Contents

Introduction

The *Celebratio Hymnal* and its supplement, *New Songs of Celebration*, now appear to ther for the first time in a combined Full Music Edition. This book pro es a collection of over eight hundred hymns and psalms, besides a gener s selection of music for the Eucharist and a section on the Liturgy of the urs. It aims to be a book which *serves* the liturgy and its structure reflec this.

There is a d erence between music which accompanies worship and music which *is lf* worship. The music we sing in the liturgy should come into the second tegory. It may accompany some action, like a procession, or it may be a 'e in itself' like the Gloria (when everybody is singing it and nothing els going on) but it is not something stuck on, it is actually part of the pray of the whole assembly.

If we are go g to choose music well, therefore, we need some knowledge of w the liturgy is about. The main occasion on which this book will be use is the Eucharist or Mass. Hymns, however, are quite a recent feature of e Mass, and we have to choose them so that they respect the form and pur se of the Mass and do not distort it.

The Mass cons ts of two parts, the Liturgy of the Word and the Liturgy of the Eucharist, ined together to form one act of worship. This mirrors the way that God ommunicates with his people: he first speaks to us and we answer by giv g thanks. God comes among us as Word and then as Nourishment.

This means tha the most important parts of the Mass are those lasting from the First Re ling to the Communion. There are also some opening rites which prepar us to celebrate, and some concluding rites which send us out into the wo d, with the Word in our hearts, to do Christ's work in the week.

So when we c ose music, we have to make sure that it fulfils the purpose of the M ss. The Church Music Committee of the Bishops' Conference of Eng nd and Wales produced, in 1987, a chart highlighting the important part This chart was in turn based on the teaching of the *General Instruction on the Roman Missal*. The explanation here closely follows that chart, hich divides the parts of the mass into five 'layers' of importance.

The most important parts to sing (i.e. the first layer) are **Acclamations**: the Gospel Acclamation and the Acclamations of the Eucharistic Prayer (Holy Holy, Memorial Acclamation and Amen.) Singing these means that you are highlighting the most sacred moments of the Mass.

Two further parts of the Mass which are **songs** (and which logically it is rather inappropriate to say and not sing) are the **Glory to God** and the **Responsorial Psalm.**

So far we have not mentioned hymns! This is because although they add richness and colour to the celebration, and underline the message of the Word, it is important first to make sure the actual texts of the liturgy are sung.

The four **hymns** that we usually sing (Entrance, Preparation of Gifts, Communion and Final) are a third layer. In a well-prepared liturgy they shouldn't be sung without the parts mentioned above; if they are, you end up with the famous 'four-hymn sandwich,' still a very common event in our churches but not something strictly in accordance with the wishes of the Missal.

In a fourth layer we could put the Penitential Rite and the Lamb of God (the 'song at the breaking of bread') which are better when sung but make sense when spoken. This layer also includes Dialogues and small Responses such as the response to the Prayer of the Faithful and the Preface Dialogue. The Our Father is best put here (although the Bishops' Committee document considers it not a sung prayer at all). There is also a fifth layer mainly containing the prayers said by the priest. (On page 6 all this is put in the form of a diagram, the columns 1–5 representing the five layers.

There is more to the liturgy than just the Eucharist, of course; there are the other sacramental rites, there are the special rites of the seasons, particularly Holy Week and the Triduum, and there is the Liturgy of the Hours, Divine Office or Prayer of the Church. This book aims to serve all of them, a task in which it could be supplemented by other more specialised publications such as the *Responsorial Psalter, The Great Week* and *Music for the Funeral Rite.* Finally, the companion volume *Planning the Liturgy with the Celebration Hymnal* is an essential part of the library of every user of the *Celebration Hymnal.* Not only does it go into much greater detail than is possible here concerning every aspect of the Liturgy, but it contains hymn lists for every Sunday, feast day and ritual occasion, providing what is the most comprehensive liturgical guide to any hymnbook published in Britain today.

Stephen Dean
February 1991

		1	2	3	4	5
Opening Rites:	Entrance/Gathering Song			●		
	Greeting					●
	Penitential Rite				●	
	Gloria		●			
	Opening Prayer					●
LITURGY OF THE WORD	*First Reading*					
	Responsorial Psalm		●			
	Second Reading					
	GOSPEL ACCLAMATION	●				
	GOSPEL					
	Homily					
	Profession of Faith					●
	Prayer of the Faithful				●	
LITURGY OF THE EUCHARIST Preparation of the Gifts:	Procession of Gifts					
	Song at the Procession			●		
Eucharistic Prayer:	Preface Dialogue and Preface				●	
	HOLY, HOLY	●			●	
	First part of prayer				●	
	MEMORIAL ACCLAMATION	●			●	
	Second part of prayer				●	
	AMEN	●			●	
Communion Rite:	Our Father				●	
	Sign of Peace					
	Breaking of Bread					
	Lamb of God				●	
	Communion Song			●		
	Communion Thanksgiving Song			●		
Concluding Rite	*Prayer after Communion*					
	Blessing					●
	Final Song			●		

MUSIC FOR THE EUCHARIST

RITE OF BLESSING OF WATER

Stephen Dean

PENITENTIAL RITE I

David Saint

(1 You were sent to heal the contrite:)* (repeated by All)
(2 Lord Jesus you raise us to new life:) Lord, have mer - cy.

(1 You came to call sinners:)
(2 Lord Jesus, you forgive our sins:) Christ, have mer - cy.

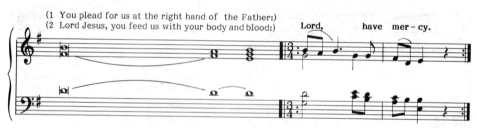

(1 You plead for us at the right hand of the Father:)
(2 Lord Jesus, you feed us with your body and blood:) Lord, have mer - cy.

* *Texts are given as examples only.*

PENITENTIAL RITE II

Seoirse Bodley

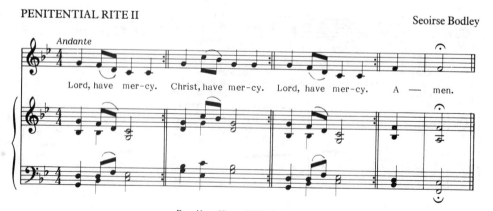

Lord, have mer-cy. Christ, have mer-cy. Lord, have mer-cy. A — men.

GLORIA I

Seoirse Bodley

Andantino

Glo-ry to God in the high-est, and peace to His peo-ple on earth.

Lord God hea-ven-ly King, Al-migh-ty God and Fa-ther. We wor-ship

you we give you thanks, we praise you for your glo-ry.

Very softly -

Lord Je-sus Christ, on-ly Son of the Fa-ther, Lord God, Lamb of God, you

take a - way the sin of the world, have mer-cy on us. You are seat-ed at the

right hand of the Fa - ther, re - ceive our prayer. For you a - lone are the

Ho-ly One. You a - lone are the Lord, you a - lone are the Most High, Je-sus

Christ, with the Ho - ly Spi-rit, in the glo - ry of God the Fa-ther. A - men.

From Mass of Peace, © 1981 Seoirse Bodley

GLORIA
(Alternative version)

* Note for choir and organist: In this version, the congregation sings only
the refrain and amen. The choir sings the rest of the music. The refrain,
which consists of the first four bars of the Gloria, is sung by all with organ
accompaniment, at each point marked 𝄋 in the music.

ALL: Glo - ry to God in the high - est, and peace to His peo - ple on earth.

CHOIR: Lord, God, heavenly King,
        Almighty God and Father,
        we worship you, we give you thanks,
        we praise you for your glory.

ALL: Glory to God in the Highest,
        and peace to His people on earth.

CHOIR: Lord Jesus Christ, only Son of the Father,
        Lord God, Lamb of God,
        you take away the sins of the world; have mercy on us.

ALL: Glory to God in the Highest,
        and peace to His people on earth.

CHOIR: You are seated at the right hand of the Father; receive our prayer.

ALL: Glory to God in the Highest,
        and peace to His people on earth.

CHOIR: For you alone are the Holy one,
        you alone are the Lord,
        you alone are the Most High, Jesus Christ,
        with the Holy Spirit, in the Glory of God the Father.

ALL: A - men.

GLORIA II

Stephen Dean

From Mass of St Andrew, © 1987 Stephen Dean

mer — cy on us. You are seat-ed at the right hand of the Fa-ther, re -

- ceive our prayer. Re - ceive our prayer. Glo-ry to God in the high-est, and

peace to his peo-ple on earth. For you a - lone are the Ho-ly One, you a -

- lone are the Lord, you a - lone are the Most High, Je-sus Christ, with the Ho — ly

Spi - rit, in the glo-ry of God the Fa-ther, A —— men!

* Glo-ry to God in the high-est, and peace to his peo-ple on earth, A — men.

Fine

* *Final refrain may be sung in alternation between two groups overlapping as shown.*

13

GLORIA III

Mike Anderson

2. Jesus, Saviour of all, Lord God, Lamb of God
   you take away our sins, Oh Lord. have mercy on us all.

3. At the Father's right hand, Lord receive our prayer,
   for you alone are the Holy One, and you alone are Lord.

4. Glory Father and Son, Glory Holy Spirit,
   to you we raise our hands up high, we glorify your name.

GLORIA IV

Jacques Berthier

Glo - ri - a, glo - ri - a, in ex - cel - sis De - o!

Glo - ri - a, glo - ri - a, al - le - lu - ia, al - le - lu - ia!

Keyboard or Instrument

Choir

(hum)

Guitar

Dm   Gm   C   F

Rhythms may be added by small percussion instruments.

1. Soprano, Tenor

Ho - di - e Chri - stus na - tus est, Sal - va - tor ap - pa - ru - it.

Al - le - lu — ia, al - le - lu — ia. (- ia) Glo - ri - a, glo - ri -

- a, in ex - cel - sis De - o. Glo - ri - a, glo - ri - a, al - le - lu — ia.

15

2. Alto, Bass *(Variation in small notes)*

Ho – di – e   Chri – stus-na-tus est,   Sal – va – tor   ap – pa — ru – it.

Ho-di – e   Chri – stus na-tus est,   Sal-va-tor   ap – pa — ru – it.

(- it)   Glo – ri – a,   glo – ri – a,   in   ex – cel – sis De –
(- ia)

– o.   Glo – ri – a,   glo – ri – a,   al – le – lu — ia.

© Les Presses de Taizé, by permission of Collins Liturgical Publications

EUCHARISTIC LITURGY I

Bernadette Farrell

INTRODUCTION

($\downarrow$. = c.56)

Melody

Ho – ly,   ho – ly,   ho – ly,

Organ

p   *p*

cresc. -

Lord God of   pow'r,   Lord God of   might,   Lord God of   pow'r and might.

16

Heav'n and earth are full of your glo-ry. Ho-san-na

in the high-est. Ho-san — na, ho-san — na, ho-

-san — na in the high-est. Bless-ed,

bless-ed, bless-ed, bless-ed is he who comes in the name, who comes in the

Lord's own name.

Ho - san — na, ho - san — na, ho - -san - na in the high — est. Ho - san — na, ho- -san — na, ho - san - na in the high - est.

MEMORIAL ACCLAMATION C

INTRODUCTION

($\textit{d}$ = c.56)

Melody

When we eat this bread and

Organ

drink this cup, we pro-claim your death, Lord Je — sus Christ, un — til you come in glo-ry. un— til you come in glo-ry, un — til you come in glo - ry, Je — sus Christ!

AMEN

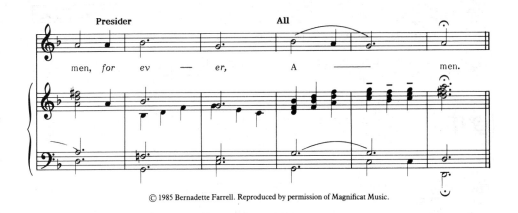

men, for ev — er, A ——— men.

EUCHARISTIC LITURGY II
(A Celtic Liturgy)

Christopher Walker

HOLY, HOLY, HOLY

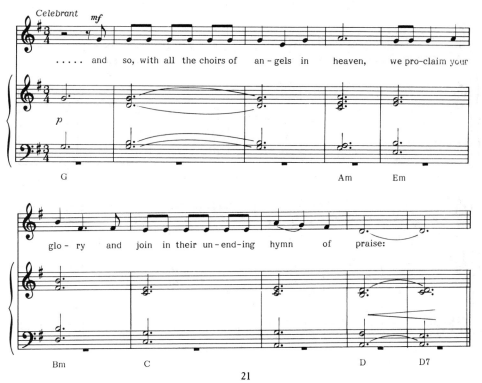

..... and so, with all the choirs of an-gels in heaven, we pro-claim your

glo- ry and join in their un-end-ing hymn of praise:

21

ACCLAMATION

DOXOLOGY AND GREAT AMEN

Through him, with him, in him, in the u-ni-ty of the Spi-rit all glo-ry and ho-nour is yours, al-might-y Fa-ther, for e - ver and e - ver. A —— men, a —— men, a —— men, a —— men.

EUCHARISTIC LITURGY III

Seoirse Bodley

Ho - ly, Ho - ly, Ho - ly Lord, God of pow'r and might.

Hea - ven and earth are full of your glo - ry. Ho - san - na in the high-est. Bless-ed is

he who comes in the name of the Lord. Ho - san - na in the high - est.

ACCLAMATION / GREAT AMEN

Christ has died, Christ is ris'n, Christ will come a — gain.
A — men, A — men, A — men, A — men.

Dy - ing you de — stroyed our death, ris — ing

you re — stored our life. Lord Je - sus come in glo - ry.

EUCHARISTIC LITURGY IV (Coventry Acclamations)

Paul Inwood

HOLY, HOLY, HOLY

HOLY, HOLY, HOLY

OPTIONAL DESCANT
2nd time only

OPTIONAL DESCANT

MELODY LINE

(Repeat hosannas (with descant) and end with the interlude)

ACCLAMATION

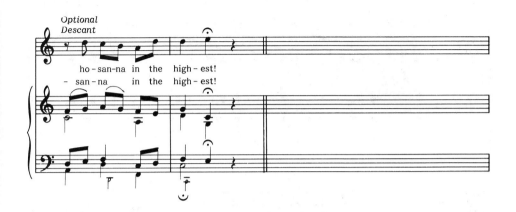

ho‑san‑na in the high‑est!
‑ san‑na in the high‑est!

GREAT AMEN

A — — — men, A ‑ men.
A — — — men, A — — men, A — — — men.

EUCHARISTIC LITURGY V (Folk Acclamations)
HOLY, HOLY

John Lillis

Christ has died, Christ has died. Christ is ris - en,
A - - - - men, A - - - men. A - - - - men,

Christ will come, will come a - gain.
A - - - - men. (A- men).

optional choir

Christ is ri - sen. Christ will come a-gain, Christ will come a-gain.
A - - - - men. A - - - men, A - - - men.

© 1981 John Lillis

EUCHARISTIC LITURGY VI

Stephen Dean

Ho — ly, ho — ly, ho — ly Lord, God of

Dm   Gm   F

pow-er and might! Heav'n and earth are full of your glo — ry. Ho -

Gm   C   Dm   A7   Dm/F   Gm   A7   Dm

ACCLAMATION I

II DYING, YOU DESTROYED OUR DEATH

Dy - ing you de — stroyed our death, ris - ing you re - stored our life. Lord Je - sus come, Lord Je - sus come, Lord Je - sus come in

Lord Je - sus, Lord Je - sus, come in glo - ry!

glo - ry. Lord Je - sus come, Lord Je - sus come, Lord Je - sus come in glo - ry!

III WHEN WE EAT THIS BREAD

When we eat this bread, when we drink this cup, we pro - claim your death, Lord Je - sus; un - til you come in glo - ry!

THROUGH HIM...

© 1987 Stephen Dean

LAMB OF GOD I

Seoirse Bodley

From Mass of Peace, © 1981 Seoirse Bodley

LAMB OF GOD II

David Clark Isele

LAMB OF GOD   III
(Communion Song 3)

Paul Inwood

Capo 5 Chords in brackets are for the last time only

General

1. Jesus, Lamb of God and source of life:
    Jesus, loving bearer of our sins:

2. Jesus, Son of God and Son of Man:
    Jesus, true redeemer of the world:

*3. Jesus Christ, our Way, our Truth, our Life:
     Jesus Christ, our living Cornerstone:

4. Jesus, Lord of life and Lord of light:
    Jesus, here in form of bread and wine:

Advent

5 = 1

6. Jesus, coming near to bring us joy:
    Jesus, Son of God, Emmanuel:

7. Jesus, bringing hope to all who fear:
    Jesus, bringing strength to all who mourn:

*8. Jesus, Saviour heralded by John:
     Jesus, Son of David's house and line:

*9 = 4

*Verses marked with an asterisk (*)
are optional and may be omitted*

38

Christmas

10. Jesus, Lamb of God, the Word made flesh:
    Jesus, Son of God, come down on earth:

11. Jesus, King of glory, Prince of Peace:
    Jesus, shining in our darkened world:

12. Jesus, King of angels, Lord of joy:
    Jesus, born to save the world from sin:

13 = 4

Lent

14. Jesus, source of everlasting life:
    Jesus, source of reconciling love:

15. Jesus, by whose suffering we are healed:
    Jesus, man of sorrows, friend of grief:

16 Jesus, crucified, transcending time:
    Jesus, Saviour, by whose death we live:

Eucharistic *(Maundy Thursday, Corpus Christi)*

17. Jesus, Lamb of God and bread of life:
    Jesus, blood that cleanses us from sin:

18. Jesus, showing how we ought to serve:
    Jesus, teaching how we ought to love:

*19. Jesus Christ, our true, eternal priest:
    Jesus, food and drink that makes us one:

20 = 4

Easter

21. Jesus, risen Lord, triumphant King:
    Jesus, true redeemer of the world:

22. Jesus, Morning Star which never sets:
    Jesus, Paschal Lamb and sacrifice:

23. Jesus, bursting from the shattered tomb:
    Jesus, mighty Victor over death:

24 = 4

Pentecost *(Spirit, healing . . .)*

25. Jesus, glorious brightness, flame of love:
    Jesus, filling hearts and minds with life:

26. Jesus, healing strength, redeeming power:
    Jesus, burning out the mark of sin:

27. Jesus, by whose truth we are inspired:
    Jesus, present here among us now:

28 = 4

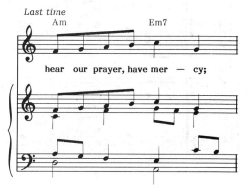

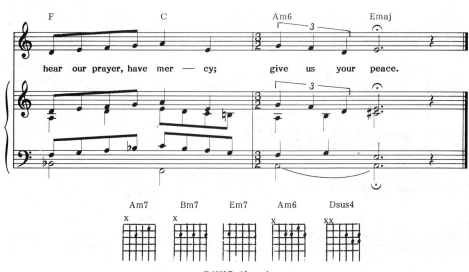

LAMB OF GOD IV

Marty Haugen

ADDITIONAL VERSES

Je-sus, Bread of Life . . .	Je-sus, Tree of Life . . .	Je-sus, Lord of Lords . . .
Je-sus, Prince of Peace . . .	Je-sus, Ancient Cup . . .	Je-sus, King of Kings . . .
Je-sus, Word of God . . .	Je-sus, Lord of Lords . . .	Je-sus, Cup of Life . . .
Je-sus, Fire of Love . . .	Je-sus, Bread of Peace . . .	Je-sus, Hope for all . . .

A NEW PEOPLE'S MASS

A. Gregory Murray OSB

NOTE. The Choir parts may be used as accompaniment; the introductions are optional.
This arrangement may also be sung by unaccompanied choir.

LORD, HAVE MERCY

Lord, have mer - cy. Lord, have mer - cy. Christ, have mer - cy.

Christ, have mer - cy. Lord, have mer - cy. Lord, have mer - cy.

GLORY TO GOD

Glo - ry to God in the high — est.

Priest's intonation and organ prelude are optional.
(eg. for Maundy Thursday/Easter Vigil)

ACCOMPANIMENT: *see note on page 42*

Glo - ry to God in the high — est, and peace to his peo-ple on earth.

Lord God, hea-ven-ly King, al - migh-ty God and Fa —

Small notes for use only when accompaniment is played from the choir part.

*Small notes for use only when accompaniment is played from the choir part.

- cy on us; you are seat-ed at the right hand of the Fa — ther, re —

- ceive our prayer. For you a - lone are the Ho — ly One, you a -

- lone are the Lord, you a - lone are the Most High, Je — sus Christ,

with the Ho - ly Spi - rit, in the glo-ry of God the Fa — ther. A — men.

HOLY, HOLY, HOLY

ACCOMPANIMENT: see note on page 42

Ho - ly, ho-ly, ho-ly Lord, God of power and might,

ORGAN

heav-en and earth are full of your glo — ry. Ho - san — na in the

high — — — est. Bless-ed is he who comes in the name

of the Lord. Ho — san — na in the high — — est.

ACCLAMATION

Christ has died, Christ is ri-sen, Christ will come a — gain.

Organ

GREAT AMEN

A men.

Organ

OUR FATHER

Our Fa-ther who art in heav-en, hallow-ed be thy name.

Thy king-dom come. Thy will be done on earth as it

LAMB OF GOD

ACCOMPANIMENT: See note on page 42.

THE COMPLETE
CELEBRATION HYMNAL

1 Abide with me

EVENTIDE (10 10 10 10)   W.H.Monk (1823–89)

A- bide with me, fast falls the e- ven- tide; the dark-ness
deepens, Lord, with me a- bide! When o- ther help-ers fail, and comforts
flee, help of the help- less, O a- bide with me.

2 Swift to its close ebbs out life's little day;
  earth's joys grow dim, its glories pass away;
  change and decay in all around I see;
  O thou who changest not, abide with me.

3 I need thy presence every passing hour;
  what but thy grace can foil the tempter's power?
  Who like thyself my guide and stay can be?
  Through cloud and sunshine, O abide with me.

4 I fear no foe with thee at hand to bless;
  ills have no weight and tears no bitterness.
  Where is death's sting? Where, grave, thy victory?
  I triumph still, if thou abide with me.

5 Hold thou thy Cross before my closing eyes;
  shine through the gloom, and point me to the skies;
  heaven's morning breaks, and earth's vain shadows flee:
  in life, in death, O Lord, abide with me!

H. F. Lyte (1793–1847)

2 Accept, O Father, in thy love

BRESLAU (88 88)   Traditional Melody adapted by F. Mendelssohn (1809–47)

Ac- cept, O Fa-ther, in thy love, these humble gifts of bread and wine, that with ourselves we of- fer thee, re- tur- ning gifts al- rea-dy thine.

2 Behold this host and chalice, Lord,
   to thee in heaven the gifts we raise;
   through them may we our homage pay,
   our adoration and our praise.

3 No earthly claim to grace is ours,
   save what thy sacrifice has won;
   grant then thy grace, fulfil our needs,
   and may thy will in ours be done.

J. Clifford Evers

3 All creation, bless the Lord

Hayward Osborne

1. All cre- a - tion, bless the Lord. Earth and hea-ven, bless the Lord. Spi - rits, pow-ers, bless the Lord. Praise him for ev - er.

F   Dm   Bb   C   F   Dm   Gm   C7   F7

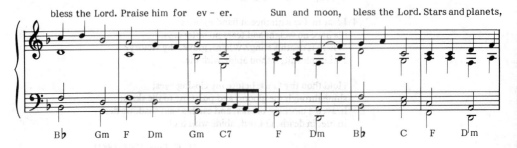

Sun and moon, bless the Lord. Stars and planets,

Bb   Gm   F   Dm   Gm   C7   F   Dm   Bb   C   F   Dm

2 Winds and breezes, bless the Lord.
  Spring and Autumn, bless the Lord.
  Winter, Summer, bless the Lord.
  Praise him for ever.
  Fire and heat, bless the Lord.
  Frost and cold, bless the Lord.
  Ice and snow, bless the Lord.
  Praise him for ever.

3 Night and daytime, bless the Lord.
  Light and darkness, bless the Lord.
  Clouds and lightning, bless the Lord.
  Praise him for ever.
  All the earth, bless the Lord.
  Hills and mountains, bless the Lord.
  Tress and flowers, bless the Lord.
  Praise him for ever.

4 Springs and rivers, bless the Lord.
  Seas and oceans, bless the Lord.
  Whales and fishes, bless the Lord.
  Praise him for ever.
  Birds and insects, bless the Lord.
  Beasts and cattle, bless the Lord.
  Let all creatures bless the Lord.
  Praise him for ever.

5 Let God's people bless the Lord.
  Men and women, bless the Lord.
  All creation, bless the Lord.
  Praise him for ever.
  Let God's people bless the Lord.
  Men and women, bless the Lord.
  All creation, bless the Lord.
  Praise him for ever.

Hayward Osborne

4 All creatures of our God and King

EASTER SONG (LASST UNS ERFREUEN)
(88 44 88 and alleluias)

Geistliche Kirchengesang, Cologne (1623)
arr. by R.Vaughan Williams (1872–1958)

2 Thou rushing wind that art so strong,
ye clouds that sail in heaven along,
O praise him, alleluia, alleluia!
Thou rising morn, in praise rejoice,
ye lights of evening, find a voice:

3 Thou flowing water, pure and clear,
make music for thy Lord to hear,
alleluia, alleluia!
Thou fire so masterful and bright,
that givest man both warmth and light:

4 Dear mother earth, who day by day
unfoldest blessings on our way,
O praise him, alleluia!
The flowers and fruits that in thee grow
let them his glory also show.

5 And all ye men of tender heart,
forgiving others, take your part,
O sing ye, alleluia!
Ye who long pain and sorrow bear,
praise God and on him cast your care.

6 And thou, most kind and gentle death,
waiting to hush our latest breath,
O praise him, alleluia!
Thou leadest home the child of God,
and Christ our Lord the way hath trod:

7 Let all things their Creator bless,
and worship him in humbleness,
O praise him, alleluia!
Praise, praise the Father, praise the Son,
and praise the Spirit, Three in One.

W. H. Draper (1855–1933)
Based on the Cantico di Frate Sole of St Francis of Assisi
(1182–1226)

5   Alleluia

2 Jesus is Lord, ...

3 And I love him, ...

4 Christ is risen, ...   *Traditional*

6 Alleluia! I will praise the Father

CONFIDO

A.Gregory Murray OSB

Al-lelu – ia, al- le-lu- ia! I will

praise the Fa-ther for all of my life. I will sing to my God as long as I live.

Last time only. Fine

Al- le-lu- ia, al- le- lu- ia, al-le-lu- ia!

al- le-lu- ia! Do not place all your trust in the pow-er of man:

he can-not save. His schemes will all per-ish when he yields up his

breath at the end of his day.

2 But so happy the man who will trust in his God:
he will find help.
For he is the maker of the heavens and earth
and of all that these hold.

3 All the searchers for justice, for freedom, for love,
he will fulfil.
The widow, the orphan, and the blind and the lame
in his love are restored.

Based on Psalm 146
by Michael Cockett

7 Alleluia! Sing to Jesus

HYFRYDOL (87 87 D)   R.H.Pritchard (1811–87)

Al- le- lu- ia, sing to Je- sus, his the
scep- tre, his the throne, al- le- lu- ia,
his the tri- umph, his the vic- tor- y a- lone:
hark! the songs of peace- ful Si- on
thun- der like a migh- ty flood;

Je- sus, out of ev- 'ry na- tion,

hath re- deemed us by his blood.

2 Alleluia, not as orphans
   are we left in sorrow now;
   alleluia, he is near us,
   faith believes, nor questions how;
   though the cloud from sight received him
   when the forty days were o'er,
   shall our hearts forget his promise,
   "I am with you evermore"?

3 Alleluia, Bread of Angels,
   thou on earth our food, our stay;
   alleluia, here the sinful
   flee to thee from day to day;
   intercessor, friend of sinners,
   earth's Redeemer, plead for me,
   where the songs of all the sinless
   sweep across the crystal sea.

4 Alleluia, King eternal
   thee the Lord of lords we own;
   alleluia, born of Mary,
   earth thy footstool, heaven thy throne;
   thou within the veil hast entered,
   robed in flesh, our great High Priest;
   thou on earth both priest and victim
   in the Eucharistic Feast.

W. Chatterton Dix (1837–98)

8 All glory, laud and honour

ST THEODULPH (76 76 D)　　　　　　　　　　　　　　Melchior Teschner (1584–1635)

Chorus

All glo-ry, laud and hon-our to thee, Re-dee-mer, King, to whom the lips of chil-dren made sweet ho-san-nas ring. 1 Thou art the King of Is-rael, thou Da-vid's ro-yal Son, who in the Lord's name com-est, the King and bles-sed one.

2 The company of angels
are praising thee on high,
and mortal men and all things
created make reply.

3 The people of the Hebrews
with palms before thee went:
our praise and prayer and anthems
before thee we present.

4 To thee before thy passion
they sang their hymns of praise;
to thee now high exalted
our melody we raise.

5 Thou didst accept their praises,
accept the prayers we bring,
who in all good delightest,
thou good and gracious king.

St Theodulph of Orleans (d.821), tr. J. M. Neale

9 All hail the power of Jesus' name

MILES LANE (86 86 extended) W. Shrubsole (1760–1806)

2 Crown him, ye martyrs of your God,
who from his altar call;
praise him whose way of pain ye trod,
and crown him Lord of all.

3 Ye prophets who our freedom won,
ye searchers, great and small,
by whom the work of truth is done,
now crown him Lord of all.

4 Sinners, whose love can ne'er forget
the wormwood and the gall,
go spread your trophies at his feet,
and crown him Lord of all.

5 Bless him, each poor oppressèd race
that Christ did upward call;
his hand in each achievement trace,
and crown him Lord of all.

6 Let every tribe and every tongue
to him their hearts enthral:
lift high the universal song,
and crown him Lord of all.

E. Perronet (1762–92), and others

10 All people that on earth do dwell

OLD HUNDREDTH (88 88)   *Genevan Psalter* (c.1551)

2 The Lord, ye know, is God indeed,
  without our aid he did us make;
  we are his folk, he doth us feed
  and for his sheep he doth us take.

3 O enter then his gates with praise,
  approach with joy his courts unto,
  praise, laud, and bless his name always,
  for it is seemly so to do.

4 For why? the Lord our God is good:
  his mercy is for ever sure;
  his truth at all times firmly stood,
  and shall from age to age endure.

5 To Father, Son and Holy Ghost,
  the God whom heaven and earth adore,
  from men and from the angel-host
  be praise and glory evermore.

William Kethe, Day's Psalter (1560)

11 All that I am

Sebastian Temple
harmony by Stephen Dean

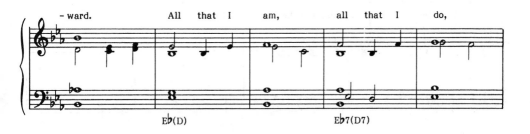

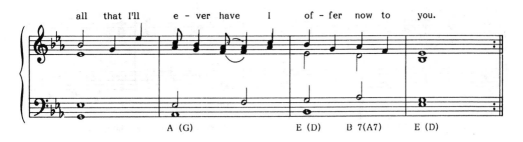

Sebastian Temple

12 All the nations of the earth

Kevin Mayhew

2 Snow capped mountains, praise the Lord.
  Alleluia.
  Rolling hills, praise the Lord.
  Alleluia.

3 Deep sea water, praise the Lord.
  Alleluia.
  Gentle rain, praise the Lord.
  Alleluia.

4 Roaring lion, praise the Lord.
  Alleluia.
  Singing birds, praise the Lord.
  Alleluia.

5 Kings and princes, praise the Lord.
  Alleluia.
  Young and old, praise the Lord.
  Alleluia.

Michael Cockett

13 All things bright and beautiful

ROYAL OAK (76 76 D)

Traditional English Melody
adapted by Martin Shaw

2 The purple-headed mountain,
  the river running by,
  the sunset and the morning,
  that brightens up the sky.

3 The cold wind in the winter,
  the pleasant summer sun,
  the ripe fruits in the garden,
  he made them every one.

4 The tall trees in the greenwood,
  the meadows for our play,
  the rushes by the water,
  to gather every day.

5 He gave us eyes to see them,
  and lips that we may tell
  how great is God Almighty,
  who has made all things well.

C. F. Alexander (1818–95)

14 All this world belongs to Jesus

Traditional Westerwald Melody
arr. W.F. Jabusch

All this world be- longs to Je- sus, ev'- ry- thing is
his by right; all on the land, all in the sea;
ev'- ry- thing is his by right.

2 Shining stars in all their beauty
are outnumbered by his gifts.
Sand on the shore, stars in the sky,
are outnumbered by his gifts.

3 Ev'ry foot that starts a-dancing
taps a rhythm full of hope;
full of his joy, full of his hope,
taps a rhythm full of hope.

4 All that's good reflects his goodness;
may it lead us back to him.
All that is good, all that is true,
may it lead us back to him.

5 So give thanks for what he's given;
touch and taste, and feet to dance;
eyes for the lights, ears for the sound,
for the wonders of our Lord.

Willard F. Jabusch

15 All ye who seek a comfort sure

ST BERNARD (86 86)

Adapted from an 18th century
melody by J.Richardson

All ye who seek a comfort sure in trou- ble and dis- tress,

what- ev- er sor-row vex the mind, or guilt the soul op- press:

2 Jesus, who gave himself for you
   upon the cross to die,
   opens to you his sacred heart;
   oh, to that heart draw nigh.

3 Ye hear how kindly he invites;
   ye hear his words so blest:
   'all ye that labour come to me,
   and I will give you rest.'

4 Jesus, thou joy of saints on high,
   thou hope of sinners here,
   attracted by those loving words
   to thee I lift my prayer.

5 Wash thou my wounds in that dear blood,
   which forth from thee doth flow;
   new grace, new hope inspire, a new
   and better heart bestow.

18th c., tr. Edward Caswall

16 Lord of light

Anthony Sharpe

voice cries in the wil – der-ness 'Pre – pare the way of the Lord, make straight the road for him, he is our God.' He will le – vel moun – tains and make the vall – eys plains. He will come in-to your hearts like a light in the dark. *Chorus* **Je — sus,**

2 And high up on a mountain
a messenger will shout,
we see His victory
He is our God.
He is like a shepherd
who cares for his flock,
He is called the Lamb of God,
for He died for our sins.

3 The Lord came and dwelt with us,
the Lord of light and truth;
the world could not recognise
He is our God,
for we know He died for us,
that we may be redeemed:
now we see He lives again,
for He rose to set us free.

Anthony Sharpe

17 Almighty Father, Lord most high

TALLIS' CANON (88 88)   Thomas Tallis (c.1510–85)

2 We offer to thee of thine own,
   ourselves and all that we can bring,
   in bread and cup before thee shown,
   our universal offering.

3 All that we have we bring to thee,
   yet all is naught when all is done,
   save that in it thy love can see
   the sacrifice of thy dear Son.

4 By this command in bread and cup,
   his body and his blood we plead;
   what on the cross he offer'd up
   is here our sacrifice indeed.

5 For all thy gifts of life and grace,
   here we thy servants humbly pray
   that thou would'st look upon the face
   of thine anointed Son today.

   Vincent Stuckley Stratton Coles (1845–1929)

18 Almighty Father, take this bread

FARRANT (86 86)

Richard Farrant (c.1530–85)

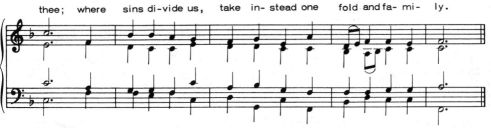

2 The wine we offer soon will be
   Christ's blood, redemption's price;
   receive it, Holy Trinity,
   this holy sacrifice.

3 O God, by angels' choirs adored,
   thy name be praised on earth;
   on all men be that peace outpoured
   once promised at his birth.

Anonymous

19 Amazing grace

AMAZING GRACE (86 86)

American Folk Hymn

2 'Twas grace that taught my heart to fear,
and grace my fears relieved.
How precious did that grace appear
the hour I first believed.

3 Through many dangers, toils and snares
I have already come.
'Tis grace hath brought me safe thus far,
and grace will lead me home.

4 The Lord has promised good to me;
his word my hope secures.
He will my shield and portion be
as long as life endures.

John Newton (1725–1807)

20 Jerusalem (And did those feet)

JERUSALEM D.L.M.   C.H.H.Parry (1848–1918)

1. And did those

feet   in an-cient   time   walk u-pon England's mountains   green? And was the

ho — ly lamb of   God   on England's pleasant pas-tures   seen? And did the

coun — te-nance di — vine shine forth u — pon our cloud-ed hills? And was Je -

- ru - sa-lem build-ed here a-mong those dark sa-ta - nic mills?

2. Bring me my bow of burn - ing

gold! Bring my my ar-rows of de — sire! Bring me my spear! O clouds un -

76

William Blake (1757–1827)

21 Angels we have heard in heaven

IRIS (87 87 and refrain)   French Traditional Melody harmonised by R.R.Terry (1865–1938)

2 Shepherds, why this exultation?
Why your rapturous strain prolong?
Tell us of the gladsome tidings,
which inspire your joyous song.

3 Come to Bethlehem, and see him
o'er whose birth the angels sing,
come, adore, devoutly kneeling,
Christ the Lord, the new-born king.

4 See him in a manger lying
whom the choir of angels praise!
Mary, Joseph, come to aid us
while our hearts in love we raise.

James Chadwick (1813–82)

22 Angels we have heard on high

IRIS (altered) (77 77 and refrain)

French Traditional Melody
harmonised by R.R.Terry (1865–1938)

2 Shepherds, why this jubilee?
  Why your rapturous strain prolong?
  Say, what may your tidings be,
  which inspire your heavenly song.

3 Come to Bethlehem and see
  him whose birth the angels sing:
  come, adore on bended knee
  the infant Christ, the new-born king.

4 See within a manger laid,
  Jesus, Lord of heaven and earth!
  Mary, Joseph, lend your aid
  to celebrate our Saviour's birth.

James Chadwick (1813–82)

23   Ask, and you will receive

Chorus: Ask, and you will re- ceive. Seek, and you will

find. Knock, and the door will be o- pened for the

love of the Lord has no end. 1. Is there an- y man

here, when his son asks for bread, would turn him a- way with a

stone in- stead? Is there an- y man here, when his son asks for

C D G D G

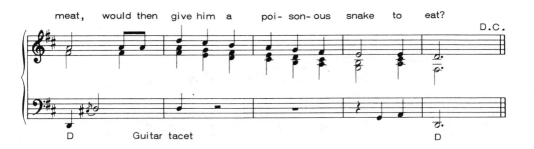

meat, would then give him a poi- son- ous snake to eat?

D.C.

D Guitar tacet D

2 So then how could your Father in heaven above,
   who knows so much more of the ways of love,
   so then how could your Father refuse what is good,
   when you ask in the name of the Son he loves.

3 So whatever you ask you will always receive,
   whatever you seek you will always find.
   For my Father will give to all those who believe
   in the Spirit of love that will never end.

Michael Cockett

24 As with gladness men of old

DIX (77 77 77)

C. Kocher (1786–1872)

2 As with joyful steps they sped,
to that lowly manger-bed,
there to bend the knee before
him whom heaven and earth adore,
so may we with willing feet
ever seek thy mercy-seat.

3 As they offered gifts most rare,
at that manger rude and bare,
so may we with holy joy,
pure, and free from sin's alloy,
all our costliest treasures bring,
Christ, to thee our heavenly King.

4 Holy Jesus, every day
keep us in the narrow way;
and, when earthly things are past,
bring our ransomed souls at last
where they need no star to guide,
where no clouds thy glory hide.

5 In the heavenly country bright
need they no created light,
thou its Light, its Joy, its Crown,
thou its Sun which goes not down;
there for ever may we sing
alleluias to our King.

William Chatterton Dix (1837–98)

25   Attend and keep this happy feast

CLAUDIUS (86 86 D)   G.W.Fink (1783–1846)

At- tend and keep this hap- py fast I preach to you this day. Is
this the fast that pleas- es me that takes your joy a- way? Do
I de-light in sor- row's dress, says God, who reigns a- bove, the
hang- ing head, the dis- mal look, will they at- tract my love?

2 But this is not the fast I choose,
  that shares the heavy load;
  that seeks to bring the poor man in
  who's weary of the road,
  that gives the hungry bread to eat,
  to strangers gives a home;
  that does not let you hide your face
  from your own flesh and bone?

3 Then like the dawn your light will break,
  to life you will be raised.
  And men will praise the Lord for you;
  be happy in your days.
  The glory of the Lord will shine,
  and in your steps his grace.
  And when you call he'll answer you;
  he will not hide his face.

Roger Ruston, after Isaiah 58:5–9

26   At the cross her station keeping

STABAT MATER

From *Mainz Gesangbuch*, 1661

2 Through her heart, his sorrow sharing,
all his bitter anguish bearing,
now at length the sword has pass'd

3 Oh, how sad and sore distress'd
was that mother highly blest,
of the sole-begotten One.

4 Christ above in torment hangs;
she beneath beholds the pangs
of her dying glorious Son.

5 Is there one who would not weep,
whelm'd in miseries so deep,
Christ's dear mother to behold?

6 Can the human heart refrain
from partaking in her pain,
in that mother's pain untold?

7 Bruised, derided, cursed, defiled,
she beheld her tender child,
all with bloody scourges rent;

8 For the sins of his own nation,
saw him hang in desolation,
till his spirit forth he sent.

9 O thou mother! fount of love!
Touch my spirit from above,
make my heart with thine accord:

10 Make me feel as thou has felt;
make my soul to glow and melt
with the love of Christ my Lord.

11 Holy Mother, pierce me through,
in my heart each wound renew
of my Saviour crucified.

12 Let me share with thee his pain
who for all my sins was slain,
who for me in torments died.

13 Let me mingle tears with thee,
mourning him who mourn'd for me,
all the days that I may live:

14 By the cross with thee to stay,
there with thee to weep and pray,
is all I ask of thee to give.

15 Virgin of all virgins best,
listen to my fond request:
let me share thy grief divine;

16 Let me, to my latest breath,
in my body bear the death
of that dying son of thine.

17 Wounded with his every wound
steep my soul till it hath swoon'd
in his very blood away.

18 Be to me, O Virgin, nigh,
lest in flames I burn and die,
in his awful judgement day.

19 Christ, when thou shalt call me hence,
be thy mother my defence,
be thy cross my victory.

20 While my body here decays,
may my soul thy goodness praise,
safe in paradise with thee.

Ascribed to Jacopone da Todi (d. 1306),
tr. E. Caswall

27 At the Lamb's high feast

Melody by J. Hintze (1622–1702)
harmonised by J. S. Bach

SALZBURG (77 77 D)

At the Lamb's high feast we sing praise to our vic- tor-ious king, who hath washed us in the tide flow-ing from his piercéd side. Praise we him whose love div- ine gives the guests his blood for wine, gives his bod-y for the feast, love the vic- tim, love the priest.

2 Where the paschal blood is poured,
Death's dark angel sheathes his sword;
Israel's hosts triumphant go
through the wave that drowns the foe.
Christ the Lamb, whose blood was shed.
Paschal victim, paschal bread;
with sincerity and love
eat we manna from above.

3 Mighty victim from the sky,
powers of hell beneath thee lie;
death is conquered in the fight;
thou hast brought us life and light,
now thy banner thou dost wave;
vanquished Satan and the grave;
angels join his praise to tell –
see o'erthrown the prince of hell.

4 Paschal triumph, paschal joy,
only sin can this destroy;
from the death of sin set free
souls re-born, dear Lord, in thee.
Hymns of glory, songs of praise,
Father, unto thee we raise.
Risen Lord, all praise to thee,
ever with the Spirit be.   *7th C., tr. Robert Campbell*

28 At the name of Jesus

FIRST TUNE

EVELYNS (65 65 D)

W.H.Monk (1823–89)

At the name of Jesus ev-'ry knee shall bow,
ev-'ry tongue con-fess him King of glo-ry now:
'tis the Fa-ther's pleas-ure we should call him Lord,
who from the beg-gin-ning was the migh-ty Word.

2 At his voice creation
  sprang at once to sight,
  all the Angel faces,
  all the hosts of light,
  thrones and dominations,
  stars upon their way,
  all the heavenly orders,
  in their great array.

3 Humbled for a season,
  to receive a name
  from the lips of sinners
  unto whom he came,
  faithfully he bore it
  spotless to the last,
  brought it back victorious
  when from death he passed.

4 Bore it up triumphant
  with its human light
  through all ranks of creatures,
  to the central height,
  to the throne of Godhead,
  to the Father's breast,
  filled it with the glory
  of that perfect rest.

5 Name him, brothers, name him,
  with love as strong as death,
  but with awe and wonder,
  and with bated breath.
  He is God the Saviour,
  he is Christ the Lord,
  ever to be worshipped,
  trusted and adored.

6 In your hearts enthrone him;
  there let him subdue
  all that is not holy,
  all that is not true;
  crown him as your captain,
  in temptation's hour
  let his will enfold you
  in its light and power.

7 Brothers, this Lord Jesus
  shall return again,
  with his Father's glory,
  with his angel train,
  for all wreaths of empire
  meet upon his brow,
  and our hearts confess him
  King of glory now.

Caroline Maria Noel (1817–77)

CAMBERWELL (65 65 D)   Michael Brierley

29 Ave Maria, O Maiden, O Mother

AVE MARIA

R.R.Terry (1865–1938,

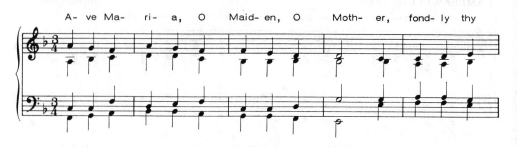

A- ve Ma- ri- a, O Maid- en, O Moth- er, fond- ly thy

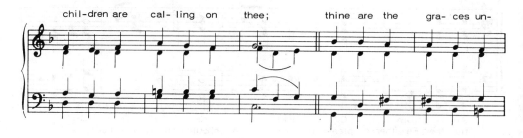

chil-dren are cal- ling on thee; thine are the gra- ces un-

claimed by an- oth- er, sin-less and beau-ti- ful, Star of the sea.

Chorus

Ma- ter Am- a- bil-is, or- a pro no- bis, pray for thy

chil- dren who call up- on thee; A- ve Sanc- tis- si-ma,

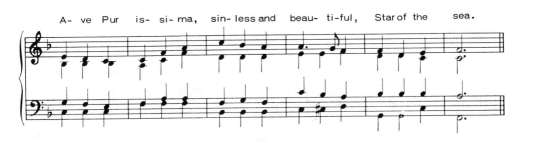

A- ve Pur is- si- ma, sin- less and beau- ti-ful, Star of the sea.

2 Ave Maria, the night shades are falling,
softly, our voices arise unto thee;
earth's lonely exiles for succour are calling,
sinless and beautiful Star of the sea.

3 Ave Maria, thy children are kneeling,
words of endearment are murmured to thee;
softly thy spirit upon us is stealing,
sinless and beautiful Star of the sea.

'Sister M'

30 Away in a manger

CRADLE SONG

J.Kirkpatrick (1838–1921)

A- way in a man- ger, no crib for a bed, the

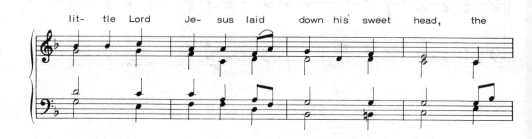

lit- tle Lord Je- sus laid down his sweet head, the

stars in the bright sky looked down where he lay, the

lit- tle Lord Je- sus a- sleep on the hay.

2 The cattle are lowing, the baby awakes,
   but little Lord Jesus no crying he makes.
   I love thee, Lord Jesus! Look down from the sky,
   any stay by my side until morning is nigh.

3 Be near me, Lord Jesus; I ask thee to stay
   close by me for ever, and love me, I pray.
   Bless all the dear children in thy tender care,
   and fit us for heaven, to live with thee there.

vv.1,2 Anonymous
v.3 J.T. McFarland (c.1906)

31 Battle is o'er

SURREXIT (888 and alleluia)   Dom Gregory Murray, O.S.B.

2 Christ who endured the shameful tree,
   o'er death triumphant welcome we,
   our adoring praise outpouring,
   alleluia.

3 On the third morn from death rose he,
   clothed with what light in heaven shall be,
   our unswerving faith deserving,
   alleluia.

4 Hell's gloomy gates yield up their key,
   paradise door thrown wide we see;
   never-tiring be our choiring,
   alleluia.

5 Lord, by the stripes men laid on thee,
   grant us to live from death set free,
   this our greeting still repeating,
   alleluia.

Simphonia Sirenum (1695)
tr. Ronald Arbuthnott Knox

32 Be still (I)

Anne Conway
Arr. Stephen Dean

Be still and know I am with you, be
still, I am the Lord. I will not
leave you orphans. I leave with
you my world, be one. _____
2. You

2 You fear the light may be fading,
  you fear to lose your way.
  Be still, and know I am near you.
  I'll lead you to the day
  and the sun.

3 Be glad the day you have sorrow,
  be glad, for then you live.
  The stars shine only in darkness,
  and in your need I give
  my peace.

Anne Conway

33 Be still (II)

Anonymous

2 I am the Lord that healeth thee,
  I am the Lord that healeth thee,
  I am the Lord that healeth thee.

3 In thee, O Lord, I put my trust,
  In thee, O Lord, I put my trust,
  In thee, O Lord, I put my trust.

Anonymous

34 Bethlehem! of noblest cities

STUTTGART (87 87)

German Melody arranged by
C.F.Witt (c.1660–1716)

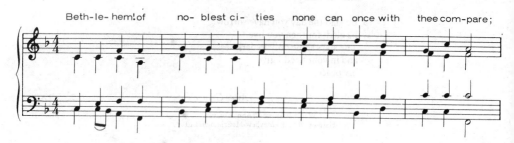

2 Fairer than the sun at morning
  was the star that told his birth,
  to the lands their God announcing,
  hid beneath a form of earth.

3 By its lambent beauty guided,
  see the eastern kings appear;
  see them bend, their gifts to offer –
  gifts of incense, gold and myrrh.

4 Solemn things of mystic meaning!
  Incense doth the God disclose;
  gold a royal child proclaimeth;
  Myrrh a future tomb foreshows.

5 Holy Jesu, in thy brightness
  to the gentile world display'd,
  with the Father and the Spirit,
  endless praise to thee be paid.

Aurelius Prudentius (348–413), tr. E. Caswall

35 Be thou my vision

SLANE (10 11 11 12)

Traditional Irish Melody,
arr. Martin Shaw (1875–1958)

naught be all else to me save that thou art;

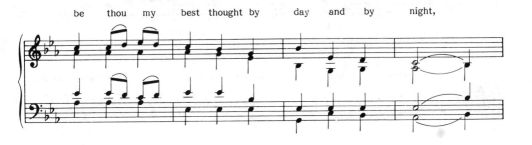

be thou my best thought by day and by night,

wak – ing or sleep – ing thy pres- ence my light.

2 Be thou my wisdom, be thou my true word,
   I ever with thee and thou with me, Lord;
   thou my great Father, and I thy true son;
   thou in me dwelling, and I with thee one.

3 Be thou my breast-plate, my sword for the fight,
   be thou my armour, and be thou my might,
   thou my soul's shelter, and thou my high tower,
   raise thou me heavenward, O Power of my power.

4 Riches I heed not, nor man's empty praise,
   thou mine inheritance through all my days;
   thou, and thou only, the first in my heart,
   high King of heaven, my treasure thou art!

5 High King of heaven, when battle is done,
   grant heaven's joy to me, O bright heaven's sun;
   Christ of my own heart, whatever befall,
   still be my vision, O Ruler of all.

Irish (8th C.), tr. Mary Byrne, versified by Eleanor Hull

36 Blest are the pure in heart

FRANCONIA (6 6 8 6)

arr. W.H.Havergal (1793–1870)

Blest are the pure in heart, for they shall see our God;

the sec-ret of the Lord is theirs, their soul is Christ's a- bode.

2 The Lord who left the heavens
   our life and peace to bring,
   to dwell in lowliness with men,
   their pattern and their king.

3 Still to the lowly soul
   he doth himself impart
   and for his dwelling and his throne
   chooseth the pure in heart.

4 Lord, we thy presence seek;
   may ours this blessing be:
   give us a pure and lowly heart,
   a temple meet for thee.

Verses 1 and 3 by John Keble (1792–1866)
verses 2 and 4 from W. J. Hall's
Psalms and Hymns (1836)

37 Breathe on me, Breath of God

CARLISLE (6 6 8 6)   C. Lockhart (1745–1815)

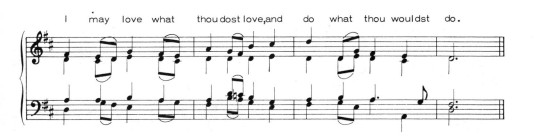

2 Breathe on me, Breath of God,
    until my heart is pure:
    until with thee I have one will
    to do and to endure.

3 Breathe on me, Breath of God.
    till I am wholly thine,
    until this earthly part of me
    glows with thy fire divine.

4 Breathe on me, Breath of God,
    so shall I never die,
    but live with thee the perfect life
    of thine Eternity.

Edwin Hatch (1835–89)

38 Bring, all ye dear-bought nations

EASTER SONG (LASST UNS ERFREUEN)
(88 44 88 and alleluias)

Geistliche Kirchengesang, (Cologne, 1623)
arr. R. Vaughan Williams (1872–1958)

Bring, all ye dear-bought na- tions bring, your

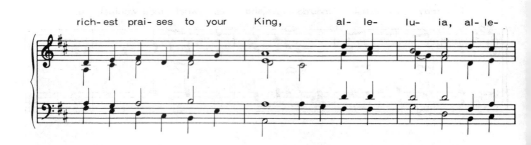

rich-est prai- ses to your King, al- le- lu- ia, al- le-

lu- ia. That spot-less Lamb, who more than due, paid

for his sheep, and those sheep you.

Chorus

Al- le- lu- ia, al- le-

98

lu- ia, al-le- lu- ia, al-le- lu- ia, al-le- lu- ia!

2 That guiltless Son, who bought your peace,
  and made his Father's anger cease,
  then, life and death together fought,
  each to a strange extreme were brought.

3 Life died, but soon revived again,
  and even death by it was slain.
  Say, happy, Magdalen, oh, say,
  what didst thou see there by the way?

4 "I saw the tomb of my dear Lord,
  I saw himself, and him adored,
  I saw the napkin and the sheet,
  that bound his head and wrapt his feet."

5 "I heard the angels witness bear,
  Jesus is ris'n; he is not here;
  go, tell his followers they shall see,
  thine and their hope in Galilee."

6 We, Lord, with faithful hearts and voice,
  on this thy rising day rejoice.
  O thou, whose power o'ercame the grave,
  by grace and love us sinners save.

  Wipo (11th C.). tr. Walter Kirkham Blount

39   Bring flowers of the rarest

Anonymous

1. Bring flowers of the rar-est, bring blossoms the fair-est, from gar-den and wood-land and hill-side and dale; our full hearts are swel-ling, our glad voi-ces tel-ling the praise of the lov-li-est flower of the vale.

Chorus

O Ma-ry we crown thee with blos-soms to-day, Queen of the An-gels and Queen of the May. O Ma-ry we crown thee with blos-soms to-day, Queen of the An-gels and Queen of the May.

2 Their lady they name thee,
  their mistress proclaim thee.
  Oh, grant that thy children on earth be as true,
  as long as the bowers
  are radiant with flowers
  as long as the azure shall keep its bright hue.

3 Sing gaily in chorus,
  the bright angels o'er us
  re-echo the strains we begin upon earth;
  their harps are repeating
  the notes of our greeting,
  for Mary herself is the cause of our mirth.

Anonymous

40 By the blood that flowed from thee

WESTMINSTER (7 7 7 7 D)   John Richardson (1816–79)

By the blood that flowed from thee in thy griev-ous a- go-ny;
by the traitor's guile-less kiss, fil- ling up thy bit-ter-ness;
Chorus Je-sus, Sav-iour, hear our cry; thou wert suff'ring once as we:
now en- thron'd in maj-es- ty countless an-gels sing to thee.

2 By the cords that, round thee cast,
  bound thee to the pillar fast,
  by the scourge so meekly borne,
  by the purple robe of scorn.

3 By the thorns that crown'd thy head,
  by the sceptre of a reed;
  by thy foes on bending knee,
  mocking at thy royalty.

4 By the people's cruel jeers;
  by the holy women's tears;
  by thy footsteps, faint and slow,
  weigh'd beneath thy cross of woe;

5 By thy weeping mother's woe;
  by the sword that pierced her through,
  when in anguish standing by,
  on the cross she saw thee die.

Frederick William Faber (1814–63)

41   Christ be beside me

BUNESSAN (5 5 5 4 D)

Traditional Gaelic Melody
arr. Stephen Dean

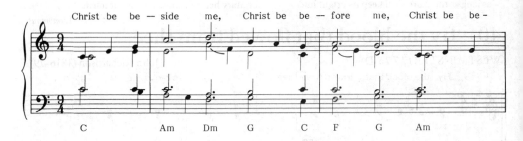

Christ be be — side me, Christ be be — fore me, Christ be be-

C   Am   Dm   G   C   F   G   Am

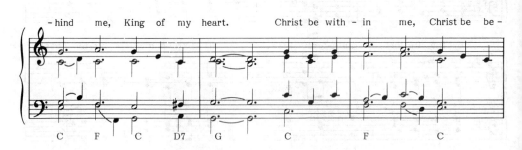

- hind   me,   King   of   my   heart.   Christ be with – in   me,   Christ be be-

C   F   C   D7   G   C   F   C

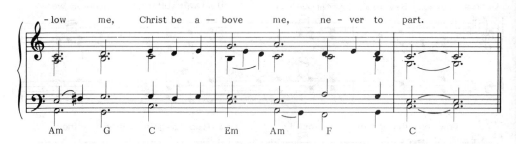

- low   me,   Christ be a — bove   me,   ne - ver   to   part.

Am   G   C   Em   Am   F   C

This may be sung by 4-part choir, following the syllabic overlay.
The chords given here fit this arrangement but differ from those
in the melody edition.

2 Christ on my right hand,
  Christ on my left hand,
  Christ all around me,
  shield in the strife.
  Christ in my sleeping,
  Christ in my sitting,
  Christ in my rising,
  light of my life.

3 Christ be in all hearts
  thinking about me,
  Christ be in all tongues
  telling of me.
  Christ be the vision
  in eyes that see me,
  in ears that hear me,
  Christ ever be.

Adapted from 'St Patrick's Breastplate' by James Quinn

42   Christ is King of earth and heaven

LAUS DEO (87 87)

German Melody adapted by
R.Redhead (1820–1901)

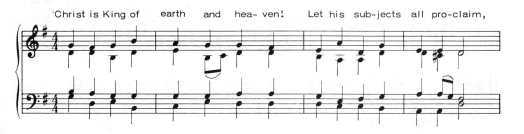

'Christ is King of earth and hea-ven! Let his sub-jects all pro-claim,

in the splendour of his tem-ple, hon-our to his ho-ly name.

2 Christ is King! No soul created
  can refuse to bend the knee
  to the God made man who reigneth
  as 'twas promised, from the tree.

3 Christ is King! Let humble sorrow
  for our past neglect atone,
  for the lack of faithful service
  to the Master whom we own.

4 Christ is King! Let joy and gladness
  greet him; let his courts resound
  with the praise of faithful subjects
  to his love in honour bound.

5 Christ is King! In health and sickness,
  till we breathe our latest breath,
  till we greet in highest heaven,
  Christ the victor over death.

Ivor J. E. Daniel (1883–1967)

43   Christ is our King

Estelle White

king, let the whole world re- joice! May all the nations sing out with one

voice! Light of the world, you have helped us to see that all men are

bro-thers and all men one day will be free!

He came to o- pen the eyes of the blind,

let-ting the sun-light pour in-to their minds. Vis-ion is wait-ing for

Em   B7   G

those who have hope, He is the light of the world.

D7   A   A7   D7

2 He came to speak tender words to the poor,
  he is the gateway and he is the door.
  Riches are waiting for all those who hope.
  He is the light of the world.

3 He came to open the doors of the gaol,
  he came to help the downtrodden and frail.
  Freedom is waiting for all those who hope.
  He is the light of the world.

4 He came to open the lips of the mute,
  letting them speak out with courage and truth.
  His words are uttered by all those who hope.
  He is the light of the world.

5 He came to heal all the crippled and lame,
  sickness took flight at the sound of his name.
  Vigour is waiting for all those who hope.
  He is the light of the world.

6 He came to love every man on this earth
  and through his Spirit he promised rebirth.
  New life is waiting for all those who hope.
  He is the light of the world.

Estelle White

105

44 Christ the Lord is ris'n today

EASTER HYMN (7 7 7 7 D)

From *Lyra Davidica* (1708)

Christ the Lord is ris'n to-day! Chris- tians haste your vows to pay,

of- fer ye your praises meet at the pas- chal victim's feet;

for the sheep the Lamb hath bled, sin- less in the sinner's stead.

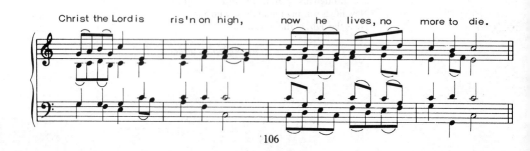

Christ the Lord is ris'n on high, now he lives, no more to die.

2 Christ, the victim undefiled,
  man to God hath reconciled
  when in strange and awful strife
  met together death and life;
  Christians, on this happy day
  haste with joy your vows to pay.
  Christ the Lord is ris'n on high;
  Now he lives, no more to die.

3 Say, O wond'ring Mary, say
  what thou sawest on thy way.
  "I beheld, where Christ had lain,
  empty tomb and angels twain,
  I beheld the glory bright
  of the rising Lord of light;
  Christ my hope is ris'n again;
  now he lives, and lives to reign."

4 Christ, who once for sinners bled,
  now the first-born from the dead,
  throned in endless might and power,
  lives and reigns for evermore.
  Hail, eternal hope on high!
  Hail, thou king of victory!
  Hail, thou Prince of life adored!
  Help and save us, gracious Lord.

Wipo 11th C., tr. Jane Elizabeth Leeson

45 Colours of day

Sue McClellan, John Pac
and Keith Ryecroft

Col- ours of day dawn in- to the mind, the sun has come

up, the night is be- hind. Go down in the ci- ty,

in- to the street, and let's give the mes- sage to the peo- ple we

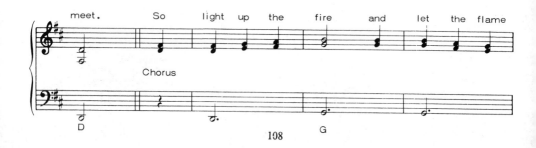

meet. So light up the fire and let the flame

Chorus

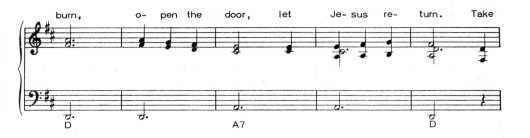

burn, o- pen the door, let Je- sus re- turn. Take

seeds of his Spi- rit, let the fruit grow, tell the

peo- ple of Je- sus, let his love show.

2 Go through the park, on into the town;
   the sun still shines on it never goes down.
   The light of the world is risen again;
   the people of darkness are needing our friend.

3 Open your eyes, look into the sky,
   the darkness has come, the sun came to die.
   The evening draws on the sun disappears,
   but Jesus is living, and his Spirit is near.

Sue McClellan, John Pac and Keith Ryecroft

109

46   Come, adore this wondrous presence

ST THOMAS (87 87 87)

Samuel Webbe (1740–1816)

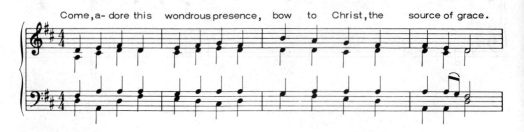

Come, a- dore this wondrous presence, bow to Christ, the source of grace.

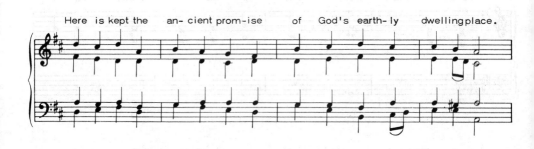

Here is kept the an- cient prom-ise of God's earth- ly dwelling place.

Sight is blind be- fore God's glo- ry, faith a- lone may see his face.

2 Glory be to God the Father,
   praise to his co-equal Son,
   adoration to the Spirit,
   bond of love, in Godhead one.
   Blest be God by all creation
   joyously while ages run.

St Thomas Aquinas (1227–74)
translated by James Quinn

47 Come, Christian people

John Glynn

2 Not much to look at
  – simply straw and hay –
  yet on that carpet
  your King was laid today.

3 Man, are you listening?
  Take heed what I say:
  Here on this planet
  your King still lives today.

John Glynn

48 Come to the manger

Traditional Melody
adapted by S.P.Waddington

2 He leaves all his glory behind,
  to be born and to die for mankind,
  with grateful beasts his cradle chooses,
  thankless man his love refuses;
  Lord, have pity and mercy on me!

3 To the manger of Bethlehem come,
  to the Saviour Emmanuel's home;
  the heav'nly hosts above are singing,
  set the Christmas bells a-ringing;
  Lord, have pity and mercy on me!

Anonymous

49 Come down, O Love divine

DOWN AMPNEY (66 11 D)   R. Vaughan Williams (1872–1958)

2 O let it freely burn,
   till earthly passions turn
   to dust and ashes in its heat consuming;
   and let thy glorious light
   shine ever on my sight,
   and clothe me round, the while my path illuming.

3 Let holy charity
   mine outward vesture be,
   and lowliness become mine inner clothing;
   true lowliness of heart,
   which takes the humbler part,
   and o'er its own shortcomings weeps with loathing.

4 And so the yearning strong,
   with which the soul will long,
   shall far outpass the power of human telling,
   for none can guess its grace,
   till he become the place
   wherein the Holy Spirit makes his dwelling.

Bianco da Siena d. 1434,
tr. Richard Frederick Littledale

50 Come, Holy Ghost

TALLIS ORDINAL (88 88)

Thomas Tallis (c. 1510–85)

Come, Ho- ly Ghost, Cre- a- tor, come from thy bright heavenly throne, come,

take pos- ses- sion of our souls, and make them all thy own.

2 Thou who art called the Paraclete,
  best gift of God above,
  the living spring, the living fire,
  sweet unction and true love.

3 Thou who art sev'nfold in thy grace,
  finger of God's right hand;
  his promise, teaching little ones
  to speak and understand.

4 O guide our minds with thy blest light,
  with love our hearts inflame;
  and with thy strength, which ne'er decays,
  confirm our mortal frame.

5 Far from us drive our deadly foe;
  true peace unto us bring;
  and through all perils lead us safe
  beneath thy sacred wing.

6 Through thee may we the Father know,
  through thee th'eternal Son,
  and thee the Spirit of them both,
  thrice-blessed Three in One.

7 All glory to the Father be,
  with his co-equal Son:
  the same to thee, great Paraclete,
  while endless ages run.

Ascribed to Rabanus Maurus (776–856)
tr. Anonymous

51 Come, Lord Jesus, come

Kevin Mayhew

2 Come, Lord Jesus, come.
Come, take my eyes, may they shine with joy.
Take them for your service, Lord.
Take them for your glory, Lord.
Come, Lord Jesus, come.
Come, Lord Jesus, take my eyes.

3 Come, Lord Jesus, come.
Come, take my lips, may they speak your truth.
Take them for your service, Lord.
Take them for your glory, Lord.
Come, Lord Jesus, come.
Come, Lord Jesus, take my lips.

4 Come, Lord Jesus, come.
Come take my feet, may they walk your path.
Take them for your service, Lord.
Take them for your glory, Lord.
Come, Lord Jesus, come.
Come, Lord Jesus, take my feet.

5 Come, Lord Jesus, come.
Come, take my heart, fill it with your love.
Take it for your service, Lord.
Take it for your glory, Lord.
Come, Lord Jesus, come.
Come, Lord Jesus, take my heart.

6 Come, Lord Jesus, come.
Come, take my life, take it for your own.
Take it for your service, Lord.
Take it for your glory, Lord.
Come, Lord Jesus, come.
Come, Lord Jesus, take my life.

Kevin Mayhew

52 Come, my brothers

Traditional

2 Come to him with songs of praise, alleluia.
Songs of praise, rejoice in him, alleluia.

3 For the Lord is a mighty God, alleluia.
He is king of all the world, alleluia.

4 In his hands are valleys deep, alleluia.
In his hands are mountain peaks, alleluia.

5 In his hands are all the seas, alleluia.
And the lands which he has made, alleluia.

6 Praise the Father, praise the Son, alleluia.
Praise the Spirit, the Holy One, alleluia.

Traditional

53 Come, praise the Lord, the almighty

LOBE DEN HERREN (14 14 47 8)   From the *Stralsund Gesangbuch* (1665)

Come, praise the Lord, the al- migh- ty, the king of all na- tions! Tell forth his fame, O ye peo-ples with loud ac- cla- ma- tions! His love is sure; faith- ful his word shall en- dure, steadfast through all ge- ne- ra- tions!

2 Praise to the Father most gracious, the Lord of creation!
Praise to his Son, the Redeemer who wrought our salvation!
O heav'nly Dove, praise to thee, fruit of their love.
Giver of all consolation!

Psalm 116, versified by James Quinn

54 Come to the Lord

Estelle White

2 Speak to the Lord and gather round his table.
  Gather round his table and speak to the Lord.

3 Sing to the Lord and gather round his table.
  Gather round his table and sing to the Lord.

4 Clap to the Lord and gather round his table.
  Gather round his table and clap to the Lord.

5 Dance to the Lord and gather round his table.
  Gather round his table and dance to the Lord.

Estelle White

55 Come ye thankful people, come

ST GEORGE (77 77 D)

G.J.Elvey (1816–93)

2 We ourselves are God's own field,
 fruit unto his praise to yield;
 wheat and tares together sown,
 unto joy or sorrow grown;
 first the blade and then the ear,
 then the full corn shall appear:
 grant, O harvest Lord, that we
 wholesome grain and pure may be.

3 For the Lord our God shall come,
 and shall take his harvest home;
 from his field shall purge away
 all that doth offend, that day,
 give his angels charge at last
 in the fire the tares to cast,
 but the fruitful ears to store
 in his garner evermore.

4 Then, thou Church triumphant, come,
 all be safely gathered in,
 free from sorrow, free from sin,
 there for ever purified
 in God's garner to abide;
 come, ten thousand angels, come,
 raise the glorious harvest-home!

Henry Alford (1810–71)

56 Crown him with many crowns

FIRST TUNE

CORONA (6686 D)

R.R.Terry (1865–1938)

Crown him with man-y crowns, the Lamb up-on his throne;

hark, how the heav'nly an-them drowns all mu-sic but its own:

a-wake, my soul, and sing of him who died for thee,

and hail him as thy matchless King through all e-ter-ni-ty.

2 Crown him the Virgin's Son,
the God incarnate born,
whose arm those crimson trophies won,
which now his brow adorn;
fruit of the mystic rose,
as of that rose the stem,
the root, whence mercy ever flows,
the babe of Bethlehem.

3 Crown him the Lord of love;
behold his hands and side,
rich wounds, yet visible above,
in beauty glorified:
no angel in the sky
can fully bear that sight,
but downward bends his burning eye
at mysteries so bright.

56

DIADEMATA (6686 D)   G.J. Elvey (1816–93)

Crown him with man- y crowns, the Lamb up- on his throne; hark, how the heavenly an- them drowns all mu- sic but its own: a- wake, my soul, and sing of him who died for thee, and hail him as thy match-less King through all e-ter-ni- ty.

4 Crown him the Lord of peace,
  whose powers a sceptre sways,
  from pole to pole, that wars may cease,
  absorbed in prayer and praise:
  his reign shall know no end,
  and round his pierced feet
  fair flowers of Paradise extend
  their fragrance ever sweet.

5 Crown him the Lord of heaven,
  one with the Father known,
  and the blest Spirit through him given
  from yonder triune throne:
  all hail, Redeemer, hail,
  for thou hast died for me;
  thy praise shall never, never fail
  throughout eternity.

Matthew Bridges (1800–94)

57 Daily, daily, sing to Mary

FIRST TUNE

DAILY DAILY (87 87 D)   from the *Paderborn Gesangbuch* (1765)

Dai-ly, dai-ly, sing to Ma-ry, sing, my soul, her praises due;

all her feasts, her ac-tions wor-ship, with the heart's de-vo-tion true.

Lost in won-d'ring con-tem-pla-tion be her maj-es-ty con-fessed:

call her moth-er, call her Vir-gin, hap-py moth-er, Virgin blest.

2 She is mighty to deliver;
  call her, trust her lovingly.
  When the tempest rages round thee,
  she will calm the troubled sea.
  Gifts of heaven she has given,
  noble Lady! to our race:
  she, the Queen, who decks her subjects,
  with the light of God's own grace.

3 Sing, my tongue, the Virgin's trophies,
  who for us her Maker bore;
  for the curse of old inflicted,
  peace and blessings to restore.
  Sing in songs of praise unending,
  sing the world's majestic Queen;
  weary not nor faint in telling
  all the gifts she gives to men.

57

LAUDES MARIAE

H.F.Hemy (1818–88)

4 All my senses, heart, affections,
 strive to sound her glory forth;
 spread abroad the sweet memorials,
 of the Virgin's priceless worth,
 where the voice of music thrilling,
 where the tongues of eloquence,
 that can utter hymns beseeming
 all her matchless excellence?

5 All our joys do flow from Mary,
 all then join her praise to sing;
 trembling sing the Virgin Mother,
 Mother of our Lord and King,
 while we sing her awful glory,
 far above our fancy's reach,
 let our hearts be quick to offer
 love the heart alone can teach.

Ascribed to St. Bernard of Cluny (12th C.), tr. Henry Bittleston

58 Day by day in the market place

Aimé Duval

Chorus

Day by day in the mar- ket place I play my flute all

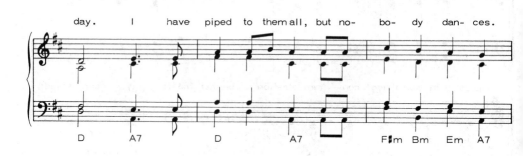

day. I have piped to them all, but no- bo- dy dan- ces.

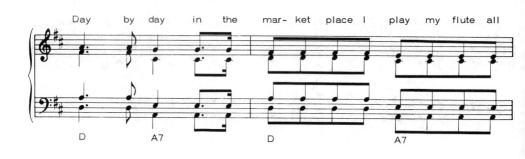

Day by day in the mar- ket place I play my flute all

day, and who- ev- er you be, won't you dance with me.

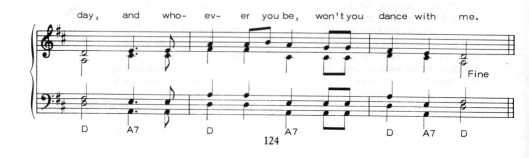

Fine

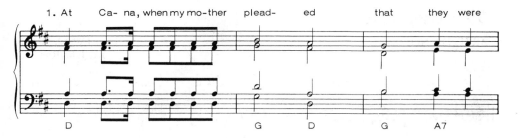

1. At Ca-na, when my mo-ther plead-ed that they were

short of wine, I gave them all the wine they

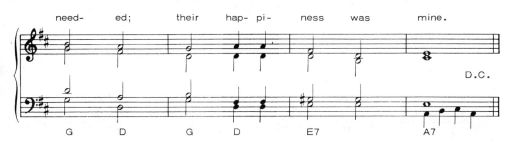

need-ed; their hap-pi-ness was mine.

D.C.

2 Once, when I found poor Peter quaking,
   I let him walk the sea.
   I filled their fishing nets to breaking
   that day in Galilee.

3 While all the world despised the sinner
   I showed him hope again,
   and gave the honours at that dinner
   to Mary Magdalene.

4 Lazarus from the tomb advancing
   once more drew life's sweet breath.
   You too will leave the churchyard dancing,
   for I have conquered death.

Aime Duval

125

59 Day is done

AR HYD Y NOS (84 84 8884)

Traditional Welsh Melody
arr. John Rombaut

Day is done, but Love un-fail- ing dwells ev- er

here; sha- dows fall, but hope, pre-vail- ing,

calms ev- 'ry fear. Lov- ing Fa- ther, none for-sa- king,

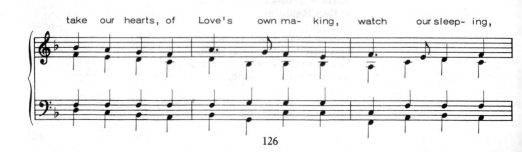

take our hearts, of Love's own ma- king, watch our sleep- ing,

guard   our wak-   ing,   be   al-   ways   near!

2 Dark descends, but Light unending
  shines through our night;
  you are with us, ever lending
  new strength to sight;
  one in love, your truth confessing,
  one in hope of heaven's blessing,
  may we see, in love's possessing,
  love's endless light!

3 Eyes will close, but you, unsleeping,
  watch by our side;
  death may come: in love's safe keeping
  still we abide.
  God of love, all evil quelling,
  sin forgiving, fear dispelling,
  stay with us, our hearts indwelling,
  this eventide!

James Quinn

60 Dear Lord and Father

REPTON (86 886)

C.H.H.Parry (1848–1918)

Dear Lord and Fa- ther of man-kind, for- give our fool- ish ways! Re- clothe us in our right- ful mind, in pur- er lives thy ser- vice find, in deep- er rev- 'rence praise, in deep- er rev- 'rence praise.

2 In simple trust like theirs who heard
   beside the Syrian sea,
   the gracious calling of the Lord,
   let us, like them, without a word,
   rise up and follow thee,
   rise up and follow thee.

3 O Sabbath rest by Galilee!
   O calm of hills above,
   where Jesus knelt to share with thee
   the silence of eternity,
   interpreted by love!
   interpreted by love!

4 Drop thy still dews of quietness,
   till all our strivings cease;
   take from our souls the strain and stress,
   and let our ordered lives confess
   The beauty of thy peace,
   The beauty of thy peace.

5 Breathe through the heats of our desire
   thy coolness and thy balm;
   let sense be dumb, let flesh retire;
   speak through the earthquake, wind and fire,
   O still small voice of calm!
   O still small voice of calm!

John Greenleaf Whittier (1807–92)

61 Dear maker of the starry skies

CREATOR ALME SIDERUM (8 8 8 8)

Based on a Plainsong Melody
Harmony by James O'Donnell

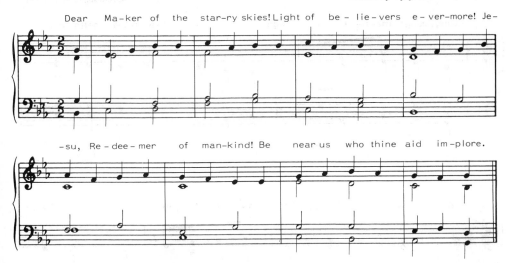

2 When man was sunk in sin and death,
lost in the depth of Satan's snare,
love brought thee down to cure our ills,
by taking of those ills a share.

3 Thou for the sake of guilty men
permitting thy pure blood to flow,
didst issue from thy virgin shrine
and to the cross a victim go.

4 So great the glory of thy might,
if we but chance thy name to sound,
at once all heaven and hell unite
in bending low with awe profound.

5 Great judge of all, in that last day,
when friends shall fail and foes combine,
be present then with us, we pray,
to guard us with thy arm divine.

6 To God the Father with the Son,
and Holy Spirit, one and three,
be honour, glory, blessing, praise,
all through the long eternity.

7th c., tr. Edward Caswall

Arrangement © 1984 Mayhew-McCrimmon Ltd

62 Ding Dong! merrily on high

BRANLE DE L'OFFICIAL (77 77 and refrain)

Melody from Arbeau's
Orchésographie, 1588

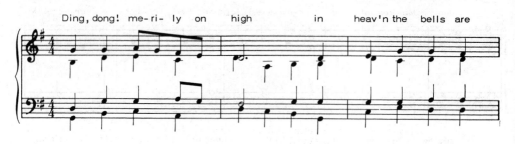

Ding, dong! me-ri-ly on high   in heav'n the bells are

ring- ing. Ding, dong! ve-ri-ly the sky is

riv'n with an- gels sing- ing.   Glo-

Chorus

ri- a. Ho- san- na in ex- cel- sis.

2 E'en so here below, below,
   let steeple bells be swungen,
   and io, io, io,
   by priest and people sungen.

3 Pray you, dutifully prime
   your matin chime, ye ringers;
   may you beautifully rime
   your evetime song, ye singers.

George Ratcliffe Woodward (1848–1934)

63 Do not worry

Sebastian Temple

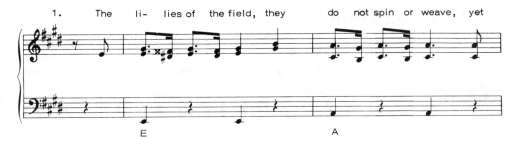

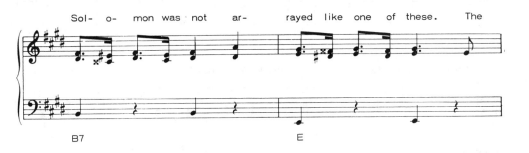

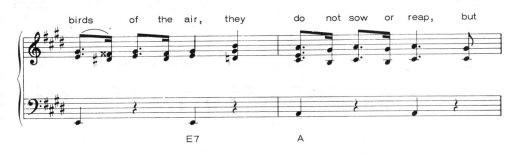

2 The Lord will guide you in his hidden way,
show you what to do and tell you what to say.
When you pray for rain, go build a dam to store
ev'ry drop of water you have asked him for.

3 The Lord knows all your needs before you ask.
Only trust in him for he will do the task
of bringing in your life whatever you must know.
He'll lead you through the darkness wherever you must go.

Sebastian Temple

64 Do you know

Sebastian Temple

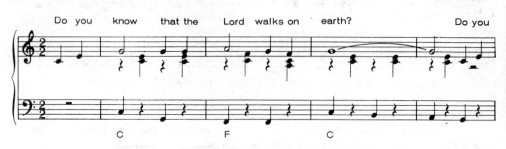

Do you know that the Lord walks on earth? Do you

know he is liv- ing here now? He is

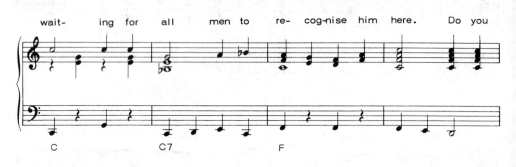

wait- ing for all men to re- cog-nise him here. Do you

know that the Lord walks on earth?

2 Do you know that he walks in disguise?
   Do you know he's in crowds ev'rywhere?
   Every place that you go, you may find that he is there.
   Do you know that the Lord's in disguise?

3 Do you know that the Lord thirsts so much?
   Do you know that he's sitting in jail?
   Ev'rywhere he is hungry and naked in the cold.
   Do you know he's rejected without care?

4 Do you know he is crucified each day?
   Do you know that he suffers and dies?
   Ev'rywhere he is lonely and waiting for a call.
   Do you know he is sick all alone?

5 Do you know that he wants to be free?
   Do you know he wants help from you and me?
   He has need of our hands and our feet and hearts to
   serve.
   Do you know he can work through men?

6 Do you know that the Lord dwells in men?
   Do you know he resides in their hearts?
   His face is shining in everyone we meet.
   Do you know he's disguised as ev'ry man?

7 Do you know that the Lord walks on earth?
   Do you know he is living here now?
   He is waiting for all men to recognise him here.
   Do you know he's disguised as ev'ry man?

Sebastian Temple

65   Draw nigh and take

GUSTATE (10 10 10 10)

Traditional Irish Melody
arr. Dom Gregory Murray O.S.B.

Draw nigh, and take the bo- dy of our Lord,
and drink the ho- ly blood for you out- poured,
saved by that bo- dy, hal- lowed by that blood,
where- by re- freshed we ren- der thanks to God.

2 Salvation's giver, Christ the only Son,
by that his cross and blood the victory won,
offered was he for greatest and for least;
himself the victim, and himself the priest.

3 Victims were offered by the law of old,
that, in a type, celestial mysteries told.
He, ransomer from death and light from shade,
giveth his holy grace his saints to aid.

4 Approach ye then with faithful hearts sincere,
and take the safeguard of salvation here,
he that in this world rules his saints and shields,
to all believers life eternal yields.

5 With heav'nly bread makes them that hunger whole,
gives living waters to the thirsty soul,
Alpha and Omega, to whom shall bow
all nations at the doom, is with us now.

From the Antiphonary of Bennchar (7th C.) tr. J. M. Neale

66 Dust, dust and ashes

Traditional

2 They crucified my saviour and nailed him to the cross...

3 And Mary came a-running her saviour for to see...

4 The angels said: "He's not here, he's gone to Galilee..."

5 He rose, he rose, he rose up, he rose up from the dead...

Traditional

67 Eternal Father, strong to save

MELITA (88 88 88)

J.B.Dykes (1823–76)

2 O Saviour, whose almighty word
   the winds and waves submissive heard,
   who walkedst on the foaming deep
   and calm amid its rage didst sleep:
   O hear us when we cry to thee
   for those in peril on the sea.

3 O sacred Spirit, who didst brood
   upon the waters dark and rude,
   and bid their angry tumult cease,
   and give, for wild confusion, peace:
   O hear us when we cry to thee
   for those in peril on the sea.

4 O Trinity of love and power,
   our brethren shield in danger's hour.
   From rock and tempest, fire and foe,
   protect them whereso'er they go,
   and ever let there rise to thee
   glad hymns of praise from land and sea.

W. Whiting (1825–78)

68 Faith of our fathers

SAWSTON (88 88 and chorus)

Traditional Melody

Faith of our fathers! living still in spite of dungeon, fire, and sword: oh, how our hearts beat high with joy when-e'er we hear that glorious word. Faith of our fathers! Holy Faith! We will be true to thee till death, we will be true to thee till death.

Chorus

2 Our fathers, chained in prisons dark,
   were still in heart and conscience free;
   how sweet would be their children's fate,
   if they, like them, could die for thee!

3 Faith of our fathers, Mary's prayers,
   shall win our country back to thee;
   and through the truth that comes from God
   England shall then indeed be free.

4 Faith of our fathers, we will love
   both friend and foe in all our strife,
   and preach thee too, as love knows how,
   by kindly words and virtuous life.

Frederick William Faber (1814–63)

69 Father and life-giver

PRINCETHORPE (65 65 D)

W. Pitts (1829–1903)

Fa- ther and life- giv- er, grace of Christ im- part;

he, the word in- car- nate - food for mind and heart.

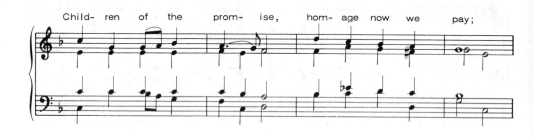

Child- ren of the prom- ise, hom- age now we pay;

sac- ri- fi- cial ban- quet cheers the des- ert way.

2 Wine and bread the symbols –
love and life convey,
offered by your people,
work and joy portray.
All we own consigning,
nothing is retained;
tokens of our service,
gifts and song contain.

3 Transformation wondrous
water into wine;
mingled in the Godhead
we are made divine.
Birth into his body
brought us life anew,
total consecration –
fruit from grafting true.

4 Christ, the head and members
　living now as one,
　offered to the Father
　by this holy Son;
　and our adoration
　purified we find,
　through the Holy Spirit
　breathing in mankind.　　　　*A.J. Newman*

70　**Father most holy**

CHRISTE SANCTORUM (11 11 11 3)

From La Feillee,
Méthode du Plain Chant (1782)

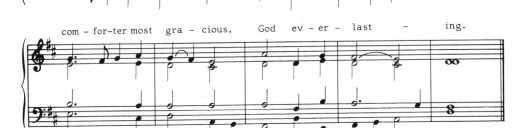

2 Three in a wondrous unity unbroken,
　one perfect Godhead, love that never faileth,
　light of the angels, succour of the needy,
　hope of all living.

3 All thy creation serveth its creator,
　thee every creature praiseth without ceasing,
　we too would sing the psalms of true devotion:
　hear, we beseech thee.

4 Lord God almighty unto thee be glory,
　one in three persons, over all exalted.
　Thine, as is meet, be honour, praise and blessing
　now and forever.

　　　　　　　10th c., tr. A. E. Alston

71 Father, within thy house today

SURREY (88 88 88)

H. Carey (1685–1743)

Fa- ther, with- n thy house to- day we

wait thy kind- ly love to see:

since thou hast said in truth that they who

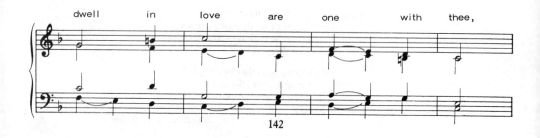

dwell in love are one with thee,

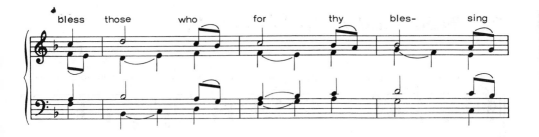

bless those who for thy bles- sing

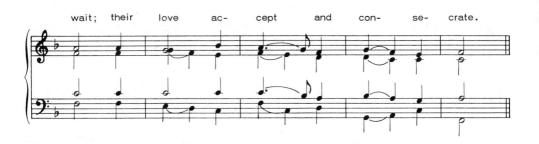

wait; their love ac- cept and con- se- crate.

2 Blest Spirit, who with life and light
didst quicken chaos to thy praise,
whose energy, in sin's despite,
still lifts our nature up to grace,
bless those who here in troth consent,
Creator, crown thy sacrament.

3 Great one in three, of whom are named
all families in earth and heaven,
hear us, who have thy promise claimed,
and let a wealth of grace be given,
grant them in life and death to be
each knit to each, and both to thee.

Robert Hugh Benson (1871–1914)

72 Feed us now

Peter Allen

2 The ones who didn't listen,
  the rich, the safe, the sure,
  they didn't think they needed
  the offering of a cure.

3 It's hard for us to listen,
  things haven't changed at all.
  We've got the things we wanted;
  we don't want to hear your call.

4 Yet millions still have hunger,
  disease, no homes, and fear.
  We offer them so little,
  and it costs them very dear.

5 So help us see the writing,
  written clear upon the wall:
  he who doesn't feed his neighbour
  will get no food at all.

Peter Allen

73 Fight the good fight

DUKE STREET (88 88)

J. Hatton (d. 1793)

Fight the good fight with all thy might! Christ is thy

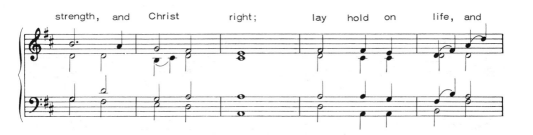

strength, and Christ right; lay hold on life, and

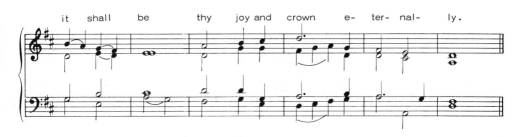

it shall be thy joy and crown e- ter- nal- ly.

2 Run the straight race through God's good grace,
  life up thine eyes and seek his face;
  life with its way before us lies,
  Christ is the path, and Christ the prize.

3 Cast care aside, upon thy Guide
  lean, and his mercy will provide
  lean, and the trusting soul shall prove
  Christ is its life, and Christ its love.

4 Faint not nor fear, his arms are near,
  he changeth not, and thou art dear;
  only believe, and thou shalt see
  that Christ is all in all to thee.

J. S. B. Monsell (1811–75)

145

74 Fill my house

Peter Kearney

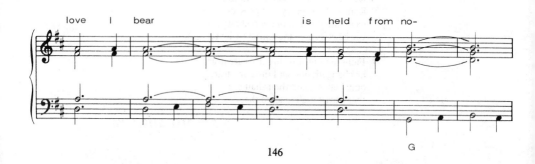

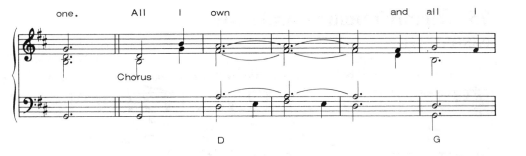

one.   All   I   own   and   all   I

Chorus

D   G

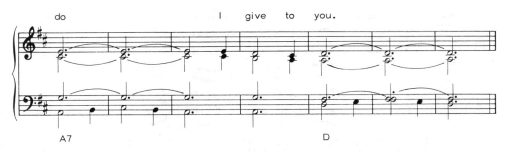

do   I   give   to   you.

A7   D

2 Take my time unto the fullest.
  Find in me the trust you seek,
  and take my hands to you outreaching.

3 Christ our Lord with love enormous
  from the cross his lesson taught
  – to love all men as I have loved you.

4 Join with me as one in Christ-love.
  May our hearts all beat as one,
  and may we give ourselves completely.

Peter Kearney

75 Firmly I believe and truly

OMNI DIE (87 87)

From *Corner's Gesangbuch*, 1631
arr. by W.S.Rockstro

2 And I trust and hope most fully
    in that manhood crucified;
    and each thought and deed unruly
    do to death, as he has died.

3 Simply to his grace and wholly
    light and life and strength belong;
    and I love supremely, solely,
    him the holy, him the strong.

4 And I hold in veneration,
    for the love of him alone,
    Holy Church, as his creation,
    and her teachings, as his own.

5 Adoration aye be given,
    with and through the angelic host,
    to the God of earth and heaven,
    Father, Son and Holy Ghost.

John Henry Newman (1801–90)

76 Follow Christ

Sebastian Temple
arr. James O'Donnell

1. Fol- low Christ and love the world as he did, when he walked u- pon the earth. Love each friend and e- ne- my as he did. In God's eyes we have e- qual worth.

2 Follow Christ and serve the world as he did
when he ministered to ev'ryone.
Serve each friend and enemy as he did
so that the Father's will be done.

3 He said: "Love each other as I love you.
By this all men will know you're mine.
As I served you I ask that you do.
This new commandment I assign."

4 Follow Christ and love the world as he did
when he walked upon the earth.
Love each friend and enemy as he did.
In God's eyes we have equal worth.

Sebastian Temple.

77   For all the saints

SINE NOMINE (10 10 10 4)

R. Vaughan Williams (1872–1958)

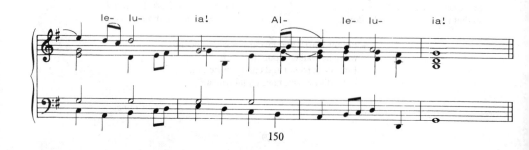

2 Thou wast their rock, their fortress, and their might;
thou, Lord, their captain in the well-fought fight;
thou in the darkness drear their one true light.

3 O may thy soldiers, faithful, true and bold,
fight as the saints who nobly fought of old,
and win, with them, the victor's crown of gold.

4 O blest communion! fellowship divine!
We feebly struggle, they in glory shine;
yet all are one in thee, for all are thine.

5 And when the strife is fierce, the warfare long,
steals on the ear the distant triumph-song,
and hearts are brave again, and arms are strong.

6 The golden evening brightens in the west;
soon, soon to faithful warriors cometh rest:
sweet is the calm of paradise the blest.

7 But lo! there breaks a yet more glorious day;
the saints triumphant rise in bright array:
the king of glory passes on his way.

8 From earth's wide bounds, from ocean's farthest coast,
through gates of pearl streams in the countless host,
singing to Father, Son and Holy Ghost.

William Walsham How (1823–97)

78 Forth in the peace of Christ

ANGEL'S SONG (Song 34)(88 88)   Orlando Gibbons (1583–1625)

Forth in the peace Christ we go; Christ to the world with

joy we bring; Christ in our minds, Christ on our

lips, Christ in our hearts, the world's true King.

A higher setting of this tune will be found at No. 79

2 King of our hearts, Christ makes us kings;
  kingship with him his servants gain;
  with Christ, the Servant-Lord of all,
  Christ's world we serve to share Christ's reign.

3 Priests of the world, Christ sends us forth
  the world of time to consecrate,
  the world of sin by grace to heal,
  Christ's world in Christ to re-create.

4 Christ's are our lips, his word we speak;
  prophets are we whose deeds proclaim
  Christ's truth in love that we may be
  Christ in the world, to spread Christ's name.

5 We are the Church; Christ bids us show
  that in his Church all nations find
  their hearth and home where Christ restores
  true peace, true love, to all mankind.

James Quinn, S.J.

See also hymn 744

79 Forth in thy name, O Lord

ANGEL'S SONG (Song 34)(88 88)   Orlando Gibbons (1583–1625)

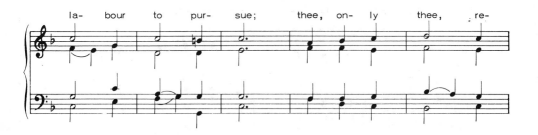

A lower setting of this tune will be found at No. 78

2 The task thy wisdom hath assigned
  O let me cheerfully fulfil;
  in all my works thy presence find,
  and prove thy good and perfect will.

3 Thee may I set at my right hand,
  whose eyes my inmost substance see,
  and labour on at thy command,
  and offer all my works to thee.

4 Give me to bear thy easy yoke,
  and every moment watch and pray,
  and still to things eternal look,
  and hasten to thy glorious day;

5 For thee delightfully employ
  whate'er thy bounteous grace hath given,
  and run my course with even joy,
  and closely walk with thee to heaven.

Charles Wesley (1707–88)

80 Forty days and forty nights

HEINLEIN (7 7 7 7)   from *Nurnbergisches Gesangbuch*, 1676

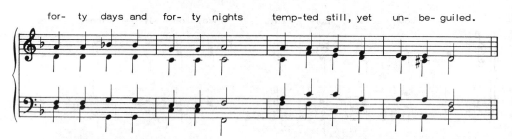

2 Sunbeams scorching all the day,
  chilly dew-drops nightly shed,
  prowling beasts about thy way,
  stones thy pillow, earth thy bed.

3 Let us thy endurance share
  and from earthly greed abstain
  with thee watching unto prayer,
  with thee strong to suffer pain.

4 Then if evil on us press,
  flesh or spirit to assail,
  victor in the wilderness,
  help us not to swerve or fail!

5 So shall peace divine be ours;
  holier gladness ours shall be,
  come to us angelic powers,
  such as ministered to thee.

6 Keep, O keep us, Saviour dear,
  ever constant by thy side,
  that with thee we may appear
  at the eternal Eastertide.

George Hunt Smyttan (1822–70) and others

81 From the deep

DE PROFUNDIS (65 65)   Kevin Mayhew

lis- ten, Lord, to my ap- peal, none but you can help.

2 If you count our grievous sins,
no man will be spared,
but your mercy still forgives,
in your love we trust.

3 Night and day my spirit waits,
longs to see my God,
like a watchman, weary, cold,
waiting for the dawn.

4 Open-handed is the Lord,
swift to pardon us:
he will lead his people free,
clean from all their sins.

5 Glory be to God our Lord,
merciful and kind,
Father, Son and Holy Ghost,
now and evermore.

Paraphrased from Psalm 129 by Luke Connaughton

82 From the depths we cry

CULBACH (77 77)

*From a chorale in
Heilige Seelenhurst, 1657*

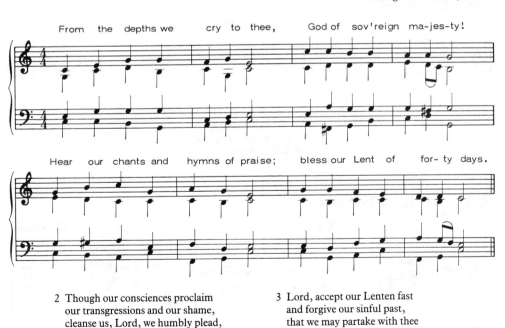

From the depths we cry to thee, God of sov'reign ma-jes-ty!

Hear our chants and hymns of praise; bless our Lent of for-ty days.

2 Though our consciences proclaim
our transgressions and our shame,
cleanse us, Lord, we humbly plead,
from our sins of thought and deed.

3 Lord, accept our Lenten fast
and forgive our sinful past,
that we may partake with thee
in the Easter mystery.

Based on Psalm 129 by Sister M. Teresine

83 Give me peace, O Lord

Estelle White

2 Give peace to the world, I pray,
let all quarrels cease today.
May we spread your light and love.
Lord, give us peace.

Estelle White

84 Sing Hosanna

Traditional

2 Give me peace in my heart, keep me resting,
  give me peace in my heart I pray.
  Give me peace in my heart, keep me resting.
  Keep me resting till the end of day.

3 Give me love in my heart, keep me serving,
  give me love in my heart, I pray.
  Give me love in my heart, keep me serving,
  keep me serving till the end of day.

Traditional

85   Give me yourself

Estelle White

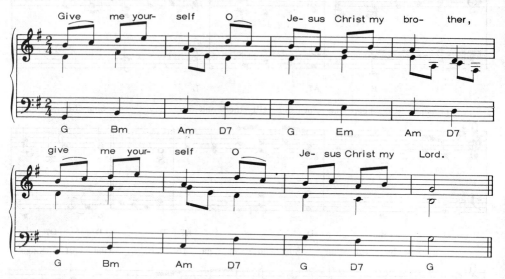

2 Give me your peace, O Jesus Christ my brother,
  give me your peace, O Jesus Christ my Lord.

3 Give me your love, O Jesus Christ my brother,
  give me your love, O Jesus Christ my Lord.

4 Give me your heart, O Jesus Christ my brother,
  give me your heart, O Jesus Christ my Lord.

Estelle White

86   Glorious God

Sebastian Temple

2 Glorious God, magnificent, holy,
  we love you, adore you, and come to you in pray'r.
  Glorious God, mighty, eternal,
  we sing your praise ev'rywhere.

Sebastian Temple

87 Glory be to God

Estelle White

Glo-ry be to God, the King of

kings. Ho-san-na, ho-san-na! Raise your voi-ces

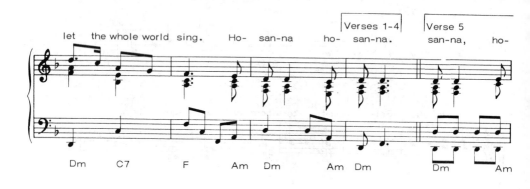

let the whole world sing. Ho-san-na ho-san-na.

Verses 1-4 | Verse 5

san-na, ho-

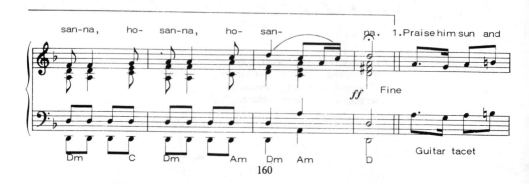

san-na, ho-san-na, ho-san- na. 1.Praise him sun and

Fine

Guitar tacet

160

2 Butterflies and silken moths and
   spiders in their webs,
   praise him streams and rounded stones that
   line a river bed.

3 Praise him concrete, glass and steel
   that form a city's face,
   piston rods and generators,
   satellites in space.

4 Praise him all the oceans and the
   waves upon the shore,
   albatross and kittiwake and
   seagulls as they soar.

5 Praise him all you people from the
   near and distant lands,
   praise him for the fruitful earth,
   his loving gift to man.

Estelle White

161

88 Glory be to Jesus

CASWALL (65 65)   F. Filitz (1804–76)

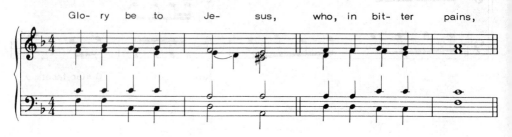

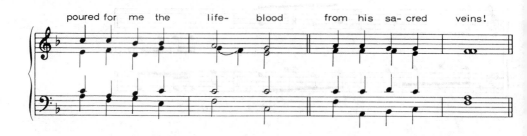

2 Grace and life eternal
   in that blood I find:
   blest be his compassion,
   infinitely kind.

3 Blest through endless ages
   be the precious streams,
   which from endless torment
   doth the world redeem.

4 There the fainting spirit
   drinks of life her fill;
   there as in a fountain
   laves herself at will.

5 Abel's blood for vengeance
   pleaded to the skies,
   but the blood of Jesus
   for our pardon cries.

6 Oft as it is sprinkled
   on our guilty hearts,
   Satan in confusion
   terror-struck departs.

7 Oft as earth exulting
   wafts its praise on high,
   hell with horror trembles;
   heaven is filled with joy.

8 Lift ye, then, your voices;
   swell the might flood;
   louder still and louder,
   praise the precious blood.

18th c., tr. Edward Caswall

89 Peruvian Gloria

Traditional Peruvian

2 Glory to God, glory to God,
Son of the Father.
Glory to God, glory to God,
Son of the Father.
To him be glory for ever.
To him be glory for ever.
Alleluia, amen.
Alleluia, amen,
alleluia, amen,
alleluia, amen.

3 Glory to God, glory to God,
glory to the Spirit.
Glory to God, glory to God,
glory to the Spirit.
To him be glory for ever.
To him be glory for ever.
Alleluia, amen.
Alleluia, amen,
alleluia, amen,
alleluia, amen.

Peruvian

This song is best sung accompanied only by bongos or a similar percussion instrument. The optional harmony notes give added effect, but those singing the tune should remain on the lower notes.

90   Glory to thee, Lord God

CORONA (66 86 D)

R.R. Terry (1865–1938)

Glo- ry to thee, Lord God! in faith and hope we sing.

Through this comple-ted sac- ri- fice our love and praise we bring.

We give thee for our sins a price beyond all worth,

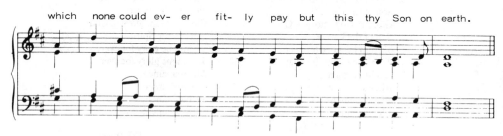

which none could ev- er fit- ly pay but this thy Son on earth.

2 Here is the Lord of all,
   to thee in glory slain;
   of worthless givers, worthy gift
   a victim without stain.
   Through him we give thee thanks,
   with him we bend the knee,
   in him be all our life, who is
   our one true way to thee.

3 So may this sacrifice
   we offer here this day,
   be joined with our poor lives in all
   we think and do and say.
   By living true to grace,
   for thee and thee alone,
   our sorrows, labours, and our joys
   will be his very own.

John Greally

91   Glory to thee, my God, this night

TALLIS' CANON (88 88)   Thomas Tallis (c.1510–85)

2 Forgive me, Lord, for thy dear Son,
the ill that I this day have done,
that with the world, myself and thee,
I, ere I sleep, at peace may be.

3 Teach me to live, that I may dread
the grave as little as my bed;
teach me to die, that so I may
rise glorious at the awful day.

4 O may my soul on thee repose
and with sweet sleep mine eyelids close,
sleep that may me more vigorous make
to serve my God when I awake.

5 Praise God, from whom all blessings flow;
praise him, all creatures here below;
praise him above, ye heavenly host;
praise Father, Son, and Holy Ghost.

T. Ken (1637–1711)

92 Go, tell it on the mountain

Traditional
arr. Stephen Dean

Chorus

Go, tell it on the moun-tain, ov-er the hills and ev'-ry where.

Go, tell it on the moun-tain that Je-sus Christ is born.

1. While shep-herds kept their watch-ing o'er wand'ring flocks by night, be-

hold from out of hea-ven there shone a ho-ly light.

2 And lo, when they had seen it,
they all bowed down and prayed,
they travelled on together
to where the Babe was laid.

3 When I was a seeker,
I sought both night and day:
I asked my Lord to help me
and he showed me the way.

4 He made me a watchman
upon the city wall,
And if I am a Christian,
I am the least of all.

Traditional

93 God be in my head

GOD BE IN MY HEAD (Irreg.)

Walford Davies (1869–1941)

God be in my head, and in my un- der-stand-ing;

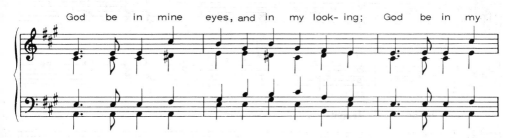

God be in mine eyes, and in my look- ing; God be in my

mouth, and in my speak- ing; God be in my heart, and in my

think- ing; God be at mine end, and at my de- part- ing.

Book of Hours (1514)

94 God everlasting

CHRISTE SANCTORUM (11 11 11 5)

From La Feillée's
Methode du Plainchant, 1782

2 Countless the mercies thou hast lavished on us,
source of all blessing to all creatures living;
to thee we render, for thy love o'erflowing.
Humble thanksgiving.

3 Now in remembrance of our great redeemer,
dying on Calvary, rising and ascending,
through him we offer what he ever offers,
sinners befriending.

4 Strength to the living rest to the departed,
grant, Holy Father, through this pure oblation:
may the life-giving bread for every bring us
health and salvation.

Harold Riley

95 Godhead here in hiding

ADORO TE (11 11 11 11)

Plainsong, harmonized by
Dom Gregory Murray O.S.B.

God-head here in hid-ing, whom I do a-dore,
masked by these bare shad-ows, shape and no-thing more,
see, Lord, at thy ser-vice low lies here a heart
lost, all lost in won-der at the God thou art.

2 Seeing, touching, tasting are in thee deceived;
how says trusty hearing? That shall be believed;
what God's Son hath told me, take for truth I do;
truth himself speaks truly, or there's nothing true.

3 On the cross thy Godhead made no sign to men;
here thy very manhood steals from human ken;
both are my confession, both are my belief;
and I pray the prayer of the dying thief.

4 I am not like Thomas, wounds I cannot see,
but can plainly call thee Lord and God as he;
this faith each day deeper be my holding of,
daily make me harder hope and dearer love.

5 O thou our reminder of Christ crucified,
living Bread, the life of us for whom he died,
lend this life to me then; feed and feast my mind,
there be thou the sweetness man was meant to find.

6 Jesu, whom I look at shrouded here below,
I beseech thee send me what I long for so,
some day to gaze on thee face to face in light
and be blest for ever with thy glory's sight.

Ascribed to St. Thomas Aquinas (1227–74), tr. Gerard Manley Hopkins

96 God is love

Anonymous

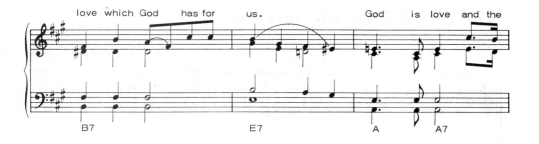

2 God is hope ...

3 God is peace ...

4 God is joy ...

Anonymous

97 God is love: his the care

THEODORIC

From *Piae Cantiones*, 1582
harmonized by John Rombaut

God is love: his the care, tending each, everywhere. God is love, all is there!

Je- sus came to show him, that man- kind might know him!

Sing a- loud, loud, loud! Sing a- loud, loud, loud!

God is good! God is truth! God is beau- ty! Praise him!

2 None can see God above;
all have here man to love;
thus may we Godward move,
finding him in others,
holding all men brothers:

3 Jesus lived here for men:
strove and died, rose again,
rules our hearts, now as then;
for he came to save us
by the truth he gave us:

4 To our Lord praise we sing,
light and life, friend and king,
coming down love to bring,
pattern for our duty,
showing God in beauty:

Percy Dearmer
(1867–1936)

98 God of mercy and compassion

AU SANG QU'UN DIEU (87 87 D)

Traditional French Melody
adapted by G. Pergolesi

God of mer-cy and com-pas-sion, look with pi-ty up-on me; Fa-ther,

let me call thee Fa-ther, 'tis thy child re-turns to thee. Je-sus,

Chorus

Lord, I ask for mer-cy; let me not im-plore in vain; all my

sins I now de-test them, nev-er will I sin a-gain.

2 By my sins I have deserved
   death and endless misery,
   hell with all its pain and torments,
   and for all eternity.

3 By my sins I have abandon'd
   right and claim to heaven above,
   where the saints rejoice for ever,
   in a boundless sea of love.

4 See our Saviour, bleeding, dying,
   on the cross of Calvary;
   to that cross my sins have nail'd him,
   yet he bleeds and dies for me.

E. Vaughan (1827–1908)

99 Go, tell everyone

Hubert Richards

174

and set the * down-trod-len free, and go

tell ev'- ry one the news that the King-dom of

God has come, and go tell ev'- ry- one the

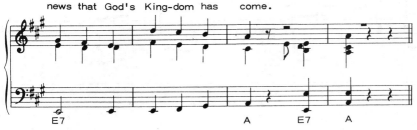

news that God's King-dom has come.

2 Just as the Father sent me,
so I'm sending you out to be
my witnesses throughout the world,
the whole of the world.

3 Don't carry a load in your pack,
you don't need two shirts on your back.
A workman can earn his own keep,
can earn his own keep.

4 Don't worry what you have to say,
don't worry because on that day
God's spirit will speak in your heart,
will speak in your heart.

Alan Dale

175

100 Going home

Traditional Spiritual

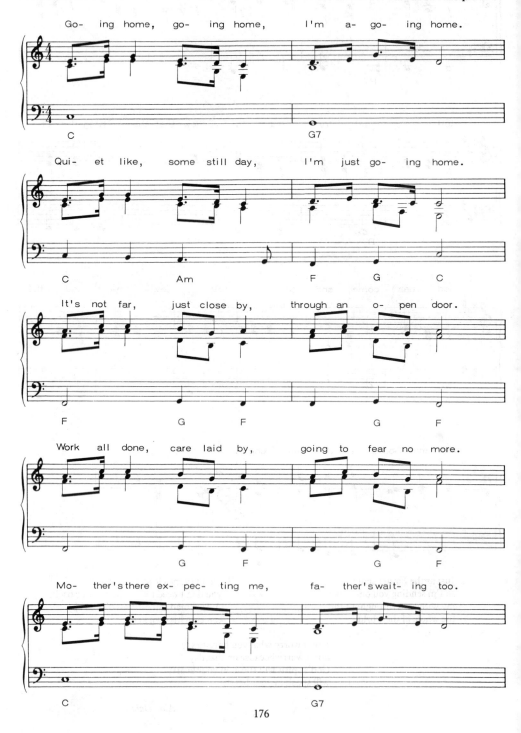

Go- ing home, go- ing home, I'm a- go- ing home.

C   G7

Qui- et like, some still day, I'm just go- ing home.

C   Am   F   G   C

It's not far, just close by, through an o- pen door.

F   G   F   G   F

Work all done, care laid by, going to fear no more.

G   F   G   F

Mo- ther's there ex- pec- ting me, fa- ther's wait- ing too.

C   G7

Lots of folk ga- thered there, all the friends I knew,

all the friends I knew.

2 Morning star lights the way,
restless dreams all done.
Shadows gone, break of day,
real life just begun.
There's no break, there's no end,
just a living on,
wide awake with a smile,
going on and on.
Going home, going home,
I'm just going home.
It's not far, just close by,
through an open door.
I'm just going home.

William Arms Fisher

101   Gonna lay down my sword and shield

Traditional Spiritual

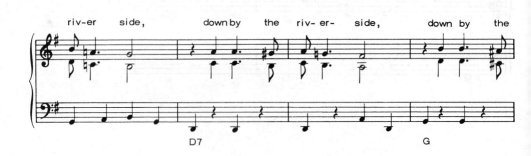

2 Gonna walk with the Prince of Peace
  down by the riverside,
  down by the riverside,
  down by the riverside.
  Gonna walk with the Prince of Peace
  down by the riverside.
  I ain't gonna study war no more.

3 Gonna shake hands around the world
  down by the riverside,
  down by the riverside,
  down by the riverside.
  Gonna shake hands around the world
  down by the riverside.
  I ain't gonna study war no more.

Traditional Spiritual

102   Go, the Mass is ended

Sr Marie L. Pereira
arr. James O'Donnell

2 Go, the Mass is ended,
  take his love to all.
Gladden all who meet you,
fill their hearts with hope and courage.
Go, the Mass is ended,
fill the world with love,
and give to all what you've received
– the peace and joy of Christ.

3 Go, the mass is ended,
  strengthened in the Lord,
lighten ev'ry burden,
spread the joy of Christ around you.
Go, the Mass is ended,
take his peace to all.
This day is yours to change the world
– to make God known and loved.

Sister Marie Lydia Pereira

Harmony © 1984 Mayhew-McCrimmon Ltd

103 Great Saint Andrew

CONTEMPLATION (87 87 D)   Felix Mendelssohn (1809–47)

Great Saint An- drew, friend of Je- sus, lov- er of his glo- rious cross,

ear- ly by his voice ef- fec- tive called from ease to pain and loss,

strong Saint An- drew, Si- mon's bro-ther, who with haste fra- ter- nal flew,

fain with him to share the trea- sure which, at Je- sus' lips he drew.

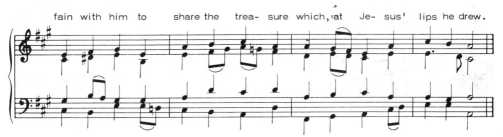

2 Blest Saint Andrew, Jesus' herald,
  true apostle, martyr bold,
  who, by deeds his words confirming,
  sealed with blood the truth he told.
  Ne'er to king was crown so beauteous,
  ne'er was prize to heart so dear,
  as to him the cross of Jesus
  when its promised joys drew near.

3 Loved Saint Andrew, Scotland's patron,
  watch thy land with heedful eye,
  rally round the cross of Jesus
  all her storied chivalry!
  To the Father, Son, and Spirit,
  front of sanctity and love,
  give we glory, now and ever,
  with the saints who reign above.

Frederick Oakeley (1802–80)

104   Guide me, O thou great Redeemer

CWM RHONDDA (87 87 47)   J. Hughes (1873–1932)

Guide me, O thou great Re-deemer, pil-grim through this bar-ren land;

I am weak, but thou art mighty; hold me with thy pow'r-ful hand:

bread of hea-ven, bread of hea-ven, feed me till I want no

more.   Feed me now till I want no more.

2 Open now the crystal fountain,
  whence the healing stream doth flow;
  let the fire and cloudy pillar
  lead me all my journey through;
  strong Deliverer,
  be thou still my strength and shield.

3 When I tread the verge of Jordan,
  bid my anxious fears subside,
  death of death, and hell's destruction,
  land me safe on Canaan's side;
  songs of praises,
  I will ever give to thee.

W. Williams (1717–91), tr. P. and W. Williams

105 Hail, glorious Saint Patrick

ST PATRICK (11 11 11 11)

Traditional Melody
arr. John Rombaut

Hail glo- rious Saint Pat- rick, dear saint of our isle, on

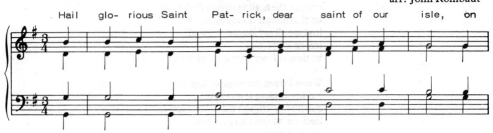

us thy poor chil-dren bes- tow a sweet smile; and now thou art high in the

man- sions ; a- bove, on E- rin's green val- leys look

down in thy love. On E- rin's green val- leys, on

Chorus

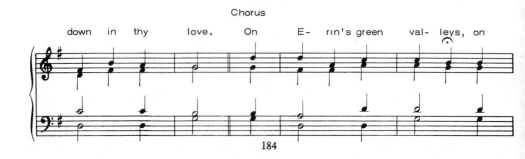

E- rin's green val- leys, on E- rin's green

val- leys look down in thy love.

2 Hail, glorious Saint Patrick! thy words were once strong
against Satan's wiles and an infidel throng;
not less is thy might where in heaven thou art;
O, come to our aid, in our battle take part.

3 In the war against sin, in the fight for the faith,
dear saint, may thy children resist unto death;
may their strength be in meekness, in penance, in prayer,
Their banner the Cross which they glory to bear.

4 Thy people, now exiles on many a shore,
shall love and revere thee till time be no more;
and the fire thou hast kindled shall ever burn bright,
Its warmth undiminished, undying its light.

5 Ever bless and defend the sweet land of our birth,
where the shamrock still blooms as when thou wert on earth,
and our hearts shall yet burn, wheresoever we roam,
For God and Saint Patrick, and our native home.

Sister Agnes

106 Hail, Queen of heaven

STELLA (88 88 88)

Traditional melody
arr. H.F.Hemy (1818–88)

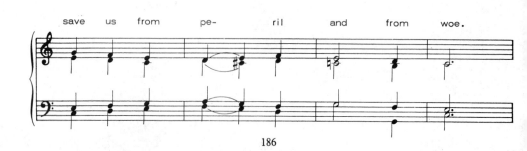

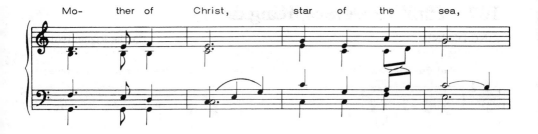

Mo- ther of Christ, star of the sea,

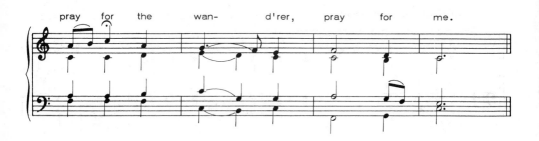

pray for the wan- d'rer, pray for me.

2 O gentle, chaste and spotless maid,
   we winners make our prayers through thee;
   remind thy son that he has paid
   the price of our iniquity.
   Virgin most pure, star of the sea,
   pray for the sinner, pray for me.

3 Sojourners in this vale of tears,
   to thee, blest advocate, we cry;
   pity our sorrows, calm our fears,
   and soothe with hope our misery.
   Refuge in grief, star of the sea,
   pray for the mourner, pray for me.

4 And while to him who reigns above,
   in Godhead One, in Persons Three,
   the source of life, of grace, of love,
   homage we pay on bended knee,
   do thou, bright Queen, star of the sea,
   pray for thy children, pray for me.

John Lingard (1771–1851)

107 Hail Redeemer, King divine

KING DIVINE (77 77 and refrain)

Charles Rigby (1901–62)

2 King whose name creation thrills,
rule our minds, our hearts, our wills,
till in peace each nation rings
with thy praises, King of kings.

3 King most holy, King of truth,
guide the lowly, guide the youth;
Christ thou King of glory bright,
be to us eternal light.

4 Shepherd-King, o'er mountains steep,
homeward bring the wandering sheep,
shelter in one royal fold
states and kingdoms, new and old.

Patrick Brennan

108   Hail the day that sees him rise

LLANFAIR (77 77 and alleluias)   R. Williams (1781–1821)

2 There for him high triumph waits;
  life your heads, eternal gates!
  He hath conquered death and sin;
  take the king of glory in!

3 Circled round with angel-powers,
  their triumphant Lord and ours;
  wide unfold the radiant scene,
  take the king of glory in!

4 Lo, the heaven its Lord receives,
  yet he loves the earth he leaves;
  though returning to his throne,
  still he calls mankind his own.

5 See! he lifts his hands above,
  see! he shows the prints of love;
  hark! his gracious lips bestow,
  blessings on his Church below.

6 Still for us he intercedes,
  his prevailing death he pleads;
  near himself prepares our place,
  he the first-fruits of our race.

7 Lord, though parted from our sight,
  far above the starry height,
  grant our hearts may thither rise,
  seeking thee above the skies.

8 Ever upward let us move,
  wafted on the wings of love;
  looking when our Lord shall come,
  longing, sighing after home.

Charles Wesley (1707–88),
Thomas Cotterill (1779–1823)
and others

109   Hail, thou star of ocean

LAUDES (65 65 D)   John Richardson (1816–79)

2 Break the captive's fetters,
  light on blindness pour,
  all our ills expelling,
  every bliss implore.
  Show thyself a mother;
  offer him our sighs,
  who for us incarnate
  did not thee despise.

3 Virgin of all virgins,
  to thy shelter take us;
  gentlest of the gentle,
  chaste and gentle make us.
  Still, as on we journey,
  help our weak endeavour;
  till with thee and Jesus
  we rejoice for ever.

4 Through the highest heaven,
  to the almighty Three,
  Father, Son and Spirit,
  One same glory be.

9th c., tr. Edward Caswall
190

110 Hail to the Lord's anointed

CRÜGER (76 76 D)

From a Melody in J.Crüger's
Gesangbuch adapted by W.H.Monk

Hail to the Lord's an-oin-ted, Great Da-vid's greater son! Hail, in the time ap-poin-ted, his reign on earth be-gun! He comes to break op-pres-sion, to set the cap-tive free, to take a-way trans-gres-sion, and rule in e-qui-ty.

2 He shall come down like showers
upon the fruitful earth,
and love, joy, hope, like flowers,
spring in his path to birth:
before him on the mountains
shall peace the herald go;
and righteousness in fountains
from hill to valley flow.

3 Kings shall fall down before him,
and gold and incense bring;
all nations shall adore him,
his praise all people sing;
to him shall prayer unceasing
and daily vows ascend;
his kingdom still increasing
a kingdom without end.

4 O'er every foe victorious,
he on his throne shall rest,
from age to age more glorious,
all-blessing and all-blest;
the tide of time shall never
his covenant remove;
his name shall stand for ever;
that name to us is love.

James Montgomery (1771–1854)

111 Happy the man

Sebastian Temple

Sebastian Temple

193

112 Hark! A herald voice

MERTON (76 76)

W.H.Monk

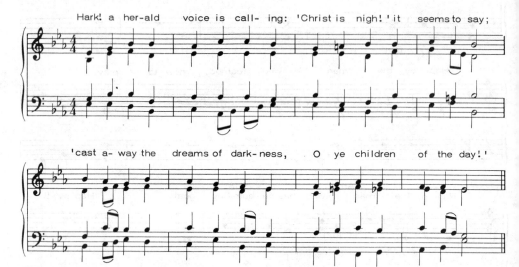

Hark! a her-ald voice is call-ing: 'Christ is nigh!' it seems to say;
'cast a-way the dreams of dark-ness, O ye children of the day!'

2 Startled at the solemn warning,
let the earth-bound soul arise;
Christ, her sun, all sloth dispelling,
shines upon the morning skies.

3 Lo! the Lamb, so long expected,
comes with pardon down from heaven;
let us haste, with tears of sorrow,
one and all to be forgiven;

4 So when next he comes with glory,
wrapping all the earth in fear,
may he then as our defender
on the clouds of heaven appear.

5 Honour, glory, virtue, merit,
to the Father and the Son,
with the co-eternal Spirit,
while unending ages run.

6th c., tr. Edward Caswall

113 Hark, the herald angels

MENDELSSOHN

Adapted from a chorus by
Felix Mendelssohn (1809–47)

Hark, the her-ald an-gels sing, glo-ry to the new-born

2 Christ, by highest heaven adored,
Christ, the everlasting Lord,
late in time behold him come,
offspring of a Virgin's womb!
Veiled in flesh the Godhead see,
hail the incarnate Deity!
Pleased as man with man to dwell,
Jesus, our Emmanuel.

3 Hail the heaven-born Prince of peace!
Hail the Son of Righteousness!
Light and life to all he brings
risen with healing in his wings;
mild he lays his glory by,
born that man no more may die,
born to raise the sons of earth,
born to give them second birth.

Charles Wesley (1743),
George Whitefield (1753),
Martin Madan (1760), and others

114 Haul, haul away

Kevin Mayhew

Haul, haul a-way. Haul, haul a-way. Cast the nets wide and

sink the nets deep and it's haul, haul a-way. Oh, he sat in the boat and he

Fine

spoke to the crowd. Haul, haul a-way. And his voice wasn't soft and his

voice wasn't loud. Haul, haul a-way. And he spoke of the just and the

pure and the free, and his voice caught the air like a net in the sea. And it's

D.C.

2 He said; "Cast your nets wide where the water
 is deep."
Haul, haul away.
"Oh, cast the nets wide, and sink the nets deep."
Haul, haul away.
"Though we've worked through the
 night and we've nothing to show,
we will try once again just because you say so."
And it's ...

3 Oh the catch it was huge and the boat it was small.
Haul, haul away.
His friends came to help when they heard Peter call.
Haul, haul away.
"You must leave us," said Peter, "for we're men
 of sin."
But he said: "Come with me and be fishers of men."
And it's ...

Michael Cockett

115 Help, Lord, the souls

BELMONT (86 86)

From *Islington Psalmody*, 1854

Help, Lord, the souls that thou hast made, the souls to
thee so dear, in pris- on for the
debt un- paid, of sins com- mit- ted here.

2 These holy souls, they suffer on,
 resigned in heart and will,
 until thy high behest is done,
 and justice has its fill.

3 For daily falls, for pardoned crime
 they joy to undergo
 the shadow of thy cross sublime,
 the remnant of thy woe.

4 Oh, by their patient of delay,
 their hope amid their pain,
 their sacred zeal to burn away
 disfigurement and stain;

5 Oh, by their fire of love, not less
 in keenness than the flame;
 oh, by their very helplessness,
 oh, by thy own great name;

6 Good Jesus, help! sweet Jesus, aid
 the souls to thee most dear,
 in prison for the debt unpaid
 of sins committed here.

John Henry Newman (1801–90)

116   Here's a child for you

Estelle White

Here's a child for you, O Lord, we shall cher-ish,
we shall care. We'll be faith-ful to your Word
for we want this child to share your love-light.

2 May he hold his head up high,
 graceful, joyful, strong of limb.
 May his eyes be clear and bright,
 seeing beauty in all things
 that you've made.

3 We were young ourselves, O Lord,
 we were eager, we were fresh
 like the opening buds of spring,
 and we wanted happiness
 in your way.

4 Then, at times, we went astray,
we were foolish, we were weak,
and the innocence we had
vanished like the trace of feet
when snow melts.

5 But we come, O Lord and king,
at your bidding, and we pray
that the precious gift we bring
will grow stronger every day
in your love.

6 By the water poured out here
and our promise, we believe,
he will master every fear,
and at last will come to see
your Godhead.

Estelle White

117 He's got the whole world

Traditional

2 He's got you and me, brother ...

3 He's got you and me, sister ...

4 He's got everybody here ...

5 He's got the whole world ...   *Traditional*

118　He was born like you and I

Hubert Richards

He was born like you and I in a bo-dy which must die, yet his

Dm　　　　　　　　　Gm

death was not for ev-er he lives on. Who is this, like you and I who was

Dm　　　　　　　A　A7　　D

born to live and die, yet his death was not for ev- er he lives on.

G　　　　　Bm　　Em　A　D

Chorus

Deep, deep, deep, is the my-ste-ry I sing. Dark, dark, dark, is the rid- dle. He was born like you and I in a bo- dy which must die yet his death was not for ev- er: he lives on.

2 Not a soul, so it is said,
saw him raised up from the dead,
yet by now the story's known throughout the world.
Who is this whom it is said
no one saw raised from the dead,
yet by now the story's known throughout the world?

3 His believers, when they've met,
know he's there with them, and yet
he's with God (what makes us think that's somewhere else?).
Who is this who, when they've met,
is right there with them, and yet
he's with God (what makes us think that's somewhere else?)

Hubert Richards

119   He who would valiant be

MONK'S GATE (11 11 12 11)

Adapted from an English traditional melody
by R. Vaughan Williams (1872–1958)

2 Who so beset him round
   with dismal stories,
   do but themselves confound:
   his strength the more is.
   No foes shall stay his might
   though he with giants fight;
   he will make good his right
   to be a pilgrim.

3 Since, Lord, thou dost defend
   us with thy Spirit,
   we know we at the end
   shall life inherit.
   Then fancies flee away!
   I'll fear not what men say,
   I'll labour night and day
   to be a pilgrim.

Percy Dearmer (1867–1936),
after John Bunyan (1628–88)

120 Holy Father, God of might

VIENNA (77 77)

J.H.Knecht (1752–1817)

2 Hear the songs your people raise,
songs of joyful thanks and praise,
calling all created things
to adore you, King of kings.

3 Christ, be with us as we go,
let this blind world see and know,
burning in our lives, the sight
of its only saving light.

4 So, all men will bless your name,
and kingship all proclaim,
praising with the heavenly host
Father, Son and Holy Ghost.

Anonymous

121 Holy God, we praise thy name

GROSSER GOTT (78 78 77)

From *Katholisches Gesangbuch*, 1774

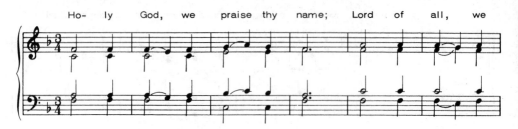

Ho- ly God, we praise thy name; Lord of all, we

bow be- fore thee! All on earth thy scep- tre own,

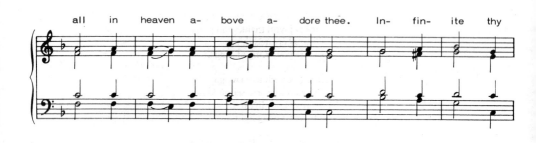

all in heaven a- bove a- dore thee. In- fin- ite thy

vast do- main, ev- er- last- ing is thy reign.

2 Hark! the loud celestial hymn,
  angel choirs above are raising;
  cherubim and seraphim,
  in unceasing chorus praising,
  fill the heavens with sweet accord,
  holy, holy, holy Lord.

3 Holy Father, holy Son,
  Holy Spirit, three we name thee.
  While in essence only one
  Undivided God we claim thee;
  and adoring bend the knee,
  while we own the mystery.

4 Spare thy people, Lord, we pray,
  by a thousand snares surrounded;
  keep us without sin to-day;
  never let us be confounded.
  Lo, I put my trust in thee,
  never, Lord, abandon me.

C. A. Walworth (1820–1900)

122 Holy holy

Jimmy Owens

2 Gracious Father, gracious Father,
  we are glad to be your children, gracious Father.
  And we lift our heads before you as a token of our love,
  gracious Father, gracious Father.

3 Precious Jesus, precious Jesus,
  we are glad you have redeemed us, precious Jesus.
  And we lift our hands before you as a token of our love,
  precious Jesus, precious Jesus.

4 Holy Spirit, Holy Spirit,
   come and fill our hearts anew, Holy Spirit.
   And we lift our voice before you as a token of our love,
   Holy Spirit, Holy Spirit.

5 Hallelujah, hallelujah,
   hallelujah, hallelujah, hallelujah.
   And we lift our hearts before you as a token of our love,
   hallelujah, hallelujah.

Jimmy Owens

123 Holy, holy, holy! Lord God almighty

NICAEA (11 12 12 10)   J.B.Dykes (1823–76)

2 Holy, holy, holy! All the saints adore thee.
   Casting down their golden crowns around the glassy sea;
   Cherubim and seraphim falling down before thee,
   which wert, and art, and evermore shall be.

3 Holy, holy, holy! Though the darkness hide thee,
   though the eye of sinful man thy glory may not see,
   only thou art holy, there is none beside thee,
   perfect in power, in love, and purity.

4 Holy, holy, holy! Lord God almighty!
   All thy works shall praise thy name, in earth, and sky, and sea;
   holy, holy, holy! Merciful and mighty!
   God in three persons, blessed Trinity!

Reginald Heber (1783–1875)

124 Holy Spirit, Lord of light

VENI SANCTE SPIRITUS (777 777) Samuel Webbe (1740–1816)

Ho-ly Spi-rit, Lord of Light, from the clear cel- est- ial height,

thy pure beam-ing ra- diance give, come, thou Fa- ther of the poor,

come with trea- sures which en- dure, come thou Light of all that live.

2 Thou, of all consolers best,
  thou, the soul's delightsome guest,
  dost refreshing peace bestow:
  thou in toil art comfort sweet;
  pleasant coolness in the heat;
  solace in the midst of woe.

3 Light immortal, light divine,
  visit thou these hearts of thine,
  and our inmost being fill:
  if thou take thy grace away,
  nothing pure in man will stay;
  all his good is turned to ill.

4 Heal our wounds, our strength renew;
  on our dryness pour thy dew;
  wash the stains of guilt away:
  Bend the stubborn heart and will;
  melt the frozen, warm the chill;
  guide the steps that go astray.

5 Thou, on those who evermore
  thee confess and thee adore,
  in thy sevenfold gifts descend:
  Give them comfort when they die;
  give them life with thee on high;
  give them joys that never end.

Ascribed to Stephen Langton (d. 1228)
tr. Edward Caswall

125 Holy Spirit of fire

John Glynn

Ho- ly Spi-rit of fire, flame ev-er- las- ting, so

G   D   C

bright and clear, speak this day in our hearts.

G   D

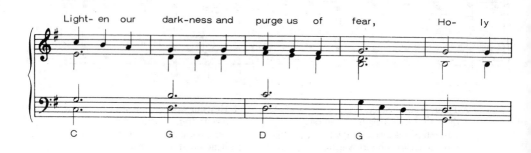

Light- en our dark-ness and purge us of fear, Ho- ly

C   G   D   G

Spi- rit of fire. The wind can blow or be still,

Fine   Chorus

D   G   C   G

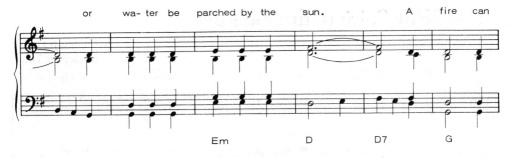

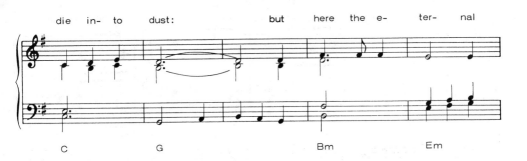

2 Holy Spirit of love,
   strong are the faithful who trust your pow'r.
   Love who conquer our will,
   teach us the words of the gospel of peace,
   Holy Spirit of love.

3 Holy Spirit of God,
   flame everlasting, so bright and clear,
   spark this day in our hearts.
   Lighten our darkness and purge us of fear,
   Holy Spirit of God.

John Glynn

126 Holy Virgin, by God's decree

VIERGE SAINTE (87 99)

Abbé P.Décha
arr. Stephen Dean

2 By your faith and loving accord,
   as the handmaid of the Lord,
   you undertook God's plan to embrace.
   Mary, we thank you, hail full of grace.

3 Refuge for your children so weak,
   sure protection all can seek.
   Problems of life you help us to face.
   Mary, we trust you, hail full of grace.

4 To our needy world of today
   love and beauty you portray,
   showing the path to Christ we must trace.
   Mary, our mother, hail, full of grace.

J. P. Lecot
tr. W. Raymond Lawrence

127 How dark was the stable

Kevin Mayhew

2 How cold was the stable where Jesus was born?
  How cold was the stable that was his first home?
  It was cold as the frost on a white window pane;
  it was cold as a heart that has known no love.

3 How light was the stable when Jesus was born?
  How light was the stable he made his first home?
  It was light as the star that was shining that night;
  it was light as an angel in splendour and might.

4 How warm was the stable when Jesus was born?
  How warm was the stable he made his first home?
  It was warm as the love of the first Christmas morn;
  it was warm as our hearts in which Jesus is born.

Michael Cockett

128   I am the bread of life

Kevin Mayhew

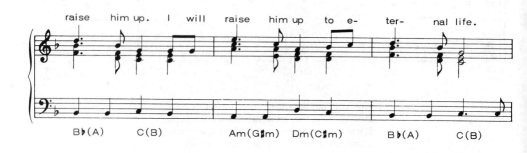

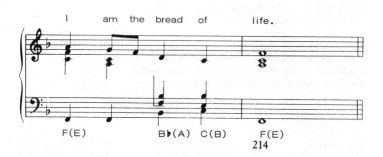

2 I am the spring of life.
   He who hopes in me will never be thirsty.
   I will raise him up. I will raise him up.
   I will raise him up to eternal life.
   I am the spring of life.

3 I am the way of life.
   He who follows me will never be lonely.
   I will raise him up. I will raise him up.
   I will raise him up to eternal life.
   I am the way of life.

4 I am the truth of life.
   He who looks for me will never seek blindly.
   I will raise him up. I will raise him up.
   I will raise him up to eternal life.
   I am the truth of life.

5 I am the life of life.
   He who dies with me will never die vainly.
   I will raise him up. I will raise him up.
   I will raise him up to eternal life.
   I am the life of life.

David Konstant

129 I believe in God almighty

Kevin Mayhew

I be- lieve in God al- migh- ty, who made heav'n and earth.

C   Cmaj7   Am   Em

I be- lieve in one Lord, Je- sus Christ, his on- ly Son.

F   Fmaj7   Dm   G

God from God and Light from Light, the one true God a- bove,

Am   Em

with the Fa- ther he is one, cre- a- tor of all things. Oh

f Chorus

F   Dm   G   G7

I be- lieve in God al- migh- ty who made heav'n and

C   Em   F   C   Dm   G

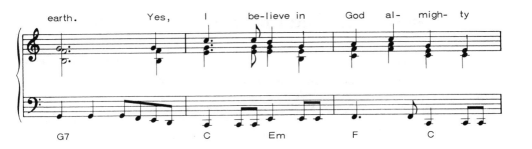

earth.   Yes,   I   be-lieve in   God   al-   migh- ty

G7   C   Em   F   C

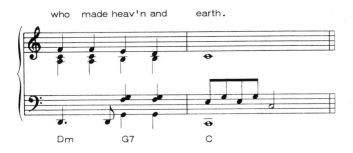

who   made heav'n and   earth.

Dm   G7   C

2 Through the Spirit, born of Mary,
  God became a man.
  For our sake he suffered death.
  They nailed him to a cross.
  But no earthly grace could hold
  the Lord of heav'n and earth;
  bursting forth he rose again,
  just as the prophets said.

3 Forty days he walked the earth,
  a dead man come alive.
  Then he bid his friends farewell,
  returning to his heav'n.
  He will come again to judge
  the living and the dead.
  He is Lord of all the worlds;
  his kingdom has no end.

4 I believe in God the Father,
  Spirit and the Son.
  I believe the Church is holy,
  universal, one.
  And through water all our guilt
  is cleansed-we are made new.
  Dying we will rise again
  to live for ever more.

Kevin Mayhew
(based on the Creed)

130 I believe in God the Father

SUSSEX (87 87)

Adapted from a traditional English Melody
by R. Vaughan Williams (1872–1958)

2 I believe what God has spoken
through his Church, whose word is true;
boldly she proclaims his Gospel,
ever old, yet ever new.

3 All my hope is in God's goodness,
shown for us by him who died,
Jesus Christ, the world's Redeemer,
spotless Victim crucified.

4 All my love is Love eternal;
in that Love I love mankind.
Take my heart, O Heart once broken,
take my soul, my strength, my mind.

5 Father, I have sinned against you;
look on me with eyes of love;
seek your wand'ring sheep, Good Shepherd;
grant heav'n's peace, O heavn'ly Dove.

6 Bless'd be God, the loving Father;
bless'd be God, his only Son;
bless'd be God, all-holy Spirit;
bless'd be God, for ever one.

James Quinn

131 Lord of the dance

Traditional Shaker tune arr. James O'Donnell

Harmony © 1984 Mayhew-McCrimmon Ltd

2 I danced for the scribe
and the pharisee,
but they would not dance
and they wouldn't follow me.
I danced for the fishermen,
for James and John;
they came with me
and the dance went on.

3 I danced on the Sabbath
and I cured the lame.
The holy people they
said it was a shame.
They whipped and they stripped
and they hung me on high,
and they left me there
on the cross to die.

4 I danced on a Friday
when the sky turned black.
It's hard to dance
with the devil on your back.
They buried my body
and they thought I'd gone
but I am the dance
and I still go on.

5 They cut me down
and I leapt up high.
I am the life
that'll never, never die.
I'll live in you
if you'll live in me.
I am the Lord
of the Dance, said he.   *Sydney Carter*

132 I'll sing a hymn to Mary

TURRIS DAVIDICA (76 76 D)

H.F.Hemy (1818–88)

2 O noble Tower of David,
 of gold and ivory,
 the Ark of God's own promise,
 the gate of heav'n to me,
 to live and not to love thee,
 would fill my soul with shame;
 when wicked men blaspheme
  thee,
 I'll love and bless thy name.

3 The Saints are high in glory,
 with golden crowns so bright;
 but brighter far is Mary,
 upon her throne of light.
 O that which God did give thee,
 let mortal ne'er disclaim;
 when wicked men blaspheme
  thee,
 I'll love and bless thy name.

4 But in the crown of Mary,
 there lies a wondrous gem,
 as Queen of all the Angels,
 which Mary shares with them:
 no sin hath e'er defiled thee,
 so doth our faith proclaim;
 when wicked men blaspheme
  thee,
 I'll love and bless thy name.

John Wyse (1825–98)

220

133 Immaculate Mary

LOURDES (65 65 and refrain)

Traditional French Melody
arr. John Rombaut

Im- mac- u- late Ma- ry! Our hearts are on fire, that
ti- tle so won-drous fills all our de- sire. A- ve, a- ve, a-
ve Ma- ri- a! A- ve, a- ve, a- ve Ma- ri- a!

2 We pray for God's glory,
  may his kingdom come!
  We pray for his vicar,
  our father, and Rome.

3 We pray for our mother
  the church upon earth,
  and bless, sweetest Lady,
  the land of our birth.

4 O Mary! O mother!
  Reign o'er us once more,
  be England thy 'dowry'
  as in days of yore.

5 We pray for all sinners,
  and souls that now stray
  from Jesus and Mary,
  in heresy's way.

6 For poor, sick, afflicted
  thy mercy we crave;
  and comfort the dying
  thou light of the grave.

7 There is no need, Mary,
  nor ever has been,
  which thou canst not succour,
  Immaculate Queen.

8 In grief and temptation,
  in joy or in pain,
  we'll ask thee, our mother,
  nor seek thee in vain.

9 O bless us, dear Lady,
  with blessings from heaven.
  And to our petitions
  let answer be given.

10 In death's solemn moment,
   our mother, be nigh;
   as children of Mary –
   O teach us to die.

11 And crown thy sweet mercy
   with this special grace,
   to behold soon in heaven
   God's ravishing face.

12 Now to God be all glory
   and worship for aye,
   and to God's virgin mother
   an endless Ave.

Anonymous

134 Immortal, invisible

ST DENIO (11 11 11 11)

Welsh hymn melody

Im- mor- tal, in- vis- i- ble, God on- ly wise, in light in- ac-

ces- si- ble hid from our eyes, most bles- sed, most glo- rious, the

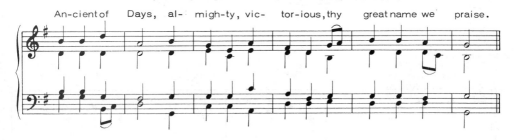

An- cient of Days, al- migh- ty, vic- tor- ious, thy great name we praise.

2 Unresting, unhasting, and silent as light;
nor wanting, nor wasting, thou rulest in might –
thy justice like mountains high-soaring above
thy clouds which are fountains of goodness and love.

3 To all life thou givest, to both great and small;
in all life thou livest, the true life of all;
we blossom and flourish as leaves on the tree,
and wither and perish; but naught changeth thee.

4 Great Father of glory, pure Father of light,
thine angels adore thee, all veiling their sight;
all laud we would render: O help us to see
'tis only the splendour of light hideth thee.

W. Chalmers Smith (1825–1908)
Based on 1 Tim. 1: 17

135 In bread we bring you

Kevin Nichols
arr. Stephen Dean

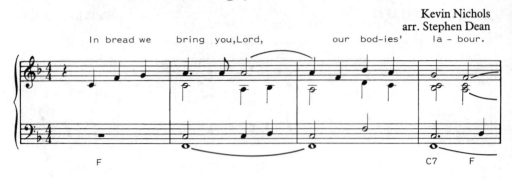

In bread we bring you, Lord, our bod-ies' la-bour.

in wine we of-fer you our Spi-rit's grief. We do not

ask you, Lord, who is my neigh-bour? But stand u-

ni-ted now, one in be-lief. Oh we have glad-ly heard

your word, your ho - ly word, and now in an - swer, Lord,

C7 F B♭ G7

our gifts we bring. Our self-ish hearts make true,

G7 F F7 B♭

our fail-ing faith make new, our lives be - long to you,

C7 F Dm D Gmaj7 G7

our Lord and King.

C7 F

2 The bread we offer you is blessed and broken,
    and it becomes for us our spirits' food.
    Over the cup we bring your Word is spoken;
    make it your gift to us your healing blood.
    Take all that daily toil plants in our heart's poor soil
    take all we start and spoil, each hopeful dream,
    the chances we have missed, the graces we resist,
    Lord, in thy Eucharist, take and redeem.

Kevin Nichols

136   In Christ there is no east nor west

McKEE (86 86)

Traditional Spiritual
arr. Stephen Dean

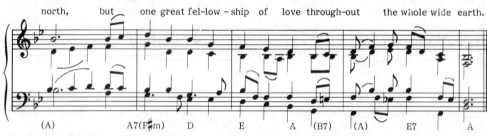

* *In the Melody Edition this tune is in A major.*
The Capo is only needed if playing in B♭.
Chords in brackets do not appear in the Melody Edition.

2 In him shall true hearts ev'rywhere
  their high communion find.
  His service is the golden cord
  close-binding all mankind.

3 Join hands, then, brothers of the faith
  whate'er your race may be.
  Who serves my Father as a son
  is surely kin to me.

4 In Christ now meet both east and west,
  in him meet south and north.
  All Christly souls are one in him
  throughout the whole wide earth.

John Oxenham (1852–1941)

137 In the bleak midwinter

CRANHAM

Gustav Holst (1847–1934)

In the bleak mid- win- ter, fros- ty wind made moan,

earth stood hard as ir- on, wa- ter like a stone;

snow had fal- len, snow on snow, snow on snow,

in the bleak mid- win- ter, long a- go.

2 Our God, heaven cannot hold him
   nor earth sustain;
   Heaven and earth shall flee away,
   when he comes to reign.
   In the bleak midwinter
   a stable-place sufficed
   the Lord God Almighty,
   Jesus Christ.

3 Enough for him, whom Cherubim
   worship night and day,
   a breastful of milk,
   and a mangerful of hay:
   enough for him, whom angels
   fall down before,
   the ox and ass and camel
   which adore.

4 Angels and archangels
   may have gathered there,
   Cherubim and Seraphim
   thronged the air.
   But only his mother
   in her maiden bliss
   worshipped the beloved
   with a kiss.

5 What can I give him,
   poor as I am?
   If I were a shepherd
   I would bring a lamb;
   if I were a wise man
   I would do my part;
   yet what I can I give him –
   give my heart.

Christina G. Rossetti (1830–94)

138 In the earth the small seed

Estelle White

2 In the vineyard branches are cut away
so that fresh young shoots may, with ev'ry day,
bend beneath the fruit as it ripens and
fills with promise.
Golden is the harvest and precious the
wine that you are
and give to us, Lord.

3 In me, Oh my Lord, plant the seed of love
nourished by your body and by your blood.
May my soul take wings and rise upward to
new awakenings!
Golden is the light of your Godhead that
by love you have,
and give to us, Lord.

Estelle White

139 Into one we all are gathered

CARITAS

Eric Welch

In- to one we all are gath-ered through the love of Christ. Let us then rejoice with glad-ness. In him we find love. Let us fear and love the liv- ing God, and love and cher-ish all man-kind.

Chorus

Where char- i-ty and love are, there is God.

2 Therefore, when we are together in the love of Christ,
  let our minds know no division, strife or bitterness,
  may the Christ our God be in our midst.
  Through Christ our Lord all love is found.

3 May we see your face in glory, Christ our loving God.
  With the blessed saints of heaven give us lasting joy.
  We will then possess true happiness,
  and love for all eternity.

*Adapted from 'Ubi Caritas et Amor'
by Michael Cockett*

140　I saw the grass

Estelle White

I saw the grass, I saw the trees and the

boats a-long the shore. I saw the shapes of ma-ny things I had

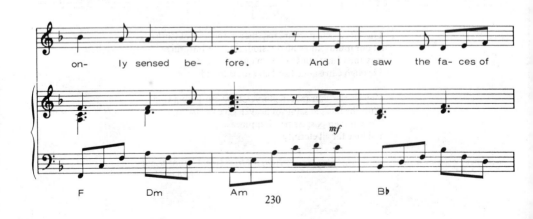

on- ly sensed be- fore. And I saw the fa- ces of

2 I hurried then away from town
to a quiet, lonely place.
I found a clear, unruffled pool
and I gazed upon my face.
And I saw the image of me more clearly
than if I had never been blind.
The line of envy around the lips
and the greed and the hate in the eyes.
And I turned away, yes, I turned away,
for I had seen the perfect face of a real and proper man,
the man who'd brought me from the dark
into light, where life began.

3 I made my way into the town,
to the busy, crowded streets,
the shops and stalls and alley-ways,
to the squalor and the heat.
And I saw the faces of men more clearly
than if I had never been blind,
the lines of sorrow around their lips
and the child looking out from their eyes,
and I turned to them, yes, I turned to them,
remembering the perfect face of a real and proper man,
the man who'd brought me from the dark
into light, where life began.

Estelle White

141   I sing a song to you, Lord

Richard Beaumont

2 Worthy is the slain Lamb,
honour him and praise.
We rejoice with gladness,
sing our love today.

3 He has used his power,
has begun his reign.
So rejoice, you heavens,
and proclaim his name.

4 Shine your light on us, Lord,
let us know your way.
Be our guide for ever,
make us yours today.

Richard Beaumont

142 I sing the Lord God's praises

MAGNIFICAT (76 76 D)

Eugene Monaghan

I sing the Lord God's prai- ses, I an- swer to his

call. His ser- vant girl he rai- ses, she

will be blessed all. The Lord God gives his

pow- er to her who loves his name; o'er

her his strength will tow- er, his mer- cies will re- main.

2 Proud-hearted men he scatters,
  the strong will pass away;
  and for the kind and gentle
  there dawns the Lord's own day.
  Woe to the rich and mighty!
  He feeds and satisfies
  those who for justice hunger,
  and to him turn their eyes.

3 A Saviour he had promised
  to Abram long ago;
  and now to his own people
  his mercy he will show.
  Come let us praise our Father,
  for he fulfils his word,
  and sends his Holy Spirit
  through Jesus Christ our Lord.

W. F. Harwood

143　It came upon the midnight clear

NOEL (86 86 D)

Traditional English Melody
arr. Arthur Sullivan (1842–1900)

2 Yet with the woes of sin and strife
the world has suffered long;
beneath the angel-strain have rolled
two thousand years of wrong;
and man, at war with man, hears not
the love-song which they bring:
O hush the noise, ye men of strife,
and hear the angels sing!

3 For lo, the days are hastening on,
by prophets seen of old,
when with the ever-circling years
shall come the time foretold,
when the new heaven and earth shall own
the prince of peace their king,
and all the world send back the song
which now the angels sing.

E. H. Sears (1810–76)

144 It's me, O Lord

Traditional

2 Not my mother or my father...

3 Not the stranger or my neighbour...

Negro Spiritual

145   I watch the sunrise

Colin Murphy

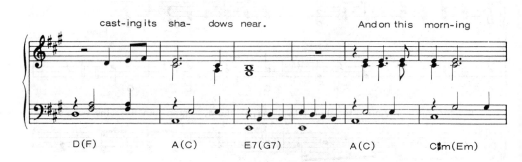

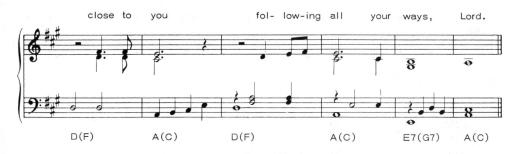

2 I watch the sunlight
   shine through the clouds,
   warming the earth below.
   And at the mid-day
   life seems to say:
   'I feel your brightness near me.'
   For you are always ...

3 I watch the sunset
   fading away,
   lighting the clouds with sleep.
   And as the evening
   closes its eyes
   I feel your presence near me.
   For you are always ...

4 I watch the moonlight
   guarding the night,
   waiting till morning comes.
   The air is silent,
   earth is at rest –
   only your peace is near me.
   Yes, you are always ...

John Glynn

239

146   I will give you glory

Malcolm Campbell-Carr

2 I will sing your praises,
   O God, my King.
   I will bless your name for ever.
   I will bless you day, after day.

3 I will give you honour,
   O God, my King.
   I will bless your name for ever.
   I will bless you day, after day.

Malcolm Campbell-Carr

For an effective second part in this song sing a third above the tune (starting on B)

147 I wonder as I wander

Traditional Melody
from N. Carolina

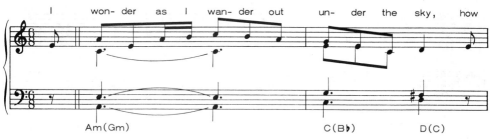

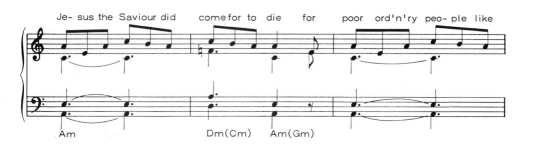

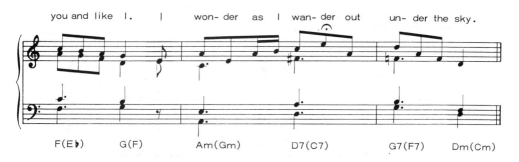

2 When Mary birthed Jesus, 'twas in a cow's stall
with wise men and farmers and shepherd and all.
But high from God's heaven a star's light did fall,
and the promise of ages it did then recall.

3 If Jesus had wanted for any wee thing,
a star in the sky, or a bird on the wing,
or all of God's angels in heav'n for to sing,
he surely could have it, 'cause he was the king.

Traditional

148 January brings the snow

Estelle White

2 March means sun and wind and rain,
  springtime flowers dancing.
  I am young, growing fast,
  wanting all the answers.

3 Maytime blossoms fill the air,
  here's a time for pleasure!
  Keep me safe, O my Lord,
  in my work and leisure.

4 In July the trees are tall,
  butterflies are roving.
  In my prime, may I be
  faithful in my loving.

5 In September's golden fields
  harvesters are reaping,
  and my mind gathers in
  mem'ries worth the keeping.

6 In November there are mists
  jewelling the grasses.
  Now my steps lose their spring;
  how each moment passes!

7 Come December days grow short
  and they say my life's through;
  but, my Lord, it's been good,
  and I want to thank you.

Estelle White

149   Jerusalem the golden

EWING 976 76 D)

A.Ewing (1830–95)

2 They stand, those halls of Sion,
   all jubilant with song,
and bright with many an angel,
   and all the martyr throng;
the prince is ever in them,
   the daylight is serene;
the pastures of the blessed
   are decked in glorious sheen.

3 There is the throne of David;
   and there, from care released,
the shout of them that triumph,
   the song of them that feast;
and they, who with their leader
   have conquered in the fight,
for ever and for ever
   are clad in robes of white.

4 O sweet and blessed country,
   the home of God's elect!
O sweet and blessed country
   that eager hearts expect!
Jesus, in mercy bring us
   to that dear land of rest;
who art, with God the Father
   and Spirit, ever blest.

From 'De Contemptu Mundi', St Bernard of Cluny,
tr. J. M. Neale

150 Jesu, Lover of my soul

ABERYSTWYTH

Joseph Parry (1841–1903)

Je- su, lov-er of my soul, let me to thy bos- om fly,

while the near- er wa-ters roll, while the tem-pest still is high:

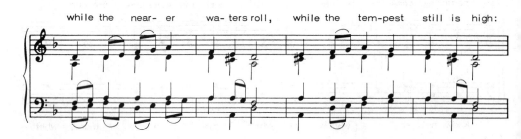

hide me, O my Sav-iour, hide, till the storm of life is past;

safe in- to the ha-ven guide, O re- ceive my soul at last.

2 Other refuge have I none;
hangs my helpless soul on thee;
leave, ah! leave me not alone,
still support and comfort me.
All my trust on thee is stayed,
all my help from thee I bring;
cover my defenceless head
with the shadow of thy wing.

3 Thou, O Christ, art all I want;
more than all in thee I find;
raise the fallen, cheer the faint,
heal the sick and lead the blind,
just and holy is thy name;
I am all unrighteousness;
false and full of sin I am,
thou art full of truth and grace.

4 Plenteous grace with thee is found,
grace to cover all my sin
let the healing streams abound;
make and keep me pure within.
Thou of life the fountain art,
freely let me take of thee;
spring thou up within my heart,
rise to all eternity.

Charles Wesley (1707–88)

151 Jesu, meek and lowly

RAVENSHAW (66 66)

Michael Weisse (1480–1534)
abridged by W.H.Monk

2 Prince of life and power,
  my salvation's tower,
  on the cross I view thee,
  calling sinners to thee.

3 There behold me gazing
  at the sight amazing;
  bending low before thee,
  helpless I adore thee.

4 See the red wounds streaming,
  with Christ's life-blood gleaming,
  blood for sinners flowing,
  pardon free bestowing,

5 Fountains rich in blessing,
  Christ's fond love expressing,
  thou my aching sadness
  turnest into gladness.

6 Lord in mercy guide me,
  be thou e'er beside me,
  In thy wings direct me,
  'neath thy wings protect me.

A. H. Collins (1827–1919)

152   Jesus, the very thought

JAZER (86 86)   A.Edmonds Tozer (1857–1910)

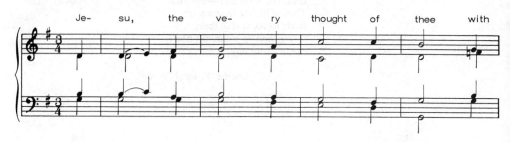

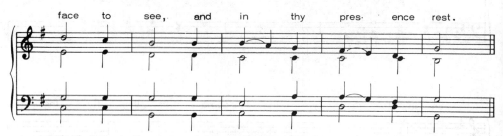

2 Nor voice can sing, nor heart can frame,
  nor can the memory find,
  a sweeter sound than thy blest name,
  O Saviour of mankind.

3 O hope of every contrite heart,
  O joy of all the meek,
  to those who fall, how kind thou art,
  how good to those who seek!

4 But what to those who find? Ah, this
  nor tongue nor pen can show;
  the love of Jesus, what it is
  none but his lovers know.

5 Jesu, our only joy be thou,
  as thou our prize wilt be;
  Jesu, be thou our glory now,
  and through eternity.

11th c., tr. Edward Caswall

153 Jesus Christ is risen today

EASTER HYMN (74 74 D)

From *Lyra Davidica* (1708)

2 Hymns of praise then let us sing, alleluia!
  Unto Christ, our heavenly king, alleluia!
  Who endured the cross and grave, alleluia!
  Sinners to redeem and save, alleluia!

3 But the pains that he endured, alleluia!
  Our salvation have procured; alleluia!
  Now above the sky he's king, alleluia!
  Where the angels ever sing, alleluia!

Lyra Davidica (1708) and the Supplement (1816).
Based partly on 'Surrexit Christus hodie'. (14th c.)

154 Jesus, gentlest Saviour

PRINCETHORPE (65 65 D)

W. Pitts (1829–1903)

Je-sus, gentlest Sav- iour, God of might and power,

thou thyself art dwel- ling in us at this hour.

Na- ture cannot hold thee, heav'n is all too strait

for thine endless glo- ry and thy roy- al state.

2 Yet the hearts of children,
   hold what worlds cannot,
   and the God of wonders
   loves the lowly spot.
   Jesus, gentlest Saviour,
   thou art in us now,
   fill us full of goodness,
   till our hearts o'erflow.

3 Pray the prayer within us
   that to heaven shall rise;
   sing the song that angels
   sing above the skies;
   multiply our graces,
   chiefly love and fear;
   and, dear Lord, the chiefest,
   grace to persevere.

Frederick William Faber (1814–63)

155 Jesus Lord, I'll sing a song

Briege O'Hare

Je- sus Lord, I'll sing a song that's soft and low for

you, so you can join with me and sing it too.

You have said that when we pray, then you are pray- ing

too, and when your Father hears us, he hears you.

Chorus

Our Fa- ther who art in hea- ven,

hal- lowed be thy name, hal- lowed be thy name.

2 I believe that you are here
with me and praying too.
Your Father loves me
because I love you.
Jesus, Lord, I'll sing a song that's
soft and low for you,
so you can join with me
and sing it too.

Briege O'Hare

156 Jesus is God!

ELLACOMBE (86 86 D)

From *St Gall Gesangbuch*, 1863

2 Jesus is God! the glorious bands
 of golden angels sing
 songs of adoring praise to him,
 their maker and their king.
 He was true God in Bethlehem's crib,
 on Calvary's cross true God,
 he who in heaven eternal reigned,
 in time on earth abode.

3 Jesus is God! Let sorrow come,
 and pain and every ill;
 all are worth while, for all are means
 his glory to fulfil;
 worth while a thousand years of life
 to speak one little word,
 if by our Credo we might own
 the Godhead of our Lord.

Frederick William Faber (1814–63)

157 Jesus, my Lord, my God, my all

CORPUS CHRISTI (88 88 88)

Crown of Jesus Hymnbook, 1864

Je-sus, my Lord, my God, my all, how can I love thee as I ought? And how rev- ere this won- drous gift, so far sur- pas- sing hope or thought? **Chorus** Sweet Sa- cra- ment, we thee a- dore; Oh, make us love thee more and more.

2 Had I but Mary's sinless heart
to love thee with, my dearest King,
Oh, with what bursts of fervent praise
thy goodness, Jesus, would I sing!

3 Ah, see! within a creature's hand
the vast Creator deigns to be,
reposing, infant-like, as though
on Joseph's arm, or Mary's knee.

4 Thy body, soul, and Godhead, all;
O mystery of love divine!
I cannot compass all I have,
for all thou hast and art are mine;

5 Sound, sound, his praises higher still,
and come, ye angels, to our aid;
'tis God, 'tis God, the very God
whose power both man and angels made.

Frederick William Faber (1814–63)

253

158   Jesus, thou art coming

PRINCETHORPE (65 65 D)   W.Pitts (1829–1903)

Je-sus, thou art com-ing, ho-ly as thou art,
thou the God who made me to my sin-ful heart.
Je-sus I be-lieve it, on thy on-ly word;
kneel-ing, I a-dore thee, as my King and Lord.

2 Who am I, my Jesus,
  that thou com'st to me?
  I have sinned against thee,
  often grievously;
  I am very sorry
  I have caused thee pain.
  I will never, never,
  wound thy heart again.

3 Put thy kind arms round me,
  feeble as I am;
  thou art my Good Shepherd,
  I, thy little lamb;
  since thou comest, Jesus,
  now to be my guest,
  I can trust thee always,
  Lord, for all the rest.

4 Dearest Lord, I love thee,
  with my whole heart,
  not for what thou givest,
  but for what thou art.
  Come, oh, come, sweet Saviour!
  Come to me, and stay,
  for I want thee, Jesus,
  more than I can say.

5 Ah! what gift or present,
  Jesus, can I bring?
  I have nothing worthy
  of my God and King;
  but thou art my shepherd:
  I, thy little lamb,
  take myself, dear Jesus,
  all I have and am.

6 Take my body, Jesus,
  eyes, and ears and tongue;
  never let them, Jesus,
  help to do thee wrong.
  Take my heart, and fill it
  full of love for thee;
  all I have I give thee,
  give thyself to me.

'S.N.D.'

159 Just a closer walk with thee

Traditional

2 Through the day of toil that's near,
if I fall, dear Lord, who cares.
Who with me my burden share?
None but thee, dear Lord, none but thee.

3 When my feeble life is o'er,
time for me will be no more.
Guide me gently, safely on
to the shore, dear Lord, to the shore.

Traditional

160 Keep we the fast

SAXONY (88 88)

From *Christliches Gesangbuch*, 1568

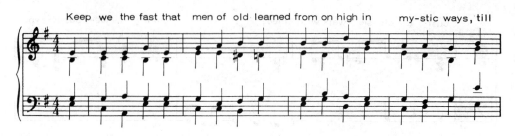

Keep we the fast that men of old learned from on high in my-stic ways, till

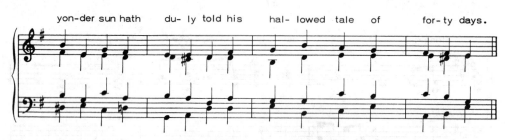

yon-der sun hath du- ly told his hal- lowed tale of for-ty days.

2 This covenant, long since revealed
   to patriarchs and ardent seers,
   Christ by his own example sealed,
   author of time, and Lord of years.

3 More wisely therefore let us walk,
   sparing of food and wine and sleep;
   over our trifles and our talk
   more jealous be the watch we keep.

4 Still by our sins, O Lord, we grieve
   thy love, so full of pardon free:
   author of mercy, still reprieve
   the souls that turn again to thee.

5 Remember whence our fashion came,
   frail creatures, yet thy creatures still,
   crush, for the glory of thy name,
   the murm'rings of our stubborn will.

6 The guilt that dooms us put away,
   with larger grace our prayers requite,
   at last, and ever from this day,
   teach us to live as in thy sight.

7 Hear us, O Trinity sublime,
   and undivided unity;
   so let this consecrated time
   bring forth thy fruits abundantly.

St Gregory the Great (540–604)
tr. R.A. Knox

161 King of glory

GWALCHMAI (74 74 D)

J.D.Jones (1827–70)

King of glo-ry, king of peace, I will love thee;
and, that love may nev-er cease, I will move thee.
Thou hast gran-ted my re-quest, thou hast heard me;
Thou didst note my work-ing breast, thou hast spared me.

2 Wherefore with my utmost art,
I will sing thee.
And the cream of all my heart
I will bring thee,
though my sins against me cried,
thou didst clear me;
and alone, when they replied,
thou didst hear me.

3 Seven whole days, not one in seven,
I will praise thee;
in my heart, though not in heaven,
I can raise thee.
Small it is, in this poor sort
to enrol thee:
e'en eternity's too short
to extol thee.

George Herbert (1593–1633)

257

162 Kum ba yah

Traditional

Kum ba yah, my Lord, kum ba yah, kum ba yah, my Lord, kum ba

C   F   C   F

yah. Kum ba yah my Lord, kum ba yah. O Lord, kum ba yah.

G C   F   C   F C G7 C

2 Someone's crying, Lord, kum ba yah,
someone's crying, Lord, kum ba yah!
Someone's crying, Lord, kum ba yah!
O Lord, kum ba yah.

3 Someone's singing, Lord, kum ba yah,
someone's singing, Lord, kum ba yah!
Someone's singing, Lord, kum ba yah!
O Lord, kum ba yah.

4 Someone's praying, Lord, kum ba yah,
someone's praying, Lord, kum ba yah!
Someone's praying, Lord, kum ba yah!
O Lord, kum ba yah.

Spiritual

163 Great St George

SWAVESEY (87 87 D)   J. Crookall (1821–87)

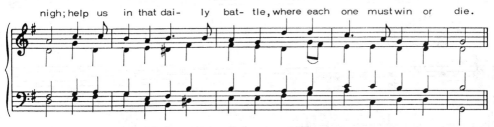

Lea- der now on earth no longer, sol-dier of th'eter- nal
king, vic- tor in the fight for hea-ven, we thy lov- ing prais- es
sing. **Chorus** Great Saint George, our pa- tron, help us, in the con- flict be thou
nigh; help us in that dai- ly bat- tle, where each one must win or die.

2 Praise him who in deadly battle
   never shrank from foeman's sword,
   proof against all earthly weapon,
   gave his life for Christ the Lord.

3 Who, when earthly war was over,
   fought, but not for earth's renown;
   fought, and won a nobler glory,
   won the martyr's purple crown.

4 Help us when temptation presses,
   we have still our crown to win,
   help us when our soul is weary
   fighting with the powers of sin.

5 Clothe us in thy shining armour,
   place thy good sword in our hand;
   teach us how to wield it, fighting
   onward towards the heavenly land.

6 Onward, till, our striving over,
   on life's battlefield we fall,
   resting then, but ever ready,
   waiting for the angel's call.   *Joseph W. Reeks (1849–1900)*

164 Lead, kindly light

FIRST TUNE

LUX BENIGNA (10 4 10 4 10 10)

J.B.Dykes (1823–76)

SANDON (10 4 10 4 10 10)   C.H.Purday (1799–1885)

2 I was not ever thus, nor prayed that thou
  shouldst lead me on;
  I loved to choose and see my path; but now
  lead thou me on.
  I loved the garish day, and, spite of fears,
  pride ruled my will; remember not past years.

3 So long thy power hath blest me, sure it still
  will lead me on
  o'er moor and fen, o'er crag and torrent, till
  the night is gone,
  and with the morn those angels faces smile
  which I have loved long since, and lost awhile.

John Henry Newman (1801–90)

165 Lead us, heavenly Father

MANNHEIM (87 87 87)

Adapted from a Chorale
by F. Filitz (1804–76)

Lead us, heav'n-ly Fa-ther, lead us o'er the world's tem- pestuous sea;

guard us, guide us, keep us, feed us, for we have no help but thee;

yet pos-ses-sing ev- ery bles-sing if our God our Fa-ther be.

2 Saviour, breathe forgiveness o'er us,
all our weakness thou dost know,
thou didst tread this earth before us,
thou didst feel its keenest woe;
lone and dreary, faint and weary,
through the desert thou didst go.

3 Spirit of our God, descending,
fill our hearts with heavenly joy,
love with every passion blending,
pleasure that can never cloy;
thus provided, pardoned, guided,
nothing can our peace destroy.

J. Edmeston (1791–1867)

166   Let all mortal flesh keep silence

PICARDY (87 87 87)   French Carol Melody

2 King of kings, yet born of Mary,
  as of old on earth he stood
  Lord of lords, in human vesture –
  in the Body and the Blood.
  He will give to all the faithful
  his own Self for heavenly Food.

3 Rank on rank the host of heaven
  spreads its vanguard on the way,
  as the Light of Light descendeth
  from the realms of endless day,
  that the powers of hell may vanish
  as the darkness clears away.

4 At his feet the six-winged Seraph;
  Cherubim with sleepless eye,
  veil their faces to the Presence,
  as with ceaseless voice they cry,
  alleluia, alleluia,
  alleluia, Lord most high.

Liturgy of St. James,
tr. G. Moultrie

263

167   Let all that is within me

Traditional

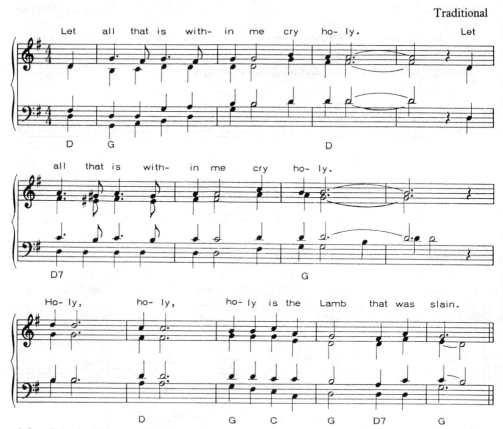

2 Let all that is within me cry mighty.
Let all that is within me cry mighty.
Mighty, mighty, mighty is the Lamb that was slain.

3 Let all that is within me cry worthy.
Let all that is within me cry worthy.
Worthy, worthy, worthy is the Lamb that was slain.

4 Let all that is within me cry blessed.
Let all that is within me cry blessed.
Blessed, blessed, blessed is the Lamb that was slain.

5 Let all that is within me cry Jesus.
Let all that is within me cry Jesus.
Jesus, Jesus, Jesus is the Lamb that was slain.

Traditional

168   Let all the world in every corner sing

LUCKINGTON   Basil Harwood (1859–1949)

God and King! The heav'ns are not too high, his
praise may thith-er fly: the earth is not too low, his
prais-es there may grow. Let all the world in
ev- 'ry cor- ner sing, my God and King!

2 Let all the world
in every corner sing,
my God and King!
The church with psalms must shout,
no door can keep them out;
but, above all, the heart
must bear the longest part.
Let all the world
in every corner sing,
my God and King!

George Herbert (1593–1633)

169   Let us break bread together

Traditional

2 Let us drink wine together ...

3 Let us praise God together ...

Traditional

170 Let's make peace in our hearts

Sebastian Temple

2 Let's take peace into the world.
Let's take peace into the world.
Let's take true peace into the world.
Let's take true peace into the world.

3 Let's share peace with ev'ryone.
Let's share peace with ev'ryone.
Let's share true peace with ev'ryone.
Let's share true peace with ev'ryone.

4 My peace I leave with you.
My peace I give to you.
Not as the world gives do I give,
but true peace I give unto you.

Sebastian Temple

171 Let us, with a gladsome mind

MONKLAND (77 77)

John Antes (1740–1811)
arr. J. Wilkes (1861)

Let us, with a gladsome mind, praise the Lord, for he is kind:

for his mercies aye en- dure, ev- er faith-ful, ev- er sure.

2 Let us blaze his name abroad,
for of gods he is the God;

3 He, with all-commanding might,
filled the new-made world with light;

4 He the golden-tressed sun
caused all day his course to run:

5 And the horned moon at night,
'mid her spangled sisters bright:

6 All things living he doth feed,
his full hand supplies their need:

7 Let us, with a gladsome mind,
praise the Lord, for he is kind.

John Milton (1608–75)
based on Ps. 136

172 Light of our darkness

GROSSER GOTT (modified)(88 88)   From *Katholisches Gesangbuch*, 1774

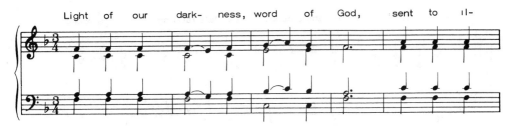

Light of our dark- ness, word of God, sent to il-

lu- mine our earth- ly night, you we sal- ute with sing- ing

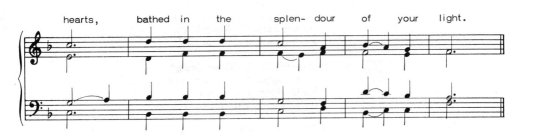

hearts, bathed in the splen- dour of your light.

2 Sword that can pierce the inmost soul,
  stripping whatever thoughts are there,
  cut to the marrow of our minds,
  enter our hearts and lay them bare.

3 Vessel of God's abundant life,
  bearer of truth that sets us free,
  breaking the deadly grasp of sin,
  work in our hearts your mystery.

4 Word that has overcome the world,
  seed of immortal destiny,
  grow in our hearts, that we may live
  sharing your deathless victory.

Richard Connolly

173 Little flower in the ground

Kevin Mayhew

2 Seeds that fall on to the ground
by the winds are scattered round.
Some will feed the Winter birds,
and some will nestle in the earth.

3 Some will last the Winter through
'till the Spring makes all things new.
See the flower newly grown
from seeds the Winter wind has sown.

4 Praise the Lord in heav'n above,
who shows us all the way of love.
Praise him for the dying year.
If Winter comes then Spring is near.

Michael Cockett

174   Little Jesus, sweetly sleep

ROCKING (10 7 88 77)

Traditional Czechoslovakian Melody
arr. John Rombaut

2 Mary's little baby sleep, sweetly sleep,
   sleep in comfort, slumber deep;
   we will rock you, rock you, rock you,
   we will rock you, rock you, rock you,
   we will serve you all we can,
   darling, darling little man.

Czech., tr. O. B. C.

175   Long ago in Bethlehem

Papuan Melody
arr. Ian Sharp

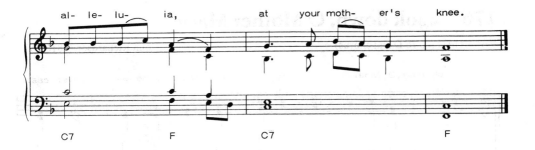

al- le- lu- ia, at your moth- er's knee.

C7 F C7 F

2 Now as King we hail the baby,
living faith proclaims the story
of that humble manger glory,
stabled in the hay.
Hosanna, alleluia,
hosanna alleluia,
hosanna, alleluia,
Christ is King today.

Ian Sharp

176 Look down, O Mother Mary

VAUGHAN (76 76 D and chorus)

John Richardson (1816–79)

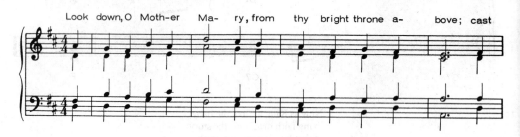

Look down, O Mother Mary, from thy bright throne a- bove; cast

down up- on thy chil- dren one on- ly glance of love; and

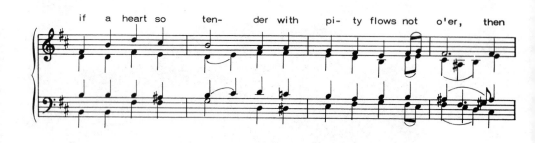

if a heart so ten- der with pi- ty flows not o'er, then

turn a- way, O Moth- er, and look on us no more. Look

Chorus

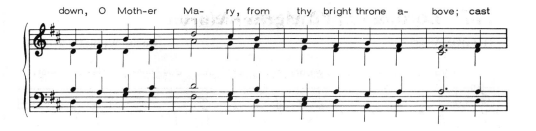

down, O Moth-er Ma- ry, from thy bright throne a- bove; cast

down up- on thy chil- dren one on- ly glance of love.

2 See how, ungrateful sinners,
  we stand before thy Son;
  his loving heart upbraids us
  the evil we have done,
  but if thou wilt appease him,
  speak for us but one word;
  for thus thou canst obtain us
  the pardon of Our Lord.

3 O Mary, dearest Mother,
  if thou wouldst have us live,
  say that we are thy children,
  and Jesus will forgive.
  Our sins make us unworthy
  that title still to bear,
  but thou art still our mother;
  then show a mother's care.

4 Unfold to us thy mantle,
  there stay we without fear;
  what evil can befall us
  if, mother, thou art near?
  O kindest, dearest mother
  thy sinful children save;
  look down on us with pity,
  who thy protection crave.

St Alphonsus (1696–1787),
tr. Edmund Vaughan

177 Lord, accept the gifts we offer

ST THOMAS (87 87 87) Samuel Webbe (1740–1816)

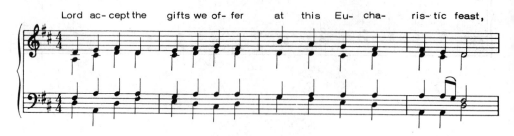

Lord ac-cept the gifts we of-fer at this Eu-cha-ris-tic feast,

bread and wine to be transformed now through the ac-tion of thy priest

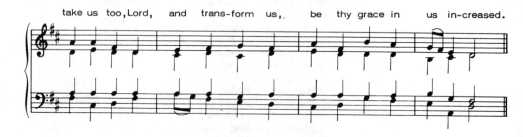

take us too, Lord, and trans-form us, be thy grace in us in-creased.

2 May our souls be pure and spotless
 as the host of wheat so fine;
 may all stain of sin be crushed out,
 like the grape that forms the wine,
 as we, too, become partakers,
 in this sacrifice divine.

3 Take our gifts, almighty Father,
 living God, eternal, true,
 which we give through Christ, our Saviour,
 pleading here for us anew
 grant salvation to all present,
 and our faith and love renew.

Sister M. Teresine

178   Lord, for tomorrow

PROVIDENCE (8 4 8 4)   R.R.Terry (1865–1938)

2 Let me both diligently work
  and duly pray;
  let me be kind in word and deed,
  just for today.

3 Let me be slow to do my will,
  prompt to obey;
  help me to mortify my flesh,
  just for today.

4 Let me no wrong or idle word
  unthinking say;
  set thou a seal upon my lips,
  just for today.

5 Let me in season, Lord, be grave,
  in season, gay;
  let me be faithful to thy grace,
  just for today.

6 And if today my tide of life
  should ebb away,
  give me thy sacraments divine,
  sweet Lord, today.

7 So, for tomorrow and its needs
  I do not pray;
  but keep me, guide me, love me, Lord,
  just for today.   *Sister M. Xavier*

179 Living Lord

LIVING LORD (9 8888 D)

Patrick Appleford

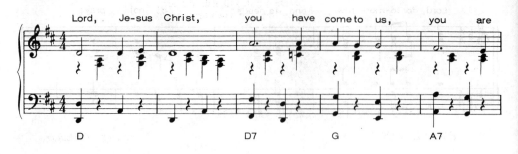

2 Lord Jesus Christ,
   now and ev'ry day
   teach us how to pray, Son of God.
   You have commanded us to do
   this in remembrance, Lord, of you
   Into our lives your pow'r breaks through,
   living Lord.

3 Lord Jesus Christ,
   you have come to us,
   born as one of us, Mary's Son.
   Led out to die on Calvary,
   risen from death to set us free,
   living Lord Jesus, help us see
   you are Lord.

4 Lord Jesus Christ,
   I would come to you,
   live my life for you, Son of God.
   All your commands I know are true,
   your many gifts will make me new,
   into my life your pow'r breaks through,
   living Lord.

Patrick Appleford

180   Lord Jesus, think on me

SOUTHWELL (6686)   From *Damon's Psalter*, 1579

Lord   Je- sus, think on   me,   and   purge a- way my   sin; from

earthborn pas-sions   set   me   free,   and   make me   pure with-   in.

2 Lord Jesus, think on me,
   with care and woe oppressed;
   let me thy loving servant be,
   and taste thy promised rest.

3 Lord Jesus, think on me
   amid the battle's strife;
   in all my pain and misery
   be thou my health and life.

4 Lord Jesus, think on me,
   nor let me go astray;
   through darkness and perplexity
   point thou the heavenly way.

5 Lord Jesus, think on me,
   when flows the tempest high:
   when on doth rush the enemy,
   O Saviour, be thou nigh.

6 Lord Jesus, think on me,
   that, when the flood is past,
   I may the eternal brightness see,
   and share thy joy at last.

Bishop Synesius (375–430)
tr. A. W. Chatfield

181 Lord of all hopefulness

SLANE (10 11 11 12)

Traditional Irish Melody
arr. Martin Shaw (1875–1958)

Lord of all hope-ful-ness, Lord of all joy, whose

trust, ev- er child- like, no cares could des- troy, be

there at our wak- ing, and give us, we pray, your

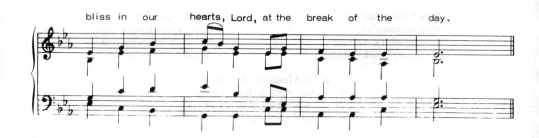

bliss in our hearts, Lord, at the break of the day.

2 Lord of all eagerness,
  Lord of all faith,
  whose strong hands were skilled
  at the plane and the lathe,
  be there at our labours,
  and give us, we pray,
  your strength in our hearts, Lord,
  at the noon of the day.

3 Lord, of all kindliness,
  Lord of all grace,
  your hands swift to welcome,
  your arms to embrace,
  be there at our homing,
  and give us, we pray,
  your love in our hearts, Lord,
  at the eve of the day.

4 Lord, of all gentleness,
  Lord of all calm,
  whose voice is contentment,
  whose presence is balm,
  be there at our sleeping,
  and give us, we pray,
  your peace in our hearts, Lord,
  at the end of the day.

Jan Struther (1901–53)

182 Lord, we pray for golden peace

Sebastian Temple

282

2 Keep all men for ever one,
   one in love and in grace.
   And wipe away all war and strife,
   give freedom to each race.

3 Let your justice reign supreme.
   Righteousness always done.
   Let goodness rule the hearts of men
   and evil overcome.

Sebastian Temple.

183   Lord, who throughout these forty days

ST FLAVIAN (86 86)   From *Day's Psalter*, 1563

Lord, who throughout these for-ty days for us didst fast and pray, teach

us with thee to mourn our sins, and at thy side to stay.

2 As thou with Satan didst contend,
   and didst the victory win,
   O give us strength in thee to fight,
   in thee to conquer sin.

3 As thirst and hunger thou didst bear,
   so teach us, gracious Lord,
   to die to self, and daily live
   by thy most holy word.

4 And through these days of penitence,
   and through thy Passiontide,
   yea, evermore, in life and death,
   Lord Christ, with us abide.

Claudia Frances Hernaman (1838–98)

283

184 Love divine, all loves excelling

LOVE DIVINE (87 87)   John Stainer (1840–1901)

Love Di- vine all loves ex- cel-ling, joy of heav'n, to earth come

down, fix in us thy humble dwelling, all thy faith-ful mer-cies crown.

2 Jesus, thou art all compassion,
    pure unbounded love thou art;
    visit us with thy salvation,
    enter every trembling heart.

3 Come, almighty to deliver,
    let us all thy life receive;
    suddenly return, and never,
    never more thy temples leave.

4 Thee we would be always blessing,
    serve thee as thy hosts above;
    pray, and praise thee without ceasing,
    glory in thy perfect love.

5 Finish then thy new creation,
    pure and sinless let us be;
    let us see thy great salvation
    perfectly restored in thee.

6 Changed from glory into glory,
    till in heaven we take our place,
    till we cast our crowns before thee,
    lost in wonder, love, and praise.

Charles Wesley (1707–88)

185   Love is his word

CRESSWELL (88 97 10 7)

Anthony Milner

Love is his word, Love is his way, feast- ing with men, fast- ing a- lone, liv- ing and dy- ing, ri- sing a- gain, love, on-ly love, is his way. Rich- er than gold is the love of my Lord: bet- ter than splen- dour and wealth.

Chorus

2 Love is his way, love is his mark,
    sharing his last Passover feast,
    Christ at his table, host to the Twelve,
    love, only love, is his mark.

3 Love is his mark, love is his sign,
    bread for our strength, wine for our joy,
    'This is my body, this is my blood,'
    love, only love, is his sign.

4 Love is his sign, love is his news,
    'Do this,' he said, 'lest you forget
    all my deep sorrow, all my dear blood,'
    love, only love, is his news.

5 Love is his news, love is his name,
    we are his own, chosen and called,
    family, brethren, cousins and kin.
    Love, only love, is his name.

6 Love is his name, love is his law.
    Hear his command, all who are his:
    'Love one another, I have loved you.'
    Love, only love, is his law.

7 Love is his law, love is his word:
    love of the Lord, Father and Word,
    love of the Spirit, God ever one,
    love, only love, is his word.

Luke Connaughton (1919–79)

186 Loving Father, from thy bounty

Picardy (87 87 87)

Traditional French Carol

Lov- ing Fa- ther, from thy boun- ty choic- est gifts un-
num- bered flow: all the bless-ings of sal-
va- tion, which to Christ thy Son we owe,
all the gifts that by thy bid- ding
na- ture's hands on us be- stow!

2 Here thy grateful children gather,
   offering gifts of bread and wine;
   these we give to thee in homage,
   of our love the loving sign,
   and restore to thee creation,
   given to man, yet ever thine!

3 Soon will come Christ's loving presence,
   on our love to set his seal!
   Body broken, Blood shed for us,
   bread and wine will then reveal!
   bread and wine, though these no longer,
   flesh and blood will yet conceal!

James Quinn, S.J.

187   Loving Shepherd of thy sheep

LÜBECK (77 77)   from *Freylinghausen's Gesangbuch*, 1704

2 Loving shepherd, thou didst give
   thine own life that I might live;
   may I love thee day by day,
   gladly thy sweet will obey.

3 Loving shepherd, ever near,
   teach me still thy voice to hear;
   suffer not my steps to stray
   from the strait and narrow way.

4 Where thou leadest may I go,
   walking in thy steps below;
   then before thy Father's throne,
   Jesu, claim me for thine own.

Jane E. Leeson (1807–82)

188　Maiden yet a mother

Traditional French Carol
harmonized by Dom Gregory Murray O.S.B.

UNE VAINE CRAINTE (65 65 D)

2 Thus his day prepared,
　he who all things made
　'mid his creatures tarried,
　in thy bosom laid;
　there his love he nourished,
　warmth that gave increase
　to the root whence flourished
　our eternal peace.

3 Noon on Sion's mountain
　is thy charity;
　hope its living fountain
　finds, on earth, in thee:
　lady, such thy power,
　he, who grace would buy
　not as of thy dower,
　without wings would fly.

Dante Alighieri (1265–1321)
tr. R. A. Knox

189   Make me a channel of your peace

Sebastian Temple

1 Make me a channel of your peace,   where
2 Make me a channel of your peace,   where

there is ha - tred, let me bring your love. ————————— Where
there's des- pair in life, let me bring hope. ——————— Where

there is in - ju -- ry, your par- don, Lord, ————————— And
there is darkness ———— on - ly light, ————————— And

where there's doubt, true faith in you.
where there's sad - ness e -- ver

2 joy.   3 O Master, grant that I may ne-ver seek

so much to be consoled as to console, to be un-der-stood

A7   D D7 G

as to un - der - stand to be loved, as to love with all my

D   E

soul.   4 Make me a chan-nel of your peace,

A   A7   D

it is in par - don - ing that we are par - doned,

                 Em (A7)

in giv - ing to all men that we re - ceive,   and in

A7

dy - ing that we're born to e - ter - nal life.

290

190 Man of Galilee

Estelle White

2 Man who healed the blind
  open up the eyes of my mind
  to the needs of my fellow man.
  Help me give with open hands.

3 Man of bread and of wine
  show me by the means of this sign
  that I share your life and your light
  with the neighbour here at my side.

4 Man of Calvary
  give me strength and will to be free
  of the weight of self-pity's chains,
  then my trials will be but gains.

5 Man at God's right hand,
  will you help me understand
  that in you, when my breath is stilled,
  all my longings will be fulfilled?

Estelle White

191 Many times have I turned

Russian Melody arr. Stephen Dean

Ma–ny times have I turned from the way of the Lord, many times have I chos–en the dark–ness.

Dm   Gm   A   Dm

In the light of the day, when the shadows are gone, all I see is my sin in its

Gm   A

Chorus

stark — ness. Je – sus came to bring us mer — cy. Je – sus

Dm   Gm   Dm

came to bring us life a – gain. He loves us, he loves us, he loves us!

Gm   Dm   Gm Dm   Gm Dm   Gm Dm

2 I confess I have sinned in the sight of the Lord,
through my pride, through my malice and weakness.
I've rejected the promise that comes from the cross
where the Lord hung above us in meekness.

3 With a word, with a deed, with a failure to act,
with a thought that was evil and hateful,
I confess to you, brothers and sisters of mine,
I have sinned and been proven ungrateful.

4 Through my fault, through my fault, through my serious fault,
I confess to you, Lord, all my sinning.
But look down on me, Lord, grant your pardon and peace;
with your help, I've a new life beginning.

Willard F. Jabusch

The chords given here are those of the Melody edition, and do not correspond to the harmonies here

192   Mary immaculate

LIEBSTER IMMANUEL (11 10 11 10)

Himmels-Lust, 1679
arr. J.S.Bach

2 Here, in an orbit of shadow and sadness
  veiling thy splendour, thy course thou hast run;
  now thou art throned in all glory and gladness,
  crowned by the hand of thy saviour and Son.

3 Sinners, we worship thy sinless perfection,
  fallen and weak, for thy pity we plead;
  grant us the shield of thy sovereign protection,
  measure thine aid by the depth of our need.

4 Frail is our nature, and strict our probation,
  watchful the foe that would lure us to wrong,
  succour our souls in the hour of temptation,
  Mary immaculate tender and strong.

5 See how the wiles of the serpent assail us,
  see how we waver and flinch in the fight;
  let thine immaculate merit avail us,
  make of our weakness a proof of thy might.

6 Bend from thy throne at the voice of our crying;
  bend to this earth which thy footsteps have trod;
  stretch our thine arms to us living and dying,
  Mary immaculate mother of God.

F. W. Weatherell

293

193   May the peace of Christ be with you

Kevin Mayhew

Kevin Mayhew

194   Merrily on

John Glynn

wa- ters that car- ry a song, a song that is sung of the

Em F G7 C Am

love of the Lord, a love that is end- less and ev- er out-

Em Am F C G7

| 1-3

poured.

| 4

C

2 Father above, Father above,
  source of our life and our strength and our love,
  as fresh as the spring that is limpid and clear,
  your presence is young and will always be near.

3 Son from on high, Son from on high,
  you who united the earth and the sky,
  Oh, cleanse us with water and fill us with peace,
  our river of mercy who never will cease.

4 Spirit of God, Spirit of God,
  breathe on the waters and flow in the flood,
  and open the flood-gates that lead to the sea
  - the ocean is open and boundless and free!

5 Merrily on, merrily on
  flow the bright waters that carry a song,
  a song that is sung of the love of the Lord,
  a love that is endless and ever outpoured.

John Glynn

195   Mine eyes have seen the glory

Traditional American
arr. Stephen Dean

BATTLE HYMN

2 I have seen him in the watchfires of a hundred circling camps.
They have gilded him an altar in the evening dews and damps.
I can read his righteous sentence by the dim and flaring lamps.
His day is marching on.

3 He has sounded forth the trumpet that shall never sound retreat.
He is sifting out the hearts of men before his judgement seat.
O, be swift my soul to answer him, be jubilant my feet!
Our God is marching on.

4 In the beauty of the lilies Christ was born across the sea
with a glory in his bosom that transfigures you and me.
As he died to make men holy, let us die to make men free.
Whilst God is marching on.

Julia Ward Howe (1819–1910)

Arrangement for Celebration Hymnal © McCrimmon Publishing Co Ltd

196 Morning has broken

BUNESSAN (55 54 D)

Traditional Gaelic Melody
arr. Stephen Dean

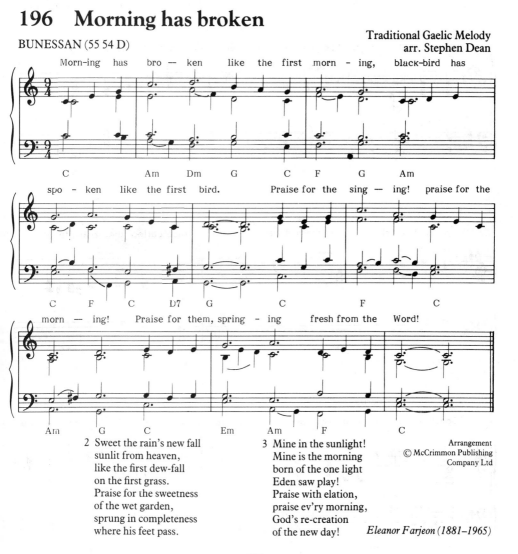

2 Sweet the rain's new fall
sunlit from heaven,
like the first dew-fall
on the first grass.
Praise for the sweetness
of the wet garden,
sprung in completeness
where his feet pass.

3 Mine in the sunlight!
Mine is the morning
born of the one light
Eden saw play!
Praise with elation,
praise ev'ry morning,
God's re-creation
of the new day!

Arrangement
© McCrimmon Publishing
Company Ltd

Eleanor Farjeon (1881–1965)

197 Moses, I know you're the man

Estelle White

"Mo-ses I know you're the man," the Lord said. "You're going to work out my

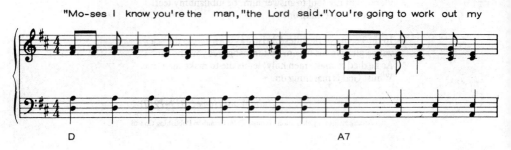

D   A7

plan," the Lord said, "Lead all the Is- rael-ites out of sla-ve- ry.

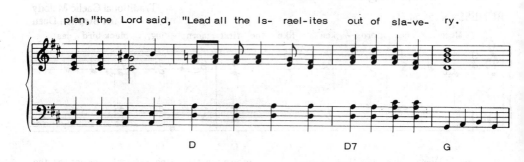

D   D7   G

And I shall make them a wan- der- ing race called the peo-ple of

E7   D   A7

Chorus

God."   So ev'ry day   we're on our   way,   for we're a

D   D7   G   D   B7

298

tra - velling, wan- der-ing   race called the peo-ple of   God.

E7   A7   D

2 "Don't get too set in your ways,"
  the Lord said.
  "Each step is only a phase,"
  the Lord said.
  "I'll go before you and I shall be a sign
  to guide my travelling, wandering race.
  You're the people of God."

3 "No matter what you may do,"
  the Lord said,
  "I shall be faithful and true,"
  the Lord said.
  "My love will strengthen you as you go along,
  for you're my travelling, wandering race.
  You're the people of God."

4 "Look at the birds in the air,"
  the Lord said,
  "They fly unhampered by care,"
  the Lord said.
  "You will move easier if you're travelling light,
  for you're a wandering vagabond race.
  You're the people of God."

5 "Foxes have places to go,"
  the Lord said.
  "But I've no home here below,"
  the Lord said.
  "So if you want to be with me all your days,
  keep up the moving and travelling on.
  You're the people of God."

Estelle White

198   Most ancient of all mysteries

ST FLAVIAN (86 86)   From *Day's Psalter*, 1563

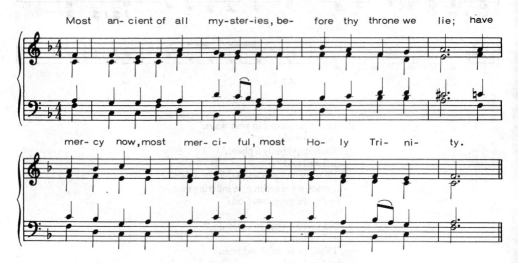

2 When heaven and earth were yet unmade,
  when time was yet unknown,
  thou, in thy bliss and majesty,
  didst live and love alone.

3 Thou wert not born; there was no fount,
  from which thy being flowed;
  there is no end which thou canst reach:
  but thou art simply God.

4 How wonderful creation is,
  the work that thou didst bless;
  and oh, what then must thou be like,
  Eternal Loveliness!

5 Most ancient of all mysteries,
  still at thy throne we lie;
  have mercy now, most merciful,
  most Holy Trinity.

Frederick William Faber (1814–63)

199   Mother of mercy

MATER MISERICORDIAE (88 88 8)   H.F. Hemy (1818–88)

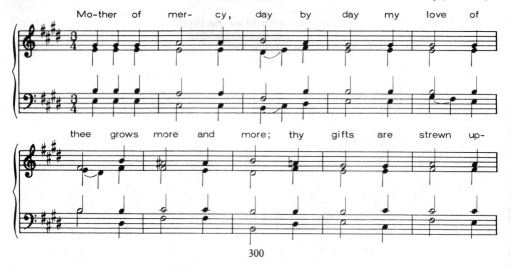

on   my   way,   like   sands   up-   on   the   great   sea

shore,   like   sands   up-   on   the   great   sea   shore.

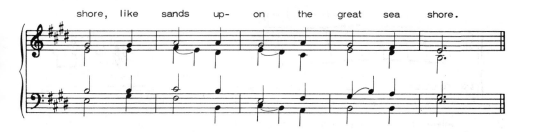

2 Though poverty and work and woe
   the masters of my life may be,
   when times are worst, who does not know
   darkness is light with love of thee?
   darkness is light with love of thee?

3 But scornful men have coldly said
   thy love was leading me from God;
   and yet in this I did but tread
   the very path my Saviour trod,
   the very path my Saviour trod.

4 They know but little of thy worth
   who speak these heartless words to me;
   for what did Jesus love on earth
   one half so tenderly as thee?
   one half so tenderly as thee.

5 Get me the grace to love thee more;
   Jesus will give if thou wilt plead;
   and, Mother! when life's care are o'er,
   oh, I shall love thee then indeed!
   oh, I shall love thee then indeed!

6 Jesus, when his three hours were run
   bequeath'd thee from the cross to me
   and oh! how can I love thy Son,
   sweet Mother! if I love not thee?
   sweet Mother! if I love not thee?

Frederick William Faber (1814–63)

200　My glory

M.J.McAlister

My glo-ry and the lif-ter of my head, my
glo-ry and the lif-ter of my head, for thou O Lord, art a
shield to me, my glo-ry and the lif-ter of my head. I
cried un-to the Lord with my voice, I cried un-to the Lord with my
voice, I cried un-to the Lord with my voice and he
heard me out of his ho-ly hill. My

Fine

D.S.

201 My God, accept my heart

BELMONT (86 86)

From *Islington Psalmody*, 1854

My God, ac-cept my heart this day, and make it whol-ly thine, that I from thee no more may stray, no more from thee de-cline.

2 Before the cross of him who died,
   behold, I prostrate fall;
   let every sin be crucified,
   and Christ be all in all.

3 Anoint me with thy heavenly grace,
   and seal me for thine own,
   that I may see thy glorious face,
   and worship at thy throne.

4 Let every thought, and work and word
   to thee be ever given,
   then life shall be thy service, Lord,
   and Death the gate of heaven.

5 All glory to the Father be,
   all glory to the Son,
   all glory, Holy Ghost, to thee,
   while endless ages run.

Matthew Bridges (1800–94)

202 My God, and is thy table spread

ROCKINGHAM (88 88)   Adapted by E.Miller

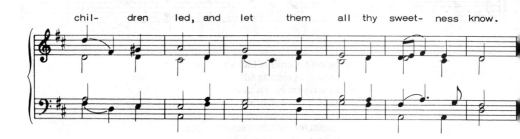

2 Hail, sacred feast, which Jesus makes!
  Rich banquet of his flesh and blood!
  Thrice happy he, who here partakes
  that sacred stream, that heavenly food.

3 O let thy table honoured be,
  and furnished well with joyful guests;
  and may each soul salvation see,
  that here its sacred pledges tastes.

Philip Doddridge (1702–51)

203 My God, how wonderful thou art

WESTMINSTER (86 86)   James Turle (1802–82)

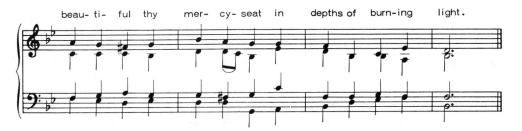

2 How dread are thine eternal years
  O everlasting Lord!
  By prostrate spirits day and night
  incessantly adored.

3 How beautiful, how beautiful
  the sight of thee must be,
  thine endless wisdom, boundless power
  and awful purity!

4 Oh, how, I fear thee, living God!
  with deepest, tenderest fears,
  and worship thee with trembling hope
  and penitential tears.

5 Yet I may love thee too, O Lord,
  almighty as thou art,
  for thou hast stooped to ask of me
  the love of my poor heart.

6 No earthly father loves like thee,
  no mother e'er so mild
  bears and forbears as thou hast done
  with me thy sinful child.

7 Father of Jesus, love's reward,
  what rapture will it be
  prostrate before thy throne to lie,
  and gaze and gaze on thee!

Frederick William Faber (1814–63)

204 My God I love thee

EVERLASTING LOVE (86 86)

R.R.Terry (1865–193.

2 Thou, O my Jesus, thou didst me
  upon the cross embrace;
  for me didst bear the nails and spear
  and manifold disgrace.

3 And griefs and torments numberless
  and sweat of agony;
  e'en death itself – and all for one
  who was thine enemy.

4 Then why, O Blessed Jesu Christ
  should I not love thee well;
  not for the sake of winning heaven,
  or of escaping hell;

5 Not with the hope of gaining aught;
  not seeking a reward,
  but, as thyself hast loved me
  O ever-loving Lord?

6 E'en so I love thee, and will love,
  and in thy praise will sing;
  solely because thou art my God
  and my eternal king.

17th c., tr. Edward Caswall

205   My God loves me

PLAISIR D'AMOUR

2 His gentle hand
  he stretches over me.
  Though storm-clouds threaten the day
  he will set me free.

3 He comes to me
  in sharing bread and wine.
  He brings me life that will reach
  past the end of time.

4 My God loves me,
  his faithful love endures.
  And I will live like a child
  held in love secure.

5 The joys of love
  as offerings now we bring.
  The pains of love will be lost
  in the praise we sing.

Verse 1 Anonymous
Verses 2–5 Sandra Joan Billington

206   My song is love unknown

LOVE UNKNOWN (66 66 44 44)   John Ireland (1879–1962)

2 He came from his blest throne,
   salvation to bestow;
   but men made strange, and none
   the longed-for Christ would know,
   but O, my friend,
   my friend indeed,
   who at my need
   his life did spend!

3 Sometimes they strew his way,
   and his sweet praises sing;
   resounding all the day
   hosannas to their King;
   then 'Crucify!'
   is all their breath,
   and for his death
   they thirst and cry.

4 Why, what hath my Lord done?
   What makes this rage and spite?
   He made the lame to run,
   he gave the blind their sight.
   Sweet injuries!
   Yet they at these
   themselves displease,
   and 'gainst him rise.

5 They rise, and needs will have
  my dear Lord made away;
  a murderer they save,
  the Prince of Life they slay.
  Yet cheerful he
  to suffering goes,
  that he his foes
  from thence might free.

6 In life, no house, no home
  my Lord on earth might have:
  in death no friendly tomb
  but what a stranger gave.
  What may I say?
  Heaven was his home;
  but mine the tomb
  wherein he lay.

7 Here might I stay and sing,
  no story so divine,
  never was love, dear King,
  never was grief like thine.
  This is my Friend,
  in whose sweet praise
  I all my days
  could gladly spend.

Samuel Crossman (c. 1624–84)

207 New praises be given

ST DENIO (11 11 11 11)   Welsh Hymn Melody (1839)

2 His glory still praising on thrice holy ground
  the apostles stood gazing, his mother around;
  with hearts that beat faster, with eyes full of love,
  they watched while their master ascended above.

3 "No star can disclose him", the bright angels said;
  "Eternity knows him, your conquering head;
  those high habitations, he leaves not again,
  till, judging all nations, on earth he shall reign".

4 Thus spoke they and straightway, where legions defend
  heaven's glittering gateway, their Lord they attend,
  and cry, looking thither, "Your portals let down
  for him who rides hither in peace and renown".

5 They asked, who keep sentry in that blessed town,
  "Who thus claimeth entry, a king of renown?"
  "The Lord of all valiance", that herald replied,
  "Who Satan's battalions laid low in their pride".

6 Grant, Lord, that our longing may follow thee there,
  on earth who are thronging thy temples with prayer;
  and unto thee gather, Redeemer, thine own
  where thou with thy Father dost sit on the throne.

St. Bede the Venerable (673–735)
tr. R. A. Knox

208 Now come to me

COME TO ME (86 86 D)

Traditional English Folk Melody

2 Now come to me all you who seek
and place your trust in me.
For I will comfort those who mourn
and make the blind to see.
However dark the stormy night
the sun will raise the dawn,
and you will live beneath the light
of love in darkness born.

3 Now come to me all you who seek
and place your trust in me.
For I bring peace to those at war
and set the captives free.
Just as in cutting sun-ripe wheat
we count the summer's worth,
so shall all those who justice seek
be there at love's new birth.

Michael Cockett

209 Now Jesus said (I)

Kevin Mayhew

2 They found the flour, they found the salt.
they found a jug of water.
But, though they searched around the town,
an ounce of yeast could not be found.
They came to him with eyes cast down
and told him of their failure.

3 Then Jesus said: "Do not be sad,
we'll mix the flour and water.
And though we bake unleavened bread,
if you will be the yeast instead,
the bread will rise up from the dead
and feed you ever after."

Michael Cockett

210 Now Jesus said (II)

Kevin Mayhew

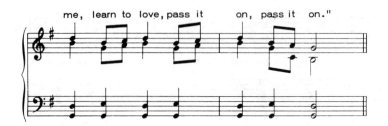

2 So Peter said:
  "You must love one another,
  pass it on, pass it on."
  So Peter said:
  "Call all men your brother,
  come to me, learn to love,
  pass it on, pass it on."

3 The people said ...

4 My Father said ...

5 Now I can say ...

Michael Cockett

211 Now thank we all our God

NUN DANKET (67 67 66 66)   J.Crüger (1598–1662)

2 O may this bounteous God
  through all our life be near us
  with ever joyful hearts
  and blessed peace to cheer us;
  and keep us in his grace,
  and guide us when perplexed,
  and free us from all ills
  in this world and the next.

3 All praise and thanks to God
  the Father now be given
  the Son and him who reigns
  with them in highest heaven,
  the one Eternal God,
  whom earth and heaven adore;
  for thus it was, is now,
  and shall be evermore.

Martin Rinkart (1586–1649),
tr. Catherine Winkworth

212 Now with the fast departing light

GROSSER GOTT (88 88)

From *Katholisches Gesangbuch*, 1774

2 Far off let idle visions fly:
   no phantom of the night molest:
   curb thou our raging enemy,
   that we in chaste repose may rest.

3 Father of mercies! hear our cry:
   hear us, O sole-begotten Son!
   Who, with the Holy Ghost most high,
   reignest while endless ages run.

7th c., tr. Edward Caswall

213 O bread of heaven

ST CATHERINE (88 88 88)   H.F.Hemy (1818–88)

O bread of hea-ven, be- neath this veil thou dost my ve- ry God con- ceal: my Je- sus, dear- est trea- sure, hail; I love thee and a- dor- ing kneel; each lov- ing soul by thee is fed with thine own self in form of bread.

2 O food of life, thou who dost give
  the pledge of immortality;
  I live; no, 'tis not I that live;
  God gives me life, God lives in me:
  he feeds my soul, he guides my ways,
  and every grief with joy repays.

3 O bond of love, that dost unite
  the servant to his living Lord;
  could I dare live, and not requite
  such love then death were meet reward:
  I cannot live unless to prove
  some love for such unmeasured love.

4 Beloved Lord in heaven above,
  there, Jesus, thou awaitest me;
  to gaze on thee with changeless love,
  yes, thus I hope, thus shall it be:
  for how can he deny me heaven
  who here on earth himself hath given?

St Alphonsus (1696–1787) tr. Edward Caswall

214　O come, all ye faithful

ADESTE FIDELES

Attributed to J.F.Wade (1710–86)

2 God of God,
light of light,
lo! he abhors not the virgin's womb;
very God,
begotten not created:

3 Sing, choirs of angels,
sing in exultation,
sing all ye citizens of heaven above;
glory to God
in the highest:

4 Yea, Lord, we greet thee,
born this happy morning,
Jesu, to thee be glory given;
word of the Father,
now in flesh appearing:

18th c., tr. Frederick Oakeley

215 O come and mourn

OLD HALL GREEN (88 88 extended)

J.Crookall (1821–87)

Chorus

2 Have we no tears to shed for him,
  while soldiers scoff and men deride?
  Ah! look how patiently he hangs;

3 How fast his feet and hands are nailed;
  his blessed tongue with thirst is tied;
  his failing eyes are blind with blood;

4 Seven times he spoke, seven words of love,
  and all three hours his silence cried
  For mercy on the souls of men;

5 O break, O break, hard heart of mine;
  thy weak self-love and guilty pride
  his Pilate and his Judas were:

6 A broken heart, a fount of tears,
  ask, and they will not be denied;
  a broken heart, love's cradle is;

7 O love of God! O sin of man!
  In this dread act your strength is tried;
  and victory remains with love;

Frederick William Faber (1814–63)

216 O come, O come, Emmanuel

VENI EMMANUEL

Adapted by T. Helmore from a French Missal
harmonized by Dom Gregory Murray O.S.B.

318

2 O come, thou Rod of Jesse, free
   thine own from Satan's tyranny;
   from depths of hell thy people save,
   and give them vict'ry o'er the grave:

3 O come, thou dayspring, come and cheer
   our spirits by thine advent here;
   disperse the gloomy clouds of night,
   and death's dark shadows put to flight:

4 O come, thou key of David, come
   and open wide our heavenly home;
   make safe the way that leads on high,
   and close the path to misery.

5 O come, O come, thou Lord of might,
   who to thy tribes on Sinai's height
   in ancient times didst give the law
   in cloud and majesty and awe:

From the 'Great O Antiphons' (12th-13th c.),
tr. John Mason Neale

217 O Father, now the hour has come

UNITY (86 86)   Sandra Seward

O Fa-ther, now the hour has come, so glo-ri-fy your Son, that he may give e-ter-nal life to those who hope in him.

2 Through Jesus Christ, your only Son,
   the Word has now been sown,
   so honour him with glory now,
   the saviour of the world.

3 O Father of the Word of Truth,
   the world has known you not,
   but through the Son that you have sent
   your love is in our hearts.

4 He is no longer in this world,
   he has returned to you.
   So, holy Father, make us one
   as he is one with you.

5 May all good men be joined as one,
   as Father with the Son,
   that through the unity of love,
   the whole world may believe.

6 Through glory given to the Son,
   the Father will reveal
   the joy complete, the bond of love,
   mysterious Three in One.

Michael Cockett

218 O Father, take in sign of love

HORSLEY (86 86)

William Horsley (1774–1858)

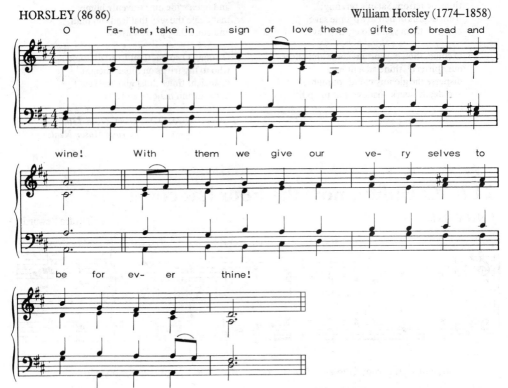

2 These gifts another gift will be,
   thy Son in very deed,
   for us a willing victim made,
   the Lamb on whom we feed!

3 These are the gifts thy Son did bless
   the night before he died.
   By which he showed himself a priest
   and victim crucified!

4 He now has given us as our own
   his offering made to thee:
   his body broken, Blood outpoured,
   for us on Calvary!

5 This bread his Body will become,
   this wine his Blood will be!
   Our humble gifts will be the gift
   that is most dear to thee!

6 This perfect gift thou wilt restore
   to greatest and to least,
   to make all one in love and joy
   in thy communion-feast!

James Quinn, S.J.

219 Of the glorious body telling

ST THOMAS (87 87 87)

Samuel Webbe (1740–1816)

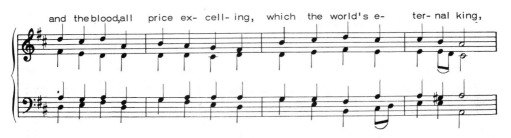

and the blood,all price ex- cell- ing, which the world's e- ter- nal king,

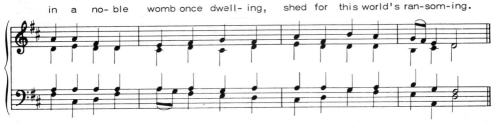

in a no- ble womb once dwell- ing, shed for this world's ran-som-ing.

2 Giv'n for us, for us descending,
   of a virgin to proceed,
   man with man in converse blending,
   scattered he the gospel seed,
   'till his sojourn drew to ending,
   which he closed in wondrous deed.

3 At the last great supper lying,
   circled by his brethren's band,
   meekly with the law complying,
   first, he finished its command.
   Then, immortal food supplying,
   gave himself with his own hand.

4 Word made flesh, by word he maketh
   very bread his flesh to be;
   man in wine Christ's blood partaketh,
   and if senses fail to see,
   faith alone the true heart waketh,
   to behold the mystery.

5 Therefore, we before him bending,
   this great sacrament revere;
   types and shadows have their ending,
   for the newer rite is here;
   faith, our outward sense befriending,
   makes the inward vision clear.

6 Glory let us give, and blessing,
   to the Father and the Son;
   honour, might and praise addressing,
   while eternal ages run;
   ever too his love confessing,
   who from both, with both is one.

St. Thomas Aquinas (1127–74),
tr. J. M. Neale, E. Caswall and others

220 O Godhead hid

AQUINAS (11 11 11 11) R.R.Terry (1865–1938)

O God-head hid, de- vout- ly I a- dore thee,

who tru- ly art with- in the forms be- fore me;

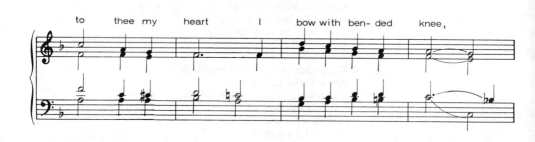

to thee my heart I bow with ben- ded knee,

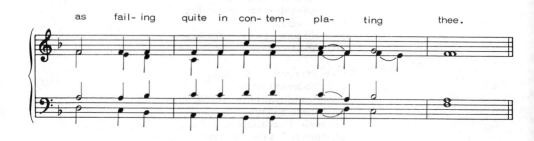

as fail- ing quite in con- tem- pla- ting thee.

2 Sight, touch, and taste in thee are each deceived,
   the ear alone most safely is believed:
   I believe all the Son of God has spoken;
   than truth's own word there is no truer token.

3 God only on the cross lay hid from view;
   but here lies hid at once the manhood too:
   and I, in both professing my belief,
   make the same prayer as the repentant thief.

4 Thy wounds, as Thomas saw, I do not see;
   yet thee confess my Lord and God to be;
   make me believe thee ever more and more,
   In thee my hope, in thee my love to store.

5 O thou memorial of our Lord's own dying!
   O bread that living art and vivifying!
   Make ever thou my soul on thee to live:
   ever a taste of heavenly sweetness give.

6 O loving Pelican! O Jesus, Lord!
   Unclean I am, but cleanse me in thy blood;
   of which a single drop, for sinners spilt,
   is ransom for a world's entire guilt.

7 Jesus, whom for the present veiled I see,
   what I so thirst for, oh, vouchsafe to me:
   that I may see thy countenance unfolding,
   and may be blest thy glory in beholding.

St. Thomas Aquinas (1227–74), tr. Edward Caswall

221 O God of earth and altar

KINGS LYNN (76 76 D)   FIRST TUNE   Traditional English Melody
arr. R. Vaughan Williams

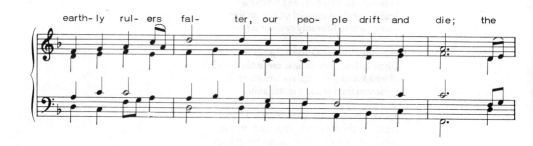

SECOND TUNE

WILLSBRIDGE (76 76 D)

R.L.de Pearsall (1795–1856)

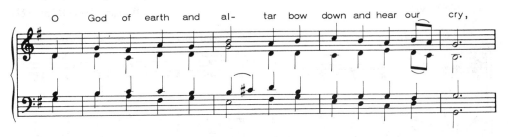

O God of earth and al- tar bow down and hear our cry,

our earth- ly ru- lers fal- ter, our peo- ple drift and die;

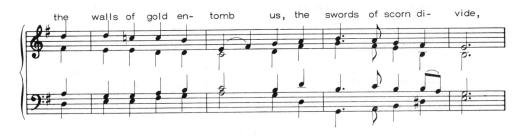

the walls of gold en- tomb us, the swords of scorn di- vide,

take not thy thun- der from us, but take a- way our pride.

2 From all that terror teaches,
  from lies of tongue and pen,
from all the easy speeches
  that comfort cruel men,
from sale and profanation
  of honour and the sword,
from sleep and from damnation,
  deliver us, good Lord!

3 Tie in a living tether
  the prince and priest and thrall,
bind all our lives together,
  smite us and save us all;
in ire and exultation
  aflame with faith, and free,
lift up a living nation,
  a single sword to thee.

G. K. Chesterton (1874–1936)

222   O God our help in ages past

ST ANNE (86 86)

William Croft (1678–1727)

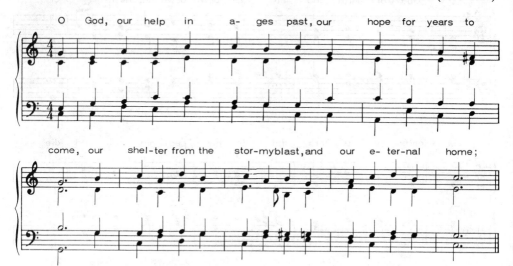

2 Beneath the shadow of thy throne,
  thy saints have dwelt secure;
  sufficient is thine arm alone,
  and our defence is sure.

3 Before the hills in order stood,
  or earth received her frame,
  from everlasting thou art God,
  to endless years the same.

4 A thousand ages in thy sight,
  are like an evening gone;
  short as the watch that ends the night
  before the rising sun.

5 Time, live an ever-rolling stream,
  bears all its sons away;
  they fly forgotten, as a dream
  dies at the opening day.

6 O God, our help in ages past,
  our hope for years to come,
  be thou our guard while troubles last,
  and our eternal home.

Isaac Watts (1674–1748)

223   O God, thy people gather

PINNER (86 86 D)

Wilfred Trotman

word, a- round thy ho- ly al- tar to

praise thy name, O Lord; for all thy lov- ing

kind- ness our grate- ful hearts we raise; but

par- don first the blind- ness of all our sin- ful ways.

2 Thou art our loving Father,
  thou art our holiest Lord,
  but we have sinned against thee,
  by thought and deed and word.
  Before the court of heaven
  we stand and humbly pray
  our sins may be forgiven,
  our faults be washed away.

3 Though sinful, we implore thee
  to turn and make us live,
  that so we may adore thee,
  and our due offering give,
  and may the prayers and voices
  of thy glad people rise,
  as thy whole Church rejoices
  in this great sacrifice.

Anthony Nye

224 O God, we give ourselves today

IRISH (86 86)

From *A Collection of hymns and Sacred Poems*, 1749

O God, we give our-selves to-day with this pure

host to thee, the self-same gift which thy dear

Son gave once on Cal-va-ry.

2 Entire and whole, our life and love
with heart and soul and mind,
for all our sins and faults and needs,
thy Church and all mankind.

3 With humble and with contrite heart
this bread and wine we give
because thy Son once gave himself
and died that we might live.

4 Though lowly now, soon by thy word
these offered gifts will be
the very body of our Lord,
his soul and deity.

5 His very body, offered up
a gift beyond all price,
he gives to us, that we may give
in loving sacrifice.

6 O Lord, who took our human life,
as water mixed with wine,
grant through this sacrifice that we
may share thy life divine.

Anthony Nye

225 O living water

Rosalie Vissing

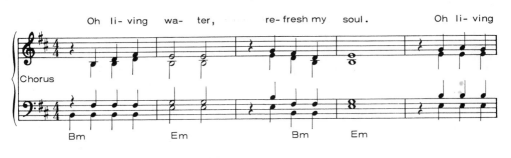

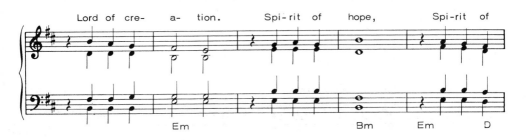

2 Oh set us free,
Oh set us free.

3 Come, pray in us,
come, pray in us.

Rosalie Vissing

226 O Lord, all the world belongs to you

ALL THINGS NEW (9 10 55 5)

Patrick Appleford

Oh Lord, all the world belongs to you, and

you are al- ways ma- king all things new. What is

wrong you for- give, and the new life you give is what's

tur- ning the world up- side down.

2 The world's only loving to its friends,
  but you have brought us love that never ends;
  loving enemies too,
  and this loving with you
  is what's turning the world upside down.

3 This world lives divided and apart.
  You draw all men together and we start
  in your body to see
  that in fellowship we
  can be turning the world upside down.

4 The world wants the wealth to live in state,
  but you show us a new way to be great;
  like a servant you came,
  and if we do the same,
  we'll be turning the world upside down.

5 Oh Lord all the world belongs to you,
  and you are always making all things new.
  Send your Spirit on all
  in your Church whom you call
  to be turning the world upside down.

Patrick Appleford

227 Oh Lord my God, when I in awesome wonder

O STØRE GUD

tr. Stuart K.Hine

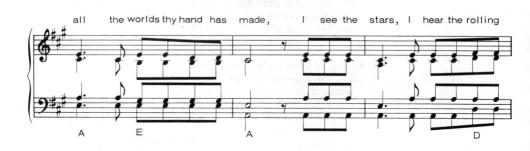

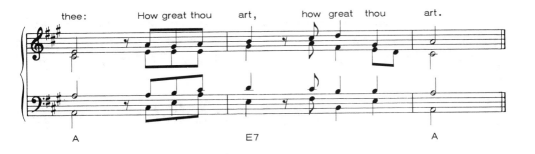

2 And when I think that God, his Son not sparing,
sent him to die, I scarce can take it in
that on the cross, my burden gladly bearing,
he bled and died to take away my sin.

3 When Christ shall come with shout of acclamation
and take me home, what joy shall fill my heart;
when I shall bow in humble adoration,
and there proclaim; my God, how great thou art.

Carl Boberg (1850–1940)
tr. Stuart K. Hine

228 O holy Lord, all adored

MIT FREUDEN ZART (87 87 887)

Later form of melody
of the Bohemian Brethren

2 To God on high be thanks and praise,
who deigns our bond to sever;
his care shall guide us all our days,
and harm shall reach us never,
on him we rest with faith assured;
of all that live he is the Lord,
for ever and for ever.

M. F. Bell (1862–1947)

334

229 Oh, sinner man

2 Run to the moon, moon won't you hide me?
  Run to the sea, sea won't you hide me?
  Run to the sun, sun won't you hide me?
  all on that day?

3 Lord said: "Sinner Man, the moon'll be a-bleeding."
  Lord said: "Sinner Man, the sea'll be a-sinking."
  Lord said: "Sinner Man, the sun'll be a-freezing."
  all on that day.

4 Run to the Lord: "Lord, won't you hide me?"
  Run to the Lord: "Lord, won't you hide me?"
  Run to the Lord: "Lord, won't you hide me?"
  all on that day.

5 Lord said: "Sinner Man, you should have been a- praying!"
  Lord said: "Sinner Man, you should have been a- praying!"
  Lord said: "Sinner Man, you should have been a- praying!"
  all on that day.

Traditional

230   Oh the Lord looked down

Traditional

Oh, the Lord looked down from his win-dow in the sky, said:

E(F)

"I cre-a- ted man but I can't re-mem- ber why!

F♯7(G7)   B7(C)

No- thing but figh- ting since cre- a- tion day. I'll

E(F)   A(B♭)

send a lit- tle wa- ter and wash them all a- way." Oh, the

E(F)   B7(C)   E(F)

Lord came down and looked a- round a spell.

2 The Lord said: "Noah, there's going to be a flood,
there's going to be some water, there's going to be some mud,
so take off your hat, Noah, take off your coat,
get Sham, Ham and Japhat and build yourself a boat."
Noah said: "Lord, I don't believe I could."
The Lord said: "Noah, get yourself some wood.
You never know what you can do till you try.
Build it fifty cubits wide and thirty cubits high."

3 Noah said: "There she is, there she is Lord!"
The Lord said: "Noah, it's time to get aboard.
Take of each creature a he and a she
and of course take Mrs Noah and the whole family."
Noah said: "Lord, it's getting mighty dark,"
The Lord said: "Noah, get those creatures in the ark."
Noah said: "Lord, it's beginning to pour."
The Lord said: "Noah, hurry up and close the door."

4 The ark rose up on the bosom of the deep.
After forty days Mr Noah took a peep.
He said: "We're not moving, Lord, where are we at?"
The Lord said: "You're sitting right on Mount Ararat."
Noah said: "Lord, it's getting nice and dry."
The Lord said: "Noah, see my rainbow in the sky.
Take all your creatures and people the earth
and be sure that you're not more trouble than you're worth."

Traditional

231 Oh the love of my Lord

Estelle White

Oh, the love of my Lord is the es-sence of
all that I love here on earth. All the
beau-ty I see he has giv-en to me and his
giv-ing is gen-tle as si-lence.

2 Every day, every hour, every moment
   have been blessed by the strength of his love.
   At the turn of each tide
   he is there at my side,
   and his touch is as gentle as silence.

3 There've been times when I've turned from his presence,
   and I've walked other paths, other ways.
   But I've called on his name
   in the dark of my shame,
   and his mercy was gentle as silence.

Estelle White

339

232 Oh when the saints

Traditional

Oh when the saints go marching in, oh when the

saints go march-ing in I want to be in that

num-ber, when the saints go march-ing in.

2 Oh when the drums begin to bang,
  oh when the drums begin to bang.
  I want to be in that number,
  when the drums begin to bang.

3 Oh when the stars fall from the sky,
  oh when the stars fall from the sky.
  I want to be in that number,
  when the stars fall from the sky.

4 Oh when the moon turns into blood,
  oh when the moon turns into blood.
  I want to be in that number,
  when the moon turns into blood.

5 Oh when the sun turns into fire,
  oh when the sun turns into fire.
  I want to be in that number,
  when the sun turns into fire.

6 Oh when the fires begin to blaze,
  oh when the fires begin to blaze.
  I want to be in that number,
  when the fires begin to blaze.

7 Oh when the Lord calls out the names,
  oh when the Lord calls out the names.
  I want to be in that number,
  when the Lord calls out the names.

Traditional

233   O Jesus Christ

AURELIA (76 76 D)   S.S.Wesley (1810–76)

2 Remember then, O Saviour,
  I supplicate of thee,
  that here I bowed before thee
  upon my bended knee;
  that here I owned thy presence,
  and did not thee deny,
  and glorified thy greatness
  though hid from human eye.

3 Accept, divine Redeemer,
  the homage of my praise;
  be thou the light and honour
  and glory of my days.
  Be thou my consolation
  when death is drawing nigh:
  be thou my only treasure
  through all eternity.

Edward Caswall (1814–78)

234   O king of might and splendour

O KING OF MIGHT (76 76 D)

Dom Gregory Murray OSB

O king of might and splen- dour, cre- a- tor most a-

dored, this sac- ri- fice we ren- der to thee as sov'- reign

Lord. May these, our gifts, be pleas- ing un- to thy maj-es-

ty, man- kind from sin re- leas- ing who have of- fen- ded thee.

2 Thy body thou hast given,
thy blood thou hast outpoured,
that sin might be forgiven,
O Jesus, loving Lord.
As now with love most tender,
thy death we celebrate,
our lives in self-surrender
to thee we consecrate.

Dom Gregory Murray, O.S.B.

235 O little town of Bethlehem

FOREST GREEN (86 86 D)

Traditional English Melody
arr. R. Vaughan Williams

O lit-tle town of Beth-le-hem, how still we see thee lie!
A-bove thy deep and dream-less sleep the si-lent stars go by.
Yet in thy dark streets shin-eth the ev-er-last-ing light;
the hopes and fears of all the years are met in thee to-night.

2 O morning stars, together
proclaim the holy birth,
and praises sing to God the King,
and peace to men on earth;
for Christ is born of Mary;
and, gathered all above,
while mortals sleep, the angels keep
their watch of wondering love.

3 How silently, how silently,
the wondrous gift is given!
So God imparts to human hearts
the blessings of his heaven.
No ear may hear his coming;
but in this world of sin,
where meek souls will receive him, still
the dear Christ enters in.

4 Where children pure and happy
pray to the blessed Child,
where misery cries out to thee,
Son of the mother mild;
where charity stands watching
and faith holds wide the door,
the dark night wakes, the glory breaks,
and Christmas comes once more.

Phillips Brooks (1835–93)

236 O Mother blest

ST URSULA (86 86 75 75)

F. Westlake (1840–98)

O Mo- ther blest, whom God bestows on sinners and on just, what

joy, what hope thou giv- est those who in thy mer-cy trust.

Chorus

Thou art cle-ment, thou art chaste, Ma- ry, thou art fair;

Of all mothers sweet-est, best; none with thee com- pare.

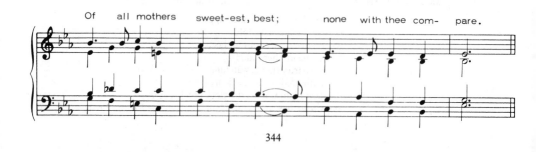

2 O heavenly mother, mistress sweet!
   It never yet was told
   that suppliant sinner left thy feet
   unpitied, unconsoled.

3 O mother pitiful and mild,
   cease not to pray for me;
   for I do love thee as a child,
   and sigh for love of thee.

4 Most powerful mother, all men know
   thy Son denies thee nought;
   thou askest, wishest it, and lo!
   his power thy will hath wrought.

5 O mother blest, for me obtain
   ungrateful though I be,
   to love that God who first could deign
   to show such love for me.

St. Alphonsus Liquori (1699–1787),
tr. Edmund Vaughan

237　O my Lord, within my heart

Estelle White

O my Lord, with- in my heart pride will have no

home, eve- ry tal- ent that I have comes from you a-

lone and like a child at rest close to its

mother's breast,   safe   in your   arms   my   soul   is   calmed.

Dm   F7   B♭   C7   F

2 Lord, my eyes do not look high
   nor my thoughts take wings,
   for I can find treasures in
   ordinary things.

3 Great affairs are not for me,
   deeds beyond my scope,
   in the simple things I do
   I find joy and hope.

Estelle White

238 Once in royal David's city

IRBY (87 87 77)

H.J.Gauntlett (1805–76)

2 He came down to earth from heaven,
who is God and Lord of all,
and his shelter was a stable
and his cradle was a stall;
with the poor, and mean, and lowly,
lived on earth our Saviour holy.

3 And through all his wondrous childhood
he would honour and obey,
love, and watch the lowly maiden
in whose gentle arms he lay;
Christian children all must be
mild, obedient, good as he.

4 For he is our childhood's pattern,
day by day like us he grew;
he was little, weak and helpless,
tears and smiles like us he knew;
and he feeleth for our sadness,
and he shareth in our gladness.

5 And our eyes at last shall see him
through his own redeeming love,
for that child so dear and gentle
is our Lord in heaven above;
and he leads his children on
to the place where he is gone.

6 Not in that poor lowly stable,
with the oxen standing by,
we shall see him; but in heaven,
set at God's right hand on high;
when like stars his children crowned
all in white shall wait around.

Cecil Francis Alexander (1818–95)

348

239 On Jordan's banks

WINCHESTER NEW (88 88)

From *Musikalisches Handbuch*, 1690

On Jor- dan's bank the Bap- tist's cry an- nounces that the Lord is nigh; come then and hear- ken, for he brings glad tid- ings from the King of kings.

2 Then cleansed be every Christian breast,
and furnished for so great a guest!
Yea, let us each our hearts prepare,
for Christ to come and enter there.

3 For thou art our salvation, Lord,
our refuge and our great reward;
without thy grace our souls must fade,
and wither like a flower decayed.

4 Stretch forth thy hand, to heal our sore,
and make us rise, to fall no more;
once more upon thy people shine,
and fill the world with love divine.

5 All praise, eternal Son, to thee
whose advent sets thy people free,
whom, with the Father, we adore,
and Holy Ghost, for evermore.

C. Coffin (1676–1749), tr. J. Chandler

240   On this house your blessing, Lord

Sister M.Pereira

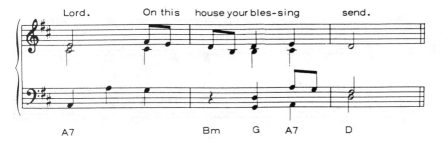

Lord. On this house your bles-sing send.

A7   Bm   G   A7   D

2 On this house your loving, Lord.
  May it overflow each day.
  On this house your loving, Lord.
  May it come and with us stay.
  Drawing us in love
  and unity
  by the love received from you.
  On this house your loving, Lord.
  May it come each day anew.

3 On this house your giving, Lord.
  May it turn and ever flow.
  On this house your giving, Lord.
  On this house your wealth bestow.
  Filling all our hopes
  and wishes, Lord,
  in the way you know is best.
  On this house your giving, Lord.
  May it come and with us rest.

4 On this house your calling, Lord.
  May it come to us each day.
  On this house your calling, Lord.
  May it come to lead the way.
  Filling us with nobler
  yearnings, Lord,
  calling us to live in you.
  On this house your calling, Lord.
  May it come each day anew.

Sister M. Pereira

241   Onward! Christian soldiers

ST GERTRUDE (65 65 triple)

Arthur Sullivan (1842–1900)

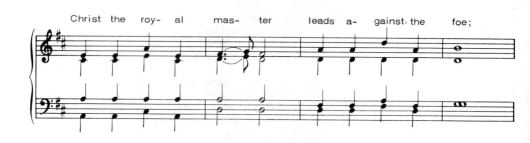

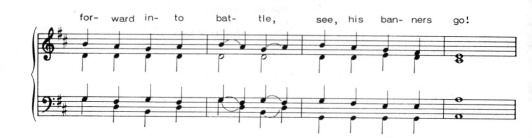

Chorus

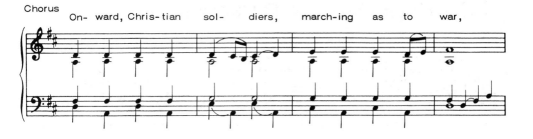

On- ward, Chris-tian sol-diers, march-ing as to war,

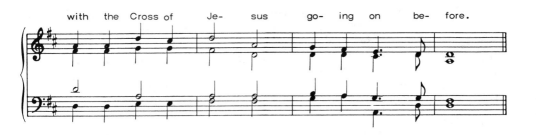

with the Cross of Je-sus go-ing on be-fore.

2 At the sign of triumph
Satan's legions flee;
on then, Christian soldiers,
on to victory.
Hell's foundations quiver
at the shout of praise;
brothers, lift your voices,
loud your anthem raise.

3 Like a might army
moves the Church of God.
Brothers, we are treading
where the Saints have trod;
we are not divided,
all one body we,
one in hope and doctrine,
one in charity.

4 Crowns and thrones may perish,
kingdoms rise and wane,
but the Church of Jesus
constant will remain;
gates of hell can never
'gainst that Church prevail;
we have Christ's own promise,
and that cannot fail.

5 Onward, then, ye people,
join our happy throng,
blend with ours your voices
in the triumph song;
glory, laud, and honour
unto Christ the King;
this through countless ages
men and angels sing.

S. Baring-Gould (1834–1924)

242   Open your ears, O Christian people

Israeli Folk Song
arr. W.F.Jabusch

O- pen your ears, O Christ- ian peo- ple, o- pen your ears and

hear Good News.   O - pen your hearts O roy- al priest- hood God has come to

Chorus

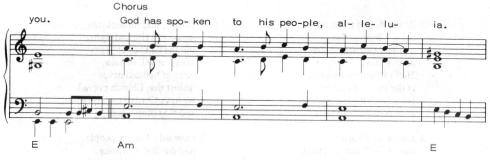

you.   God has spo- ken to his peo- ple, al- le- lu- ia.

And his words are words of wis- dom, al- le- lu- ia.

2 Israel comes to greet the Saviour,
Judah is glad to see his day.
From East and West the peoples travel,
he will show the way.

3 He who has ears to hear his message;
he who has ears, then let him hear.
He who would learn the way of wisdom,
let him hear God's words.

W. F. Jabusch

354

243 O perfect love

STRENGTH AND STAY (11 10 11 10)

J.B.Dykes (1823–76)

O per-fect love, all hu-man thought tran-scen-ding,
low-ly we kneel in prayer be-fore thy throne,
That theirs may be the love which knows no end-ing
whom thou for ev-er-more dost join in one.

2 O perfect life, be thou their full assurance
   of tender charity and steadfast faith,
   of patient hope, and quiet, brave endurance,
   with childlike trust that fears nor pain nor death.

3 Grant them the joy which brightens earthly sorrow,
   grant them the peace which calms all earthly strife;
   and to life's day the glorious unknown morrow
   that dawns upon eternal love and life.

Dorothy Francis Gurney (1858–1932)

244　O praise ye the Lord!

LAUDATE DOMINUM (10 10 11 11)

C.Hubert H.Parry (1848–1918)

2 O praise ye the Lord! praise him upon earth,
in tuneful accord, ye sons of new birth.
Praise him who hath brought you his grace from above,
praise him who hath taught you to sing of his love.

3 O praise ye the Lord, all things that give sound;
each jubilant chord re-echo around;
loud organs, his glory forth tell in deep tone,
and, sweet harp, the story of what he hath done.

4 O praise ye the Lord! thanksgiving and song
to him be outpoured all ages along;
for love in creation, for heaven restored,
for grace of salvation, O praise ye the Lord!

Henry Williams Baker (1821–77),
based on Psalms 148 and 150

245 O priest and victim

MELCOMBE (88 88)   Samuel Webbe (1740–1816)

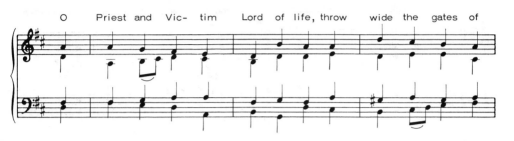

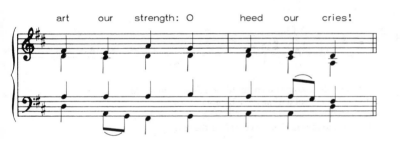

2 To Father, Son and Spirit blest,
one only God, be ceaseless praise!
May he in goodness grant us rest
in heav'n, our home, for endless days!

St Thomas Aquinas (1227–74)
tr. James Quinn, S.J.

357

246 O purest of creatures

MARIA ZU LIEBEN (11 11 11 11)

From *Paderborn Gesangbuch*, 1765

O pur-est of crea-tures! sweet mo-ther, sweet maid; the one spotless womb where-in Je-sus was laid. Dark night hath come down on us, mo-ther, and we look out for thy shin- ing, sweet star of the sea.

2 Deep night hath come down on this rough-spoken world.
And the banners of darkness are boldly unfurled;
and the tempest-tossed Church, all her eyes are on thee.
They look to thy shining, sweet star of the sea.

3 He gazed on thy soul, it was spotless and fair;
for the empire of sin, it had never been there;
none ever had owned thee, dear mother, but he,
and he blessed thy clear shining, sweet star of the sea.

4 Earth gave him one lodging; 'twas deep in thy breast,
and God found a home where the sinner finds rest,
his home and his hiding-place, both were in thee;
he was won by thy shining, sweet star of the sea.

5 Oh, blissful and calm was the wonderful rest
that thou gavest thy God in thy virginal breast;
for the heaven he left he found heaven in thee,
and he shone in thy shining, sweet star of the sea.

Frederick William Faber (1814–63)

247 O sacred head sore wounded

PASSION CHORALE (76 76 D)

H.L.Hassler (1564–1612),
harmonized by J.S.Bach

O sacred head sore woun- ded, de- filed and put to scorn;

O king- ly head sur- roun- ded with mock- ing crown of thorn:

what sor- row mars thy gran- deur? Can death thy bloom de-

flower? O coun-tenance whose splen- dour the hosts of heav'n a- dore.

2 Thy beauty, long-desired,
hath vanished from our sight;
thy power is all expired,
and quenched the light of light.
Ah me! for whom thou diest,
hide not so far thy grace:
show me, O love most highest,
the brightness of thy face.

3 I pray thee, Jesu, own me,
me, shepherd good, for thine;
who to thy fold hast won me,
and fed with truth divine.
Me guilty, me refuse not;
incline thy face to me,
this comfort that I lose not
on earth to comfort thee.

4 In thy most bitter passion
my heart to share doth cry,
with thee for my salvation
upon the cross to die.
Ah, keep my heart thus moved
to stand thy cross beneath,
to mourn thee, well-beloved,
yet thank thee for thy death.

5 My days are few, O fail not,
with thine immortal power,
to hold me that I quail not
in death's most fearful hour:

that I may fight befriended,
and see in my last strife
to me thine arms extended
upon the cross of life.

Paulus Gerhardt (1607–76), tr. Robert Bridges

248 O sacred heart

LAURENCE (4 7 99 4)

R.R. Terry (1865–1938)

O sa- cred heart, our home lies deep in

thee; on earth thou art an ex- ile's rest, in

heav'n the glo- ry of the blest, O sa- cred heart.

2 O Sacred Heart,
   thou fount of contrite tears;
   where'er those living waters flow,
   new life to sinners they bestow,
   O Sacred Heart.

3 O Sacred Heart,
   bless our dear native land;
   may England's sons in truth e'er stand,
   with faith's bright banner still in hand,
   O Sacred Heart.

4 O Sacred Heart,
  our trust is all in thee,
  for though earth's night be dark and drear,
  thou breathest rest where thou art near,
  O Sacred Heart.

5 O Sacred Heart,
  when shades of death shall fall,
  receive us 'neath thy gentle care,
  and save us from the tempter's snare,
  O Sacred Heart.

6 O Sacred Heart,
  lead exiled children home,
  where we may ever rest near thee,
  in peace and joy eternally,
  O Sacred Heart.

Francis Stanfield (1835–1914)

249   O thou, who at thy Eucharist

SONG 1 (10 10 10 10 10 10)   Orlando Gibbons (1583–1625)

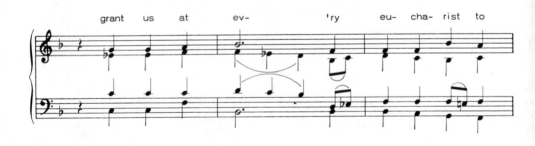

2 For all thy Church, O Lord, we intercede;
  make thou our sad divisions soon to cease;
  draw us the nearer each to each, we plead,
  by drawing all to thee, O Prince of peace;
  thus may we all one bread, one body be,
  one through this sacrament of unity.

3 We pray thee too for wanderers from thy fold,
  O bring them back, good shepherd of the sheep,
  back to the faith which saints believed of old,
  back to the Church which still that faith doth keep;
  soon may we all one bread, one body be,
  one through this sacrament of unity.

4 So, Lord, at length when sacraments shall cease,
  may we be one with all they Church above,
  one with thy saints in one unbroken peace,
  one with thy saints in one unbounded love:
  more blessed still, in peace and love to be
  one with the Trinity in unity.

William Harry Turton (1856–1938)

250   O Trinity, most blessed light

(88 88)

Lines 1–2 from the tune WINSCOTT
by S.S.Wesley (1810–76)
The origin of lines 3–4 is unknown

O Tri-ni- ty, most bles-sed light, O un-i- ty of sov'reign might

as now the fier- y sun de- parts, shed thou thy beams with- in our hearts.

2 To thee our morning song of praise,
  to thee our evening prayer we raise;
  thee may our souls for evermore,
  in lowly reverence adore.

3 All praise to God the Father be,
  all praise, eternal Son, to thee,
  whom with the Spirit we adore,
  for ever and for evermore.

St. Ambrose (340–397), tr. J. M. Neale

364

251 Caribbean Our Father

Traditional Caribbean

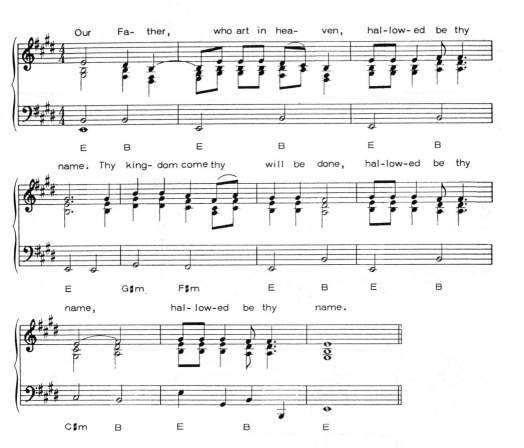

2 On earth as it is in heaven,
   hallowed be thy name.
   Give us this day our daily bread,
   hallowed be thy name,
   hallowed be thy name.

3 Forgive us our trespasses,
   hallowed be thy name,
   as we forgive those who trespass against us,
   hallowed be thy name,
   hallowed be thy name.

4 And lead us not into temptation,
   hallowed be thy name,
   but deliver us from all that is evil,
   hallowed be thy name,
   hallowed be thy name.

5 For thine is the kingdom, the power and the glory,
   hallowed be thy name,
   for ever, and for ever and ever,
   hallowed be thy name,
   hallowed be thy name.

6 Amen, amen, it shall be so,
   hallowed be thy name.
   Amen, amen, it shall be so,
   hallowed be thy name,
   hallowed be thy name.

Traditional Caribbean

252 Out and away

John Glynn

Out and a- way

G   Em   C   D7   G

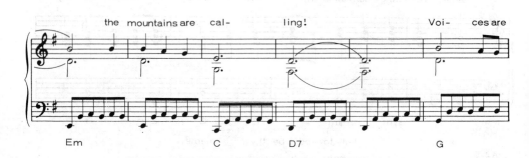

the mountains are cal- ling! Voi- ces are

Em   C   D7   G

clear and wide as the sky! Where is the

Em   D7   G

mus- ic I hear in my heart: soars ov- er val- leys as

Em   C   D7   G   Em

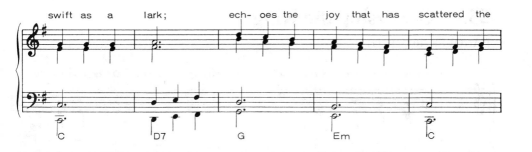

2 Hear the wind sigh through leaves that are falling;
   see the wind sway the trees that are dry.
   Silent the darkness where thunder-clouds form;
   still is the world as it waits for the storm;
   now comes the lighting that heralds the dawn of the rain.

3 Water is clear, as clear as the moonlight;
   dew on the ground, a tear in the eye.
   Rivers and torrents have vanished before;
   oceans have coastlines and continents shores:
   Boundless the flow that's unlocking the doors of my heart.

4 Free as the day my spirit is flying:
   eagles have wings, but none strong as these!
   Where have I found it, this life newly-grown?
   Gently, my heart says it's not of my own:
   deeper beyond me the Spirit has blown – he is love.

John Glynn

253 O worship the King

HANOVER (10 10 11 11)
W.Croft (1678–1727)

O wor-ship the King all glo-rious a- bove; O grate-ful- ly

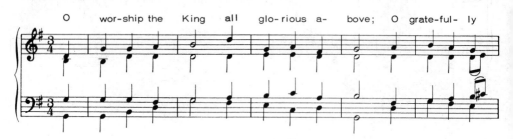

sing his power and his love: our shield and de- fen- der, the

an-cient of days, pav- il- ioned in splen-dour, and gir-ded with praise.

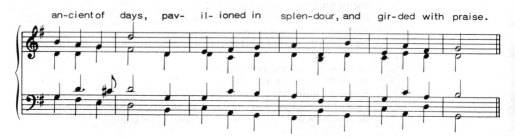

2 O tell of his might,
O sing of his grace,
whose robe is the light,
whose canopy space.
His chariots of wrath,
the deep thunder-clouds form,
and dark is his path
on the wings of the storm.

3 This earth, with its store
of wonders untold,
almighty, thy power
hath founded of old;
hath stablished it fast
by a changeless decree;
and round it hath cast,
like a mantle, the sea.

4 Thy bountiful care
what tongue can recite?
It breathes in the air,
it shines in the light;
it streams from the hills,
it descends to the plain,
and sweetly distils
in the dew and the rain.

5 Frail children of dust,
and feeble as frail,
in thee do we trust,
nor find thee to fail;
thy mercies how tender!
How firm to the end!
Our maker, defender,
redeemer, and friend.

6 O measureless might,
  ineffable love,
  while angels delight
  to hymn thee above,
  thy humbler creation,
  though feeble their lays,
  with true adoration
  shall sing to thy praise.

Robert Grant (1779–1838)

254 Peace is flowing like a river

Anonymous

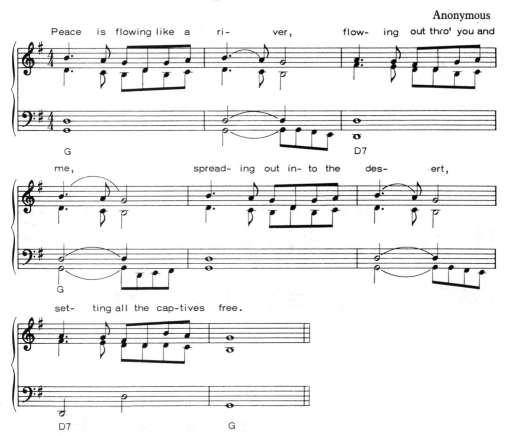

Peace is flowing like a ri- ver, flow- ing out thro' you and me, spread- ing out in- to the des- ert, set- ting all the cap-tives free.

G   D7   G   D7   G

2 Love is flowing like a river ...

3 Joy is flowing like a river ...

4 Hope is flowing like a river ...

Anonymous

369

255　Peace is the gift of heaven to earth

John Glynn

2 Peace is the gift of Christ to his Church,
wound of the lance of his love.
Love is the pain he suffered for man,
offered to us:
Oh, to accept the wound that brings us peace!

3 Joy is the gift the Spirit imparts,
born of the heavens and earth.
We are his children, children of joy,
people of God:
He is our Lord, our peace, our love, our joy!

John Glynn

256   Peacemakers

Malcolm Campbell-Carr

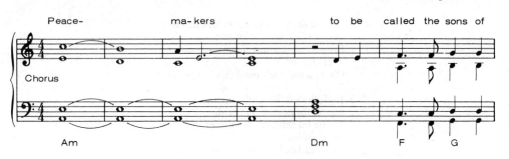

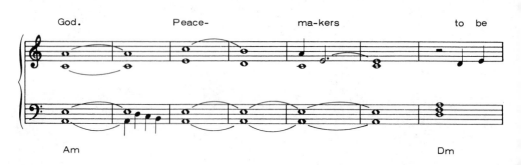

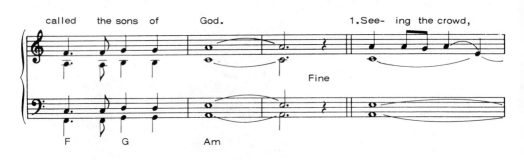

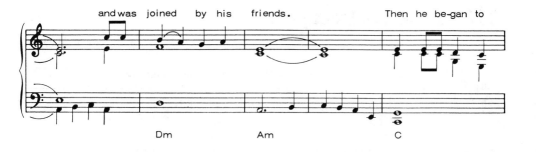

and was joined by his friends.   Then he be-gan to

Dm   Am   C

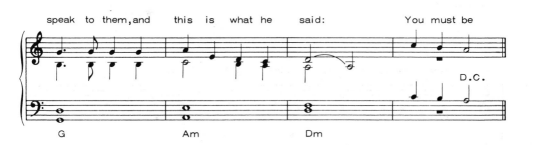

speak to them, and   this is what he   said: You must be

G   Am   Dm

D.C.

2 Happy the gentle,
for I give to them the earth.
Happy the mourners,
I will comfort their distress.
Happy are those who thirst and
hunger after what is right.
They shall be ...

Malcolm Campbell-Carr

257 Peace, perfect peace

Kevin Mayhew

2 Love, perfect love ...

3 Faith, perfect faith ...

4 Hope, perfect hope ...

5 Joy, perfect joy ...

Kevin Mayhew

258 People of God

PRAISE (97 97 D)

Kevin Mayhew

People of God, give praise to his name, praise ev- er- last-ing is

A   D   E   A   D

his,   brought to his feast   as   guests in his house,

E   F♯m   D   Bm   E

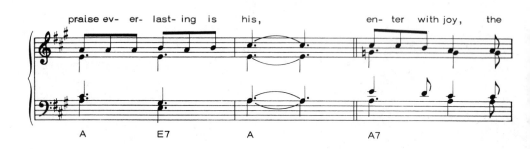

praise ev- er- last- ing is   his,   en- ter with joy,   the

A   E7   A   A7

Spi- rit is here,   praise ev- er- last- ing is   his.

D   C♯   Bm   E7   F♯m

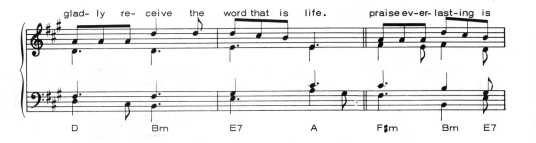

2 Sing with one voice, one love in your heart,
   praise everlasting is his,
   love that the Saviour bears to us all;
   praise everlasting is his,
   friend for the friendless, neighbour for foe,
   praise everlasting is his,
   Christ for all peoples, we are his sign
   praise everlasting is his.

3 All that we have and all that we are,
   praise everlasting is his,
   all is his gift, his token of love,
   praise everlasting is his,
   all to be loved, made profit for love,
   praise everlasting is his,
   all to be taken home to the Lord,
   praise everlasting is his.

4 Praise for his glory, thanks for his gifts,
   praise everlasting is his,
   God everlasting, one that is three,
   praise everlasting is his,
   offer him praise, the Lord of all might,
   praise everlasting is his,
   majesty, glory, age upon age,
   praise everlasting is his.

Luke Connaughton

377

259 Praise him in the morning

Anonymous

Praise him, praise him, praise him in the morn-ing
praise him in the noon-time. Praise him, praise him,
praise him when the sun goes down.

G   B7   Em   C
Am   D7   G   B7   Em
C   D7   G

2 Love him, ...

3 Trust him, ...

4 Serve him, ...

5 Jesus, ...

Anonymous

260 Praise, my soul, the king of heaven

PRAISE MY SOUL (87 87 87)

John Goss (1800–80)

Praise, my soul, the king of hea- ven, to his feet thy

tri-bute bring. Ran-somed, healed, re-stored, for-giv-en,

who like me his praise should sing? Praise him! Praise him!

Praise him! Praise him! Praise the ev-er-last-ing king!

2 Praise him for his grace and favour
to our fathers in distress;
praise him still the same for ever,
slow to chide and swift to bless.
Praise him! Praise him!
Praise him! Praise him!
Glorious in his faithfulness!

3 Father-like he tends and spares us;
well our feeble frame he knows;
in his hands he gently bears us,
rescues us from all our our foes.
Praise him! Praise him!
Praise him! Praise him!
Widely as his mercy flows!

4 Angels, help us to adore him;
ye behold him face to face;
sun and moon bow down before him,
dwellers all in time and space.
Praise him! Praise him!
Praise him! Praise him!
Praise with us the God of grace!

Henry Francis Lyte (1793–1847)

379

261 Praise the Lord and sing Hallelujah

Gerald O'Mahony

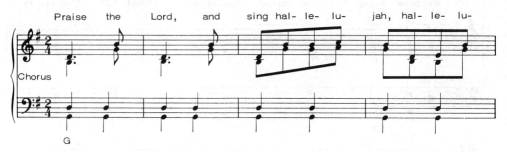

2 Praise him when you're happy,
  praise him when you're sad,
  hallelujah, hallelujah.
  He's the God who saves us
  and his message makes us glad,
  hallelujah, hallelujah.

3 Praise him in the morning,
  praise him in the night,
  hallelujah, hallelujah.
  Praise him in the thunder
  for he is the God of might,
  hallelujah, hallelujah.

Gerald O'Mahony

262 Praise to the holiest

BILLING (88 86)

R.R.Terry (1865–1938)

Praise to the ho-liest in the height, and in the depth be praise, in

all his words most won- der- ful, most sure in all his ways.

2 O loving wisdom of our God!
  When all was sin and shame,
  a second Adam to the fight,
  and to the rescue came.

3 O wisest love! that flesh and blood
  which did in Adam fail,
  should strive afresh against the foe,
  should strive and should prevail;

4 And that a higher gift than grace
  should flesh and blood refine,
  God's presence and his very self,
  and Essence all divine.

5 O generous love! that he who smote
  in man for man the foe,
  the double agony in man
  for man should undergo.

6 And in the garden secretly
  and on the Cross on high,
  should teach his brethren, and inspire
  to suffer and to die.

7 Praise to the Holiest in the height,
  and in the depth be praise,
  in all his words most wonderful,
  most sure in all his ways.

John Henry Newman (1801–90)

263 Praise to the Lord our God

Anonymous

This song may be performed either in unison
repeating it as many times as needed, or as a round.

Praise to the Lord our God, let us sing to-geth-er, lift- ing our hearts and our

voic- es to sing with joy and glad- ness.

Come a- long, a- long, a- long, and sing with

Estelle White

383

264   Praise to the Lord, the Almighty

LOBE DEN HERREN (14 14 4 7 8)

From *Stralsund Gesangbuch*, 1665

2 Praise to the Lord, let us offer our gifts at his altar;
let not our sins and transgressions now cause us to falter.
Christ, the High Priest, bids us all join in his feast.
Victims with him on the altar.

3 Praise to the Lord, oh, let all that is in us adore him!
All that has life and breath, come now in praises before him.
Let the Amen sound from his people again,
now as we worship before him.

Joachim Neander (1650–80),
tr. C. Winkworth

265 Praise we now the Lord our God

TE DEUM LAUDAMUS (76 7776)

William McClelland

Praise we now the Lord our God,
all mankind in chorus;
ceaselessly let seraphim,
angels, pow'rs and cherubim
sing with joy their praise of him,
holy, Lord of Sabaoth.

2 All the earth and sea and sky,
   glorify their maker,
   blessed martyrs, prophets grand,
   Christ's beloved apostle-band
   holy Church in every land.
   Sing his praise for ever.

3 Hail thou king of glory, Christ,
   born before all ages!
   Born of Mary, Virgin pure,
   thou didst us from death secure,
   opening wide to mankind poor,
   stores of heavenly treasure.

4 Seated now at God's right hand,
   bless thy chosen people;
   rule o'er us, dear Lord, we pray,
   keep us free from sin this day,
   save us, Lord, without delay,
   lest we be confounded.

5 In the solemn day of doom,
   we shall hear thy judgement;
   but remember, Lord, we cry,
   in that day when we shall die,
   how thy blood on us did lie,
   signing us thy people.

6 Praise we yet the Lord our God,
   throned in triune splendour;
   praise the Father, Lord of might,
   praise the Son, redeemer bright,
   praise the Spirit, source of light,
   through eternal ages.

D. McRoberts

266 Praise we our God with joy

NUN DANKET (67 67 66 66)   J.Crüger (1598–1662)

Praise we our God with joy, and gladness nev-er end-ing; angels and saints with us their grate-ful voi-ces blend-ing. He
is our Fath-er dear, o'er filled with par-ent's love; mercies un-sought, un-known, he show-ers from a-bove.

2 He is our shepherd true;
   with watchful care unsleeping,
   on us, his erring sheep
   an eye of pity keeping;
   he with a mighty arm
   the bonds of sin doth break,
   and to our burden'd hearts
   in words of peace doth speak.

3 Graces in copious stream
   from that pure fount are welling,
   where, in our heart of hearts,
   our God hath set his dwelling.
   His word our lantern is;
   his peace our comfort still;
   his sweetness all our rest;
   our law, our life, his will.

Frederick Oakeley (1802–80) and others

267 Promised Lord and Christ is he

HARK MY SOUL (77 68 7)

Early American Folk Song
arr. John Rombaut

2 Teaching, healing once was he,
   may we soon his kingdom see.

3 Dead and buried once was he,
   may we soon his kingdom see.

4 Risen from the dead is he,
   may we soon his kingdom see.

5 Soon to come again is he,
   may we soon his kingdom see.
   Come, O Lord, quickly come,
   in our lifetime, in our lifetime,
   in our lifetime may it be.

Roger Ruston, based on a Jewish Passover Song

268 Reap me the earth

JUCUNDA LAUDATIO (10 7 10 7 10 6 6)

Dom Gregory Murray O.S.B.

2 Go with your song and your music with joy,
go to the altar of God.
Carry your offerings, fruits of the earth,
work of your labouring hands.

3 Gladness and pity and passion and pain,
all that is mortal in man,
lay all before him, return him his gift,
God, to whom all shall go home.

Peter Icarus

269 Rejoice in the Lord

Evelyn Tarner

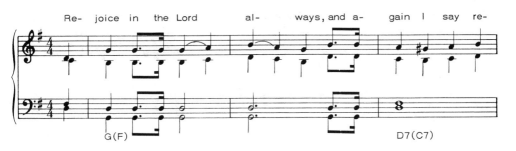

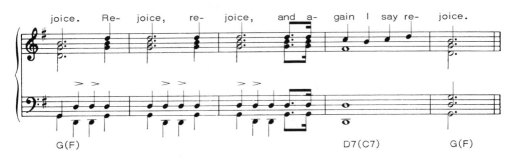

270 Rejoice! the Lord is King!

GOPSAL (66 66 88)

G.F.Handel (1685–1759)

2 Jesus the Saviour reigns,
the God of truth and love;
when he had purged our stains,
he took his seat above:

3 His kingdom cannot fail;
he rules o'er earth and heaven;
the keys of death and hell
are to our Jesus given:

4 He sits at God's right hand
till all his foes submit,
and bow to his command,
and fall beneath his feet:

Charles Wesley (1707–88)

271 Ride on! ride on in majesty

WINCHESTER NEW (88 88)

Adapted from a Chorale in
Musikalisches Handbuch, 1690

2 Ride on! ride on in majesty!
In lowly pomp ride on to die;
O Christ, thy triumphs now begin
o'er captive death and conquered sin.

3 Ride on! ride on in majesty!
The wingèd squadrons of the sky,
look down with sad and wondering eyes
to see the approaching sacrifice.

4 Ride on! ride on in majesty!
Thy last and fiercest strife is nigh;
the Father, on his sapphire throne
expects his own anointed Son.

5 Ride on! ride on in majesty!
In lowly pomp ride on to die;
bow thy meek head to mortal pain,
then take, O God, thy power, and reign.

H. H. Milman (1791–1868)

272   Round me falls the night

Mary Kennedy

Alternative tune: SEELENBRÄUTIGAM, 763 (New Songs of Celebration, 41)

2 Earthly work is done,
    earthly sounds are none;
    rest in sleep and silence seeking,
    let me hear thee softly speaking;
    in my spirit's ear
    whisper: "I am near".

3 Blessed heav'nly light
    shining through earth's night;
    voice that oft of love has told me,
    arms, so strong, to clasp and hold me;
    thou thy watch will keep,
    Saviour, o'er my sleep.

W. Romanis

273   Seasons come, seasons go

Kevin Mayhew

2 Seasons come, seasons go,
  petals fall though flowers grow;
  and when I doubt love lifts a hand
  and scatters stars like grains of sand.
  Oh love, my love, I see you passing by
  like birds that fearlessly possess the sky.

3 Seasons come, seasons go,
  times to reap and times to sow;
  but you are love, a fruitful vine,
  in ev'ry season yielding wine.
  I hear my love in laughter and in song,
  no day too short, no winter night too long.

Michael Cockett

274 See, amid the winter's snow

HUMILITY (OXFORD)

John Goss (1800–80)

See, amid the win-ter's snow, born for us on earth below,

see, the ten-der lamb ap-pears, promised from e-ter-nal years.

Chorus

Hail, thou ev-er-blessed morn, hail, redemption's hap-py dawn!

Sing through all Je-ru-sa-lem, Christ is born in Beth-le-hem.

2 Lo, within a manger lies
he who built the starry skies;
he who, throned in heights sublime,
sits amid the cherubim.

3 Say, ye holy shepherds, say,
what your joyful news today?
Wherefore have ye left your sheep
on the lonely mountain steep?

4 'As we watched at dead of night,
lo, we saw a wondrous light;
angels, singing peace on earth,
told us of the Saviour's birth.'

5 Sacred infant, all divine,
what a tender love was thine,
thus to come from highest bliss,
down to such a world as this!

6 Virgin mother, Mary blest,
by the joys that fill thy breast,
pray for us, that we may prove
worthy of the Saviour's love.

Edward Caswall (1814–78)

275 See us, Lord, about thine altar

LAUS DEO (87 87)   R.Redhead (1820–1901)

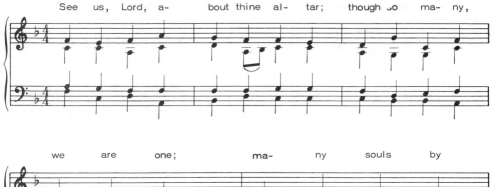

See us, Lord, a- bout thine al- tar; though so ma- ny,

we are one; ma- ny souls by

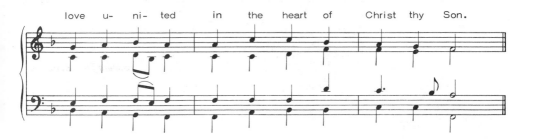

love u- ni- ted in the heart of Christ thy Son.

2 Hear our prayers, O loving Father,
  hear in them thy Son, our Lord;
  hear him speak our love and worship,
  as we sing with one accord.

3 Once were seen the blood and water;
  now he seems but bread and wine;
  then in human form he suffered,
  now his form is but a sign.

4 Wheat and grape contain the meaning;
  food and drink he is to all;
  one in him, we kneel adoring,
  gathered by his loving call.

5 Hear us yet; so much is needful
  in our frail, disorded life;
  stay with us and tend our weakness
  till that day of no more strife.

6 Members of his mystic body
  now we know our prayer is heard,
  heard by thee, because thy children
  have received th' eternal word.

John Greally

276 Shalom

Traditional Israeli Melody

Sandra Joan Billington

277   Silent night

STILLE NACHT

Franz Grüber (1787–1863),
arr. Sandra Joan Billington

2 Silent night, holy night.
Shepherds quake at the sight,
glories stream from heaven afar,
heavenly hosts sing alleluia;
Christ, the Saviour is born,
Christ, the Saviour is born.

3 Silent night, holy night.
Son of God, love's pure light
radiant beams from thy holy face,
with the dawn of redeeming grace:
Jesus, Lord, at thy birth,
Jesus, Lord, at thy birth.

Joseph Mohr (1792–1848), tr. J. Young

278 Sing my soul

Estelle White

Sing my soul. Sing, my soul.

Sing, my soul of his mer-cy.

Sing, my soul. Sing, my soul. Sing, my soul

of his mer-cy. The Lord is good to me.

Fine

His light will shine on me. When ci-ty lights would blind my

2 The Lord is good to me.
   his word will set me free
   when men would tie me to the ground.
   He mocks my foolish ways
   with love that never fails.
   When I'm most lost then I'm found.

3 The Lord is good to me.
   I hear him speak to me.
   His voice is in the rain that falls.
   He whispers in the air
   of his unending care.
   If I will hear, then he calls.

Michael Cockett

399

279 Sing, my tongue, the glorious battle

ST THOMAS (87 87 87)

Samuel Webbe (1740–1816)

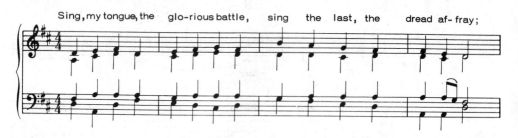

Sing, my tongue, the glo-rious battle, sing the last, the dread af-fray;

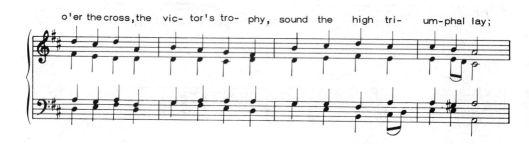

o'er the cross, the vic-tor's tro-phy, sound the high tri-um-phal lay;

how, the pains of death en-dur-ing, earth's re-deem-er won the day.

2 Faithful cross! above all other,
one and only noble tree!
None in foliage, none in blossom,
none in fruit thy peer may be;
sweetest wood and sweetest iron!
Sweetest weight is hung on thee.

3 Bend, O lofty tree, thy branches,
thy too rigid sinews bend;
and awhile the stubborn hardness,
which thy birth bestowed, suspend;
and the limbs of heaven's high monarch,
gently on thine arms extend.

400

4 Thou alone wast counted worthy
   this world's ransom to sustain,
   that by thee a wrecked creation
   might its ark and haven gain,
   with the sacred blood anointed
   of the Lamb that hath been slain.

5 Praise and honour to the Father,
   praise and honour to the Son,
   praise and honour to the Spirit,
   ever three and ever one,
   one in might and one in glory,
   while eternal ages run.

Venantius Fortunatus (530–609),
tr. J. M. Neale

280   Sing of the bride

Johnny Pearson

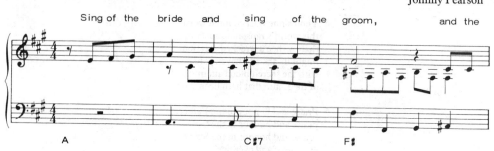

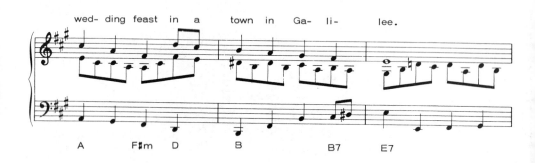

Chorus

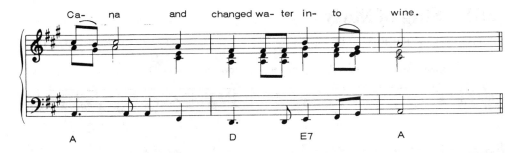

Ca- na and changed wa- ter in- to wine.

A   D   E7   A

2 Sing of the bride and sing of the groom,
  and the feasting all night and day,
  with the wine running short at the wedding feast
  to the steward's sad dismay.

3 "Please will you help, they have no more wine,"
  said a mother to her only son.
  He said: "Woman, don't you know you can't turn to me,
  for my time has not yet come."

4 "Wait till the day and wait till the time
  for the cross and for Calvary,
  but until that time here's a fine new wine
  with a taste that's fine and free."

5 Drink to the bride and drink to the groom
  at the wedding in Galilee,
  and drink to the life that is like new wine
  to all men who wish to be free.

Michael Cockett

281   Sing of Mary

PLEADING SAVIOUR (87 87 D)

From *The Christian Lyre*, 1831

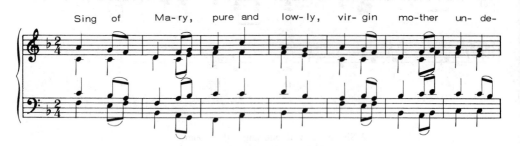

Sing of Mary, pure and lowly, virgin mother unde-

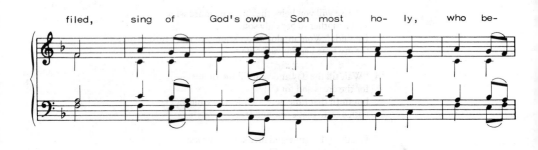

filed, sing of God's own Son most holy, who be-

came her little child. Fairest child of fairest

mother, God, the Lord, who came to earth, word made

flesh, our ve-ry bro-ther, takes our na-ture by his birth.

2 Sing of Jesus, son of Mary,
   in the home at Nazareth.
   Toil and labour cannot weary
   love enduring unto death.
   Constant was the love he gave her,
   though he went forth from her side,
   forth to preach and heal and suffer,
   till on Calvary he died.

3 Glory be to God the Father,
   glory be to God the Son;
   glory be to God the Spirit,
   glory to the three in one.
   From the heart of blessed Mary,
   from all saints the song ascends
   and the Church the strain re-echoes
   unto earth's remotest ends.

Roland F. Palmer, SSJE

282 Sing, sing, sing

Sebastian Temple

Sing, sing, sing, sing, sing, sing! Sing! peo-ple of God, Sing! Sing with one ac- cord. Sing! peo-ple of God, sing your prais- es to the Lord.

Fine

1. O Lord, how glo- ri- ous o- ver all the good earth is your name. You have ex-al-ted your maj-es- ty o-ver ev'ry hill and

406

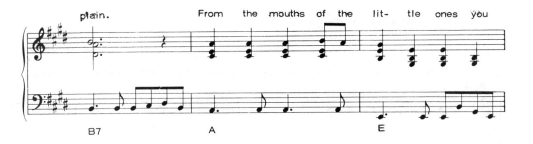

plain. From the mouths of the lit- tle ones you

B7   A   E

fash- ion end- less praise to si- - lence all the

A   E   A

venge- ful ones and glo- ri- fy your ways.

E   G   D   E

D.C.

2 When we behold the heavens
where your creation shines,
the moon and stars you set in place
to stand the test of time,
what is man that you should mind,
his sons that you should care?
A little less than angels
you have crowned him ev'rywhere.

3 You've given us dominion
over all that you have made.
We're masters of your handiwork
and rule them unafraid.
We're lords of the fish and birds,
of beasts both wild and tame.
O Lord, how glorious over all
the good earth is your name.

Sebastian Temple

407

283 Sing praises to God

Anonymous

2 Give glory to God, give glory.
  give glory to God, give glory,
  for he is the king of all the earth,
  give glory to his name.

3 Give honour to God, give honour,
  give honour to God, give honour,
  for he is the king of all the earth,
  give honour to his name.

Anonymous

284   Sing praises to the living God

Sebastian Temple,
arr. Stephen Dean

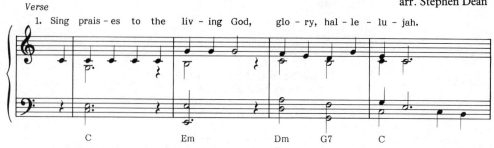

Verse

1. Sing prais - es to the liv - ing God, glo - ry, hal - le - lu - jah.

C   Em   Dm   G7   C

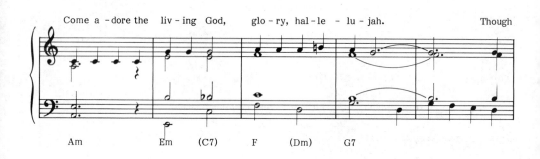

Come a - dore the liv - ing God, glo - ry, hal - le - lu - jah.   Though

Am   Em   (C7)   F   (Dm)   G7

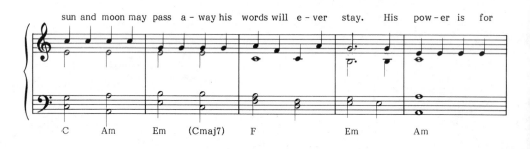

sun and moon may pass a - way his words will e - ver stay. His pow - er is for

C   Am   Em   (Cmaj7)   F   Em   Am

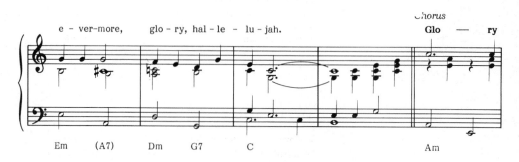

e - ver - more, glo - ry, hal - le - lu - jah.   *Chorus*   **Glo — ry**

Em   (A7)   Dm   G7   C   Am

to the Tri - ni - ty.   The un - di - vi - ded Un - i -

Em   F   Dm

- ty,————————————the Fa——ther, Son and Spi - rit one,

Em   Am   F   Dm

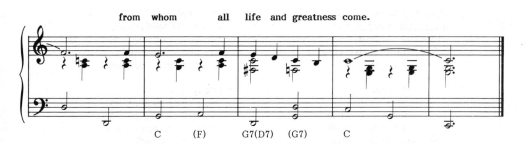

from whom   all   life and greatness come.

C   (F)   G7(D7)   (G7)   C

2 And to the living God we sing,
glory, hallelujah.
Let our love and praises ring,
glory, hallelujah.
To all his sons he always gives
his mercy and his love.
So praise him now for evermore,
glory, hallelujah.

3 And to the God who cannot die,
glory hallelujah.
To the living God we cry,
glory hallelujah.
He promised to be with us and
he live in ev'ry one.
We love him now for evermore,
glory hallelujah.

Arrangement © 1987
McCrimmon Publishing Co Ltd

Sebastian Temple

411

285 Sleep, holy babe

EDGBASTON (4 6 8 8 6)   Traditional English Melody

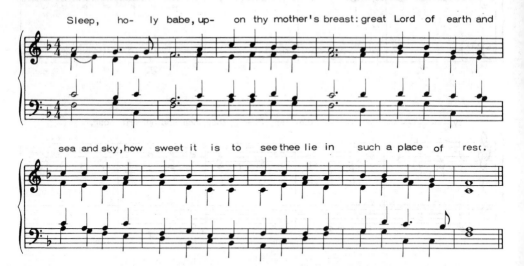

2 Sleep, holy babe;
   thine angels watch around,
   all bending low, with folded wings,
   before th'incarnate King of kings,
   in reverent awe profound.

3 Sleep, holy babe,
   while I with Mary gaze
   in joy upon that face awhile,
   upon the loving infant smile,
   which there divinely plays.

4 Sleep, holy babe,
   ah, take thy brief repose,
   too quickly will thy slumbers break,
   and thou to lengthen'd pains awake,
   that death alone shall close.

5 O lady blest,
   sweet Virgin, hear my cry;
   forgive the wrong that I have done
   to thee, in causing thy dear Son
   upon the cross to die.

Edward Caswall (1814–78)

286 Songs of thankfulness and praise

ST EDMUND (77 77 D)   Charles Stegall (1826–1905)

ma- ni- fes- ted by the star to the sa- ges
from a- far; branch of roy- al Da- vid's stem
in thy birth at Beth- le- hem; an- thems be to
thee ad- dressed; God in man made ma- ni- fest.

2 Manifest at Jordan's stream,
  prophet, Priest and King supreme,
  and at Cana wedding-guest,
  in thy Godhead manifest,
  manifest in power divine,
  changing water into wine;
  anthems be to thee addressed;
  God in man made manifest.

3 Manifest in making whole,
  palsied limbs and fainting soul,
  manifest in valiant fight,
  quelling all the devil's might,
  manifest in gracious will,
  ever bringing good from ill;
  anthems be to thee addressed;
  God in man made manifest.

4 Sun and moon shall darkened be,
  stars shall fall, the heavens shall flee.
  Christ will then like lightning shine.
  All will see his glorious sign.
  All will see the judge appear;
  all will then the trumpet hear;
  thou by all wilt be confessed;
  God in man made manifest.

5 Grant us grace to see thee, Lord,
  mirrored in thy holy word;
  may we imitate thee now
  and be pure, as pure art thou;
  that we like to thee may be
  at thy great Epiphany,
  and may praise thee, ever blest,
  God in man made manifest.

Christopher Wordsworth (1807–85)

287 Sons of God

James Thiem

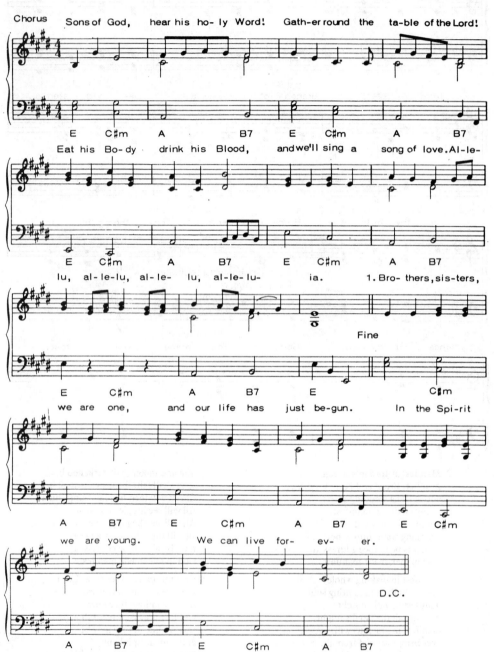

Chorus
Sons of God, hear his holy Word! Gath-er round the ta-ble of the Lord!
E C♯m A B7 E C♯m A B7
Eat his Bo-dy drink his Blood, and we'll sing a song of love. Al-le-
E C♯m A B7 E C♯m A B7
lu, al-le-lu, al-le- lu, al-le-lu- ia. 1. Bro- thers, sis-ters,
Fine
E C♯m A B7 E C♯m
we are one, and our life has just be-gun. In the Spi-rit
A B7 E C♯m A B7 E C♯m
we are young. We can live for- ev- er.
D.C.
A B7 E C♯m A B7

2 Shout together to the Lord
who has promised our reward:
happiness a hundredfold,
and we'll live forever.

3 Jesus gave a new command
that we love our fellow man
till we reach the promised land,
where we'll live forever.

4 If we want to live with him;
we must also die with him;
die to selfishness and sin,
and we'll rise forever.

5 Make the world a unity,
make all men one family
till we meet the Trinity
and live with them forever.

6 With the Church we celebrate;
Jesus' coming we await,
so we make a holiday,
so we'll live forever.

James Theim

288   Soul of my Saviour

ANIMA CHRISTI (10 10 10 10)

W.J.Maher (1823–77)

2 Strength and protection may thy Passion be;
O Blessed Jesus hear and answer me;
deep in thy wounds, Lord, hide and shelter me;
so shall I never, never part from thee.

3 Guard and defend me from the foe malign;
in death's dread moments make me only thine;
call me, and bid me come to thee on high,
when I may praise thee with thy saints for aye.

Ascribed to John XXII (1249–1334), tr. Anonymous

289 Spirit of the living Lord

Daniel Iverson
arr. James O'Donnell

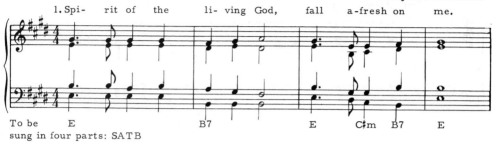

To be sung in four parts: SATB

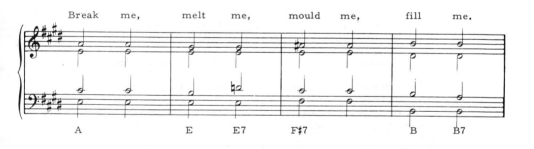

290 Star of ocean, lead us

AVE MARIS STELLA (66 66)   Caspar Ett (1788–1847)

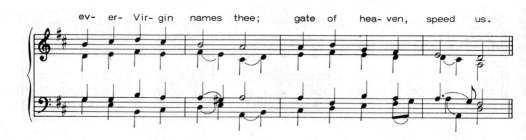

2 Ave to thee crying
  Gabriel went before us;
  peace do thou restore us,
  Eva's knot untying.

3 Loose the bonds that chain us,
  darkened eyes enlighten,
  clouded prospects brighten,
  heavenly mercies gain us.

4 For thy sons thou carest;
  offer Christ our praying –
  still thy word obeying –
  whom on earth thou barest.

5 Purer, kinder maiden
  God did never fashion;
  pureness and compassion
  grant to hearts sin-laden.

6 From that sin release us,
  shield us, heavenward faring,
  heaven, that is but sharing
  in thy joy with Jesus.

7 Honour, praise and merit
  to our God address we;
  Three in One confess we,
  Father, Son and Spirit.

9th c., tr. R. A. Knox

291 Steal away to Jesus

Spiritual

Steal a-way, steal a-way, steal a-way to Je-sus.

Chorus

D   Bm   F♯m   G   A7   D

Steal a-way, steal a-way home. I ain't got long to stay here.

D   Bm   F♯m   G   A7   D

fine

My Lord, he calls me. He calls me by the thun-der. The

G   Bm   F♯m   Bm

trum-pet sounds with-in my soul. I ain't got long to stay here.

D.C.

D   Bm   F♯m   G   A7   D

2 Green trees are bending,
the sinner stands a-trembling.
The trumpet sounds within my soul;
I ain't got long to stay here.

3 My Lord, he calls me,
he calls me by the lightning.
The trumpet sounds within my soul;
I ain't got long to stay here.

Negro Spiritual

292 Suffer little children

Philip Green

Suf-fer lit-tle chil-dren to come un-to me, for theirs is the king-dom of

D   F#dim   Em   A

hea- ven. Suf-fer lit-tle chil-dren to come un-to me, for

D   F#dim   Em   A

theirs is the king-dom of the Lord.

Fine

D

1. There came un-to him chil-dren, lit-tle chil-dren, that

D   Bm   F♯m   F♯   Bm

he might lay his hands up- on them,

G   A   D

pray for and bless them, chil-dren lit-tle chil-dren,

Bm   G   G♯dim   D

ga- thered round our Lord.   D.C.

D.C.

Em7   A7   D

421

2 The disciples said:
   "Children, little children,
   leave the Master to his prayer.
   Begone and stay not,
   children, little children,
   gathered round our Lord."

3 But Jesus said:
   "Children, little children,
   stay my blessing to receive.
   Forbid you not that
   children, little children,
   shall gather round the Lord."

4 "For you must be like
   children, little children,
   humble, simple, pure in heart.
   For it is to these
   children, little children,
   the kingdom of heav'n belongs."

Philip Green

293   **Sweet heart of Jesus**

Traditional

grate- ful, and make them, Lord, thine own for ev- er-

Chorus

more. Sweet heart of Je- sus, we im-

plore, O make us love thee more and more.

2 Sweet heart of Jesus, make us know and love thee,
   unfold to us the treasures of thy grace;
   that so our hearts, from things of earth uplifted,
   may long alone to gaze upon thy face.

3 Sweet heart of Jesus, make us pure and gentle,
   and teach us how to do thy blessed will;
   to follow close the print of thy dear footsteps,
   and when we fall – sweet heart, oh, love us still.

4 Sweet heart of Jesus, bless all hearts that love thee,
   and may thine own heart ever blessed be,
   bless us, dear Lord, and bless the friends we cherish,
   and keep us true to Mary and to thee.

Traditional

294 Sweet sacrament divine

FIRST TUNE

SANCTISSIMUM (66 66 88 6)   Dom Gregory Murray O.S.B.

Sweet sa-cra-ment di- vine, hid in thy earth- ly home lo!
round thy low- ly shrine, with sup- pliant hearts we
come; Je- sus, to thee our voice we raise, in
songs of love and heart- felt praise, sweet sa- cra- ment di- vine.

SECOND TUNE

DIVINE MYSTERIES (66 66 88 6)   Francis Stanfield (1835–1914)

Sweet sa- cra- ment div- ine, hid in thy earth- ly

424

home, lo! round thy low-ly shrine, with
sup-pliant hearts we come; Je-sus, to thee our
voice we raise, in songs of love and heart-felt praise, sweet
sa-cra-ment div-ine, sweet sa-cra-ment div-ine.

2 Sweet sacrament of peace,
   dear home of every heart,
   where restless yearnings cease,
   and sorrows all depart,
   there in thine ear all trustfully
   we tell our tale of misery,
   sweet sacrament of peace.

3 Sweet sacrament of rest,
   Ark from the ocean's roar,
   within thy shelter blest
   soon may we reach the shore,
   save us, for still the tempest raves;
   save, lest we sink beneath the waves
   sweet sacrament of rest.

4 Sweet sacrament divine,
   earth's light and jubilee,
   in thy far depths doth shine
   thy Godhead's majesty;
   sweet light, so shine on us, we pray,
   that earthly joys may fade away,
   sweet sacrament divine.

Francis Stanfield (1835–1914)

295 Sweet Saviour, bless us 'ere we go

SUNSET (88 88 88)

George Herbert (1817–1906)

Sweet Sav- iour, bless us ere we go, thy word into our minds in- stil; and make our luke- warm
hearts to glow with low- ly love and fer- vent
will.

Chorus

Through life's long day and death's dark

night,　　　　O　gen- tle　Je- sus,　be　our　light.

2 The day is done; its hours have run,
　and thou hast taken count of all,
　the scanty triumphs grace has won,
　the broken vow, the frequent fall.

3 Grant us, dear Lord, from evil ways,
　true absolution and release;
　and bless us more than in past days
　with purity and inward peace.

4 Do more than pardon; give us joy,
　sweet fear and sober liberty,
　and loving hearts without alloy,
　that only long to be like thee.

5 Labour is sweet, for thou hast toiled,
　and care is light, for thou hast cared;
　let not our works with self be soiled.
　Nor in unsimple ways ensnared.

6 For all we love – the poor, the sad,
　the sinful – unto thee we call;
　oh let thy mercy make us glad,
　thou art our Jesus and our all.

Frederick William Faber (1814–63)

296   Take my hands

Sebastian Temple
arr. Stephen Dean

1. Take my hands and make them as your own, and use them for your

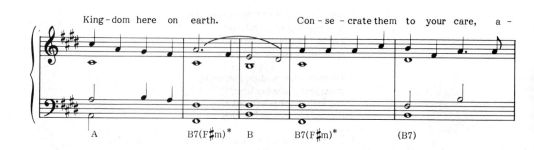

King - dom here on earth. Con - se - crate them to your care, a -

- noint them for your ser - vice where you may need your gos - pel to be sown.

* *Harmonies in brackets may differ from
those in the melody/guitar edition.*

Optional ending

Take my hands, take my hands O Lord.

2 Take my hands. They speak now for my heart,
   and by their actions they will show their love.
   Guard them on their daily course,
   be their strength and guiding force
   to ever serve the Trinity above.

3 Take my hands. I give them to you, Lord.
   Prepare them for the service of your name.
   Open them to human need
   and by their love they'll sow your seed
   so all may know the love and hope you give.

Sebastian Temple

297   Take our bread

Joe Wise

Take our bread, we ask you, take our hearts, we love you, take our
Chorus

D   Bm   G   Em

lives, oh Fa-ther, we are yours, we are yours. 1. Yours as we
Fin.

D   Em   A7   D

stand at the ta-ble you set, yours as we eat the bread our hearts can't for-

Bm   D   Bm   D   G   Em

get. We are the signs of your life with us yet; we are

A7   D   Bm   D   Bm
yours, we are yours.

D.C.

Em   A7

2 Your holy people stand washed in your blood,
  Spirit filled, yet hungry, we await your food.
  Poor though we are, we have brought ourselves to you:
  we are yours, we are yours.

Joseph Wise

298 Thank you

Martin G. Schneider,
arr. Stephen Dean

Thank you for giving me the morning. Thank you for ev'-ry day that's new.

G   Em   Am7   D9   Em   G   Am7   D

Thank you that I can know my wor-ries can be cast on you.

G   G7   C   Am   A7   D   G

2 Thank you for all my friends and brothers.
  Thank you for all the men that live.
  Thank you for even greatest enemies
  I can forgive.

3 Thank you, I have my occupation.
  Thank you for ev'ry pleasure small.
  Thank you for music, light and gladness.
  Thank you for them all.

4 Thank you for many little sorrows.
  Thank you for ev'ry kindly word.
  Thank you for ev'rywhere your guidance
  reaches ev'ry land.

5 Thank you, I see your Word has meaning.
  Thank you, I know your Spirit here.
  Thank you because you love all people,
  those both far and near.

6 Thank you, O Lord, you spoke unto us.
  Thank you that for our words you care.
  Thank you, O Lord, you came among us,
  bread and wine to share.

7 Thank you, O Lord, your love is boundless.
  Thank you that I am full of you.
  Thank you, you made me feel so glad and
  thankful as I do.

Walter van der Haas and Peter-Paul van Lelyveld

Harmony © 1984 Mayhew-McCrimmon Ltd

299   The baker woman

Hubert Richards

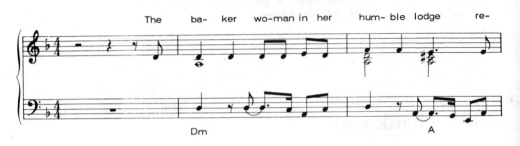

The ba- ker wo-man in her hum- ble lodge re-

Dm   A

ceived a grain of wheat from God. For nine whole months the

Dm   A   F

grain she stored. Be- hold the hand-maid of the Lord. Make us the bread,

Gm   A   Dm   A   D   D

Ma- ry, Ma- ry. Make us the bread, we need to be fed.

G   D   A7   D

2 The bakerwoman took the road which led
   to Bethlehem, the house of bread.
   To knead the bread she laboured through the night,
   and brought it forth about midnight.
   Bake us the bread, Mary, Mary.
   Bake us the bread, we need to be fed.

3 She baked the bread for thirty years
   by the fire of her love and the salt of her tears,
   by the warmth of a heart so tender and bright,
   and the bread was golden brown and white.
   Bring us the bread, Mary, Mary.
   bring us the bread, we need to be fed.

4 After thirty years the bread was done.
   It was taken to town by her only son;
   the soft white bread to be given free
   to the hungry people of Galilee.
   Give us the bread, Mary, Mary.
   Give us the bread, we need to be fed.

5 For thirty coins the bread was sold,
   and a thousand teeth so cold, so cold
   tore it to pieces on a Friday noon
   when the sun turned black and red the moon.
   Break us the bread, Mary, Mary.
   Break us the bread, we need to be fed.

6 And when she saw the bread so white,
   the living bread she had made at night,
   devoured as wolves might devour a sheep,
   the bakerwoman began to weep.
   Weep for the bread, Mary, Mary.
   Weep for the bread, we need to be fed.

7 But the bakerwoman's only son
   appeared to his friends when three days had run
   on the road which to Emmaus led,
   and they knew him in the breaking of bread.
   Lift up your head, Mary, Mary.
   Lift up your head, for now we've been fed.

Hubert Richards

300 The Church's one foundation

AURELIA (76 76 D)

S.S. Wesley (1810–76)

2 Elect from every nation,
    yet one o'er all the earth,
    her charter of salvation
    one Lord, one faith, one birth;
    one holy name she blesses,
    partakes one holy food,
    and to one hope she presses,
    with every grace endued.

3 'Mid toil, and tribulation,
    and tumult of her war,
    she waits the consummation
    of peace for evermore;
    till with the vision glorious
    her longing eyes are blest,
    and the great Church victorious
    shall be the Church at rest.

4 Yet she on earth hath union
    with God the Three in One,
    and mystic sweet communion
    with those whose rest is won:
    O happy ones and holy!
    Lord, give us grace that we
    like them, the meek and lowly
    on high may dwell with thee.

S. J. Stone (1830–1900)

301 The coming of our God

OPTATUS (6 6 8 6)

Traditional Melody,
harmonised by G.R.Woodward

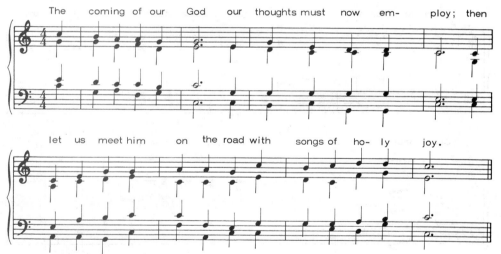

The coming of our God our thoughts must now em-ploy; then
let us meet him on the road with songs of ho-ly joy.

2 The co-eternal Son,
    a maiden's offspring see;
    a servant's form Christ putteth on,
    to set his people free.

3 Daughter of Sion, rise
    to greet thine infant king,
    nor let thy stubborn heart despise
    the pardon he doth bring.

4 In glory from his throne
    again will Christ descend,
    and summon all that are his own
    to joys that never end.

5 Let deeds of darkness fly
    before the approaching morn,
    for unto sin 'tis ours to die,
    and serve the virgin-born.

6 Our joyful praises sing
    to Christ, then set us free;
    like tribute to the Father bring,
    and, Holy Ghost, to thee.

Charles Coffin (1676–1749),
tr. R. Campbell

435

302 The day of resurrection

ELLACOMBE (76 76 D)   *Würtemberg Gesangbuch (1784)*

2 Our hearts be pure from evil,
   that we may see aright
   the Lord in rays eternal
   of resurrection-light;
   And listening to his accents,
   may hear so calm and plain
   his own 'All hail' and, hearing,
   may raise the victor strain.

3 Now let the heavens be joyful,
   and earth her song begin,
   the round world keep high triumph,
   and all that is therein;
   Let all things seen and unseen
   their notes of gladness blend,
   for Christ the Lord hath risen,
   our joy that hath no end.

*St. John Damascene (c. 750),
tr. J. M. Neale*

303 The day thou gavest

ST CLEMENT (98 98)   C.C.Scholefield (1839–1904)

The day thou gav- est, Lord, is en- ded, the dark- ness falls at thy be- hest; to thee our morn- ing hymns asc- en- ded, thy praise shall sanc- ti- fy our rest.

2 We thank thee that thy Church unsleeping,
   while earth rolls onward into light,
   through all the world her watch is keeping,
   and rests not now by day or night.

3 As o'er each continent and island
   the dawn leads on another day,
   the voice of prayer is never silent,
   nor dies the strain of praise away.

4 The sun that bids us rest is waking
   our brethren 'neath the western sky
   and hour by hour fresh lips are making
   thy wondrous doings heard on high.

5 So be it, Lord; thy throne shall never,
   like earth's proud empire, pass away;
   thy kingdom stands, and grows for ever,
   till all thy creatures own thy sway.

John Ellerton (1826–93)

304 The farmer

Roger Haines and John Murphy

2 An enemy with darnel seed is
   sowing, sowing.
   The weed that fights the growing corn is
   choking, choking, choking, choking.

3 Together till the harvest they'll be
   growing, growing.
   But then what has been sown we will be
   reaping, reaping, reaping, reaping.

4 The corn is taken to the barn for
   storing, storing.
   The weed is cast into the fire for
   burning, burning, burning, burning.

Michael Cockett

305 The first Nowell

THE FIRST NOWELL

Traditional Melody,
harmonised by John Stainer

2 They looked up and saw a star,
  shining in the east, beyond them far,
  and to the earth it gave great light,
  and so it continued both day and night.

3 And by the light of that same star,
  three wise men came from country far.
  To seek for a king was their intent,
  and to follow the star wherever it went.

4 This star drew nigh to the north-west,
  o'er Bethlehem it took its rest,
  and there it did both stop and stay
  right over the place where Jesus lay.

5 Then entered in those wise men three,
  full reverently upon their knee,
  and offered there in his presence,
  their gold and myrrh and frankincense.

6 Then let us all with one accord
  sing praises to our heavenly Lord,
  that hath made heaven and earth of nought,
  and with his blood mankind hath bought.

Traditional Old English

306 The God whom earth and sea and sky

EISENACH (88 88)

Johann Hermann Schein (1586–1630)

The God whom earth and sea, and sky, a-
dore and laud and mag-ni-fy, who o'er their three-fold
fab-ric reigns, the Vir-gin's spot-less womb con-tains.

2 The God whose will by moon and sun,
and all things in due course is done,
is borne upon a maiden's breast
by fullest heavenly grace possessed.

3 How blest that mother, in whose shrine
the great Artificer divine,
whose hand contains the earth and sky,
vouchsafed, as in his ark, to lie!

4 Blest, in the message Gabriel brought;
blest, by the work the Spirit wrought;
from whom the great desire of earth,
took human flesh and human birth.

5 All honour, laud and glory be,
O Jesus, virgin-born, to thee!
All glory, as is ever meet
to Father and to Paraclete.

Ascribed to Venantius Fortunatus (530–609),
tr. J. M. Neale

307　The green life rises from the earth

CHILDHOOD (88 86 and refrain)　　　　　　University of Wales (Students' Hymnal)
　　　　　　　　　　　　　　　　　　　　　　　　　1923 (Walford Davies)

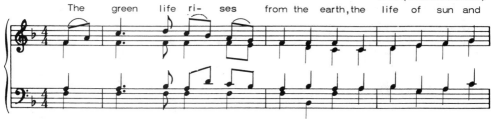

The green life ri- ses from the earth, the life of sun and

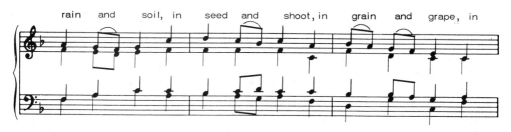

rain and soil, in seed and shoot, in grain and grape, in

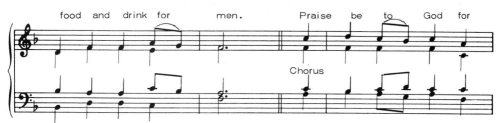

food and drink for men. Praise be to God for

Chorus

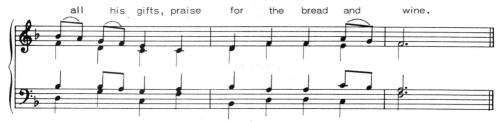

all his gifts, praise for the bread and wine.

2　The Lord of Spring, the Lord of Life,
　made bread his body, wine his blood.
　The life of earth, the life of God,
　becomes the life of man.

3　We take in hand the bread and wine,
　reminder of the dying Lord.
　This food, this drink, this feast of joy
　gives Christ's own life to us.

4　"The Son of Man must die," said he,
　"my death will raise you all to life.
　No blade is born, no harvest reaped,
　until the seed has died.

5　"These are the signs of death and life,
　the bread you break, the cup you share:
　my dying gift in which I live,
　my death is life to you."

6　Give praise to God who gave this gift,
　his very Son, to bring us life.
　The Father's life in him is ours,
　his Spirit breathes in us.

Luke Connaughton (1919–79)

441

308 The head that once was crowned with thorns

ST MAGNUS (86 86)   J.Clarke (1659–1707)

The head that once was crowned with thorns is crowned with glo- ry

now: a roy-al di-a- dem a-dorns the migh- ty vic- tor's brow.

2 The highest place that heaven affords
  is his, is his by right.
  The King of kings and Lord of lords,
  and heaven's eternal light;

3 The joy of all who dwell above,
  the joy of all below,
  to whom he manifests his love,
  and grants his name to know.

4 To them the cross, with all its shame
  with all its grace is given;
  their name an everlasting name,
  their joy the joy of heaven.

5 They suffer with their Lord below,
  they reign with him above,
  their profit and their joy to know
  the mystery of his love.

6 The cross he bore is life and health,
  though shame and death to him;
  his people's hope, his people's wealth,
  their everlasting theme.

                    Thomas Kelly (1769–1854)

309 The heavenly Word, proceeding forth

DUGUET (88 88)

Abbé Duguet (c.1767)

2 By false disciple to be giv'n
  to foemen for his life athirst,
  himself, the very bread of heav'n,
  he gave to his disciples first.

3 He gave himself in either kind,
  he gave his flesh, he gave his blood;
  in love's own fullness thus designed,
  of the whole man to be the food.

4 O saving victim, opening wide
  the gate of heav'n to man below,
  our foes press on from every side;
  thine aid supply, thy strength bestow.

5 To thy great name be endless praise,
  Immortal Godhead, one in three:
  O grant us endless length of days
  in our true native land with thee.

St. Thomas Aquinas (1227–74),
tr. J. M. Neale

310 The King of glory

Israeli Folk Song

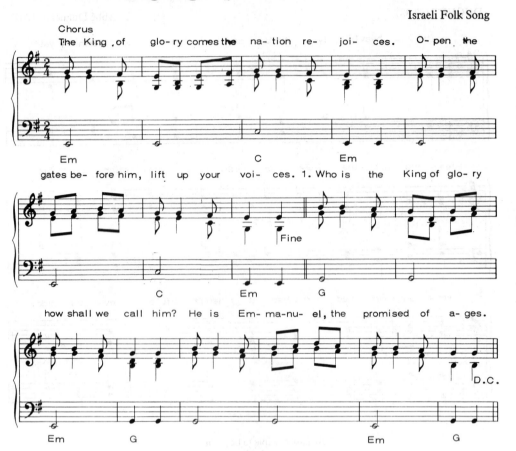

Chorus

The King of glory comes the nation rejoices. Open the gates before him, lift up your voices. 1. Who is the King of glory how shall we call him? He is Emmanuel, the promised of ages.

2 In all of Galilee,
in city and village,
he goes among his people,
curing their illness.

3 Sing then of David's Son,
our Saviour and brother;
in all of Galilee
was never another.

4 He gave his life for us,
the pledge of salvation.
He took upon himself
the sins of the nation.

5 He conquered sin and death;
he truly has risen.
And he will share with us
his heavenly vision.

W. F. Jabusch

444

311 The King of love my Shepherd is

DOMINUS REGIT ME (87 87)

J.B.Dykes (1823–76)

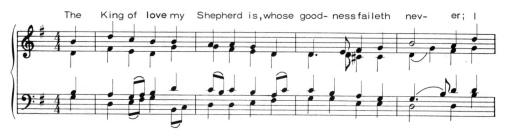

2 Where streams of living water flow
  my ransomed soul he leadeth,
  and where the verdant pastures grow
  with food celestial feedeth.

3 Perverse and foolish oft I strayed
  but yet in love he sought me,
  and on his shoulder gently laid,
  and home, rejoicing, brought me.

4 In death's dark vale I fear no ill
  with thee, dear Lord, beside me;
  thy rod and staff my comfort still,
  thy cross before to guide me.

5 Thou spread'st at a table in my sight,
  thy unction grace bestoweth:
  and O what transport of delight
  from thy pure chalice floweth!

6 And so through all the length of days
  thy goodness faileth never;
  good Shepherd, may I sing thy praise
  within thy house for ever.

Henry Williams Baker (1821–77)

445

312 The Lord's my shepherd

CRIMOND (86 86)   J. Irvine (1836–87)

The Lord's my shep- herd, I'll not want, he makes me down to lie in

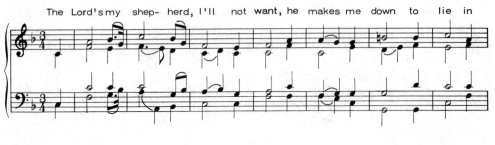

pas- tures green. He lead- eth me the qui- et wa- ters by.

2 My soul he doth restore again,
   and me to walk doth make
   within the paths of righteousness,
   e'en for his own name's sake.

3 Yea, though I walk in death's dark vale,
   yet will I fear none ill.
   For thou art with me, and thy rod
   and staff me comfort still.

4 My table thou hast furnished
   in presence of my foes,
   my head thou dost with oil anoint,
   and my cup overflows.

5 Goodness and mercy all my life
   shall surely follow me.
   And in God's house for evermore
   my dwelling-place shall be.

Paraphrased from Ps.22(23)
in the 'Scottish Psalter' 1650

313 The Mass is ended

Sebastian Temple

The Mass is end-ed, all go in peace.
Bb(A)   Eb(D)   Cm (Bm)

We must di-min-ish, and Christ in-crease.
F (E)   F7(E7)   Bb(A)

We take him with us where-e'er we go
Eb(D)   Cm(Bm)

that through our ac-tions his life may show.
F7(E7)   Bb(A)

2 We witness his love to ev'ryone
by our communion with Christ the Son.
We take the Mass to where men may be,
so Christ may shine forth for all to see.

3 Thanks to the Father who shows the way.
His life within us throughout each day.
Let all our living and loving be
to praise and honour the Trinity.

4 The Mass is ended, all go in peace.
We must diminish and Christ increase.
We take him with us where'er we go
that through our actions his life may show.

Sebastian Temple

314 The prophet in his hunger

CHALKWELL

John Rombaut

The pro-phet in his
hun-ger asked for bread.

He asked the poor and
fa-mine was their guest.

They saw star-va-tion

448

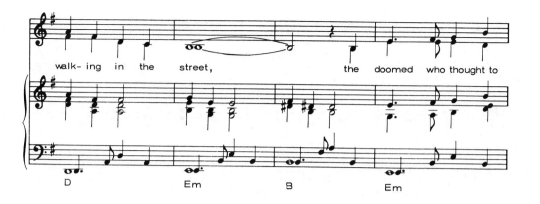

walk-ing in the street, the doomed who thought to

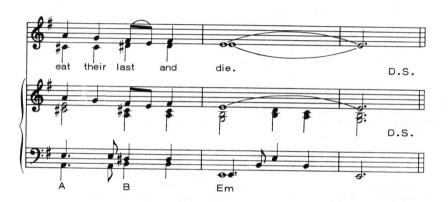

eat their last and die. D.S.

2 It is the Lord who lights the blinded eye,
   who lends the poor his wealth, the weak his strength,
   who feeds us with his everlasting love,
   and pours for men his justice like strong wine.

3 Because the widow offered of her last,
   and opened to his need her empty hand,
   Elijah promised her: "You shall not want.
   Your larder never shall be clean of food."

4 The widow and the orphan are his care;
   whom none will else defend, he will defend:
   he puts the strutting pride of tyrants down,
   and raises up the lowly from the dust.

5 See, in the temple, how with gestures wide,
   the rich men cast their casual gold to God,
   the widow offers all her dwindling purse,
   the pence of poverty – a richer gift.

Luke Connaughton (1919–79)

315 The race that long in darkness pined

ST FULBERT (86 86)   H.J.Gauntlett (1805–76)

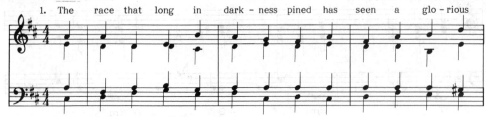

1. The race that long in dark-ness pined has seen a glo-rious light: the peo-ple dwell in day, who dwelt in death's sur-round-ing night.

2 To hail thy rise, thou better sun,
the gathering nations come,
joyous as when the reapers bear
the harvest treasures home.

3 To us a child of hope is born,
to us a Son is given;
him shall the tribes of earth obey,
him all the hosts of heaven.

4 His name shall be the Prince of Peace
for evermore adored,
the Wonderful, the Counsellor
the great and mighty Lord.

5 His power increasing still shall spread,
his reign no end shall know;
justice shall guard his throne above,
and peace abound below.

John Morison (1749–98)

DUNDEE (86 86)   *Scottish Psalter,* 1615

316 There is a green hill far away

HORSLEY (86 86)   W.Horsley (1774–1858)

2 We may not know, we cannot tell,
what pains he had to bear,
but we believe it was for us
he hung and suffered there.

3 He died that we might be forgiven,
he died to make us good;
that we might go at last to heaven,
saved by his precious blood.

4 There was no other good enough
to pay the price of sin;
he only could unlock the gate
of heaven, and let us in.

5 O, dearly, dearly has he loved,
and we must love him too,
and trust in his redeeming blood,
and try his works to do.

Cecil Frances Alexander (1818–95)

317 There is a world

Estelle White

There is a world where people come and go a-bout their ways and

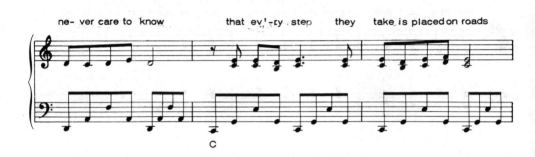

ne-ver care to know that ev'-ry step they take is placed on roads

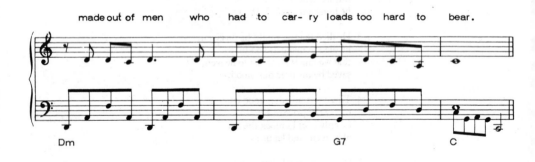

made out of men who had to car-ry loads too hard to bear.

Chorus

"That world's not ours," that's what we al-ways say. "We'll build a new one,

but some other day." When will we wake from comfort and from ease,

C

and strive to-geth- er to cre- ate a world of love and peace?

Dm   G7   C

2 There is a world where people walk alone,
   and have around them men with hearts of stone,
   who would not spare one second of their day,
   or spend their breath in order just to say: 'Your pain is mine.'

3 There is a world where brothers cannot meet
   with one another where the tramp of feet
   brings men of ice, men who would force apart
   friends of all races having but one heart, a heart of love.

Estelle White

To give added effect to this song, verse two may be played in D,
modulating by one bar of A7; and verse three in E, modulating
by one bar of B7.

318 The royal banners forward go

FIRST TUNE

TRURO (88 88)   *Psalmodia Evangelica*, 1789

The roy-al ban-ners for-ward go, the cross shines forth in

my-stic glow; where he in flesh, our flesh who made our

sen- tence bore, our ran- som paid.

SECOND TUNE

EISENACH (88 88)   J.H.Schein (1586–1630)

The roy- al ban- ners for- ward go, the

cross shines forth in mys- tic glow; where he in flesh, our

flesh who made, our sen- tence bore, our ran- som paid.

2 There whilst he hung, his sacred side
   by soldier's spear was open'd wide,
   to cleanse us in the precious flood
   of water mingled with his blood.

3 Fulfill'd is now what David told
   in true prophetic song of old,
   how God the heathen's king should be;
   for God is reigning from the tree.

4 O tree of glory, tree most fair,
   ordain'd those holy limbs to bear,
   how bright in purple robe it stood,
   the purple of a saviour's blood!

5 Upon its arms, like balance true,
   he weigh'd the price for sinners due,
   the price which none but he could pay:
   and spoil'd the spoiler of his prey.

6 To thee, eternal Three in One,
   let homage meet by all be done,
   as by the cross thou dost restore,
   so rule and guide us evermore.

Verantius Fortunatus (530–609),
tr. J. M. Neale and others

455

319 The Spirit of the Lord

Anonymous

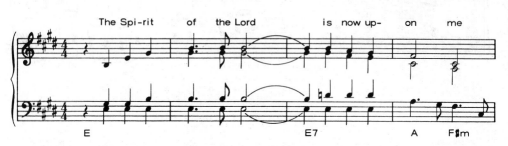

The Spi-rit of the Lord is now up- on me

to heal the bro- ken heart and set the cap- tives free,

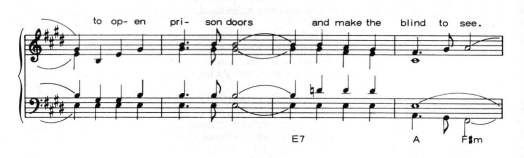

to op- en pri- son doors and make the blind to see.

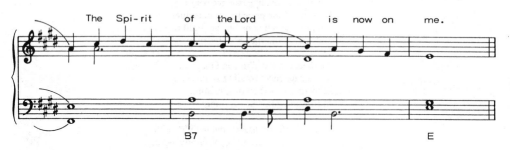

The Spi-rit of the Lord is now on me.

320 The kingdom

Mike Anderson

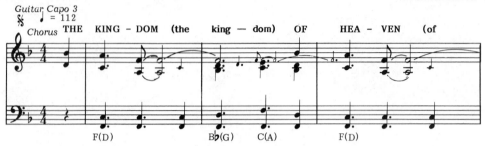

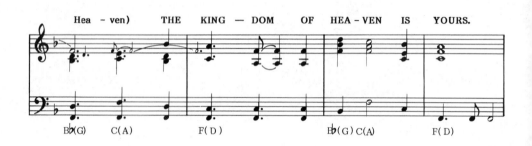

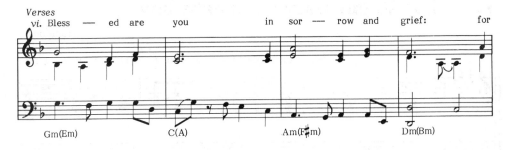

Verses
vi. Bless — ed are you   in sor — row and   grief: for

Gm(Em)   C(A)   Am(F#m)   Dm(Bm)

you   shall all   be con - soled.

B♭(G)   F (D)   C(A)

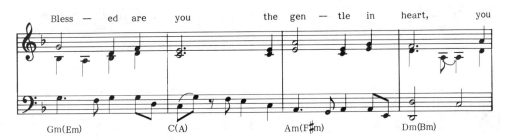

Bless — ed are you   the gen — tle in   heart,   you

Gm(Em)   C(A)   Am(F#m)   Dm(Bm)

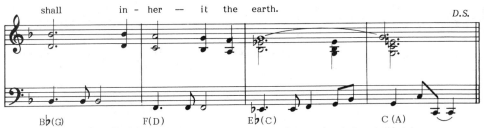

shall   in - her — it   the earth.   *D.S.*

B♭(G)   F(D)   E♭(C)   C (A)

2 Blessed are you who hunger for right:
  for you shall be satisfied.
  Blessed are you the merciful ones:
  for you shall be pardoned too.

3 Blessed are you whose hearts are pure:
  your eyes shall gaze on the Lord.
  Blessed are you who strive after peace:
  the Lord will call you His own.

4 Blessed are you who suffer for right:
  the Heavenly Kingdom is yours.
  Blessed are you who suffer for me:
  for you shall reap your reward.

Words & Music © 1983 Mike Anderson

Mike Anderson

321   The Virgin Mary had a baby boy

Traditional

Chorus

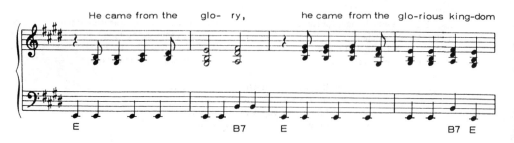

He came from the glo-ry, he came from the glorious kingdom.

Oh yes, be-lie-ver, Oh yes, be-lie-ver.

He came from the glo-ry, he came from the glorious kingdom.

2 The angels sang when the baby was born ...
   and proclaimed him the Saviour Jesus.

3 The wise men saw where the baby was born ...
   and they saw that his name was Jesus.

Traditional West Indian

461

322 The wandering flock of Israel

PASTOR BONUS (99 99 10 9)

Dom Gregory Murray O.S.B.

The wan- der- ing flock of

Em D Em D Em D Em G

Is- ra- el is scattered and far from home and hope; the

A D G A G B

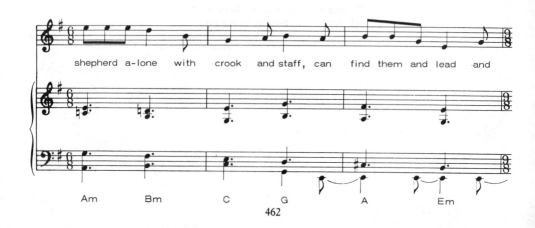

shepherd a-lone with crook and staff, can find them and lead and

Am Bm C G A Em

2 I walk on the heights, I climb and cling,
the terror beneath, the ice aloft.
I look for his tracks, await his hand
to help and to hold, to guide and save.

3 I thirst for his word as grass in drought,
dry, brittle and barren, parched and brown;
no shower can fall, no sap rise green
no hope, if the Lord should send no rain.

4 Creator of all, your craftsman's care
with fashioning hand caressed our clay;
this vine is the work your hands have wrought,
your love is the sun, our soil of growth.

J. Smith

463

323 They hung him on a cross

Spiritual

2 They whipped him up the hill, ...

3 They speared him in the side, ...

4 The blood came streaming down, ...

5 He hung his head and died, ...

6 He's coming back again, ...

Spiritual

324   They say I am wise

Kevin Mayhew

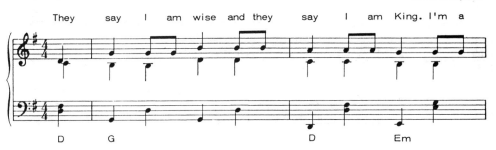

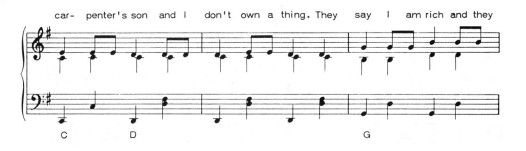

2 They asked me for bread and they asked for a sign.
  I gave them some bread and I gave them some wine.
  The bread was my body, the wine was my blood.
  They still turned away from me looking for food.

3 They shouted with joy. They laid palms on the road,
  but into the town on a donkey I rode.
  They said: "Do not go for we can't stand the loss."
  The very next morning they gave me a cross.

4 They brought me down low though they hung me up high.
  They brought me to life though they left me to die.
  They buried me deep with a stone at my head,
  but I am the living and they are the dead.

Michael Cockett

465

325   This day God gives me

BUNESSAN (5554 D)

Scots Gaelic Melody

This day God gives me strength of high hea- ven, sun and moon

shin- ing, flame in my hearth, flash- ing of

light- ning, wind in its swift- ness, deeps of the

o- cean, firm- ness of earth.

2 This day God sends me
  strength as my steersman,
  might to uphold me, wisdom as guide.
  Your eyes are watchful,
  your ears are listening,
  your lips are speaking, friend at my side.

3 God's way is my way,
  God's shield is round me,
  God's host defends me, saving from ill.
  Angels of heaven,
  drive from me always
  all that would harm me, stand by me still.

4 Rising, I thank you,
  mighty and strong One,
  King of creation, giver of rest,
  firmly confessing
  Threeness of Persons,
  Oneness of Godhead, Trinity blest.

Adapted from St Patrick's Breastplate
James Quinn, S.J.

326   This is the image of the Queen

IVER (86 86 D)

H.F.Hemy (1818–88)

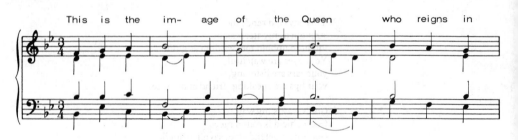

This is the im-age of the Queen who reigns in

bliss a-bove; of her who is the hope of men,

whom men and an-gels love. Most ho-ly Ma-ry, at thy

feet I bend a sup-pli-ant knee; in this thy own sweet

month of May, do thou re-mem-ber me.

2 The homage offered at the feet
of Mary's image here
to Mary's self at once ascends
above the starry sphere.
Most holy Mary, at thy feet
I bend a suppliant knee;
in all my joy, in all my pain,
do thou remember me.

3 How fair soever be the form
which here your eyes behold,
its beauty is by Mary's self
excell'd a thousandfold.
Most holy Mary, at thy feet,
I bend a suppliant knee;
in my temptations each and all,
do thou remember me.

4 Sweet are the flow'rets we have culled,
this image to adorn;
but sweeter far is Mary's self,
that rose without a thorn.
most holy Mary, at thy feet
I bend a suppliant knee;
when on the bed of death I lie,
do thou remember me.

5 O lady, by the stars that make
a glory round thy head;
and by the pure uplifted hands,
that for thy children plead;
when at the judgement-seat I stand,
and my dread saviour see;
when waves of night around me roll
O then remember me.

Edward Caswall (1814–78)

327   This is my will, my one command

SUANTRAI (88 88)

Traditional Irish Melody,
Harmony by James O'Donnell

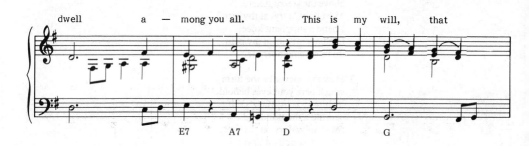

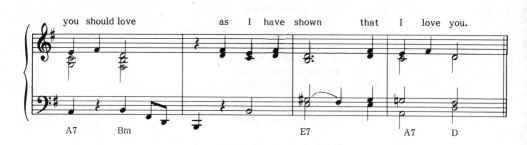

2 No greater love
a man can have
than that he die
to save his friends.
You are my friends
if you obey
all I command
that you should do.

3 I call you now
no longer slaves;
no slave knows all
his master does.
I call you friends,
for all I hear
my Father say
you hear from me.

4 You chose not me,
but I chose you,
that you should go
and bear much fruit.
I called you out
that you in me
should bear much fruit
that will abide.

5 All that you ask
my Father dear
for my name's sake
you shall receive.
This is my will,
my one command,
that love should dwell
in each, in all.

James Quinn S.J.

Alternative Harmonisation   Stephen Dean

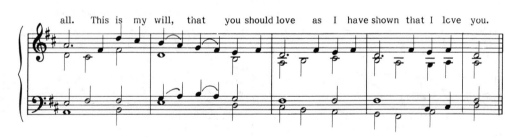

328 This joyful Eastertide

VRUECHTEN (67 67 D)   Dutch Melody, 17th century

Chorus

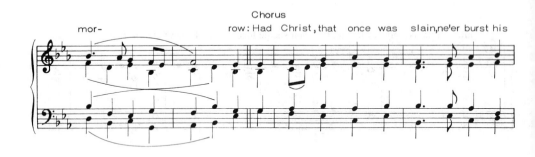

2 My flesh in hope shall rest,
 and for a season slumber:
 till trump from east to west
 shall wake the dead in number:

3 Death's flood hath lost his chill,
 since Jesus crossed the river:
 lover of souls, from ill
 my passing soul deliver:

*George Ratcliffe Woodward
(1849–1934)*

329 This little light of mine

Traditional

474

2 On Monday he gave me the gift of love,
  Tuesday peace came from above.
  On Wednesday he told me to have more faith,
  on Thursday he gave me a little more grace.

Friday he told me just to watch and pray,
Saturday he told me just what to say.
On Sunday he gave me the power divine
to let my little light shine.

Traditional

330 Thou wilt keep him in perfect peace

Anonymous

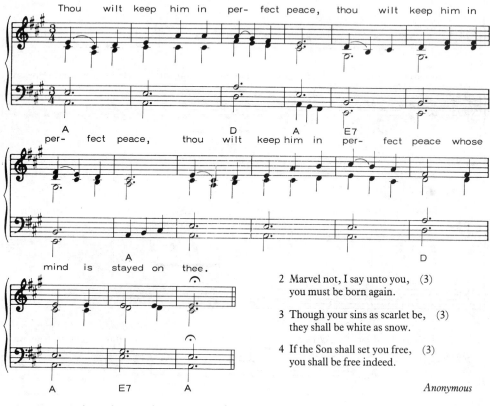

2 Marvel not, I say unto you, (3)
you must be born again.

3 Though your sins as scarlet be, (3)
they shall be white as snow.

4 If the Son shall set you free, (3)
you shall be free indeed.

Anonymous

331 Thy hand, O God, has guided

THORNBURY (76 76 D)

Basil Harwood (1859–1949)

fa-thers owned thy good-ness, and we their deeds re-cord; and
both of this bear wit-ness: one Church, one
faith, one Lord.

2 Thy heralds brought glad tidings
   to greatest, as to least;
   they bade men rise, and hasten
   to share the great king's feast;
   and this was all their teaching,
   in every deed and word,
   to all alike proclaiming
   one Church, one Faith, one Lord.

3 When shadows thick were falling,
   and all seemed sunk in night,
   thou, Lord, didst send thy servants,
   thy chosen sons of light.
   On them and on thy people
   thy plenteous grace was poured,
   and this was still their message:
   one Church, one Faith, one Lord.

4 Through many a day of darkness,
   through many a scene of strife,
   the faithful few fought bravely,
   to guard the nation's life.
   Their gospel of redemption,
   sin pardoned, man restored,
   was all in this enfolded:
   one Church, one Faith, one Lord.

5 And we, shall we be faithless?
   Shall hearts fail, hands hang down?
   Shall we evade the conflict,
   and cast away our crown?
   Not so: in God's deep counsels
   some better thing is stored;
   we will maintain, unflinching,
   one Church, one Faith, one Lord.

6 Thy mercy will not fail us,
   nor leave thy work undone;
   with thy right hand to help us
   the vict'ry shall be won;
   and then, by men and angels
   thy name shall be adored.
   And this shall be their anthem:
   one Church, one Faith, one Lord.

E. H. Plumptre (1821–91)

332   To Christ the Lord of worlds

DEUS TUORUM MILITUM (GRENOBLE) (88 88)   Grenoble Church Melody

To Christ the Lord of worlds we sing, the na-tions' un-i-ver-sal king. Hail, con-quering Christ, whose reign a-lone o-ver our hearts and souls we own.

A lower setting of this hymn will be found at No. 405.

2 Christ, who art known the prince of peace,
 bid all rebellious tumults cease;
 call home thy straying sheep, and hold
 for ever in one faithful fold.

3 For this, thine arms, on Calvary,
 were stretched across th' empurpled tree,
 and the sharp spear that through thee ran
 laid bare the heart that burned for man.

4 For this, in forms of bread and wine
 lies hid the plenitude divine,
 and from thy wounded body runs
 the stream of life to all thy sons.

5 May those who rule o'er men below
 thee for their greater sovereign know,
 and human wisdom, arts, and laws,
 in thee repose as in their cause.

6 Let kingly signs of pomp and state
 unto thy name be dedicate,
 city and hearth and household be
 under thy gentle sceptre free.

7 Praise be to Christ, whose name and throne
 o'er every throne and name we own;
 and equal praises still repeat
 the Father and the Paraclete.

Roman Breviary, tr. W. H. Shewring

333 To Christ, the Prince of Peace

NARENZA (66 86)

J.Leisentritt,
Catholicum Hymnologium Germanicum, 1587

2 Deep in his heart for us
  the wound of love he bore:
  that love wherewith he still inflames
  the hearts that him adore.

3 O Jesu, victim blest,
  what else but love divine
  could thee constrain to open thus
  that sacred heart of thine?

4 O fount of endless life,
  O spring of water clear,
  O flame celestial, cleansing all
  who unto thee draw near!

5 Hide us in thy dear heart,
  for thither we do fly;
  there seek thy grace through life, in death
  thine immortality.

6 Praise to the Father be,
  and sole-begotten Son;
  praise, holy Paraclete, to thee
  while endless ages run.

Catholicum Hymnologium Germanicum (1587)
tr. E. Caswall

334 To Jesus' Heart, all burning

Traditional Melody

To Je-sus' Heart, all burn-ing with fer-vent love for men, my

heart with fond-est yearn-ing shall raise its joy-ful strain. While

Chorus

a-ges course a-long, blest be with loud-est song the

sa-cred heart of Je-sus by ev-'ry heart and tongue. The

sa-cred heart of Je-sus by ev-'ry heart and tongue.

480

2 O Heart, for me on fire
with love no man can speak,
my yet untold desire
God gives me for thy sake.

3 Too true, I have forsaken
thy love for wilful sin;
yet now let me be taken
back by thy grace again.

4 As thou art meek and lowly,
and ever pure of heart,
so may my heart be wholly
of thine the counterpart.

5 When life away is flying,
and earth's false glare is done;
still, Sacred Heart, in dying
I'll say I'm all thine own.

Aloys Schlor
(1805–52),
tr. A. J. Christie

335   To the name that brings salvation

ORIEL (87 87 87)

Caspar Ett (1788–1847)

To the name that brings sal-va-tion hon- our, wor- ship, laud we pay:

that for many a gen- er- a- tion hid in God's fore- know- ledge lay;

but to ev- 'ry tongue and na- tion Ho- ly Church pro- claims to- day.

2 Name of gladness, name of pleasure,
by the tongue ineffable,
name of sweetness passing measure,
to the ear delectable;
'tis our safeguard and our treasure,
'tis our help 'gainst sin and hell.

3 'Tis the name of adoration,
'tis the name of victory;
'tis the name for meditation
in the vale of misery;
'tis the name for veneration
by the citizens on high.

4 'Tis the name by right exalted
over every other name:
that when we are sore assaulted
puts our enemies to shame:
strength to them that else had halted,
eyes to blind, and feet to lame.

5 Jesu, we thy name adoring,
long to see thee as thou art:
of thy clemency imploring
so to write it in our heart,
that hereafter, upward soaring,
we with angels may have part.

15th c., tr. J. M. Neale

336 Trust is in the eyes of a tiny babe

Estelle White

Guitar Capo 3
Bouncy

Trust is in the eyes of a ti-ny babe
lean-ing on his mother's breast. In the ea-ger beat of a
young bird's wings on the day it leaves the nest. It is the

Chorus

Dm G7   C   C   Em   Am
F   C   G7   C   Em
Am   F   G7   C   G   D7   G7

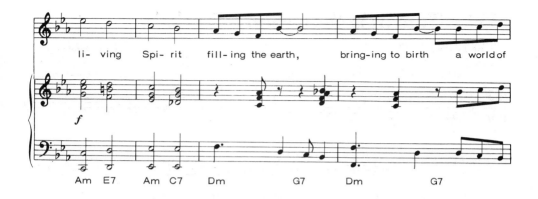

li- ving Spi- rit fill- ing the earth, bring-ing to birth a world of

Am E7 Am C7 Dm G7 Dm G7

D.S.

love and laugh-ter, joy in the light of the Lord.

Am E7 Am C7 Dm G7 C

D.S.

2 Hope is in the rain that makes crystal streams
tumble down a mountain side,
and in every man who repairs his nets,
waiting for the rising tide.

3 Love is in the hearts of all those who seek
freedom for the human race.
Love is in the touch of the hand that heals,
and the smile that lights a face.

4 Strength is in the wind as it bends the trees,
warmth is in the bright red flame,
light is in the sun and the candle-glow,
cleansing are the ocean's waves.

Estelle White

337 Unto us is born a Son

PUER NOBIS (77 77)

Melody from *Piae Cantiones*, 1582

Unison

Un-to us is born a Son, King of quires su- per- nal;
see on earth his life be- gun, of lords the Lord e-
ter- nal, of lords the Lord e- ter- nal.

2 Christ, from heav'n descending low,
comes on earth a stranger:
ox and ass their owner know
becradled in a manger,
becradled in a manger.

3 This did Herod sore affray,
and grievously bewilder:
so he gave the word to slay,
and slew the little childer,
and slew the little childer.

4 Of his love and mercy mild
this the Christmas story,
and O that Mary's gentle Child
might lead us up to glory!
Might lead us up to glory!

5 O and A and A and O
cum cantibus in choro,
let the merry organ go,
Benedicamus Domino,
Benedicamus Domino.

15th c.,
tr. G. R. Woodward

338 Vaster far than any ocean

Russian Folk Tune

Vast- er far than an- y o- cean, deep- er

E   484   B7

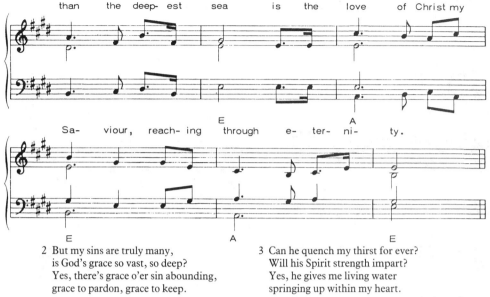

than the deep-est sea is the love of Christ my Sa-viour, reach-ing through e-ter-ni-ty.

2 But my sins are truly many,
is God's grace so vast, so deep?
Yes, there's grace o'er sin abounding,
grace to pardon, grace to keep.

3 Can he quench my thirst for ever?
Will his Spirit strength impart?
Yes, he gives me living water
springing up within my heart.

Author unknown

339 Virgin, wholly marvellous

ORIENTIS PARTIBUS (77 77)   Pierre de Corbeil (d.1222)

Vir-gin, whol-ly mar-vel-lous, who didst bear God's Son for us,

worth-less is my tongue and weak of thy pur-i-ty to speak.

2 Who can praise thee as he ought?
Gifts, with every blessing fraught,
gifts that bring the eternal life,
thou didst grant us, Maiden-Wife.

3 God became thy lowly Son,
made himself thy little one,
raising men to tell thy worth
high in heav'n as here on earth.

4 Heav'n and earth, and all that is
thrill today with ecstasies,
chanting glory unto thee,
singing praise with festal glee.

5 Cherubim with fourfold face,
are no peers of thine in grace;
and the six-wing'd seraphim
shine, amid thy splendour, dim.

6 Purer art thou than are all
heav'nly hosts angelical,
who delight with pomp and
state
on thy beauteous Child to wait.

St. Ephrem Syrus (c. 307–373),
tr. J. W. Atkinson

340 Walk with me, oh my Lord

Estelle White

Chorus

Walk with me oh my Lord through the dark- est night and bright- est day. Be at my side O Lord, hold my hand and

guide me on my way. 1. Sometimes the road seems long my en-er-gy is spent. Then, Lord, I think of you and I am gi-ven strength.

Fine

D   Bm

F♯m   Bm   F♯m   Bm

F♯m   E7   A7

2 Stones often bar my path
   and there are times I fall,
   but you are always there
   to help me when I call.

3 Just as you calmed the wind
   and walked upon the sea,
   conquer, my living Lord,
   the storms that threaten me.

4 Help me to pierce the mists
   that cloud my heart and mind
   so that I shall not fear
   the steepest mountain-side.

5 As one you helped the lame
   and gave sight to the blind,
   help me when I'm downcast
   to hold my head up high.

Estelle White

487

341   We are gathering together

Anonymous

2 We are offering together unto him.

3 We are singing together unto him.

4 We are praying together unto him.

Anonymous

342   We are one in the Spirit

ST BRENDAN'S

Peter Scholtes

We are one in the Spi-rit, we are one in the Lord, we are

Em

one in the Spi-rit, we are one in the Lord, and we pray that all

Am   *Em*   *Chorus*   *Am*

u-ni-ty may one day be res-tored. And they'll know we are Christians by our

Em   *C*

love, by our love, yes, they'll know we are Christians by our love.

Em   *Am*   *Em*   *Am*   *Em*

2 We will walk with each other,
we will walk hand in hand,
we will walk with each other,
we will walk hand in hand.
And together we'll spread the news
that God is in our land.

3 We will work with each other,
we will work side by side.
We will work with each other,
we will work side by side.
And we'll guard each man's dignity
and save each man's pride.

4 All praise to the Father
from whom all things come,
and all praise to Christ Jesus,
his only Son,
and all praise to the Spirit
who makes us one.

Peter Scholtes   © 1966 F.E.L. Publications

489

343   We bring our gifts to the Lord

Estelle White

2 We bring our love to the Lord, our God.
   We bring our love to the Lord, our God.

3 We bring ourselves to the Lord, our God.
   We bring ourselves to the Lord, our God.

Estelle White

344   We celebrate this festive day

Willard F. Jabusch, after J.S. Bach
arr. Stephen Dean

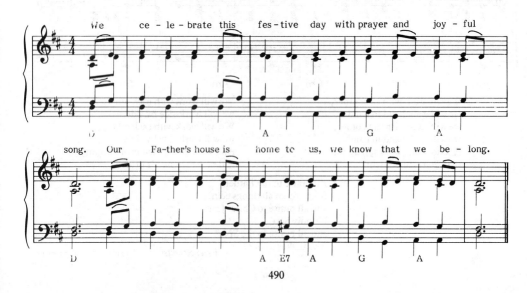

Chorus

The bread is bro-ken, wine is poured, a feast to lift us up! Then

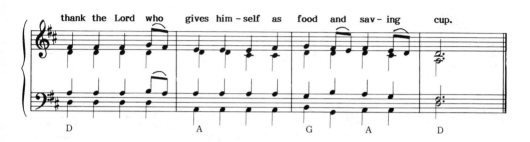

thank the Lord who gives him–self as food and sav–ing cup.

*The chords given here fit this arrangement but
differ from those in the melody edition.*

2 The door is open, enter in
and take your place by right.
For you've been chosen as his guest
to share his love and light.

3 We came together as the twelve
came to the Upper Room.
Our host is Jesus Christ the Lord,
now risen from the tomb.

4 Who travels needs both food and drink
to help him on his way.
refreshed and strong we'll journey on
and face another day.

5 Who shares this meal receives the Lord
who lives, though he was dead.
So death can hold no terrors now
for those who eat this bread.

Willard F. Jabusch

Arrangement © 1986 McCrimmon Publishing Company Ltd

345 We gather together as brothers and sisters

Polish Folk Melody,
arr. Stephen Dean

We ga-ther to-geth-er as broth-ers and sis-ters, for Je-sus, our Lord, tru-ly lives. He's ri-sen in glo-ry; the full Gos-pel sto-ry, what free-dom and cou-rage it gives. He binds up the woun-ded and the bro-ken, he gives the poor his chal-ice and his bread. The

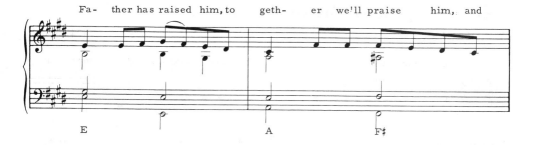

2 For mother and father,
  for sister and brother,
  for children and husband and wife,
  his Word spreads like flame,
  for all people came,
  bringing peace and the seeds of new life.

3 God takes what is foolish,
  he chooses the weakest
  to put wise and strong both to shame.
  Give thanks to the Father,
  we live in Christ Jesus,
  bow low and sing sweetly his name.

Willard F. Jabusch

346   We plough the fields and scatter

WIR PFLÜGEN

J.A.P.Schulz (1747–1800)

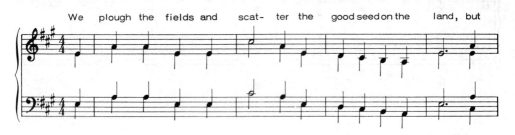

We plough the fields and scat- ter the good seed on the land, but

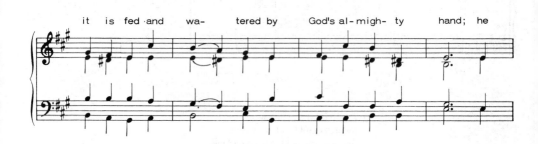

it is fed and wa- tered by God's al- migh- ty hand; he

sends the snow in win- ter, the warmth to swell the grain, the

breez- es and the sun- shine, and soft re- freshing rain:

Chorus

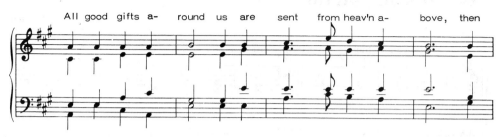

All good gifts a- round us are sent from heav'n a- bove, then

thank the Lord, O thank the Lord, for all his love.

2 He only is the maker
   of all things near and far;
   he paints the wayside flower,
   he lights the ev'ning star.
   The winds and waves obey him,
   by him the birds are fed:
   much more to us his children,
   he gives our daily bread.

3 We thank thee then, O Father,
   for all things bright and good:
   the seed-time and the harvest,
   our life, our health, our food.
   No gifts have we to offer
   for all thy love imparts,
   but that which thou desirest,
   our humble, thankful hearts.

M. Claudius (1740–1815),
tr. J. M. Campbell

495

347 Were you there

Spiritual

2 Were you there when they nailed him to a tree? ...

3 Were you there when they pierced him in the side? ...

4 Were you there when the sun refused to shine? ...

5 Were you there when they laid him in the tomb? ...

6 Were you there when he rose from out the tomb? ...

Negro Spiritual

348   We shall overcome

Traditional

We shall o- ver come,   we shall o- ver come,   we shall o- ver

C   F   C   Am   C   F   C   Am   C   Am

come some day.   Oh,   deep   in   my   heart

F   Dm   G   F   G   C

I   do be- lieve   that   we shall o- ver   come some   day.

F   G   Am   C   F   C   G   C

2 We'll walk hand in hand ...

3 We shall live in peace ...

4 We shall live with him ...

Traditional

349 We three kings

KINGS OF ORIENT   John Henry Hopkins (1822–1900)

We three kings of O-ri-ent are; bear-ing gifts we traverse a- far,

field and foun-tain, moor and moun-tain, fol-lowing yon- der star. O

Star of won- der, star of night, star with roy- al beau-ty bright,

west-ward lead- ing, still pro- ceed-ing, guide us to thy per- fect light.

2 Born a King on Bethlehem plain,
gold I bring, to crown him again,
King for ever, ceasing never,
over us all to reign.

3 Frankincense to offer have I,
Incense owns a Deity nigh.
Prayer and praising, all men raising,
worship him, God most high.

4 Myrrh is mine, its bitter perfume
breathes a life of gathering gloom;
sorrowing, sighing, bleeding, dying,
sealed in the stone-cold tomb.

5 Glorious now behold him arise,
King and God and sacrifice;
alleluia, alleluia,
earth to heaven replies.

John Henry Hopkins (1822–1900)

350 We will walk through the valley

Spiritual, adapted by Kevin Mayhew

We will walk through the val- ley in the sha- dow of death. We will walk through the dark- ness with- out fear.

Though the night may be long, the dark en- clo- sing, we know Je- sus, our morn- ing light is near.

2 He has walked through the valley of the shadow of death,
he has walked through the night of fear alone.
Though the darkness had gathered to destroy him
he was there at the rising of the sun.

3 We will walk in the glory of the bright morning sun,
we will walk in the light that guides our way.
For with Jesus the lord of light beside us
we will walk in the glory of the day.

Michael Cockett

351 What can we offer you

Tom Shelley

What can we of- fer you, Lord our God? How can we

D Bm Em A7 D

wor- ship you as you de- serve? We can on-ly of- fer what our

Bm Em A7 D Bm

lips do pro- claim. We can on-ly of- fer you hum-ble acts of

G A7 D Bm Em

praise. But we offer this with Je- sus our bro-ther, Je- sus your

A7 D Bm Em A7

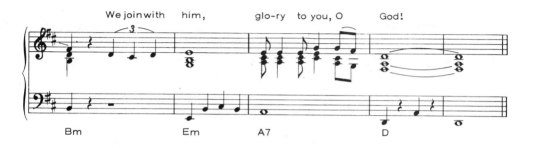

2 What can we offer you, Lord our God?
   How can we thank you for all that you've done?
   We can only say it, Lord God, we thank you so.
   We can only try to live grateful lives, O Lord.
   But we offer this with Jesus, our brother, Jesus your Son.
   We join with him, our thanks to you, O God.
   We join with him, our thanks to you, O God.

3 What can we offer you, Lord our God?
   How do we prove we are truly sorry, Lord?
   We can say it often, God, sorry that we are.
   We can try to prove it, Lord, by the way we live.
   And we offer this with Jesus, our brother, Jesus, your Son.
   We join with him, forgive our sins, O God.
   We join with him, forgive our sins, O God.

4 What can we offer you, Lord our God?
   Dare we present you with another call for help?
   We just have to say it, Lord God, we need you so.
   We just have to beg you, Lord, take us by the hand.
   And we offer this with Jesus, our brother, Jesus, your Son.
   We join with him, Lord, we need you so.
   We join with him, Lord, we need you so.

Tom Shelley

352   Whatsoever you do

W.F. Jabusch

2 When I was homeless
you opened your door.
When I was naked
you gave me your coat.
Now enter into the
home of my Father.

3 When I was weary
you helped me find rest.
When I was anxious
you calmed all me fears.
Now enter into the
home of my Father.

4 When in a prison
you came to my cell.
When on a sick bed
you cared for my needs.
Now enter into the
home of my Father.

5 Hurt in a battle
   you bound up my wounds.
   Searching for kindness
   you held out your hands.
   Now enter into the
   home of my Father.

6 When I was Negro
   or Chinese or White,
   mocked and insulted,
   you carried my cross.
   Now enter into the
   home of my Father.

7 When I was aged
   you bothered to smile.
   When I was restless
   you listened and cared.
   Now enter into the
   home of my Father.

8 When I was laughed at
   you stood by my side.
   When I was happy
   you shared in my joy.
   Now enter into the
   home of my Father.

W. F. Jabusch

353 When I needed a neighbour

Sydney Carter

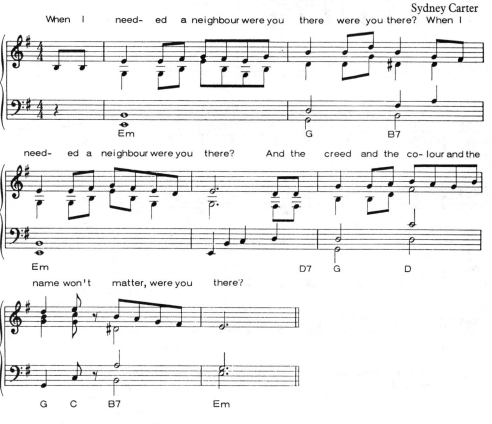

2 I was hungry and thirsty, ...

3 I was cold, I was naked, ...

4 When I needed a shelter, ...

5 When I needed a healer, ...

6 Wherever you travel, I'll be there I'll be there.
   Wherever you travel, I'll be there.
   And the creed and the colour and the name won't matter
   I'll be there.   *Sydney Carter*

354   When Israel was in Egypt's land

Spiritual

2 The Lord told Moses what to do,
   let my people go,
   to lead the children of Israel through,
   let my people go.

3 Your foes shall not before you stand
   let my people go,
   and you'll possess fair Canaan's land,
   let my people go.

4 O let us all from bondage flee,
   let my people go,
   and let us all in Christ be free,
   let my people go.

5 I do believe without a doubt,
   let my people go,
   a Christian has a right to shout,
   let my people go.

Traditional Spiritual

355   When I survey the wondrous cross

ROCKINGHAM (88 88)

E.Miller (1731–1807)

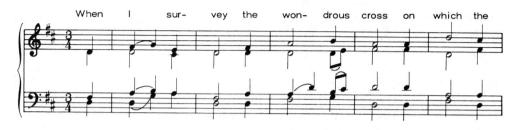

When I sur- vey the won- drous cross on which the

Prince of Glo- ry died, my rich- est gain I

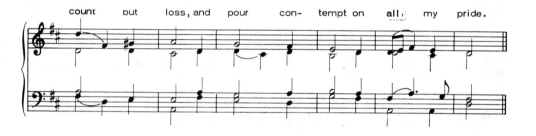

count but loss, and pour con- tempt on all my pride.

2 Forbid it, Lord, that I should boast,
   save in the death of Christ, my God:
   all the vain things that charm me most,
   I sacrifice them to his blood.

3 See from his head, his hands, his feet,
   sorrow and love flow mingled down;
   did e'er such love and sorrow meet,
   or thorns compose so rich a crown?

4 Were the whole realm of nature mine,
   that were an offering far too small;
   love so amazing, so divine,
   demands my soul, my life, my all.

Isaac Watts (1674–1748)

356 Where are you bound, Mary?

John Glynn

506

2 Mary heard the word spoken in her inmost heart;
Mary bore the Word and held him in her arms.
Sorrow she has known, seeing him upon the cross
-greater joy to see him rise again.

3 Where are we all bound, carrying the Word of God?
Time and place are ours to make his glory known.
Mary bore him first, we will tell the whole wide
    world;
Let it be according to his word.

John Glynn

357 Where does the wind come from?

Sister Mary Oswin

2 Whence does the Spirit come?
Where is his dwelling?
You see the weary world
so wilful, so rebelling.
But still the Spirit breathes,
and where,
there is no telling.

Sister Mary Oswin

358   Where is love and loving kindness

UBI CARITAS (12 12 12 12 and refrain)   Dom Gregory Murray O.S.B.

Where is love and lov- ing kind- ness, God is fain to dwell.

Flock of Christ, who loved us, in one fold con- tain- ĕd,

joy and mirth be ours, for mirth and joy he giv- eth;

fear we still and love the God who ev- er liv- eth,

each   to   o-   ther joined   by   char- i-   ty   un- feign-   èd.

2 Where is love and loving-kindness, God is fain to dwell.
   Therefore, when we meet, the flock of Christ, so loving,
   take we heed lest bitterness be there engendered;
   all our spiteful thoughts and quarrels be surrendered,
   seeing Christ is there, divine among us moving.

3 Where is love and loving-kindness, God is fain to dwell.
   So may we be gathered once again, beholding
   glorified the glory, Christ, of thy unveiling,
   there, where never ending joy, and never failing
   age succeeds to age eternally unfolding.

From the Office of the Mandatum, tr. R. A. Knox

359   Let trumpets sound

Kevin Mayhew

Ah_____ Ah_____ Ah_____

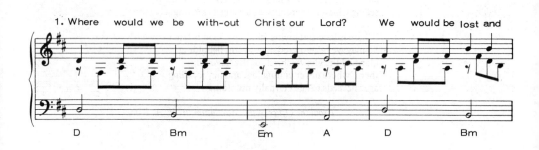

D   Bm   Em   A

1. Where would we be with-out Christ our Lord? We would be lost and

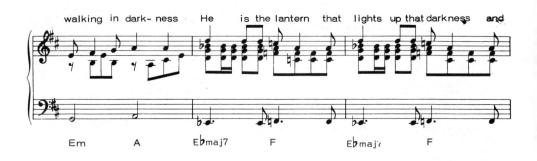

D   Bm   Em   A   D   Bm

walking in dark-ness   He   is the lantern   that   lights up that darkness   and

Em   A   E♭maj7   F   E♭maj7   F

Chorus

he   is the shep-herd who   finds   the right path.   So let the

G   Dm   G   A   D

trum- pet sound to the glo-ry of God. He is our

Bm   A   Em   D   A   Bm   A   Bm

Lord, loving and wise.

p

Fine

G   A   D   Bm   Em   A

2 Where would we be without Christ our Lord?
  We would be left to wander the desert.
  He is the beacon that leads us to safety,
  and he is the water that brings us new life.

3 Where would we be without Christ our Lord?
  We would be cold and starving and thirsty.
  He is the bread that is food for the spirit,
  and he is the wine of the new covenant.

4 Where would we be without Christ our Lord?
  He is the Son who saves all the nations.
  Through Christ the Son we are given the Spirit,
  and this is the Spirit who brings us new life.

Michael Cockett

360 While shepherds watched

WINCHESTER OLD (86 86)

Este's Psalter, 1592

2 "Fear not," said he, (for mighty dread
　　had seized their troubled mind)
　　"Glad tidings of great joy I bring
　　to you and all mankind.

3 "To you in David's town this day
　　is born of David's line
　　a Saviour, who is Christ the Lord;
　　and this shall be the sign:

4 "The heavenly Babe you there shall find
　　to human view displayed,
　　all meanly wrapped in swathing bands,
　　and in a manger laid."

5 Thus spoke the Seraph; and forthwith
　　appeared a shining throng
　　of Angels praising God, who thus
　　addressed their joyful song:

6 "all glory be to God on high,
　　and on the earth be peace,
　　goodwill henceforth from heaven to men
　　begin and never cease".

Nahum Tate (1652–1715)

361   With a song in our hearts

Estelle White

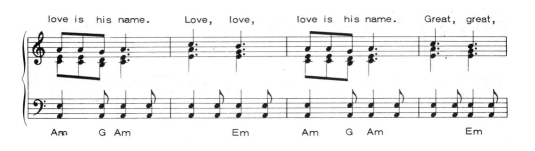

362 Yahweh, you are my strength

Estelle White

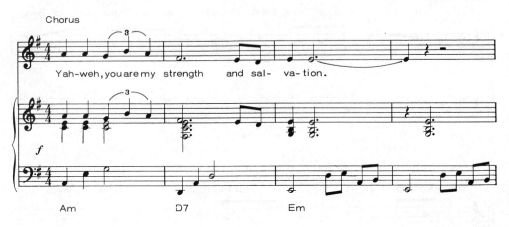

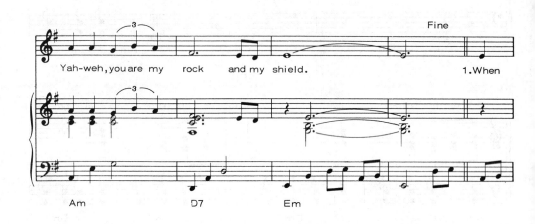

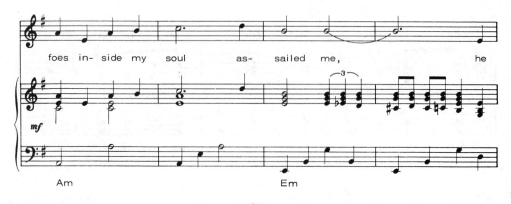

heard my cry for help and came to my aid.

Am   **Em**

2 He bent the heav'ns and came in thunder.
He flew to me and soared on wings of the wind.

3 The depths within my mind he showed me,
the hidden thoughts that I did not know were there.

4 His arm stretched from on high and held me.
He drew me from the deep, wild waters of self.

5 He is the lamp who lights the darkness.
he guides me as I leap the ramparts of life.

6 I raise my, voice and sing his glory.
With all my heart I praise the God of my joy.

Estelle White

363   Ye choirs of new Jerusalem

ST FULBERT (86 86)   H.J.Gauntlett (1805–76)

Ye choirs of new Je- ru- sa- lem, your sweet-est notes employ, the Paschal vic-to ry to hymn in strains of ho- ly joy.

2 How Judah's Lion burst his chains,
and crushed the serpent's head;
and brought with him, from death's domain,
the long-imprisoned dead.

3 From hell's devouring jaws the prey
alone our leader bore;
his ransomed hosts pursue their way
where he hath gone before.

4 Triumphant in his glory now
his sceptre ruleth all:
earth, heaven, and hell before him bow
and at his footstool fall.

5 While joyful thus his praise we sing,
his mercy we implore,
into his palace bright to bring,
and keep us evermore.

6 All glory to the Father be,
all glory to the Son,
all glory, Holy Ghost, to thee,
while endless ages run.

St. Fulbert of Chartres (c. 1000),
tr. R. Campbell

364 Ye sons and daughters of the Lord

O FILII ET FILIAE (888 and alleluias)

French Melody (17th century)

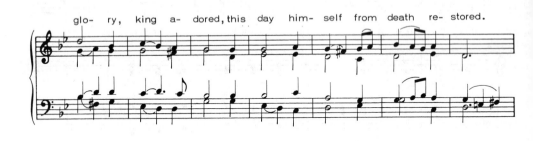

2 All in the early morning grey
   went holy women on their way
   to see the tomb where Jesus lay.

3 Of spices pure a precious store
   in their pure hands those women bore,
   to anoint the sacred body o'er.

4 Then straightaway one in white they see,
   who saith, "Ye seek the Lord; but he
   is risen, and gone to Galilee".

5 This told they Peter, told they John:
   who forthwith to to the tomb are gone,
   but Peter is by John outrun.

6 That self-same night, while out of fear
   the doors were shut, their Lord most dear
   to his apostles did appear.

7 But Thomas, when of this he heard,
   was doubtful of his brethren's word:
   wherefore again there comes the Lord.

8 "Thomas, behold my side." saith he:
   "My hands, my feet, my body see,
   and doubt not, but believe in me".

9 When Thomas saw that wounded side,
   the truth no longer he denied:
   "Thou art my Lord and God!" he cried.

10 Now let us praise the Lord most high,
   and strive his name to magnify
   on this great day, through earth and sky.

11 Whose mercy ever runneth o'er,
   whom men and angel hosts adore;
   to him be glory evermore.

17th c., tr. E. Caswall

365 Ye who own the faith of Jesus

DEN DES SINN GEBOREN (87 87 87 6)   J.A.Freylinghausen (1670–1739)

Ye who own the faith of Je- sus sing the won- ders

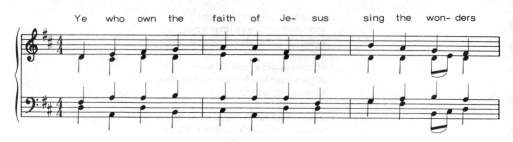

that were done, when the love of God the Fa- ther

o'er our sin the vic- t'ry won, when he made the Vir- gin Ma-ry

Mo- ther of his on- ly Son. Hail, Ma-ry, full of grace.

2 Blessed were the chosen people
  out of whom the Lord did come,
  blessed was the land of promise
  fashioned for his earthly home;
  but more blessed far the mother
  she who bore him in her womb.

3 Wherefore let all faithful people
  tell the honour of her name,
  let the Church in her foreshadowed
  part in her thanksgiving claim;
  what Christ's mother sang in gladness
  let Christ's people sing the same.

4 May the Mother's intercessions
  on our homes a blessing win,
  that the children all be prospered
  strong and fair and pure within,
  following our Lord's own footsteps,
  firm in faith and free from sin.

5 For the sick and for the aged,
  for our dear ones far away,
  for the hearts that mourn in secret,
  all who need our prayers today,
  for the faithful gone before us,
  may the holy Virgin pray.

6 Praise, O Mary, praise the Father,
  praise thy Saviour and thy Son,
  praise the everlasting Spirit,
  who hath made thee ark and throne.
  O'er all creatures high exalted,
  lowly praise the three in one.

V. S. S. Coles (1845–1929)

366 American Eucharist

Lord, have mer-cy. Lord, have mer-cy, on your
ser-vants, Lord, have mer-cy. God Al-migh-ty, just and
faith-ful, Lord have mer-cy. Lord, have mer-cy.

Christ, have mercy. Christ, have mercy,
gift from heaven, Christ have mercy.
Light of truth, and light of justice,
Christ, have mercy. Christ have mercy.

Lord, have mercy. Lord, have mercy,
on your servants, Lord, have mercy.
God almighty, just and faithful,
Lord, have mercy. Lord, have mercy.

Holy, holy, holy

Holy, holy, holy, holy,
Lord of hosts. You fill with glory
all the earth and all the heavens.
Sing hosanna, sing hosanna.

Blest and holy, blest and holy
he who comes now in the Lord's name.
In the highest sing hosanna,
in the highest sing hosanna.

Lamb of God

Jesus, Lamb of God, have mercy,
bearer of our sins, have mercy.
Jesus, Lamb of God, have mercy,
bearer of our sins, have mercy.

Saviour of the world, Lord Jesus,
may your peace be with us always.
Saviour of the world, Lord Jesus,
may your peace be with us always.

Sandra Joan Billington

367 Israeli Mass

Israeli Folk Melody
adapted by Anthony Hamson

Christ, have mercy. Christ, have mercy.
Christ, have mercy on us all.
Christ, have mercy. Christ, have mercy.
Christ, have mercy on us all.

Lord, have mercy. Lord, have mercy.
Lord, have mercy on us all.
Lord, have mercy. Lord, have mercy.
Lord, have mercy on us all.

Holy, holy, holy

Holy, holy, holy, holy
Lord of power, Lord of might.
heav'n and earth are filled with glory.
Sing hosanna evermore.

Blest and holy, blest and holy
he who comes from God on high.
Raise your voices, sing his glory,
praise his name for evermore.

Lamb of God

Lamb of God, you take away the sin,
the sin of all the world.
Give us mercy, give us mercy,
give us mercy, Lamb of God.   *(Repeat)*

Lamb of God, you take away the sin,
the sin of all the world.
Grant us peace, Lord, grant us peace, Lord,
grant us peace, O Lamb of God.

Anthony Hamson

368 Geordie Mass

English Folk Melody
adapted by Anthony Hamson

Christ, have mercy on us all.
Christ, have mercy on us.
Christ, have mercy on us all.
Christ, have mercy on us.

Lord, have mercy on us all.
Lord, have mercy on us.
Lord, have mercy on us all.
Lord, have mercy on us.

Holy, holy, holy
   Holy, holy, holy Lord
   God of might and God of pow'r.
   Glory fills all heav'n and earth.
   Sing to him hosanna!

   Blessed is the one who comes
   in the name of Christ our Lord.
   Holy, holy, holy Lord.
   Sing to him hosanna!

Lamb of God
   Lamb of God, you take our sins,
   take away our sins, Lord.
   So have mercy on us all,
   so have mercy on us.   *(Repeat)*

   Lamb of God, you take our sins,
   take our sins, Lord.
   Grant us peace, O grant us peace,
   grant us peace for ever.

Anthony Hamson

369 Monmouthshire Mass

Welsh Folk Melody
adapted by Anthony Hamson

Christ, have mercy on us all.
Christ have mercy on us.
Christ, have mercy on us all.
Christ have mercy on us.

Lord, have mercy on us all.
Lord, have mercy on us.
Lord, have mercy on us all.
Lord, have mercy on us.

Holy, holy, holy
Holy, holy, holy Lord,
God of might and power.
Glory fills all heav'n and earth.
Sing to him hosanna!

Blessed is the one who comes
brining this great glory.
Praise and honour be to God.
Sing to him hosanna!

Lamb of God
Lamb of God, you take away
the sin of all the world.
Lamb of God, you take away
the sin of all the world.

Lamb of God, you take away
the sin of all the world.
Grant us peace, O Lamb of God,
grant us peace for ever.

Anthony Hamson

370 Swedish Mass

Swedish Folk Melody
adapted by Anthony Hamson

Christ, have mercy on us all.
Christ, have mercy on us.
Christ, have mercy on us all.
Christ, have mercy on us.

Lord, have mercy on us all.
Lord, have mercy on us.
Lord, have mercy on us all.
Lord, have mercy on us.

Holy, holy, holy

Holy, holy, holy Lord,
earth is full of your glory.
Glory fills the heavens too.
Sing to him hosanna!

Blessed is the one who comes
bringing this great glory.
Holy, holy, holy Lord.
Sing to him hosanna!

Lamb of God

Lamb of God, O Jesus Christ,
take away our sins,
and have mercy on us all,
and have mercy on us.   *(Repeat)*

Lamb of God, O Jesus Christ,
take away our sins.
Grant us peace, O grant us peace,
grant us peace for ever.

Anthony Hamson

524

371 Pilgrim's Mass

LORD HAVE MERCY

Gordon Rock

Lord, have mer- cy on my soul. Lord, have mer- cy on my
Christ, have mer- cy on my soul. Christ, have mer- cy on my

F   Bb   Gm   C   Am   Dm   Gm

soul. Lord, have mer- cy, Lord, have mer- cy, Lord, have mer-cy
soul. Christ, have mer- cy, Christ, have mer- cy, Christ, have mer-cy

C   Cm   D7   Gm   C7   F7   Bb

on my soul. Pray for me, pray for me,
on my soul.

fine

C   F   Bb   C7   F   Bb   C7   Cm   D7

bro- thers and sis- ters, pray for me. Lord, have mer- cy

Gm   Bb   Gm   C7   F   G7

GLORIA

527

2 Peace on earth to all creation,
   peace on earth to all God's friends,
   peace on earth to everyone
   through the mercy of our Lord Jesus Christ.

3 Jesus Christ, the Son of the Father,
   Jesus Christ, the Son of Man,
   Jesus Christ, the Lamb of God
   who takes away the sins of the world.

4 Lamb of God, right hand of the Father,
   Lamb of God the sacrifice.
   Lamb of God who bore our sins,
   have mercy on us, receive our pray'r.

5 You alone are the Lord of creation,
   you alone are the Holy One,
   you alone are the three in one,
   the Father, the Son and the Spirit.

6 Glory be, glory be,
   glory be, glory be.   Amen.

CREED

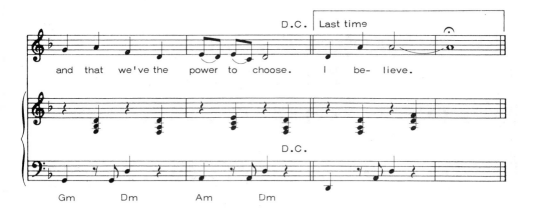

and that we've the power to choose. I be- lieve.

Gm   Dm   Am   Dm

2 I believe.
  I believe in God the Father.
  I believe in God the Son.
  I believe that he was born
  on earth to save us every one.

3 I believe.
  I believe he loved and suffered,
  taught us how to live and die,
  showed us all the way to heaven
  in our hearts, not in the sky.

4 I believe.
  I believe that God the Spirit
  ever was since time began.
  I believe that he will judge our
  actions when we've lived our span.

5 I believe.
  I believe the church is holy,
  I believe the church is true.
  I believe the church was made for
  all men, not just me and you.

6 I believe.
  Doubts and fears will fall upon us;
  we must trust that God will guide.
  Faith and hope and love will help us,
  and in joy we will abide.

SANCTUS

Ho- ly, ho- ly, ho- ly Lord
Ho- ly, ho- ly, ho- ly Lord

D   G   A4   A   F

God   of   hosts.   Your glo- ry fills all hea- ven and
God   of   hosts.   Blessed is   he   who comes in your

G   A4   A   Bm   F#m   G

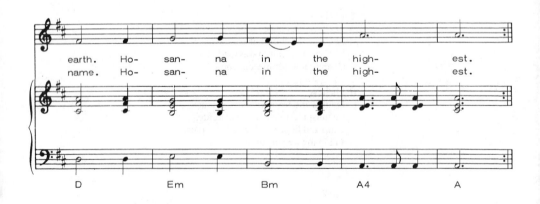

earth. Ho- san- na   in   the high-   est.
name. Ho- san- na   in   the high-   est.

D   Em   Bm   A4   A

Chorus

Our Fa-ther, king of heav'n and earth, we praise thy sa-cred name.

D Em D Em D A7 D

Verses

1 Thy king-dom come, thy will be done, in

Bm Em Bm Em

thought and word not in words a-lone.

Bm Em E7 A7

2 Give us this day our daily bread,
  our spirits and our bodies fed.

3 And forgive us all our trespasses,
  while we in turn will do no less.

4 And keep us from temptation's way,
  and help us when we go astray.

531

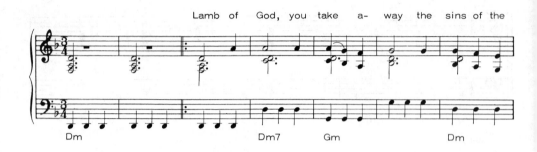

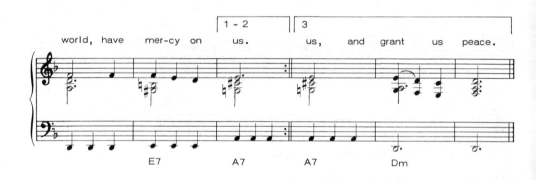

Gordon Rock

372/373 O salutaris/O saving victim

MELCOMBE   Samuel Webbe (1740–1816)

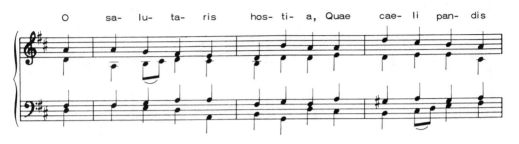

O sa- lu- ta- ris hos- ti- a, Quae cae- li pan- dis

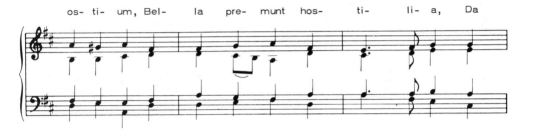

os- ti- um, Bel- la pre- munt hos- ti- li- a, Da

ro- bur, fer aux- il- i- um. A- men.

2 Uni trinoque Domino
Sit sempiterna gloria,
Qui vitam sine termino
Nobis donet in patria. Amen.

English version (see also nos. 245,309)

1 O saving victim, opening wide
The gate of heav'n to man below;
Our foes press on from ev'ry side;
Thine aid supply, thy strength bestow.

2 To thy great name be endless praise,
Immortal Godhead, one in three;
O grant us endless length of days
In our true native land with thee.

Amen.

*St. Thomas Aquinas (1227–74),
tr. J. M. Neale, E. Caswall and others*

374/375 Tantum ergo/Therefore we, before him bending

ST THOMAS (87 87 87) Samuel Webbe (1740–1816)

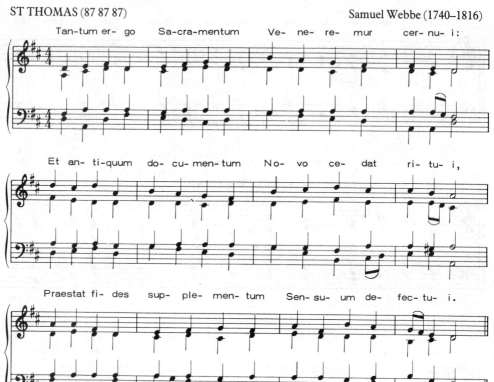

English version (see also nos. 46, 219)

2 Genitori, genitoque
  Laus et jubiliatio,
  Salus, honor, virtus quoque
  Sit et benedictio;
  Procedenti ab utroque
  Compar sit laudatio. Amen.

1 Therefore we, before him bending,
  This great sacrament revere;
  Types and shadows have their ending,
  For the newer rite is here;
  Faith, our outward sense befriending,
  Makes the inward vision clear.

2 Glory let us give, and blessing
  To the Father and the Son,
  Honour, might, and praise addressing,
  While eternal ages run;
  Ever too his love confessing
  Who from both, with both is one.
  Amen.

St. Thomas Aquinas (1227–74),
tr. J. M. Neale, E. Caswall and others

375a Amen

Traditional

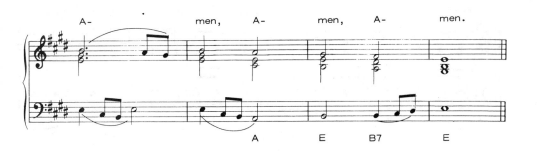

375b Our Father

Estelle White

Our Fa-ther who art in hea-ven hal-lowed be thy name. Thy

G   C   G   C   G D7

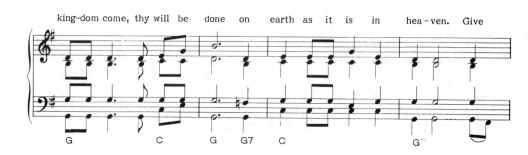

king-dom come, thy will be done on earth as it is in hea-ven. Give

G   C   G G7 C   G

us this day our dai-ly bread and for — give us our tres-pas-ses, as

Em   Am   D   D7   G

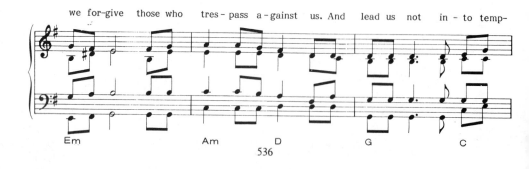

we for-give those who tres-pass a-gainst us. And lead us not in-to temp-

Em   Am   D   G   C

376 A Certain Traveller

Mary Lu Walker
Harmony by James O'Donnell

Verse

A cer-tain trav'ller on his way was robbed and left to die;
helpless by the road he lay and no-one heard his cry. A
cer-tain priest came down that way, a man most dig-ni-fied; "I
will not get in-volved" said he, and passed on the oth-er

Refrain

side. Don't pass your neigh-bour by, my friend, don't

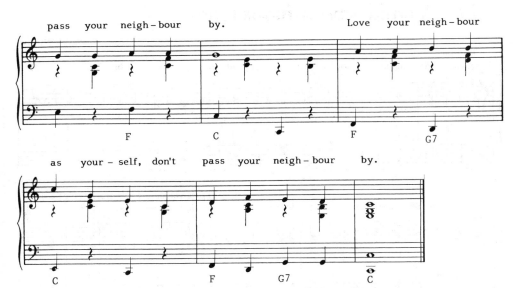

pass   your   neigh – bour   by.   Love   your   neigh – bour

F   C   F   G7

as   your – self, don't   pass   your   neigh – bour   by.

C   F   G7   C

2 A certain Levite came that way
  a man of wealth and pride,
  'I'm much too busy to stop' said he,
  and passed on the other side.
  But a certain man from Samaria,
  a stranger in the land,
  took pity on the injured man
  and lent a helping hand.

Based on Luke 10:25–37
by Mary Lu Walker

377 A child is born for us today

Gregory Norbet

Final Refrain

A child is born for us to-day, al — le — — lu - ia. He
is our Sa - viour and our God, al - le — — lu — ia, al —
— le — — lu — ia, al — le — — lu — ia. *Fine*

Verses

1 Let our hearts resound with joy
and sing a song of gladness
for the Lord, our brother,
is come and we are redeemed.

2 Tell the world of our good news:
Jesus the Christ is among us,
and his presence we celebrate
offering peace and our joy to all.

3 Christ is born, the Christ has come!
Sing everyone 'Alleluia!'
Caught in wonder at this birth
we worship God become man for us.

4 Glory to God, born today
of the Virgin Mary,
in a cave at Bethlehem:
is there room in our lives for him?

5 His name shall be 'Emmanuel!':
'God-who-lives-among-us',
angels sing and shepherds cry:
'Born is the saviour, our Lord!'

6 The magi went and worshipped him
with gifts so precious and costly.
In the fervour of their faith
they sought the child who is Lord and King.

7 The Lord will make integrity
and peace to grow in our times.
A covenant he offers us:
lasting joy will be ours to share.

8 Arise! Shine out, Jerusalem!
The glory of Yahweh★ has come to you.
Lift up your eyes and look around!
Radiant is your salvation!

★ *Instead of 'Yahweh' you may prefer
to substitute 'God'*

Gregory Norbert

378 A child is born in Bethlehem

Plainchant
accpt. by Thedore Marier

Verses

1. A child is born in Beth- le- hem, al- le- lu- ia:

So leap with joy Je- ru- sa- lem, al- le- lu- ia, al- le- lu- ia.

Refrain

A new song let us sing for Christ is born let us a- dore

542

and let our glad-ness ring.

2 Through Gabriel the word has come,
  alleluia:
  the Virgin will conceive a son,
  alleluia, alleluia.

3 Within a manger now he lies,
  alleluia:
  who reigns on high beyond the skies,
  alleluia, alleluia.

4 The shepherds hear the angel's word,
  alleluia:
  this child is truly Christ the Lord,
  alleluia, alleluia.

5 From Saba, from the rising sun,
  alleluia:
  with incense, gold, and myrrh they come,
  alleluia, alleluia.

6 Till with their gifts they enter in,
  alleluia:
  and kings adore the new-born King,
  alleluia, alleluia.

7 From virgin's womb this child is born,
  alleluia:
  the Light from Light who brings the dawn,
  alleluia, alleluia.

8 He comes to free us from our strife,
  alleluia:
  and share with us the Father's life,
  alleluia, alleluia.

9 At this the coming of the Word,
  alleluia;
  O come, let us adore the Lord,
  alleluia, alleluia.

10 To Father, Son, and Spirit praise,
  alleluia:
  from all his creatures all their days,
  alleluia, alleluia.

Latin, 14th Century,
tr Ralph Wright, OSB

© 1980 ICEL

379 A mighty stronghold

EIN' FESTE BURG (87 87 66 667)

Later form of melody by Martin Luther
Harmony by J.S.Bach (1685–1750)

544

1 A mighty stronghold is our God,
a sure defence and weapon.
He'll help us out of every need
whatever now may happen.
The ancient evil fiend
has deadly ill in mind;
great power and craft are his,
his armour gruesome is
on earth is not his equal.

2 With our own strength is nothing done
soon we are lost, dejected;
but for us fights the rightful Man
whom God himself elected.
You ask: Who may this be?
Christ Jesus it is he,
the Lord Saboath's Son,
our God, and he alone
shall hold the field victorious.

3 And though the world were full of fiends
all lurking to devour us,
we tremble not nor fear their bands,
they shall not overpower us.
The prince of this world's ill
may scowl upon us still,
he cannot do us harm,
to judgement he has come;
one word can swiftly fell him.

4 The Word they must allow to stand –
for this they win no merit;
upon the field, so near at hand,
he gives to us his Spirit.
And though they take our life,
goods, honour, child, and wife,
though we must let all go,
they will not profit so:
to us remains the Kingdom.

Martin Luther (1483–1546)
tr by Honor Mary Thwaites

380 A new commandment

Source unknown
Harmony by Stephen Dean

A new com- mandment I give un- to you, that you love one a- noth- er as I have loved you, that you love one a- noth- er as I have loved you. By this shall all men know that you are my di- sci- ples, if

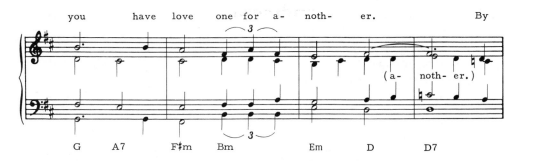

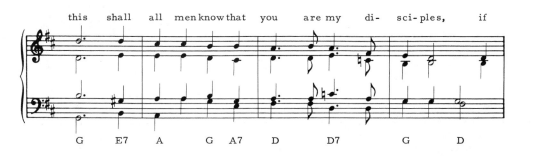

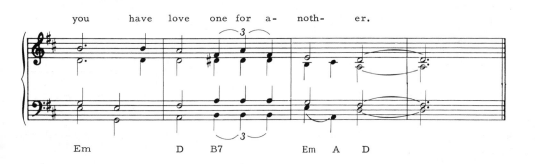

Source unknown, based on John 13:34–35

381　A noble flower of Juda

ES IST EIN' ROS'
(76 76 676)

Alte Catholische Geistliche Kirchengesang (1509)
Harmony by M. Praetorius (1571–1621)

1 A noble flow'r of Juda
from tender roots has sprung,
a rose from stem of Jesse,
as prophets long had sung;
a blossom fair and bright,
that in the midst of winter
will change to dawn our night.

2 The rose of grace and beauty
of which Isaiah sings
is Mary, virgin mother,
and Christ the flow'r she brings.
By God's divine decree
she bore our loving Saviour
who died to set us free.

3 To Mary, dearest mother,
with fervent hearts we pray:
grant that your tender infant
will cast our sins away,
and guide us with his love
that we shall ever serve him
and live with him above.

German, 15th Century,
paraphrased by Anthony G. Petti

© Faber Music Ltd

382　A sign is seen in Heaven

(76 76D)

Patrick G.Fitzpatrick

E   B   A

E A   E   B   E

1 A sign is seen in heaven,
a maiden-mother fair;
her mantle is the sunlight,
and stars adorn her hair.
The maiden's name is Mary;
in love she brings to birth
the Lord of all the ages,
the King of all the earth.

2 Like moonlight on the hilltops
she shines on all below,
like sunlight on the mountains
her Child outshines the snow.
O Mary, Queen of mothers,
still smile on young and old;
bless hearth and home and harvest,
bless farm and field and fold.

3 Pray, Mother, Queen in glory,
before the Father's throne;
praise God's eternal Wisdom,
the child who is your own;
rejoice in God the Spirit,
whose power let you conceive
the Child of Eden's promise,
O new and sinless Eve.

James Quinn, SJ

383 Abba, Abba, Father

Carey Landry

552

Abba, Abba, Father,
you are the potter,
we are the clay,
the work of your hands.

2 Father,
   may we be one in you
   as he is in you
   and you are in him,
   and you are in him.

3 Glory,
   glory and praise to you,
   glory and praise to you
   for ever. Amen.
   For ever. Amen.

Carey Landry

384 Abba, Father, send your Spirit

Ginny Vissing

2 I will give you living water . . .

3 If you seek me you will find me . . .

4 If you listen you will hear me . . .

5 Come, my children, I will teach you . . .

6 I'm your shepherd, I will lead you . . .

7 Peace I leave you, peace I give you . . .

8 I'm your life and resurrection . . .

9 Glory Father, glory Spirit . . .

Other words from Scripture may be substituted according to the occasion or the season. For example, in Advent:

1 Come, Lord Jesus, Light of nations . . .

2 Come, Lord Jesus, born of Mary . . .

3 Come, and show the Father's glory . . .

Ginny Vissing

385 Across the years there echoes still

ST COLUMBA (Erin) (87 87)   Irish traditional melody

1 Across the years there echoes still
the Baptist's bold assertion:
the call of God to change of heart,
repentance and conversion.

2 The word that John more boldly spoke
in dying than in living
now Christ takes up as he proclaims
a Father all-forgiving.

3 The erring son he welcomes home
when all is spent and squandered.
He lovingly pursues the sheep
that from the flock has wandered.

4 Forgive us, Lord, all we have done
to you and one another.
So often we have gone our way,
forgetful of each other.

5 Forgetful of the cross they bear
of hunger, want, oppression –
grant, Lord, that we may make amends
who humbly make confession.

Denis E.Hurley

386 Again the Lord's own day is here

CHURCH TRIUMPHANT (88 88)

J.W.Elliott (1833–1915)

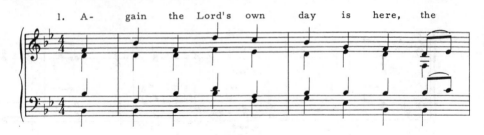

1. A- gain the Lord's own day is here, the

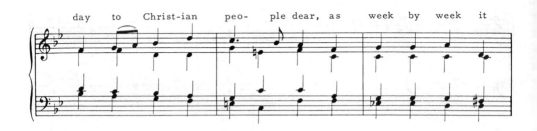

day to Christ-ian peo- ple dear, as week by week it

bids them tell how Je- sus rose from death and hell..

2 For by his flock the Lord declared
  his resurrection should be shared;
  and we who trust in him to save
  with him are risen from the grave.

3 We, one and all, of him possessed,
  are with exceeding treasures blest;
  for all he did and all he bore
  is shared by us for evermore.

4 Eternal glory, rest on high,
  a blesséd immortality
  true peace and gladness, and a throne,
  are all his gifts and all our own.

5 And therefore unto thee we sing,
  O Lord of peace, eternal King;
  thy love we praise, thy name adore,
  both on this day and evermore.

Attributed to St Thomas a Kempis (1380–1471)
tr by J.M.Neale (1818–66) and others

387 Alabaré

Source unknown,
Harmony by Rosalind Pitcher

559

(Alabaré a mi Señor is Spanish for 'I will praise my Lord')

388 All for Jesus

ALL FOR JESUS (87 87)

John Stainer (1840–1901)

1 All for Jesus, all for Jesus,
   this our song shall ever be;
   for we have no hope, nor Saviour,
   if we have not hope in thee.

2 All for Jesus, thou wilt give us
   strength to serve thee, hour by hour;
   none can move us from thy presence,
   while we trust thy love and power.

3 All for Jesus, at thine altar
   thou wilt give us sweet content;
   there, dear Lord, we shall receive thee
   in the solemn sacrament.

4 All for Jesus, thou hast loved us;
   all for Jesus, thou hast died;
   all for Jesus, thou art with us;
   all for Jesus crucified.

5 All for Jesus, all for Jesus,
   this the Church's song must be;
   till, at last, her sons are gathered
   one in love and one in thee.

J.Sparrow-Simpson

389 All my hope on God is founded

MICHAEL (87 87 33 7)   Herbert Howells (1892–1983)

1. All my hope on God is founded; he doth still my
trust re-new. Me through change and chance he guid-eth, on-ly
good and on-ly true. God un-known, he a-lone calls my
heart to be his own.

2 Pride of man and earthly glory,
  sword and crown betray God's trust;
  what with lavish care man buildeth,
  tower and temple, fall to dust.
  But God's power, hour by hour,
  is my temple and my tower.

3 God's great goodness ay endureth,
  deep his wisdom, passing thought:
  splendour, light and life attend him,
  beauty springeth out of nought.
  Evermore, from his store
  new-born worlds rise and adore.

4 Still from man to God eternal
  sacrifice of praise be done,
  high above all praises praising
  for the gift of Christ his Son.
  Christ doth call one and all;
  ye who follow shall not fall.

J.Neander (1650–80),
paraphrased by
R.S.Bridges (1844–1930)

390 All the earth proclaim the Lord

Lucien Deiss

2 Know that the Lord is our creator.
   Yes he is our Father; we are his sons.

3 We are the sheep of his green pasture,
   for we are his people; he is our God.

4 Enter his gates bringing thanksgiving,
   O enter his courts while singing his praise.

5 Our Lord is good, his love enduring,
   his word is abiding now with all men.

6 Honour and praise be to the Father,
   the Son, and the Spirit, world without end.

Based on Psalm 99(100)
by Lucien Deiss

391   All you nations

Lucien Deiss

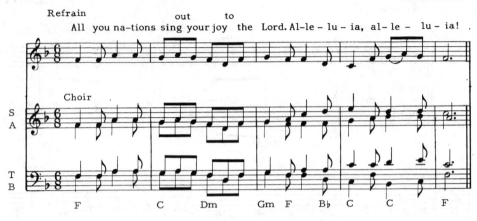

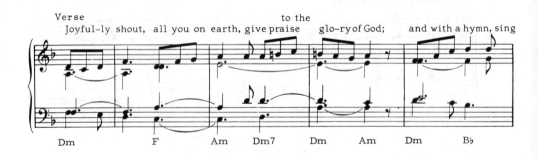

All you nations,
sing out your joy in the Lord:
alleluia, alleluia!

1 Joyfully shout, all you on earth,
 give praise to the glory of God;
 and with a hymn,
 sing out his glorious praise:
 Alleluia!

2 Lift up your hearts, sing to your God:
 tremendous his deeds among men!
 Vanquished your foes,
 struck down by power and might:
 Alleluia!

3 Let all the earth kneel in his sight,
 extolling his marvellous fame;
 honour his name,
 in highest heaven give praise:
 Alleluia!

4 Come forth and see all the great works
 that God has brought forth by his might;
 fall on your knees
 before his glorious throne:
 Alleluia!

5 Parting the seas with might and pow'r,
 he rescued his people from shame;
 let us give thanks
 for all his merciful deeds:
 Alleluia!

6 His eyes keep watch on all the earth,
 his strength is forever renewed;
 and let no man
 rebel against his commands;
 Alleluia!

7 Tested are we by God the Lord,
 as silver is tested by fire;
 burdened with pain,
 we fall ensnared in our sins:
 Alleluia!

8 Over our heads wicked men rode,
 we passed through the fire and the flood;
 then, Lord, you brought
 your people into your peace:
 Alleluia!

9 Glory and thanks be to the Father;
 honour and praise to the Son;
 and to the Spirit,
 source of life and of love:
 Alleluia!

Based on Psalm 65(66)
by Lucien Deiss

392 Alleluia, Jesus is alive

Bonaventure Hinwood
Harmony by John Rombaut

Alleluia, alleluia, alleluia, Jesus is alive!

1 Praise the Lord
for he is good eternally,
and his loving kindness for us
never fails.

2 His strong right hand
overcomes and lifts us up;
I'll never die, but live
to praise his power to save.

3 For the stone rejected
by the builder's sin
has become the cornerstone
of God's new House.

4 And he gives us the light
wherewith to see;
his intention is
that we should live with him.

Based on Psalm 117(118)

393 Alleluia, may God's Spirit come

Tune as for no. 392

Alleluia, alleluia, alleluia, may God's Spirit come!

1 Bless the Lord, my soul,
for he is great and good:
earth he has enriched
with all his mighty works.

2 You send forth your Spirit,
then creation starts,
and you still renew
all things upon the earth.

3 May the Lord find joy
in all that he creates;
and my thoughts about him
fill my heart with joy.

Based on Psalm 103(104)

394　Alleluia! Sons of God, arise

Mimi Farra
Harmony by John Rombaut

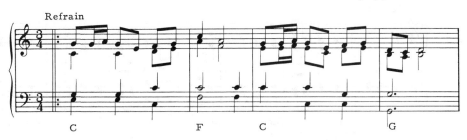

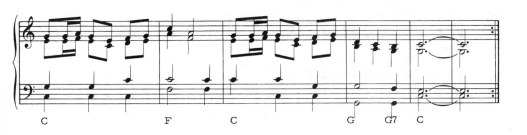

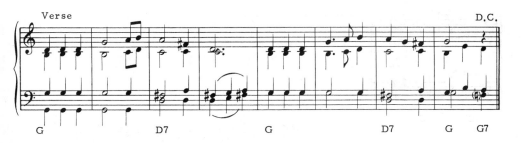

Alleluia! Alleluia! Alleluia,
Sons of God arise and follow.
Alleluia! Alleluia!
Sons of God arise and follow the Lord.

1 Come and be clothed in his righteousness;
  come join the band who are called by his name.

2 Look at the world which is bound by sin;
  walk into the midst of it proclaiming my life.

Mimi Farra

395 Alleluia, give thanks to the risen Lord

Donald Fishel
Harmony by Eric Welch

Alleluia, alleluia,
give thanks to the risen Lord.
Alleluia, alleluia,
give praise to his name.

1 Jesus is Lord of all the earth.
He is the King of creation.

2 Spread the good news o'er all the earth.
Jesus has died and has risen.

3 We have been crucified with Christ.
Now we shall live for ever.

4 God has proclaimed the just reward.
Life for all men, alleluia.

5 Come, let us praise the living God,
joyfully sing to our Saviour.

Don Fishel

396 Canticle of the Lamb

Patrick G. Fitzpatrick

Refrain

Al – le – lu – ia, al – le – lu – ia!

Verse 1

1. Sal va tion and glory and pow'r be-long to our God,

Semi-chorus · To refrain

al – le – lu – ia! His judge-ments are true and just.

Verse 2

2. Praise our God, all you his ser – vants,

Semi-chorus　　　　　　　　　　　　　　　　　　　　　To refrain

al – le – lu – ia!　You　who　fear　him　great　and　small

Verse 3

3.　The　Lord　our　God,　the　al – migh – ty,　reigns,

Semi-chorus

al – le-lu – ia!　let us re- joice and e- xult and give him the　Glory

Refrain

Al – le – lu – ia,　al – le – lu – ia!

4. The mar-riage of the Lamb has come,

Semi chorus.

To refrain

al – le–lu – ia! and his Bride has made her–self rea – dy.

Based on Revelation 19:1–2,5–7 from The Divine Office

397 Almighty Father, who for us

NETHERLANDS
(12 12 12 12)

Melody as in A. Valerius'
Nederlandstache Gedenck-Clanck (1626)
Harmony by John Wilson

1. Al- migh- ty Fa- ther, who for us thy Son didst give, that men and na- tions through his pre- cious death might live, in mer- cy guard us, lest by sloth and self- ish pride we cause to stum- ble those for whom the Sa- viour died.

(small notes organ only)

2 We are thy stewards; thine our talents, wisdom, skill;
   our only glory that we may thy trust fulfil;
   that we thy pleasure in our neighbours' good pursue,
   if thou but workest in us both to will and do.

3 On just and unjust thou thy care dost freely shower;
   make us, thy children, free from greed and lust for power,
   lest human justice, yoked with man's unequal laws,
   oppress the needy and neglect the humble cause.

4 Let not thy worship blind us to the claims of love;
   but let thy manna lead us to the feast above,
   to seek the country which by faith we now possess,
   where Christ, our treasure, reigns in peace and righteousness.

George B. Caird

398 Angel-voices ever singing

ANGEL VOICES (85 85 87)   E.G.Monk (1819–1900)

1 Angel-voices ever singing
   round thy throne of light,
   angel-harps for ever ringing,
   rest-not day nor night;
   thousands only live to bless thee
   and confess thee Lord of might.

2 Thou who art beyond the farthest
   mortal eye can scan,
   can it be that thou regardest
   songs of sinful man?
   Can we know that thou art near us,
   and wilt hear us? Yes, we can.

3 Yes, we know that thou rejoicest
   o'er each work of thine;
   thou didst ears and hands and voices
   for thy praise design;
   craftsman's art and music's measure
   for thy pleasure all combine.

4 In thy house, great God, we offer
   of thine own to thee;
   and for thine acceptance proffer
   all unworthily;
   hearts and minds and hands and voices
   in our choicest psalmody.

5 Honour, glory, might and merit
   thine shall ever be,
   Father, Son and Holy Spirit,
   Blessed Trinity!
   Of the best that thou hast given
   earth and heaven render thee.

Francis Pott (1832–1909)

399　An Upper Room

FOLKSONG (O WALY WALY) (98 98)

Traditional English melody,
arranged by John Wilson

If any of verses 1 – 3 are sung by the Choir alone, they may be in Harmony, with A.T.B. humming or singing a vowel sound; but verse 4 should always be in unison.

2 A lasting gift Jesus gave his own:
　to share his bread, his loving cup.
　Whatever burdens may bow us down,
　he by his cross shall lift us up.

3 And after Supper he washed their feet,
　for service, too, is sacrament.
　In him our joy shall be made complete –
　sent out to serve, as he was sent.

4 No end there is! We depart in peace.
　He loves beyond our uttermost:
　in every room in our Father's house
　he will be there, as Lord and Host.

F.Pratt Green

400 As earth that is dry

Anne Conway

1 As earth that is dry and parched in the sun
   lies waiting for rain,
   my soul is a desert, arid and waste;
   it longs for your Word, O Lord.

   Come to the waters, all you who thirst;
   come now, and eat my bread.

2 Though you have no money, come, buy my corn,
   and drink my red wine.
   Why spend precious gold on what will not last?
   Hear me, and your soul will live.

3 As one on a journey strays from the road
   and falls in the dark,
   my mind is a wanderer, choosing wrong paths
   and longing to find a star.

4 The Lord is your light, the Lord is your strength;
   turn back to him now.
   For his ways are not the ways you would choose,
   and his thoughts are always new.

5 As rain from the mountains falls on the land
   and brings forth the seed,
   the word of the Lord sinks deep in our hearts,
   creating the flower of truth.

Isaiah 55: 1, 2, 6, 9 & 12
paraphrased by Anne Conway

401 As I kneel before you

Maria Parkinson

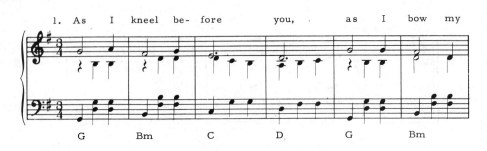

1. As I kneel be- fore you, as I bow my

G   Bm   C   D   G   Bm

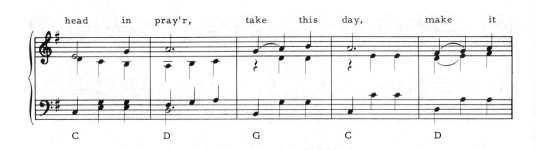

head   in pray'r, take this day, make it

C   D   G   C   D

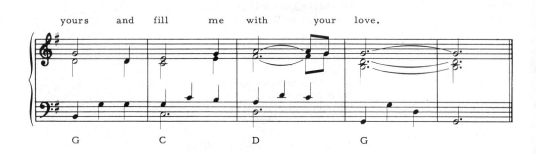

yours and fill   me with   your love.

G   C   D   G

Chorus*

A-   ve, Ma - ri -   a,   gra -   ti -   a

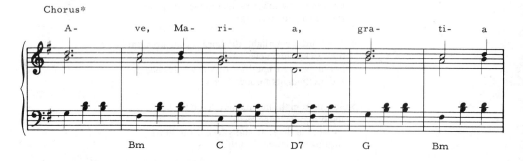

Bm   C   D7   G   Bm

* The lower notes are the tune.

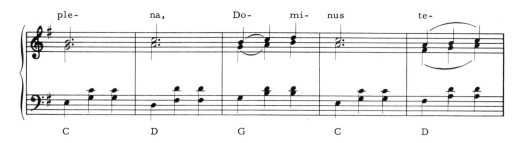

2 All I have I give you,
   ev'ry dream and wish are yours.
   Mother of Christ, Mother of mine,
   present them to my Lord.

3 As I kneel before you,
   and I see your smiling face,
   ev'ry thought, ev'ry word
   is lost in your embrace.

Maria Parkinson

402　As long as men on earth

LES COMMANDEMENS DE DIEU (98.98)

Composed or adapted by L. Bourgeois
in the *Genevan Psalter* (1543)

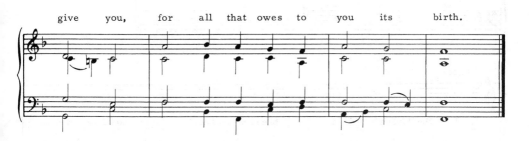

2 You are our light and life and Saviour,
　you rescue us when we are dead.
　You gave your Son to be our neighbour.
　He feeds us with his living bread.

3 As long as human words are spoken
　and for each other we exist,
　your steadfastness remains unbroken;
　for Jesus' sake, your name be blessed.

4 You are the one who clothes the flowers,
　you feed the birds in all the land.
　You are our shelter: all my hours
　and all my days are in your hand.

5 Therefore, let all the world adore you.
　It is your love that brought it forth.
　You live among us, we before you.
　Your offspring are we. Praise the Lord!

Huub Oosterhuis and C.M. De Vries

403   As one body

Jean-Paul Lecot

Refrain

As one bo – dy we are wed by par – tak – ing
of the self – same Bread; and Je – sus Christ of that bo – dy is the
head: the ho – ly Church of God.

Verses

1. I am the living bread which has come down from heaven.

Anyone who eats this bread will live for ever

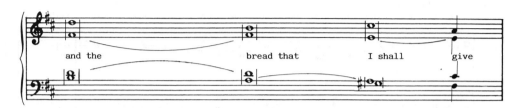

and the   bread that   I shall   give

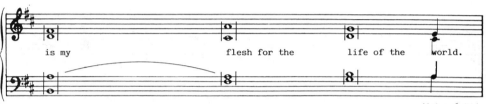

is my   flesh for the   life of the   world.

(John 6:51)

2 On the same night that he was bet*rayed*, the Lord Jesus *took* some *bread*
   thanked *God* for it, and *broke* it, and *said:*
   '*This* is my *body*, which is *given* up for *you*.
   Do this in *memory* of *me*.

                                    (1 Cor.11:23b-24)

3 *In* the same way, after *supper*, he *took* the cup and *said:*
   '*This cup* is the new *covenant* in my *blood*.
   Do this in *memory* of *me*.'
   So doing, we proclaim his *death*, until he *comes again*.

                                    (1 Cor.11:25–26)

4 *Just* as a human *body*, though it is *made* up of many *parts*
   these parts, though *many*, *make* one *body*.
   In the one *Spirit* we were *all* bapt*ised*,
   one Spirit given to us *all to drink*.

                                    (1 Cor.11:12–13)

5 *There* is one *body*, *there* is one *Spirit*
   just as we were *called* into *one* and the same *hope*.
   There is one *Lord*, one *faith*, one *baptism*
   and one *God*, who is *Father* over *all*.

                                    (Ephesians 4:4–6)

Words from Scripture: Jean-Paul Lecot,
W.R.Lawrence, R.B.Kelly

404   As the bridegroom to his chosen

BRIDEGROOM (87 87 6)   Peter Cutts

A and B may be sung by contrasted groups of voices.

2 As the fountain in the garden,
  as the candle in the dark,
  as the treasure in the coffer,
  as the manna in the ark,
  so, Lord, art thou to me.

3 As the music at the banquet,
  as the stamp unto the seal,
  as the medicine to the fainting,
  as the wine-cup at the meal
  so, Lord, art thou to me.

4 As the ruby in the setting,
  as the honey in the comb,
  as the light within the lantern,
  as the father in the home,
  so, Lord, art thou to me.

5 As the sunshine in the heavens,
  as the image in the glass,
  as the fruit unto the fig-tree,
  as the dew unto the grass,
  so, Lord, art thou to me.

Para from John Tauler (1330–61)
by Emma Frances Bevan (1827–1909)

405   Awake, awake: fling off the night

DEUS TUORUM MILITUM (88 88)

Grenoble Antiphoner, 1753
Harmony by Redmund Shaw

Another setting of this hymn (in C will be found at No. 332)

2 Awake and rise, like men renewed,
men with the Spirit's power endued.
The light of life in us must glow,
and fruits of truth and goodness show.

3 Let in the light; all sin expose
to Christ, whose life no darkness knows.
Before his cross for guidance kneel;
his light will judge and, judging, heal.

4 Awake, and rise up from the dead,
and Christ his light on you will shed.
Its power will wrong desires destroy,
and your whole nature fill with joy.

5 Then sing for joy, and use each day;
give thanks for everything alway.
Lift up your hearts; with one accord
praise God through Jesus Christ our Lord.

J.R.Peacey (1896–1971)
based on Ephesians 5:6–20

406 Bartimaeus

FIRST TUNE

Joan McCrimmon

SECOND TUNE

Bill Tamblyn

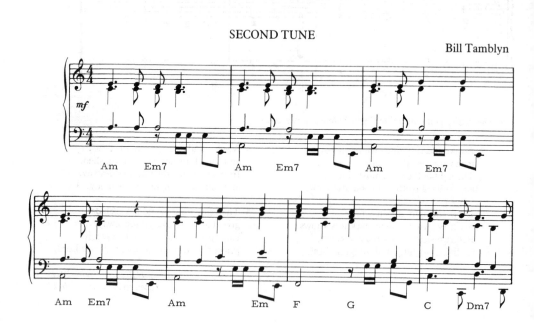

F   E   D   F   A   C

v.4 ending

Em   Dm   C   G   Am7   G

1 'Bartimaeus, Bartimaeus,
   do you hear them, do you know?
   They have seen the prophet Jesus
   in the streets of Jericho.
   Bartimaeus, it is he!
   What a shame you cannot see.'

2 'Son of David, Son of David
   walking in the blessed light,
   I a beggar ask no money.
   Lord, may I receive my sight?
   Son of David, pity me.
   You have power to make me see.'

3 'Bartimaeus, Bartimaeus,
   you have eyes to know your need;
   you have eyes to know the Giver;
   surely this is sight indeed!
   Bartimaeus, come to me.
   Bartimaeus, you shall see.'

4 Son of David, Son of David
   kindle in the human soul.
   One blind faith like Bartimaeus;
   call us out, and make us whole.
   Son of David, source of light,
   Lord, may we receive our sight?

Michael Hewlett

407   Be still, my soul

FINLANDIA (10 10. 10 10.10 10)   Jan Sibelius (1865–1957)

1 Be still, my soul: the Lord is on your side;
  bear patiently the cross of grief and pain;
  leave to your God to order and provide;
  in every change he faithful will remain.
  Be still my soul: your best, your heavenly friend
  through thorny ways lead to a joyful end.

2 Be still, my soul: your God will undertake
  to guide the future as he has the past.
  Your hope, your confidence let nothing shake,
  all now mysterious shall be clear at last.
  Be still, my soul: the tempests still obey
  his voice, who ruled them once on Galilee.

3 Be still, my soul: the hour is hastening on
  when we shall be for ever with the Lord,
  when disappointment, grief and fear are gone,
  sorrow forgotten, love's pure joy restored.
  Be still, my soul: when change and tears are past,
  all safe and blessed we shall meet at last.

Katharina von Schlegel,
tr by Jane L.Borthwick (1813–1897)

408 Before Christ died

LINDISFARNE (86 86)

Eric Welch

1 Before Christ died he took some bread,
  and then he took some wine.
  'My body and my blood,' he said,
  'a sacrificial sign.'

2 'Now eat and drink, I am your food.
  I promise you will see
  your lives transformed, your hearts renewed;
  you'll die and live with me.'

3 We drink this wine, we eat this bread,
  as Jesus bade us do.
  The covenant for which he bled
  today we must renew.

4 By faith, in broken bread we see
  the body of our Lord.
  By faith, we know the wine to be
  his holy blood outpoured.

5 Each time the church, for memory's sake,
  repeats Christ's holy act,
  each time we of that meal partake,
  Christ's death we re-enact.

6 From sunrise to the setting sun
  this death we will proclaim.
  Each day Christ promises to come
  until he comes again.

Peter de Rosa

409   Bind us together

B. Gillman

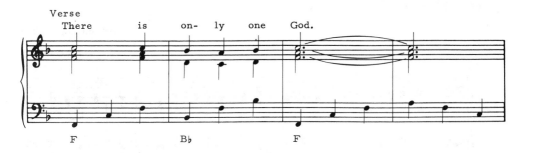

Verse

There is on-ly one God.

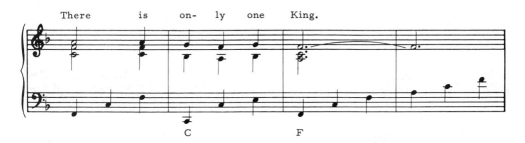

There is on-ly one King.

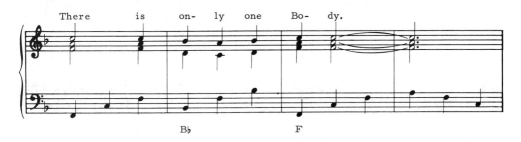

There is on-ly one Bo-dy.

That is why we sing.

D.C. al fine

2 Made for the glory of God,
  purchased by His precious Son,
  born with the right to be clean,
  for Jesus the victory has won.

3 You are the family of God,
  you are the promise divine,
  you are God's chosen desire,
  you are the glorious new wine.

Bob Gillman

410 Blessed be God!

Aniceto Nazareth

1 Blest are you, Lord, God of all creation,
   thanks to your goodness this bread we offer:
   fruit of the earth, work of our hands,
   it will become the bread of life.

Blessed be God! Blessed be God!
Blessed be God forever! Amen!
Blessed be God! Blessed be God!
Blessed be God forever! Amen!

2 Blest are you, Lord, God of all creation,
   thanks to your goodness this wine we offer:
   fruit of the earth, work of our hands,
   it will become the cup of life.

Aniceto Nazareth

411   Blest be the Lord

Daniel L. Schutte
harmony by Sr Theophane Hytrek OSF

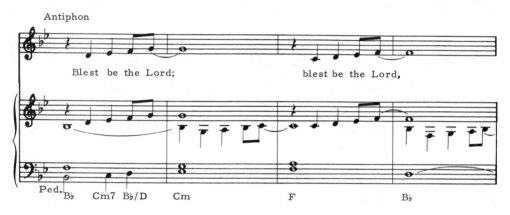

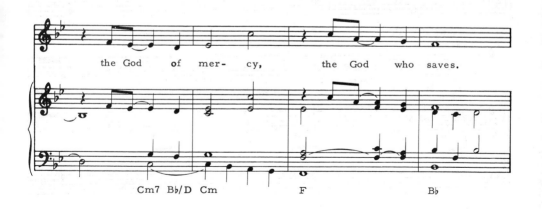

I shall not fear the dark of night,

Cm7 Bb6 Cm   F   Bb

nor the ar- row that flies by day.

Cm7 Bb6 Cm   F   Bb

Last time

Fine

Bb Cm7 Bb Cm   F   Eb   Bb

Verses

1. He will re-lease me from the nets of all my foes.

Eb   F   Eb

He will pro-tect me from their wick-ed hands.

Be-neath the shad-ow of his wings I will rejoice

to find a dwell-ing place se-cure.

2 I need not shrink before the terrors of the night,
   nor stand alone before the light of day.
   No harm shall come to me, no arrow strike me down,
   no evil settle in my soul.

3 Although a thousand strong have fallen at my side,
   I'll not be shaken with the Lord at hand.
   His faithful love is all the armour that I need
   to wage my battle with the foe.

based on Psalm 90(91) by Daniel L. Schutte SJ

412   Bread of the world

WEISSE (98 98)

Composer unknown
Harmony by J.S.Bach (1685–1750)

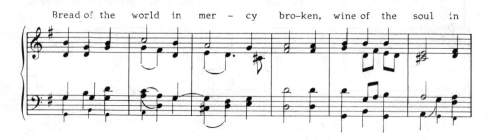

Bread of the world in mer – cy bro–ken, wine of the soul in

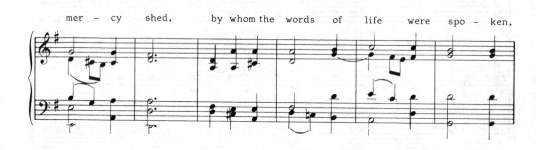

mer – cy shed, by whom the words of life were spo – ken,

and in whose death our sins are dead.

2 Look on the heart by sorrow broken,
look on the tears by sinners shed;
and be your feast to us the token
that by your grace our souls are fed.

Reginald Heber (1783–1826)

413 Break not the circle

LEYTONEN (10 11.10 11)

Doreen Potter

1 Break not the circle of enabling love,
  where people grow, forgiven and forgiving;
  break not that circle, make it wider still,
  till it includes, embraces all the living.

2 Come, wonder at this love that comes to life,
  where words of freedom are with humour spoken
  and people keep no score of wrong and guilt,
  but will that human bonds remain unbroken.

3 Come, wonder at the Lord who came and comes
  to teach the world the craft of hopeful craving
  for peace and wholeness that will fill the earth:
  he calls his people to creative living.

4 Join then the movement of the love that frees,
  till people of whatever race or nation,
  will truly be themselves, stand on their feet,
  see eye to eye with laughter and elation.

Fred Kaan

414 Breathing the words (The Magnificat)

Liz Powell and Jean Henriot
Harmony by Andrew Wright

Refrain

Breathing the words of hum–ble o – be – dience true

Am7   Dsus4/A

Let it be so, and let it be done for

Am7

you. I am the

Dsus4/A   Cmaj7

hand–maid of the Lord

Gsus4   G   A   A4   A

Verse (1)

My soul mag-ni-fies the Lord ———, and my Spi-rit ——— re-joic-es in God my King ———. Hence-forth ——— all

Dmaj7   C#m7   Bm7   A   Asus4   Dmaj7   C#m7

2. His mer - cy ——— spans ge - ne - ra - tions,——— for those —— who fear him, ——— ho - ly ——— is his name.——— He has shown —— the might —— of —— his —— arm.-
3. The migh - ty ——— flung from——— their thrones ——— and ex - al - ted ———the low - ly. ——— He has filled —— the hun-gry— with — good — things.
4. In all his ——— mer - cy he —— has helped ——— Is - ra - el ——— the home ——— of our fa - thers.——— As he cared ——— for — A - bra - ham,-
5. Give praise to — the Fa - ther—— Al - migh - ty,——— to his Son,——— Je - sus —— Christ our Lord. ——— To the Spi-rit ——— who dwells —— in —— our —— hearts,

Dmaj7   Bm7   A   Asus4   Dmaj7   C#m7

men will call me bles – sed ————, be–cause my

C#m7

God ———— has done great things for me ————

Bm7 Cmaj7 G6/B

To Refrain

Am Esus4/G E Emsus4G E

Bm7

2. —— The proud he's scattered ———— in their con –
3. —— The rich he's sent —— emp – ty hand – ed —— a –
4. —— so —— he cares for us —— un – til the
5. —— now and– for– e – ver. ———— A –

Cmaj7 G6/B Am Emsus4G E Esus4 E

2. – ceit.
3. – way.
4. end.
5. – men.

*Based on Luke 1:46–56 by Liz Powell and
Jean Henriot*

598

415 Bright star of morning

Estelle White

1. Bright star of morn- ing dawn on our dark- ness,
Je- sus our Mas- ter, our Lord and King,
our hearts we give you now and for- ev- er,
all that we care for to you we bring.

2 All of life's troubles, each daily burden
are eased and lightened when you are near.
Help us to stay close, trusting and child-like,
calmed by your presence and free from fear.

3 Immortal Saviour, forgive our weakness,
for you have known, Lord, our frailty.
May we walk with you, safe in your love-light,
each day until eternity.

Estelle White

599

416 Brother Sun and Sister Moon

Moderato

Donovan

Verses

1. Bro - ther Sun and Sis - ter Moon,
2. Bro - ther Wind and Sis - ter Air,

I sel-dom hear you, sel - dom hear your tune.
O - pen my eyes to vi-sions pure and fair

Pre - oc - cu - pied with sel-fish mi - se - ry.
that I may see the glo - ry a - round me.

I am God's crea - ture, of him I am

St Francis of Assisi,
adapted by Donovan

601

417 And be like your Father (But I say unto you)

Beverlee Paine

Gently
1. But I say un-to you, love your en-e-mies and
pray for those who hurt you. Give to those who
ask, don't turn a- way. And be like your Father in hea-ven a-bove who caus-es his
sun to shine on e- vil and good, and sends down his rain

to quench all our thirst. In him we live and

G   Em   Am   F

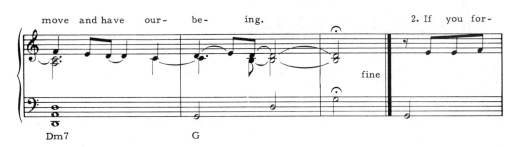

move and have our- be- ing.   2. If you for-

fine

Dm7   G

give each oth- er,   so will God for- give you.

C   F   G

Do not judge lest   you be judg'd your - selves.   And

D.S.

C   F   G

3 When you see the hungry,
  feed them from your table.
  For the poor and weary,
  be their wat'ring place.

Based on Luke 6:27ff.
Beverlee Paine

418   Christ suffered for you

Joseph Walshe

Where a bar is empty, it has to be omitted completely: the accompanist must also omit the equivalent bars

1. Christ suf-fer'd for you,

2. He com-mit-ted no sin; no guile was found on his lips.

3. When he suf-fer'd he did not threa-ten;

4. He him-self bore our sins in his bo-dy on the tree, that

5. For you were stra-ying like sheep, but now have re-turned to the

lea-ving you an e- xam-ple that you should fol - low in his steps. **D.S.**

when he was re- -viled, he did not re- vile in re- turn. **D.S.**

but he trus-ted in him who jud-ges just - ly. **D.S.**

we might die to sin and live to righ-teous-ness. **D.S.**

shep-herd and guardian of your souls. **D.S.**

F G Am Am7 C Dm Em **D.S.**

By his wounds we have been healed.

1 Peter 2:21,24

© Joseph Walshe, OSCO

605

419 By the Cross

Joseph Gelineau

1. By the Cross which did to death our on-ly Sa - viour, this bles-sed vine from which grapes are gathered in: Je - sus Christ, we thank and bless you. By the Cross which casts down fire upon our pla - net, this liv -ing branch which can heal our ev' - ry sin: Je- sus

(Choir)

Christ, we glo – ri – fy you. By the Cross on Calv'ry's hill se – cure – ly plan – ted, this liv–ing branch which can heal our ev'ry sin: Conqu'ring God, we your Church pro – claim you.

(Choir)

2 By the Blood which which we marked the wooden lintels
for our protection the night when God passed by:
Jesus Christ, we thank and bless you.
By the Blood which in our Exodus once saved us,
when hell was sealed up by God's engulfing sea:
Jesus Christ, we glorify you.
By the Blood which kills the poison in bad fruitage,
and gives new life to the dead sap in the tree:
conquering God, we your Church proclaim you!

3 By the Death on Calv'ry's hill of him the First-born,
who bears the wood and the flame for his own pyre:
Jesus Christ, we thank and bless you.
By the Death, amid the thorns, of God's own Shepherd,
the Paschal Lamb who was pierced by our despair:
Jesus Christ, we glorify you.
By the Death of God's belov'd outside his vineyard,
that he might change us from murd'rer into heir:
conquering God, we your Church proclaim you!

4 By the Wood which sings a song of nuptial
     gladness,
  of God who takers for bride our human race:
  Jesus Christ, we thank and bless you.
  By the Wood which raises up in his full vigour
  the Son of Man who draws all men by his grace:
  Jesus Christ, we glorify you.
  By the Wood where he perfects his royal Priesthood
  in one High Priest who for sin is sacrifice:
  conquering God. we your Church proclaim you!

5 Holy Tree which reaches up from earth to heaven
  that all the world may exult in Jacob's God:
  Jesus Christ, we thank and bless you.
  Mighty Ship which snatches us from God's deep
     anger,
  saves us, with Noah, from drowning in the Flood:
  Jesus Christ, we glorify you.
  Tender Wood which gives to brackish water
     sweetness,
  and from the Rock shall strike fountains for our food:
  conquering God, we your Church proclaim you

Dider Rimaud, tr by F. Pratt Green

420   Called to be servants

James G. Johnston
Harmony by Roger Humphrey

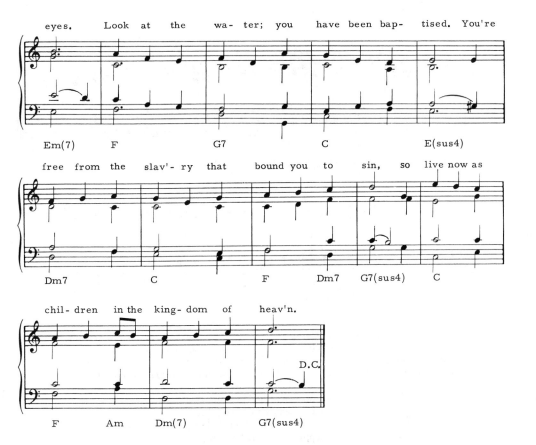

2 We are saints! Forgiveness is sure
not of ourselves, but the cross Christ endured.
We're free from the Law that said 'You must provide!'
We're free to be servants; we're called; we're baptised.

3 Jesus closed the dark pit of death.
He has breathed on us with his holy breath.
He gives us the faith to respond to his News.
We're free to show mercy, to love, to be bruised.

James G. Johnston

421   Child in the manger

BUNESSAN (53 53D)

Traditional Scottish

1 Child in the manger, infant of Mary;
  outcast and stranger, Lord of all;
  child who inherits all our transgressions,
  all our demerits on him fall.

2 Once the most holy child of salvation
  gently and lowly lived below;
  now as our glorious mighty Redeemer,
  see him victorious o'er each foe.

3 Prophets foretold him, infant of wonder;
  angels behold him on his throne:
  worthy our Saviour of all their praises;
  happy for ever are his own.

Mary MacDonald (1789–1872),
tr by Lachlan MacBean (1853–1931)

422   Christ be my way (Congress Hymn)

Anthony Milner

1 Christ be my way, my path to find the Father,
my guide when there's no trusting sound or sight;
Christ fill my mind to cleanse the understanding,
to be my truth, a beacon blazing bright;
Christ all I hope for, strengthening, upholding,
my breath of life, my pride and my delight.

*Truth on my tongue, his way to guide my walking
and I shall live, not I but Christ in me!*

2 No way but Christ, his cross the only signpost
and he our road through death to blessedness;
no safety else, no footing for the pilgrim,
without his leading there's no guide nor guess:
our way to where the Father waits to welcome
to greet us home from night and wilderness.

3 We name him Lord, Truth rising like a tower
above the world his coming shook and stirred:
truth born in time, a child, and shown to shepherds
when God's great glory on the hills was heard;
truth born beyond all time, when first the Father
pronounced his mighty all-creating Word.

4 Christ, Life of man, creation's mind and maker,
hid deep in God before the world began,
God born of God, the everlasting mercy,
the Father's love, who stopped and put on man:
man's life that ebbed beneath the nails, the crowning,
then burst in one white dawn death's narrow span.

Luke Connaughton (1919–79)

423 Christ has arisen. Alleluia!

Haya traditional melody
Harmony by Frances and Robert Kelly

1 Christ has risen, Alleluia!
Rejoice and praise him; Alleluia!
For our Redeemer burst from the tomb,
even from death, dispelling its gloom.

Let us sing praise to him with endless joy.
Death's fearful sting he has come to destroy.
Our sins forgiving, Alleluia!
Jesus is living, Alleluia!

2 For three long days the grave did its worst,
until its strength by God was dispersed.
He who gives life did death undergo,
and in its conquest his might did show.

3 The angel said to them, 'Do not fear,
you look for Jesus who is not here.
See for yourselves, the tomb is all bare:
only the grave-clothes are lying there.'

4 Go spread the news, he's not in the grave.
He has arisen, mankind to save.
Jesus' redeeming labours are done.
Even the battle with sin is won.

Tr from Swahili by Howard S. Olsen

424   Christ is alive, with joy we sing

VULPIUS (888 + Alleluias)   Melchior Vulpius (1560–1615)
For an alternative harmonization, see hymn 486

1 Christ is alive, with joy we sing;
   we celebrate our risen Lord,
   praising the glory of his name.
     Alleluia, alleluia, alleluia.

2 He is the grain of wheat that died;
   sown in distress and reaped in joy,
   yielding a harvest of new life.
     Alleluia, alleluia, alleluia.

3 He is the sun which brings the dawn:
   he is the light of all the world,
   setting us free from death and sin.
     Alleluia, alleluia, alleluia.

4 He is the vine set in the earth,
   sharing our life, becoming man,
   that man might share in God's own life.
     Alleluia, alleluia, alleluia.

5 Christ is alive, with joy we sing;
   we celebrate our risen Lord,
   Praising the glory of his name.
     Alleluia, alleluia, alleluia.

Pamela Stotter

425   Christ is arisen

CHRIST IS ERSTANDEN

Latin melody (11th cent.)
Harmony by Stephen Dean

(Optional repeat)

1 Christ is arisen from the grave's dark prison.
We now rejoice with gladness;
Christ will end all sadness.
Lord, have mercy.

2 All our hopes were ended had Jesus not ascended
from the grave triumphantly.
For this, Lord Christ, we worship Thee.
Lord, have mercy.

3 Alleluia! Alleluia! Alleluia!
We now rejoice with gladness;
Christ will end all sadness.
Lord, have mercy.

Anon (11th Century)
tr by Gustave Polack

* *As a penitential rite for Eastertide, use the verses as tropes:*

in verses 1 & 3, have the people repeat the final Lord, have mercy.
in verse 2, use instead Christ, have mercy repeated by all.

426 Christ is coming to set the captives free

N. & K. Donnelly

1 Christ is coming to set the captives free,
He is coming to rescue you and me.

Christ is coming from above
bringing joy and bringing love.
He is coming for you and me.

2 Christ has come to a stable cold and bare;
He is coming to a world where no one cares.

3 Christ is coming, bringing light where darkness
reigned;
He is coming where we gather in his name.

4 Christ is coming to this altar in our Mass;
He is coming to a new home in our hearts.

5 Christ is coming, the Father's only Son;
He is coming – his spirit makes us one.

N. & K. Donnelly

427 Christ is made the sure foundation

WESTMINSTER ABBEY
(87 87 87)

Adapted from an anthem by Henry Purcell (1659–1695)
by Ernest Hawkins (1802–68)

1. Christ is made the sure foun- da- tion, Christ the head and corn- er stone, cho- sen of the Lord, and pre- cious, bind- ing all the Church in one, ho- ly Si- on's help for ev- er, and her con- fid- ence a- lone.

2 All that dedicated city,
dearly loved of God on high,
in exultant jubilation
pours perpetual melody,
God the One in Three adoring
in glad hymns eternally.

3 To this temple where we call you
come, O Lord of Host, today;
with your wonted loving kindness
hear your people as they pray,
and your fullest benediction
shed within its walls alway.

4 Here vouchsafe to all your servants
what they ask of you to gain,
what they gain of you forever
with the blessed to retain,
and hereafter in your glory
evermore with you to reign.

5 Praise and honour to the Father,
praise and honour to the Son,
praise and honour to the Spirit,
ever Three and ever One,
consubstantial, co-eternal,
while unending ages run.

*Latin 7th or 8th Century,
tr J.M. Neale (1818–66 alt)*

617

428　Christ is the World's Light

CHRISTE SANCTORUM (11 11 11 5)　　　　　　　From the *Paris Antiphoner* (1681)

1 Christ is the world's light,
　he and no other;
　born in our darkness,
　he became our brother.
　If we have seen him,
　we have seen the Father:
　glory to God on high.

2 Christ is the world's peace,
　he and no other;
　no man can serve him
　and despise his brother.
　Who else unites us,
　one in God the Father?
　glory to God on high.

3 Christ is the world's life,
　he and no other;
　sold once for silver,
　murdered here, our brother
　he who redeems us,
　reigns with God the Father:
　glory to God on high.

4 Give God the glory,
　God and no other;
　give God the glory,
　Spirit, Son and Father;
　give God the glory,
　God in man, my brother:
　glory to God in high.

F. Pratt Green

618

429 Christ is the world's redeemer

MOVILLE (76 76D)

Irish Traditional

1 Christ is the world's redeemer,
the lover of the pure,
the fount of heavenly wisdom,
our trust and hope secure,
the armour of his soldiers,
the lord of earth and sky,
our health while we are living,
our life when we shall die.

2 Christ has our host surrounded
with clouds of martyrs bright
who wave their psalm in triumph
and fire us for the fight.
For Christ the cross ascended
to save a world undone
and suffering for the sinful
and full redemption won.

3 Down in the realm of darkness
he lay a captive bound,
but at the hour appointed
he rose, a victor crowned,
and now, to heaven ascended,
he sits upon the throne
in glorious dominion,
his Father's and his own.

St Columba (521–97)
tr by Duncan McGregor

619

430 Christ our Lord has come to save his people

Jean-Paul Lecot

REFRAIN
People

Christ our Lord has come to save his peo- ple! Al- le- lu-

ia! Al- le- lu- ia! Al- le- lu- ia!

VERSES

1. Baptised in Christ our Lord, re-born to new life in our Sa-viour and
2. O come then, bless the Lord, the Fa - ther of all, who is love with-out

Lord, al - le - lu - ia. For we are the peo - ple whom God made his
end, al - le - lu - ia. Be-fore he cre - a - ted the world with great

own through the blood of his own Son, our Lord Je - sus Christ.
pow'r we were cho - sen then in Christ, God made us his own.

3 Since time itself began
   God loved us and planned to adopt us in Christ, alleluia!
   He chose us to live in his glorious name,
   as his children and his friends, a people redeemed.

4 Be joyful in the Lord,
   rejoice and give thanks to the Father of all, alleluia!
   For Christ is alive and we live now in him;
   we are filled now with his life. Rejoice, praise his name!

5 With Christ we are made heirs
   and called to belong to the fam'ly of God, alleluia!
   Christ freed us from sin by his death on the cross,
   and has raised us up to life, a life without end.

6 Give glory to our God, the Father of all;
   to his Son, Jesus Christ, alleluia!
   And praise to the Spirit, the gift of his love.
   Let us sing out to the Lord for ever. Amen.

Paul Decha,
tr by Sr Mary Lucia and Robert B. Kelly

621

431 Christ our Pasch

Lucien Deiss

ANTIPHON

Christ our Pasch has been slain, al-le – lu – ia! Sing with joy.

F   Dm   C   F   C   G   Dm   Bb

Al – le – lu – ia, al – le – lu – ia, al – le – lu – ia!   Fine

F   Am   Em   Dm   C   G   Dm   Am   Dm   D

VERSES

1. Pasch of the New Law, the Spi – rit's ho – ly feast; O
2. Pasch of the New Law, O joy of all man – kind; the
3. Pasch of the New Law, the ban – quet hall is full of
4. Pasch of the New Law, be – hold your bap – tized saints in
5. Pasch of the New Law, our soul's im – mor – tal flame shines
6. Pasch of the New Law, O Christ who lives a – gain: the
7. Pasch of the New Law, we pray to you, O Lord: stretch
8. Pasch of the New Law, O Christ re – ceive our songs; to

Bb   F   C   F   Dm   C   G

1. Pasch of Christ the Lord, who for us has come to earth!
2. doors of life are wide, giv – ing life to us once more.
3. guests the Lord has called, that all men may share his feast.
4. robes of pur – est white for the mar – riage of the Lamb.
5. forth in splen – dor bright, ne – ver – more to cease its light.
6. pow'r of death you crushed, you have giv – en us your life.
7. forth your bless – ed hands on the peo – ple you have saved.
8. you be glo – ry, Lord, with all joy and praise. A – men!

C   Am   F   Em   Dm   Bb   Am

© 1965, 1966, 1973 World Library Publications Inc. Reprinted with permission.

Lucien Deiss

622

432 City of God, how broad and far

RICHMOND (86 86)

Adapted from T. Haweis (1734–1820)
by S. Webbe (the younger) (c. 1770–1843)

1 City of God, how broad and far
outspread thy walls sublime!
The true thy chartered freeman are,
of every age and clime.

2 One holy Church, one army strong,
one steadfast, high intent;
one working band, one harvest song
one King Omnipotent.

3 How purely hath thy speech come down
from man's primeval youth!
How grandly hath thine empire grown,
of freedom, love and truth!

4 How gleam thy watch-fires through the night
with never-fainting ray!
How rise thy towers, serene and bright,
to meet the dawning day!

5 In vain the surge's angry shock,
in vain the drifting sands:
unharmed upon the eternal Rock
the eternal City stands.

Samuel Johnson (1822–82)

433 Come, God's people, sing for joy

AVE VIRGO VIRGINUM (76 76D)

Melody from
Horn's *Gesangbuch* (1544)

1 Come, God's people, sing for joy,
shout your songs of gladness;
for the hope of Easter day
overcomes our sadness.
Come with all his people here,
who with true affection,
join again to celebrate
Jesus' resurrection.

2 Years before, as Moses led
Israel's sons and daughters
from their bonds to Exodus
through the Red Sea waters:
so the living Lord of life
speaks through our baptism
of the new life that we share
with him who is risen.

3 That first Easter he arose,
his disciples greeting;
Christians now throughout the world,
still their Lord are meeting.
Christ, who dies for all mankind,
in his death brings healing;
and his rising from the grave,
God's power is revealing.

St John Damascene (d.754),
freely paraphrased by Keith D. Pearson

434 Come, holy Lord, our faith renew

John Glynn
Harmony by John Rombaut

1 Come, holy Lord, our faith renew,
   our little praise enough for you.

   We ask your mercy, Lord,
   who bear your sacred name;
   your healing touch
   the glorious blessing we can claim.

2 O Jesus, come, our hope on earth,
   from heaven you came to share our birth.

3 Come, Spirit blest, our love revive;
   our failing prayer is made alive.

John Glynn

435   Come, let us sing out our joy (Psalm 95)

Stephen Dean

Chorus

Come let us sing out our joy to the Lord! Hail the rock of sal-vation, come in-to his presence to give him thanks, sing-ing psalms of tri-umph.

Verses (cantor or choir)

1. In his hands are the depths of the earth, the moun-tain peaks be-
2. Bow down be-fore him in prayer, kneel be-fore the
3. Lis-ten to the voice of the Lord, do not grow stubborn nor
4. Praise the Fa-ther who made all things, praise the Son who

man.

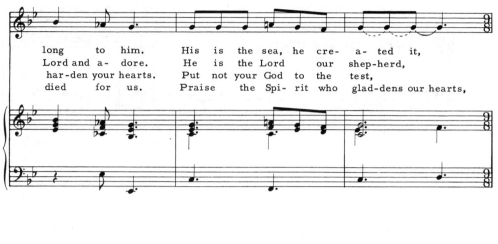

long to him. / Lord and a- dore. / har-den your hearts. / died for us.

His is the sea, he cre- a- ted it, / He is the Lord our shep-herd, / Put not your God to the test, / Praise the Spi- rit who glad-dens our hearts,

His is the dry land, formed by his hands. / We his peo-ple, the flock that he feeds. / Well you know how he cares for us. / Praise un- cea-sing fill hea- ven and earth.

CHORUS

Stephen Dean, based on Psalm 94(95)

436 Come, Lord Jesus

Garfield Rochard
Harmony by James O'Donnell

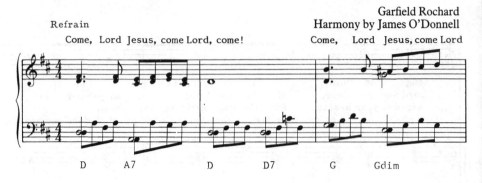

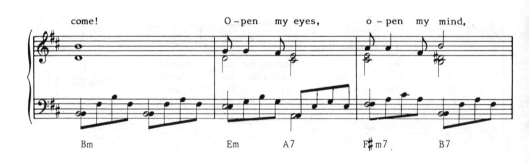

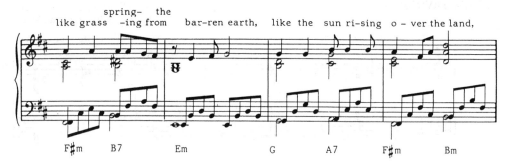

spring– the
like grass –ing from bar–ren earth, like the sun ri–sing o – ver the land,

F♯m   B7   Em   G   A7   F♯m   Bm

her–alds new life and a new re – birth

A   E7   A   A7

2 So he comes bringing righteousness,
   bringing justice to all the land;
   so he comes as a man among men,
   Saviour and Lord of all mankind.

3 Wonder Counsellor and Prince of Peace,
   a man of such integrity!
   Come Lord Jesus, we plead to you,
   come and give us liberty.

Psalm 71(72) and Isaiah 9:6,
adapted by Garfield Rochard

437 Come, O divine Messiah

VENEZ, DIVIN MESSIE

16th Century French Carol
Harmony by Stephen Dean

O di- vine Mes- si- ah! The world in si-lence waits the day when

hope shall sing its tri- umph, and sad-ness flee a- way.

2 O Thou, whom nations sighed for,
   whom priests and prophets long foretold,
   wilt break the captive fetters,
   redeem the long-lost fold.

3 Shalt come in peace and meekness,
   and lowly will thy cradle be:
   all clothed in human weakness
   shall we thy Godhead see.

French 18th Century,
tr Sr Mary of St Phillip

438 Come, O Lord, to my heart today

Douglas Rowe
Harmony by John Rombaut

Come, O Lord, to my heart today
and stay with me all the day.
Come, O Lord, to my heart today
and stay with me all the day.

1 Your flesh is food and your blood is drink,
and these you give to me your life.

2 This is the bread come down from heaven
which, if a man eats, he'll live for ever.

3 He who takes my flesh and blood
lives in me and I in him.

4 When you give your self to us,
you bind us to yourself and each other.

Based on John 50,55,56,
by Douglas Rowe

439 Come, thou long-expected Jesus

FIRST TUNE

CROSS OF JESUS (87 87)

John Stainer (1840–1901)

1 Come, thou long-expected Jesus,
  born to set thy people free,
  from our fears and sins release us,
  let us find our rest in thee.

2 Israel's strength and consolation,
  hope of all the earth thou art;
  dear desire of every nation,
  joy of every longing heart.

3 Born thy people to deliver,
  born a child and yet a king,
  born to reign in us for ever,
  now thy gracious kingdom bring.

4 By thine own eternal Spirit
  rule in all our hearts alone;
  by thine all-sufficient merit
  raise us to thy glorious throne.

Charles Wesley (1707–88)

SECOND TUNE

STUTTGART

C.F.Witt (1660–1716)

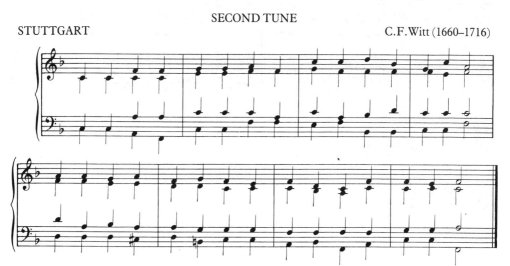

440 Day and night the heavens are telling

WACHET AUF

Melody by P.Nicolai (1556–1608)
adapted and harmonized by J.S.Bach (1685–1750)

1 Day and night the heav'ns are telling
   the glory which with us is dwelling,
   the works of God to us made known.
   Dawn and dusk are still with wonder.
   The wind cries out, the waters thunder,
   displaying his almighty power.
   Our God is great indeed.
   He knows our constant need, our creator.
   So with creation we proclaim
   his goodness as we praise his name.

2 Lord, we stand in awe before you,
   your people coming to adore you,
   so cleanse our hearts, renew our minds.
   See us now in shadows dwelling,
   and come like sun, the clouds dispelling,
   enlighten, heal us, Lord of love.
   Your Spirit in us prays.
   He teaches us your ways, as we listen.
   Touch once again with living flame
   your people gathered in your name.

Pamela Stotter

441 Day by day

D. Austin

St Richard of Chichester,
arr by D. Austin

442 Dear love of my heart

DUAN CHROI IOSA (11 11 11 11)

Irish traditional melody

1 Dear love of my heart, O heart of Christ, my Lord,
what treasure you leave within my heart, O Guest!
You come to my heart O heart on fire with love,
and leave me your heart: O how my heart is blest!

2 My heart cannot tell, O King of angel hosts,
how great was that pain you bore upon the cross:
so small is my heart, so deep your wounds of love,
so precious the crown of those you save from loss!

3 Your death has restored your likeness in my heart,
your cross in my shield, your loving heart my gain!
How sad is my heart when I recall my sins!
How could I have loved what gave your heart such pain?

4 O King of all bliss, all glory set aside,
what heart could have known the pain within your breast?
The wound in your side laid bare your burning love,
and opened for all the heart where all find rest!

Based on the Irish of Tadhg Gaelach O Suilleabhain
by James Quinn, SJ

637

443   Divided our pathways

Christopher Coelho OFM

Unison
Refrain

Di – vi– ded our path–ways, and hea–vy our guilt; bur–den'd, un–

see–ing, we grope for the one way. Far from our home, O Fa–ther, we

call out, 'Heal us, for –give us: bring us to– ge–ther in Je–sus your Son!'

Fine

Verse
Voice

1. Holy Father, keep those you have   gi–ven me true to   your Name,
2. Father, may they be one in us as you are in me   and I   am in   you,
3. I have given them the   glo–ry that you gave to   me,
4. With me in them and you in me may they be so com–plete–ly u – nited,

1. so   that they   may   all   be one   as we   are   one.
2. so   that the world   may come to be-lieve it   was you who sent   me.
3. that   they   may   all   be one   as we   are   one.

4. that   the   world may know that it was   you   who   sent   me,

and that you love them as   much as you   love   me.

From John 17:11–21–23
by Christopher Coelho

444 Do not be afraid

Gerald Markland

Chorus
Do not be a- fraid, for I have re- deemed you.
I have called you by your name; you are
mine. 1. When you walk through the wa-ters I'll be
with you. You will nev- er sink be- neath the waves.

2 When the fire is burning all around you,
   you will never be consumed by the flames.

3 When the fear of loneliness is looming,
   then remember I am at your side.

4 When you dwell in the exile of the stranger,
   remember you are precious in my eyes.

5 You are mine, O my child, I am your Father,
   and I love you with a perfect love.

Gerald Markland,
based on Isaiah 43:1–4

445 Do you really love me?

Carey Landry

Verses 1 and 2

'Do you real-ly love me?' Je-sus said to Pe-ter. 'Do you real-ly love me?' Je-sus said a - gain. 'Lord you know I love you!' Pe-ter said with joy. 'Then feed my lambs,' said he 'Pe-ter, feed my lambs.'

2 'Do you really love me?' Jesus said to Peter.
'Do you really love me?' Jesus said again.
'Lord, you know I love you!' Peter said with joy.
'Then feed my sheep,' he said, 'Peter, feed my sheep.'

Verse 3

Carey Landry

446 Each morning with its new born light

ALL MORGEN IST GANZ FRISCH(88 88)   Johann Walther (1496–1570)
Alternative tunes: see metrical index

1 Each morning with its new born light
  proclaims the Lord of life is great!
  His faithfulness will have no end;
  to him our songs of praise ascend.

2 The gift of light that fills the sky
  helps us to see and choose our way;
  then let us order our affairs
  in praise of him who for us cares.

3 Lord, let our eyes, the body's light,
  be drawn to what is good and right
  and to yourself, the source of life,
  our hope in fear, our peace in strife.

4 You, Lord of all creation, are
  as brilliant as the morning star;
  light in our hearts your holy flame
  and make us fit to bear your name.

5 Dispel the darkness from our days
  and free us from all bitterness,
  from haughty mind and blinded sight,
  and lead us forward day and night.

6 To walk as in the light of day,
  be steadfast always, come what may,
  we turn in faith to you, our Friend,
  and pray: sustain us to the end.

Johannes Zwick (1496–1542)
tr by Fred Kaan

447   Faith in God can move the mountains

Aniceto Nazareth

Refrain *Calmly*

Faith in God can move the moun-tains; trust in him can calm the sea.

Dmaj7   D7/9   Em7   A7/9♭   Dmaj7   Bm   E7   Gm6 A7

He's   my for-tress, he's   my strong-hold; he's the rock who res-cues me.

Dmaj7   D7/9   Em7   A7   D   Am7 B7   Gm6 A7   D

Verse

Lord, you are my re - fuge;   ne - ver let me be a - shamed.

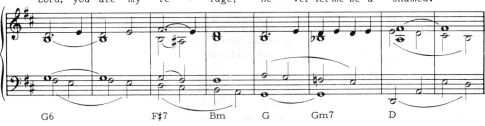

G6   F♯7   Bm   G   Gm7   D

                                      and

In your jus - tice res - cue me;   turn to me hear my prayer.

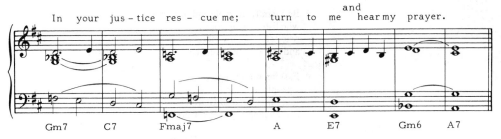

Gm7   C7   Fmaj7   A   E7   Gm6   A7

2 You are my salvation;
  from oppression set me free.
  Ever since my childhood
  you have been my only hope.

3 Bitter troubles burden me,
  but you fill me with new life.
  From the grave you raise me up,
  so my tongue will sing your praise.

Words paraphrased from Scripture
by Aniceto Nazareth

448   Fashion me a people

Carol McCollin
Harmony by Eric Welch

The metre of this hymn is irregular. The slurs in the melody apply to verse 1 only.

1 Fashion me a people,
  a people set apart;
  that I may be your God,
  and you will give me your heart.

2 Come together in community,
  a sign of my love here on earth,
  to share the life of Nazareth,
  and incarnate the myst'ry of my birth.

3 Be a fam'ly, humble and forgiving,
  who listen to my voice,
  who call upon my mercy,
  and at my coming rejoice.

4 Fashion me a people,
  a people set apart;
  that I may be your God,
  and I will give you my heart.

Carol Gordon

449 Father, hear the prayer we offer

SUSSEX (87 87)

English traditional melody,
Coll. and arr. by R. Vaughan Williams (1872–1958)

1. Fa-ther, hear the prayer we off-er: not for ease that prayer shall be,

but for strength that we may ev- er live our lives cour- a-geous-ly.

2 Not for ever in green pastures
do we ask our way to be;
but the steep and rugged pathway
may we tread rejoicingly.

3 Not for ever by still waters
would we idly rest and stay;
but would smite the living fountains
from the rocks along the way.

4 Be our strength in hours of weakness,
in our wanderings be our guide;
through endeavour, failure, danger,
Father, be there at our side.

Love Maria Willis (1824–1908)
and others

450   Father, I place into your hands

FIRST TUNE

Two sample accompaniments (repeat over and over again, or
improvise ad lib.) when verses are sung as a round:-

Ernest Sands

Accompaniment when verses are sung in unison:-

1. Fa- ther, I   place in-to your   hands the things that   I   can't do;

E   A   B7   E

Fa- ther   I   place in- to your   hands the times that   I've been through;

E   A   B7   E

Fa- ther I place in- to your hands the way that I should go,

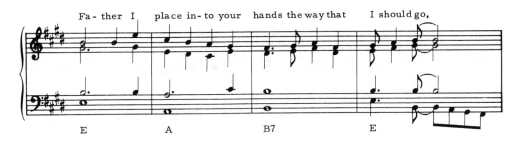

E A B7 E

For I know I al-ways can trust you.

E A B7 E

2 Father, I place into your hands
   my friends and family.
   Father, I place into your hands
   the things that trouble me.
   Father, I place into your hands
   the person I would be,
   for I know I always can trust you.

3 Father, we love to see your face,
   we love to hear your voice.
   Father, we love to sing your praise
   and in your name rejoice.
   Father, we love to walk with you
   and in your presence rest,
   for we know we always can trust you.

4 Father, I want to be with you
   and do the things you do.
   Father, I want to speak the words
   that you are speaking too.
   Father, I want to love the ones
   that you will draw to you,
   for I know that I am one with you.

J. Hewer

SECOND TUNE

J.Hewer

1. Fa-ther, I place in — to your hands the things I can—not do,

F(E)   C(B7)

Fa-ther, I place in — to your hands the times that I've been through.

F(E)

Fa-ther, I place in — to your hands the way that I should go, for I

F7(E7)   Bb6(A6)   Bbm(Am)

know I al - ways can trust you. ------------

F(E)   C(B7)   F(C)

451 Father in heaven

HALAD (55 55 55 54)

Traditional Filipino melody
Arr. by Elena G. Maquiso

1 Father in heaven,
   grant to your children
   mercy and blessing,
   songs never ceasing,
   love to unite us,
   grace to redeem us,
   Father in heaven,
   Father our God.

2 Jesus, Redeemer,
   may we remember
   your gracious Passion,
   your resurrection.
   Worship we bring you,
   praise we shall sing you
   Jesus, Redeemer,
   Jesus our God.

3 Spirit descending
   whose is the blessing –
   strength for the weary,
   help for the needy,
   sealed in our worship –
   Spirit unending,
   Spirit adored.

D.T.Niles

452 Father, in my life I see

TRINITY SONG

Frank Anderson MSC

Effective when men's voices sing one line, and women's the other.

Fa-ther, in my life I see, you are God, who walks with me. You hold my life in your hands: close be-side you I will stand.

GROUP 2: Fa-ther, in my life I see, you are God, who walks with me. You hold my life in your hands: close be-

I give all my life to you:

side you I will stand. I give all my life to

Em   Am

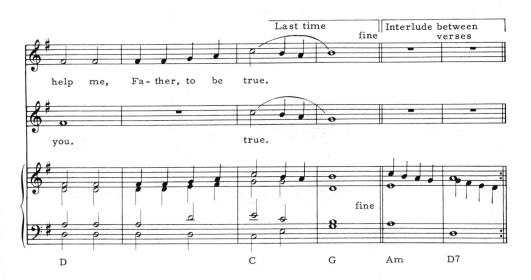

Last time
fine

Interlude between
verses

help me, Fa-ther, to be true.

you. true.

fine

D   C   G   Am   D7

2 Jesus, in my life I see . . .

3 Spirit, in my life I see . . .

Frank Anderson, MSC

453　Father, Lord of all creation

ABBOTS LEIGH (87 87D)

Cyril Taylor

1. Fa- ther, Lord of all cre- a- tion, ground of

be- ing, life and love; height and depth be-

yond de- scription, on- ly life in you can

prove: you are mor- tal life's de- pen- dence: thought, speech,

sight   are   ours   by   grace;   yours   is   ev- ery   hour's   ex-

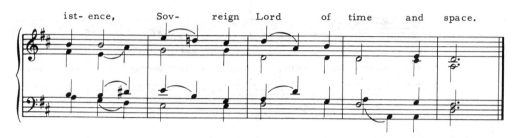

ist- ence,   Sov- reign   Lord   of   time   and   space.

2 Jesus Christ, the man for others,
we, your people, make our prayer:
give us grace to love as brothers
all whose burdens we can share.
Where your name binds us together
you, Lord, Christ, will surely be;
where no selfishness can sever
there your love may all men see.

3 Holy Spirit, rushing, burning
wind and flame of Pentecost,
fire our hearts afresh with yearning
to regain what we have lost.
May your love unite our action,
nevermore to speak alone:
God, in us abolish faction,
God, through us your love make known.

Stewart Cross

472   Glorious things of you are spoken

Tune as no. 453

1 Glorious things of you are spoken,
Sion, city of our God:
he whose word cannot be broken
formed you for his own abode.
On the Rock of Ages founded,
what can shake your sure repose?
With salvation's walls surrounded,
you may smile at all your foes.

2 See, the streams of living waters,
springing from eternal love,
well supply your sons and daughters
and all fear of want remove:
who can faint while such a river
ever flows their thirst to assuage –
grace, which like the Lord the giver
never fails from age to age?

3 Blest inhabitants of Sion,
washed in their Redeemer's blood;
Jesus, whom their souls rely on,
makes them Kings and priests to God.
'Tis his love his people raises
over self to reign as kings,
and as priests, his solemn praises
each for a thank-offering brings.

4 Saviour, since of Sion's city
I, through grace, a member am,
let the world deride or pity,
I will glory in your name:
fading is the worldling's pleasure,
all his boasted pomp and show;
solid joys and lasting treasure
none but Sion's children know.

John Newton (1725–1807)

454 Father of heaven, whose love profound

SONG 5 (88 88)

Melody and bass
by Orlando Gibbons (1583–1625)

1. Fa-ther of heav'n, whose love pro-found a ran-som for our souls hath found, be-fore thy throne we sin-ners bend, to us thy pard'-ning love ex-tend.

2 Almighty Son, incarnate Word,
   our prophet, priest, Redeemer, Lord,
   before thy throne we sinners bend,
   to us thy saving grace extend.

3 Eternal Spirit, by whose breath
   the soul is raised from sin and death,
   before thy throne we sinners bend,
   to us thy quickening power extend.

4 Thrice Holy Father, Spirit, Son;
   mysterious Godhead, Three in One,
   before thy throne we sinners bend,
   grace, pardon, life to us extend.

E. Cooper (1770–1833)

656

455   Father we praise you, now the night is over

CHRISTE SANCTORUM (11 11 11 5)   *Paris Antiphoner* (1681)

1 Father, we praise you now the night is over;
  active and watchful, stand we all before you;
  singing, we offer pray'r and meditation:
  thus we adore you.

2 Monarch of all things, fit us for your kingdom;
  banish our weakness, health and wholeness sending;
  bring us to heaven, where your saints united
  joy without ending.

3 All holy Father, Son and equal Spirit,
  Trinity blessed, send us your salvation;
  yours is the glory gleaming and resounding
  through all creation.

St Gregory the Great (540–604)
tr by Percy Dearmer (1867–1936),
slightly altered

456   Fear not, for I have redeemed you

Jodi Page

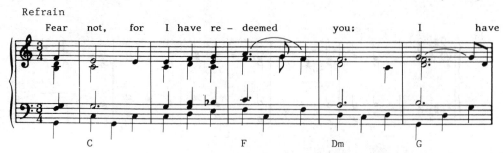

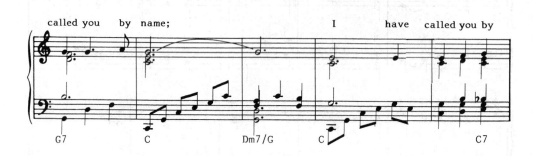

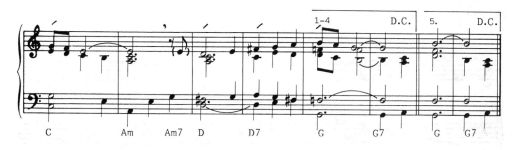

1 When you pass through the waters
  I will be with you;
  and through rivers,
  they will not overwhelm you.
  When you walk through the fire
  you will not be burned,
  the flames shall not consume you.

2 Because you are precious,
  and I love you;
  you whom I formed
  for my glory;
  you whom I called
  by my name,
  I will gather together.

3 You are my witness;
  I have chosen you
  that you may know
  and believe me.
  You are my servants
  for the world to see
  I am the Lord, I'm among you.

4 It's time now to lay aside
  the former things;
  a new day has dawned,
  do you see it.
  I'm making a way
  in the wilderness
  and rivers to flow in the desert.

5 The rivers that flow
  in the desert
  give drink
  to my chosen people;
  to quench their thirst
  and to strengthen them,
  that they might show forth my praise.

Based on Isaiah 43:4,10,18–20,
by Jodi Page

457　Fear not, rejoice and be glad

Priscilla Wright Porter

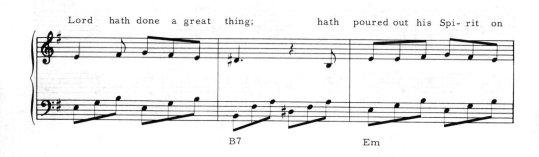

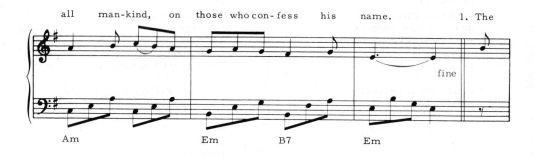

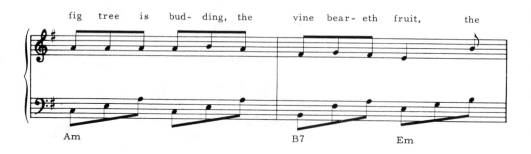

wheat-fields are gol-den with grain.   Thrust in the sick-le, the

Am   E   Am

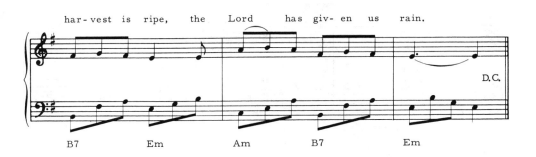

har-vest is ripe, the Lord has giv-en us rain.

B7   Em   Am   B7   Em

D.C.

2 Ye shall eat in plenty and be satisfied,
  the mountains will drip with sweet wine.
  My children shall drink of the fountain of life,
  my children will know they are mine,

3 My people shall know that I am the Lord,
  their shame I have taken away.
  My Spirit will lead them together again,
  my Spirit will show them the way.

4 My children shall dwell in a body of love,
  a light to the world they will be.
  Life shall come forth from the Father above,
  my body will set mankind free.

Priscilla Wright

458 Feed my lambs

Charles A. Buffham
Harmony by F. and R. Kelly

1 'Feed my lambs, my son, feed my sheep;
  if you love me, do not sleep.
  In the fields, my son, work and weep;
  feed my lambs, my son, feed my sheep.'

2 To the servant girl first he lied:
  'You were with him!' this she cried.
  But the Master he denied;
  on the following day, Jesus died.

3 Someone questioned him quietly,
  'Aren't you Peter of Galilee?
  I can tell you by your speech, you see.'
  Peter swore and said, 'It's not me!'

4 Peter heard the cock when it crew;
  as he left, he wept – and he knew!
  Ev'ry one of us is guilty too;
  yet Christ died for us, me and you.

5 Feed my lambs, my son, feed my sheep;
  if you love me, do not sleep.
  In the fields, my son, work and weep;
  feed my lambs, my son, feed my sheep.

Charles A. Buffham (altered)

459 Firm is our faith in our true God

LUMEN DE LUMINE (88 88)   Moira G. Kearney

Alternative tune: GROSSER GOTT (212)

1 Firm is our faith in one true God,
   loving Father and King supreme,
   mighty creator, Lord of all,
   visible world and world unseen.

2 And we believe in God's own Son,
   one with him from eternal dawn,
   who by the Spirit was conceived,
   and of his Virgin Mother born.

3 Man he was made and man he lived,
   man he suffered in cruel strife
   when on the Cross he fought with death,
   conquered and rose to deathless life.

4 This is our faith in the Spirit too:
   Lord and giver of life is he,
   one with the Father and the Son,
   spirit of love and unity.

5 Faith we profess in one true Church,
   sin forgiven and grace restored,
   hope for the vict'ry over death,
   life without end in Christ the Lord.

Denis E. Hurley

460 Follow me

Sister Madeleine, F.C.J.

Chorus

Fol-low me, fol-low me, leave your home and fa-mi-

ly, leave your fish-ing nets and boats up-on the shore.

Leave the seed that you have sown, leave the crops that you've

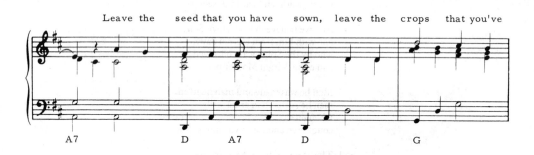

grown, leave the peo-ple you have known and fol-low me.

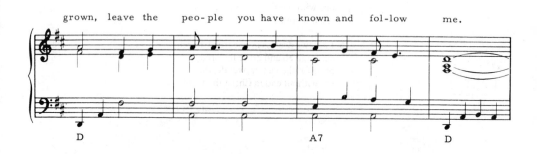

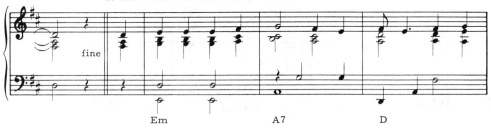

1. The fox- es have their holes and the swal-lows have their

nests, but the Son of man has no place to lay down.

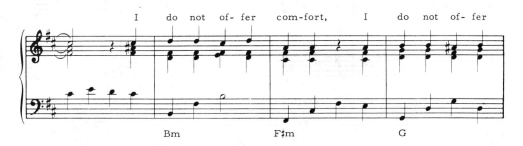

I do not of- fer com-fort, I do not of- fer

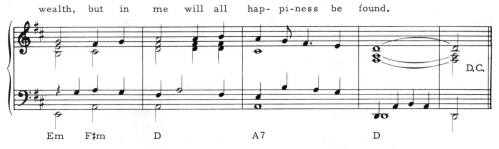

wealth, but in me will all hap- pi-ness be found.

2 If you would follow me,
  you must leave old ways behind.
  You must take my cross and follow on my path.
  You may be far from loved ones,
  you may be far from home
  but my Father will welcome you at last.

3 Although I go away
  you will never be alone,
  for the Spirit will be there to comfort you.
  Though all of you may scatter,
  each follow his own path,
  still the Spirit of love will lead you home.

Michael Cockett

461   For the fruits of his creation

EAST ACKLAM   Francis Jackson

1. For the fruits of his cre-a-tion, thanks be to God;

for his gifts to ev-'ry na-tion, thanks be to God;

for the ploughing, sow-ing, reaping, si-lent growth while men are sleeping,

fu-ture needs in earth's safe keep-ing, thanks be to God.

Alternative tune: AR HYD Y NOS (59)

2 In the just reward of labour,
  God's will is done;
in the help we give our neighbour,
  God's will is done;
in our world-wide task of caring
for the hungry and despairing
in the harvests men are sharing,
  God's will is done.

3 For the harvests of his Spirit,
  thanks be to God;
for the good all men inherit,
  thanks be to God;
for the wonders that astound us,
for the truths that still confound us,
most of all, that love has found us,
  thanks be to God.

F. Pratt Green

462   For the healing of the nations

PICARDY (87 87 87)

French traditional carol

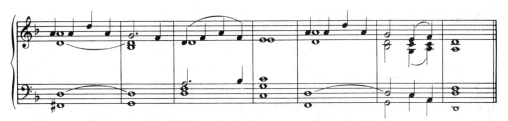

Alternative tune: Mannheim (165)

1 For the healing of the nations,
  Lord, we pray with one accord,
for a just and equal sharing
  of the things that earth affords.
To a life of love in action
  help us rise and pledge our word.

2 Lead us, father, into freedom,
  from despair your world release,
that, redeemed from war and hatred,
  men may come and go in peace.
Show us how through care and goodness
  fear will die and hope increase.

3 All that kills abundant living,
  let it from the earth be banned;
pride of status, race or schooling,
  dogmas keeping man from man.
In our common quest for justice
  may we hallow life's brief span.

4 You, creator-God, have written
  your great name on all mankind;
for our growing in your likeness
  bring the life of Christ to mind;
that by our response and service
  earth its destiny may find.

Fred Kaan

463   For to those who love God

Enrico Garzilli

2 In the face of all this
  what is there left to say?
  For if God is with us,
  who can be against us?

3 What can separate us
  from the love of Christ?
  Neither trouble, nor pain,
  nor persecution.

4 What can separate us
  from the love of Christ?
  Not the past, the present,
  nor the future.

Enrico Garzilli
Based on Romans 8:29,31–35

464 For unto us a child is born

Source unknown
Arranged by Roger Humphrey

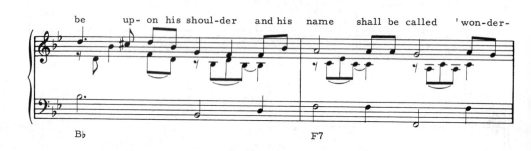

ev- er- last- ing Fath- er', and 'the

Eb   Bb

Prince of peace' is he.

F7   Bb

Based on Isaiah 9:6

465   Freely I give to you

J.Garrity
Arranged by Roger Humphrey

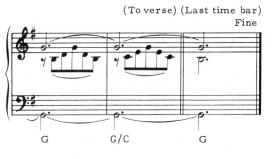

G   G/C   G

Verses

1. Call him E- man- uel, for your God is

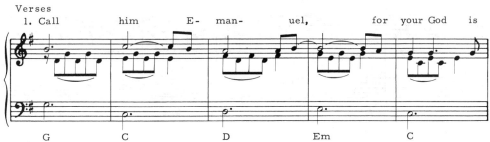

G   C   D   Em   C

with you this day. He'll be by your side

G   D   Em   C

shar-ing your joy and your pain.

D.C.

G   A   D   Dsus(9/4)   D   D(sus4)

2. Call him Je- sus, for Yah- weh

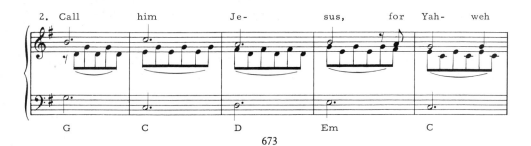

G   C   D   Em   C

673

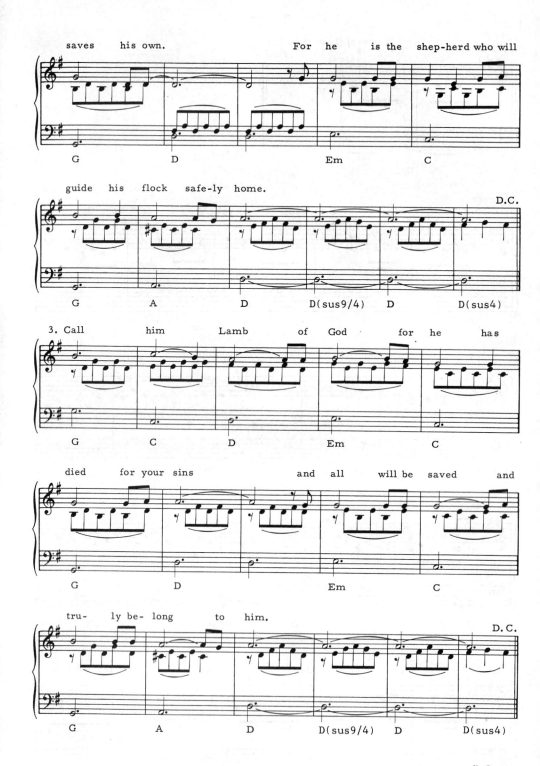

J. Garrity

466　From the depths of sin and sadness

Russian traditional melody
Arranged by Willard F. Jabusch

1 From the depths of sin and sadness
　I have called unto the Lord;
　be not deaf to my poor pleading,
　in your mercy, hear my voice.
　Be not deaf to my poor pleading,
　in your mercy, hear my voice.

2 If you, Lord, record our sinning
　who could then before you stand?
　But with you there is forgiveness;
　you shall ever be revered.
　But with you there is forgiveness;
　you shall ever be revered.

3 For the Lord my heart is waiting,
　for his word I hope and wait.
　More than watchmen wait for sunrise
　I am waiting for the Lord.
　More than watchmen wait for sunrise
　I am waiting for the Lord.

4 Hope, O people, in your Saviour,
　he will save you from your sin.
　Jesus from his cross is praying,
　　'Father, forgive them,
　they know not what they do.'
　Jesus from his cross is praying,
　　'Father, forgive them,
　they know not what they do.

Willard F. Jabusch
Based on Psalm 129(130)

467 Gather Christians

Garfield Rochard
Harmony by Eric Welch

Gather Christian, let's now celebrate;
gather Christians, the Lord we now await;
gather Christians, behold he comes;
rejoice and sing, for the Lord is King!

1 To God the Father, let's give him praise;
   to God the Father, our voice we raise;
   to God the Father, who reigns above;
   praise the Lord for his mercy and his love.

2 As we stand here before our God,
   with Christ Jesus, our saving Lord,
   we'll hear his word now, and break the bread,
   as we proclaim: he's risen from the dead!

3 Let us all now, as one community,
   praise and honour the Trinity.
   Let us all now with one accord
   sing out our praise to the living Lord!

Garfield Rochard

676

468   Gathered here from many churches

Doreen Potter

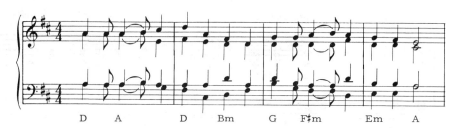

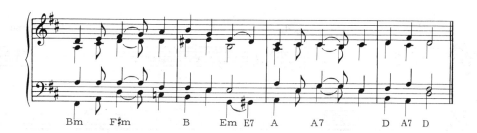

1 Gathered here from many churches,*
one in worship and intent,
let us for the days that face us
all our hopes to God present,
that our life and work may be
symbols of our unity.

2 May the spring of all our actions
be, O Lord, your love for man;
may your word be seen and spoken
and your will be clearly done.
Help us, who your image bear,
for the good of each to care.

   * or *Gathered here from many nations,*

3 Give us grace to match our calling,
faith to overcome the past;
show us how to meet the future,
planning boldly, acting fast.
Let the servant-mind of Christ
in our life be manifest.

4 Now ourselves anew committing
to each other and to you,
Lord, we ask that you will train us
for the truth we have to do;
that the world may soon become
your great city of shalom.

Fred Kaan

469　Gifts of bread and wine

Christine McCann

Gifts of bread and wine, gifts we've of-fered,

D　Em　A　G　D

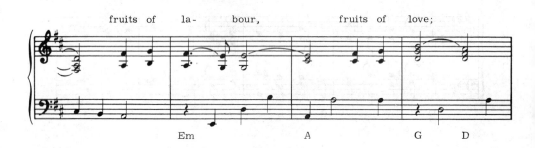

fruits of la-bour, fruits of love;

Em　A　G　D

ta-ken, of-fered, sanc-ti-fied, blessed and

Bm　G

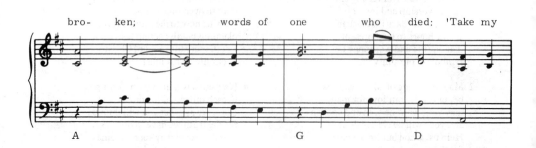

bro-ken; words of one who died: 'Take my

A　G　D

678

bo- dy; take my sav- ing blood.' Gifts of

bread and wine: Christ our Lord.

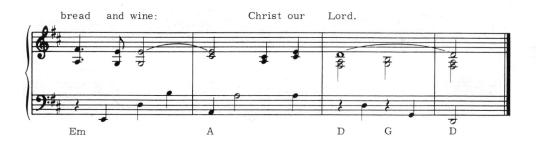

2 Christ our Saviour, living presence here,
   as he promised while on earth:
   'I am with you for all time,
   I am with you in this bread and wine.
   Take my body, take my saving blood.'
   Gifts of bread and wine: Christ our Lord.

3 Through the Father, with the Spirit,
   one in union with the Son,
   for God's people, joined in prayer
   faith is strengthened by the food we share.
   'Take my body, take my saving blood.'
   Gifts of bread and wine: Christ our Lord.

Christine McCann

470 Give praise to the Lord (Psalm 113)

Lucien Deiss

Note: Guitar chords should not be played with the organ accompaniment.

1. Give praise to the Lord, all you men, al-le-lu – ia! O praise the

name of the Lord, al-le – lu – ia! Blessed be the name of the Lord, al-le-lu –

ia, al – le – lu-ia! 2. Now and ev-er-more, al-le-lu – ia! From dawn to

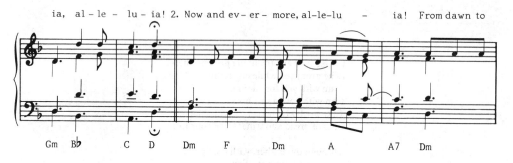

close of the day, al – le – lu – ia! Blessed be the name of the

Lord, al- le - lu - ia, al - le - lu - ia! 3. On high a- bove the earth is the
Dm F Gm B♭ C Dm C F
Lord, al-le-lu - ia! His glo-ry a - bove the sky al - le - lu - ia!
Dm A A7 Dm G C F A
There is none like the Lord our God, al - le - lu - ia, al - le-lu - ia! 4. En-
A7 Dm F Dm F Gm B♭ C Dm
throned in heaven on high, al-le-lu - ia! He views the earth and the sky, al-le-
F Dm A A7 Dm G C
lu - ia! To those in need he gives his help, al-le - lu - ia,
F A A7 Dm F Dm F Gm

al – le – lu – ia!   5. From   the dust   he   rais–es the poor, al – le –

Bb   C   Dm   C   F   Dm

lu   –   ia! He makes them sit   a–mong   kings, al-le-lu   –   ia!   A–mong the

A   A7   F   G   C   F   A7   Dm

kings of the earth, al-le – lu – ia,   al – le-lu – ia!   6. Be – hold the bar–ren

C   Dm   F   Gm   Bb   C   Dm   F

wife,   al – le – lu   –   ia! Now   a – bides in her home al – le – lu   –   ia!

Dm   A   A7   G   C   F   A

As   the hap–py   mo–ther of sons, al-le – lu – ia,   al-le-lu – ia!

A7   Dm   F   Dm   F   Gm   Bb   C   Dm

7. Let us sing to the Lord, al-le-lu — ia! Sing-ing glo-ry and praise al-le-

F   Dm   A   A7   G   C

lu — ia! Both now and ev-er-more, Amen, al-le-lu - ia, al-le-lu - ia!

F   A   A7   Dm   C   Dm   F   Gm   B♭   C   Dm

Based on Psalm 112(113)
by Lucien Deiss

471 Give us the will to listen

Kurt Rommel
Harmony by Eric Welch

Em Bm Em Am Em D   G   Bm G   D Bm Em Am Em

1 Give us the will to listen
   to the message you impart:
   we thank you, Lord,
   for showing us your heart!

2 Give us the will to persevere
   though meaning disappears:
   we thank you, Lord,
   for calming all our fears.

3 Give us the will to work on
   at what we may like the least:
   we thank you, Lord,
   for ev'ry bird and beast.

4 Give us the will to work and serve
   where we are needed most:
   we thank you, Lord,
   for staying with us close.

5 Give us the will to seek you
   in the quiet and the calm:
   we thank you, Lord,
   for keeping us from harm.

6 Give us the will to see you
   as our God, as man, as friend;
   we thank you, Lord,
   for your love has no end.

Kurt Rommel,
tr by Eileen M. Burzynska

472 Glorious things of you are spoken

See hymn no. 453

473 Glory and praise to our God

Daniel L. Schutte
Harmony by Sr. Theophane Hytrek, OSF

Spirited, very deliberate (♩ = 162)

Ped.

G   D   Em   Bm   C

Em   D   D9/ C   G/ B   D/A

ANTIPHON

Glo- ry and praise to our God, who a- lone gives

G   D   Em   G

light to our days. Man- y are the blessings he

D   Am   C   G

bears to those who trust in his ways. (Verses)

Ped.

Verses 1 - 3

Bm   C   D   G

1. We, the daughters and sons of him who built the val-leys and

Dm7   C   Am   D   D

plains, praise the won-ders our God has done in

G   Dm7   C   Bm7

cresc.

ev-'ry heart that sings. (Antiphon)

Em   A   D   D9/C   G/B   D/A

2 In His wisdom He strengthens us,
   like gold that's tested in fire,
   though the power of sin prevails,
   our God is there to save.

3 Ev'ry moment of ev'ry day
   our God is waiting to save,
   always ready to seek the lost,
   to answer those who pray.

*verse 4
overleaf*

Verse 4

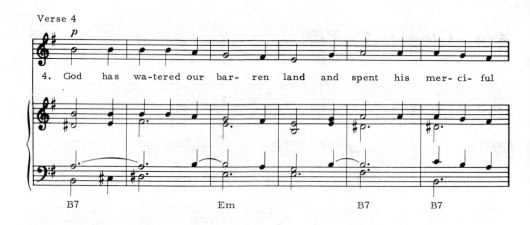

4. God has wa-tered our bar- ren land and spent his mer-ci-ful

B7   Em   B7   B7

. rain.   Now   the   riv- ers   of   life   run   full   for

Em   C   G   Em

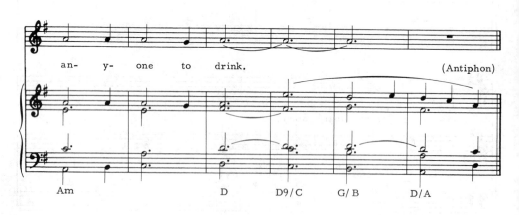

an- y- one   to   drink.   (Antiphon)

Am   D   D9/C   G/B   D/A

Dan Schutte, SJ

474 Glory to God! Peace to all men

Jacques Berthier

Glory to God! Peace to all men,
joy to earth comes from heaven.

1 For all your wonders, O Lord God,
   your people come to thank you.
   Our gracious friend, we bless your name,
   for your Kingdom which comes!
   To you we bring our praises
   through the love of the Son and of the Spirit.

2 The world's redeemer, Jesus Christ,
   receive the pray'r we bring you.
   O Lamb of God, you conquered death;
   now have mercy on us.
   Most holy Jesus, Son of God:
   living Lord of all worlds, our Lord God!

José Weber,
Tr by Eric Routley (1917–1982)

475 God, at creation's dawn

MOSCOW (664 6664)

Adapted from
Felice de Giardini (1716–96)

1 God, at creation's dawn,
over a world unborn,
your Spirit soared.
By word and water deign
that this same Spirit reign
in those now born again,
through Christ our Lord.

2 We, who in Adam fell,
are, as the Scriptures tell,
saved and restored.
For, when these rites are done,
dying we are made one,
rising we overcome,
with Christ our Lord.

3 Hear us, your Church, rejoice,
singing with grateful voice,
Father adored;
telling our faith anew,
greeting with welcome true
children new born to you,
in Christ our Lord.

Denis E. Hurley

476 God be with you till we meet again

RANDOLPH (98 89)   R. Vaughan Williams (1872–1958

1 God be with you till we meet again;
  by his counsels guide, uphold you,
  with his sheep securely fold you:
  God be with you till we meet again.

2 God be with you till we meet again;
  'neath his wings protecting hide you,
  daily manna still provide you:
  God be with you till we meet again.

3 God be with you till we meet again;
  when life's perils thick confound you,
  put his arm unfailing round you:
  God be with you till we meet again.

4 God be with you till we meet again;
  keep love's banner floating o'er you,
  smite death's threatening wave before you:
  God be with you till we meet again.

J.E. Rankin (1828–1904)

477   God forgave my sin (Freely, freely)

Carol Owens

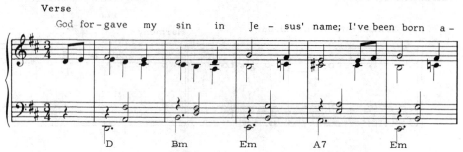

Verse

God for-gave my sin in Je - sus' name; I've been born a -

- gain in Je - sus name; and in Je - sus' name I come to you to

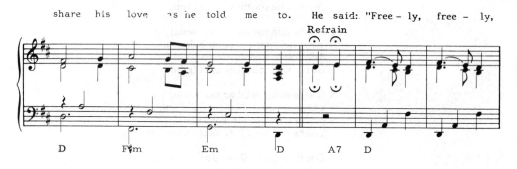

share his love as he told me to. He said: "Free - ly, free - ly,

Refrain

you have re - ceived; free - ly, free - ly, give. Go in my

name, and be—cause you be – lieve, othe–rs will know that I live."

Em   A7   A7   D

2 All pow'r is giv'n in Jesus' name,
   in earth and heav'n in Jesus' name;
   and in Jesus' name I come to you
   to share his pow'r as he told me to.

3 God gives us life in Jesus' name,
   he lives in us in Jesus' name;
   and in Jesus' name I come to you
   to share his peace as he told me to.

Carol Owens

478 God gives us harvest

Michael Coy

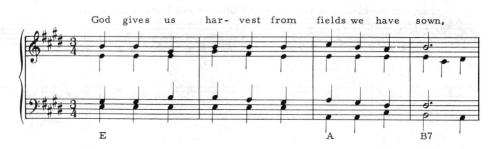

God gives us har- vest from fields we have sown,

E · A · B7

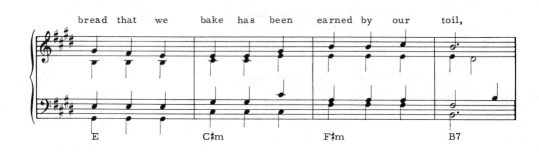

bread that we bake has been earned by our toil,

E · C♯m · F♯m · B7

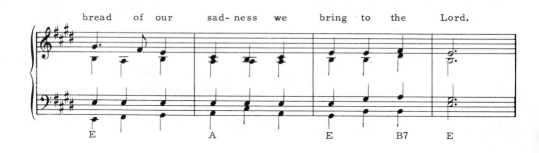

bread of our sad- ness we bring to the Lord.

E · A · E · B7 · E

LEADER

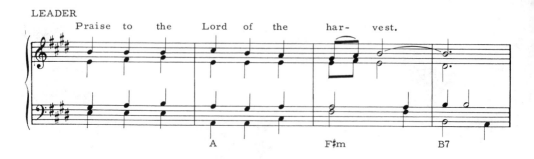

Praise to the Lord of the har- vest.

A · F♯m · B7

ALL

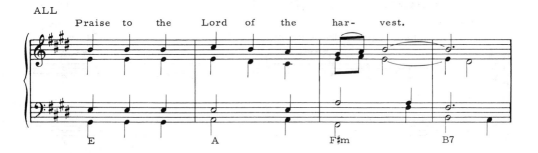

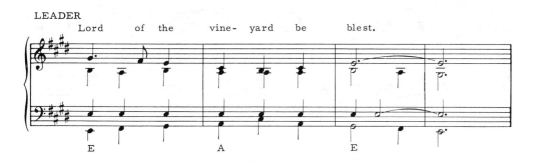

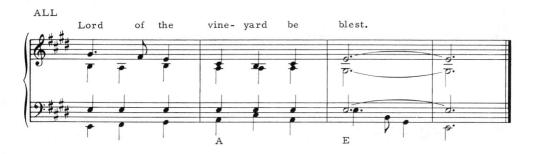

2 God has made fruitful the vines we have grown,
   wine that we make has been pressed for our joy,
   wine of our gladness we bring to the Lord.

Patrick Lee

479 God has gladdened my heart (Lourdes Magnificat)

Paul Décha

Chorus

God has glad – dened my heart with joy, al – le – lu –

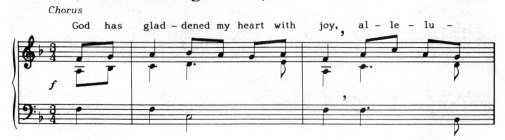

ia! He has vest – ed me with ho – li – ness, al – le – lu –

Verse 1 (Soloist)

ia! Sing my soul of the glo – ry of the Lord;

with God's Spi – rit I'm full to ov – er flow – ing!

Verse 2 (Choir, Ad.Lib.)

See the love that God show – ers on the poor: see the

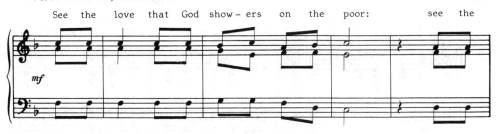

Lord ov – er – shad – ow those who fear him.

Alternate verses as above

3 All the world will join in this song of praise,
   for through me they now know the Lord is with them.

4 To fulfil what he promised from of old
   God has chosen me! Bless his name for ever.

5 Day by day, year by year, God's love is sure;
   those who listen and keep his word will know it.

6 See the pow'r of the Lord destroy the strong!
   Those who think themselves strong, the Lord will humble.

7 Empty pride, self conceit, the Lord ignores;
   but he raises the poor who call upon him.

8 No more thirst, no more hunger with the Lord;
   unsurpassed in his goodness to his people.

9 See the care that the Lord shows to us all.
   Day by day, year by year, God's love unending.

10 Praise the Father, the Son, the Spirit, praise!
   May the glory of God be sung for ever.

Words based on Luke 1:46–55,
Jean Paul Lecot, W.R. Lawrence,
R.B. Kelly

480 God is working his purpose out

FIRST TUNE

BENSON (Irregular)

Millicent D. Kingham (1866–1927)

earth shall be filled with the glo- ry of God as the

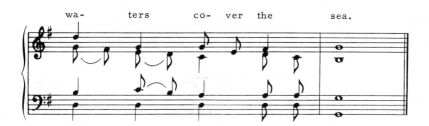

wa- ters co- ver the sea.

2 From utmost east to utmost west where-e'er man's foot hath trod,
by the mouth of many messengers goes forth the voice of God.
'Give ear to me, ye continents, ye isles give ear to me,
that the earth may be filled with the glory of God as the waters cover
the sea.'

3 What can we do to work God's work, to prosper and increase
the brotherhood of all mankind, the reign of the Prince of Peace?
What can we do to hasten the time, the time that shall surely be,
when the earth shall be filled with the glory of God as the waters
cover the sea?

4 March we forth in the strength of God with the banner of Christ
unfurled,
that the light of the glorious Gospel of truth may shine throughout
the world.
Fight we the fight with sorrow and sin, to set their captives free,
that the earth may be filled with the glory of God as the waters cover
the sea.

5 All we can do is nothing worth unless God blesses the deed;
vainly we hope for the harvest-tide till God gives life to the seed;
yet nearer and nearer draws the time, the time that shall surely be,
when the earth shall be filled with the glory of God as the waters
cover the sea.

A.C. Ainger (1841–1919)

697

PURPOSE (Irregular)   Martin Shaw (1875–1958)

1. God is work-ing his pur-pose out as year suc-ceeds to
2. From ut-most east to ut-most west where-'er man's foot hath
3. What can we do to work God's work, to pros-per and in-
4. March we forth in the strength of God with the banner of Christ un-
5. All we can do is noth-ing worth un - less God blesses the

year; God is work-ing his pur-pose out and the
trod, by the mouth of man-y mes-sen-gers goes
crease the bro-ther-hood of all man-kind, the
furled, that the light of the glo-rious gos-pel of truth may
deed; vain-ly we hope for the har-vest-tide till

time is draw-ing near; near-er and near-er
forth the voice of God, 'give ear to me, you
reign of the Prince of Peace? What can we do to
shine through-out the world; fight we the fight with
God gives life to the seed; yet near-er and near-er

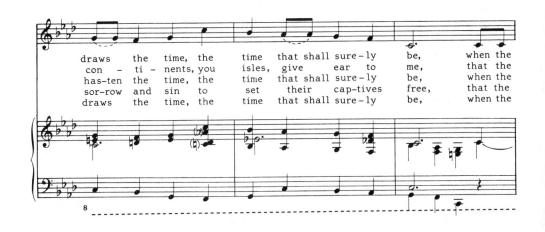

draws   the   time, the   time that shall sure–ly be,   when the
con   – ti – nents, you   isles,   give   ear   to me,   that the
has–ten the   time, the   time that shall sure–ly be,   when the
sor–row and   sin   to   set   their cap–tives free,   that the
draws   the   time, the   time that shall sure–ly be,   when the

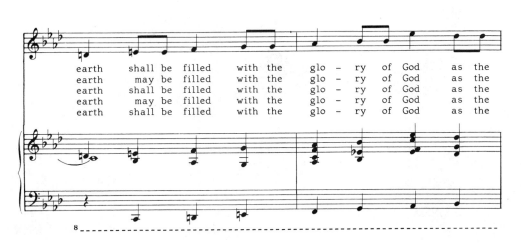

earth   shall be filled   with the   glo – ry of God   as the
earth   may be filled   with the   glo – ry of God   as the
earth   shall be filled   with the   glo – ry of God   as the
earth   may be filled   with the   glo – ry of God   as the
earth   shall be filled   with the   glo – ry of God   as the

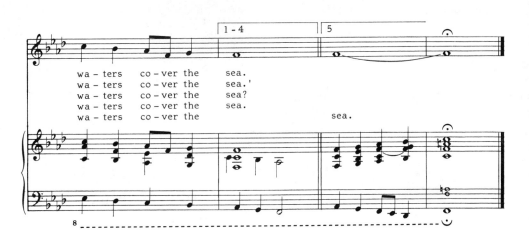

wa – ters co – ver the   sea.
wa – ters co – ver the   sea.'
wa – ters co – ver the   sea?
wa – ters co – ver the   sea.
wa – ters co – ver the   sea.

481 God made the birds

Paschal Jordan
Harmony by James O'Donnell

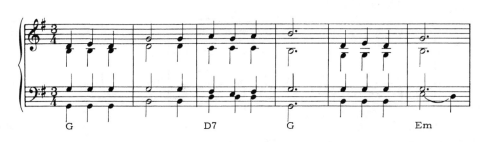

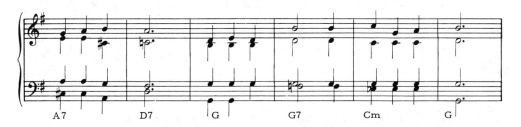

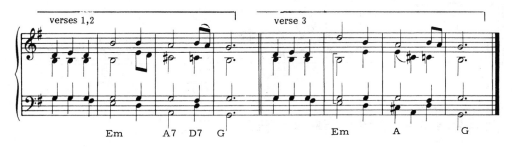

1 God made the birds, their home is the air;
God made the beasts, each in its lair;
God made the fish, their their home is the sea;
but God himself is home for me.

2 Birds find their food in their home of the air;
beasts find theirs too, 'most everywhere;
the fish find theirs in the paths of the sea;
but God himself is food for me.

3 God loves the birds, they answer in song;
God loves the beasts, so pow'rfully strong;
God loves the fish as they swim in the sea;
but God himself is love for me.

Magnus Wenninger

482 God most high of all creation

Joseph Gelineau

1 God most high of all creation, glory be to you!
 Living God, we come before you, glory be to you!
 Hosts of Heav'n, your praises are singing.
 Shouts of joy and thanks are ringing.
 We on earth re-echo their praises; glory be to you!

2 God of light, our darkness ending, glory be to you!
 Glory of truth, our doubts dispelling, glory be to you!
 Light of God on all men dawning,
 Christ the rising sun brings morning.
 You have shed your light on our pathway; glory be to you!

3 Mighty God, who brings us freedom, glory be to you!
 Faithful God who keeps his promise, glory be to you!
 As your Church we gather before you,
 and with thanks, we sing and adore you.
 Now made one in Christ, let us praise you; glory be to you!

4 God of love, your ways are gentle, glory be to you!
God of peace, you heal our sadness, glory be to you!
Called by you, we hasten to meet you,
and together pray as we greet you.
With your loving kindness surround us, glory be to you!

5 Sing your praise to God our Father, glory be to you!
Praise the Son and Holy Spirit, glory be to you!
Abba, Father, Lord of creation,
Jesus Lord, who brought salvation.
Holy Spirit, dwelling within us, glory be to you!

French, tr and adapted
by Pamela Stotter

483 God our maker, mighty Father

REX GLORIAE (87 87D)

Henry Smart (1813–1879)

1 God, our maker, mighty Father, all creation sings your praise,
sun and stars in all their splendour, moon in ev'ry changing phase,
earth with all its trees and grasses, sparkling rivers, ocean blue,
all unite to pay you homage, singing joyously to you.

2 Provident and wise creator, as your mighty plan unfurled,
man you made to share your labour in the building of the world.
Man and woman you created, that united, heart and home,
they might work and strive together till your endless kingdom come.

3 God of truth and love unbounded, further still your mercy went,
when uniting earth with heaven, your incarnate Son you sent:
first-born of your vast creation, holding all in unity,
leading all in power and wisdom to a glorious destiny.

Denis E. Hurley

484 God rest you merry, Gentlemen

English traditional melody
Harmony by Roger Humphrey

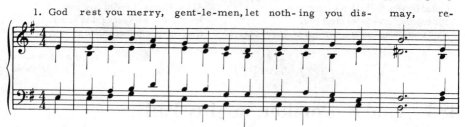

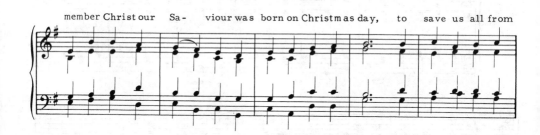

2 In Bethlehem, in Jewry,
  this blessed Babe was born,
  and laid within a manger,
  upon this blessed morn;
  the which His Mother Mary,
  did nothing take in scorn.

3 From God our heavenly Father,
  a blessed Angel came;
  and unto certain Shepherds
  brought tidings of the same;
  how that in Bethlehem was born
  the Son of God by Name:

4 'Fear not then,' said the Angel,
  'Let nothing you affright,
  this day is born a Saviour
  of a pure Virgin bright,
  to free all those who trust in Him
  from Satan's power and might.'

5 The shepherds at those tidings
  rejoicéd much in mind,
  and left their flocks a-feeding,
  in tempest, storm and wind;
  and went to Bethlehem straightway,
  the Son of God to find.

6 And when they came to Bethlehem
  where our dear Saviour lay,
  they found Him in a manger,
  where oxen feed on hay;
  His Mother Mary kneeling down,
  unto the Lord did pray.

7 Now to the Lord sing praises,
  all you within this place,
  and with true love and brotherhood
  each other now embrace;
  this holy tide of Christmas
  all other doth deface.

English Traditional Carol

485 God's Spirit precedes us

Bonaventure Hinwood
Harmony by John Rombaut

God's Spirit precedes us,
guides and gently leads us.
Alleluia, alleluia!
God's Spirit precedes us,
guides and gently leads us.
Alleluia, alleluia!

1 Through mountains and valleys
he journeys with us,
all his work
entrusts to our control;
and those who know not
what God wants from them
must silently wait
on the voice of our God.

2 In sorrow and gladness,
he's always near us,
and his love,
he gives to everyone;
and those who know not
God's presence with them
must just take a look
at the life all around.

*Tr from the Dutch by Bonaventure Hinwood,
based on Psalm 65(66)*

706

486 Good Christian men

VULPIUS (888 + Alleluias)

Melchior Vulpius (1560–1615)
Harmony by F.Layriz (1844)

For an alternative harmonization, see hymn 486

1. Good Christ-ian men, re- joice and sing!
Now is the tri- umph of our King!
To all the world glad news we bring:
Al- le- lu- ia! Al- le- lu- ia! Al- le- lu- ia!

2 The Lord of Life is risen for ay:
   bring flowers of song to strew his way;
   let all mankind rejoice and say: Alleluia!

3 Praise we in songs of victory
   that Love, that Life, which cannot die,
   and sing with hearts uplifted high: Alleluia!

4 Thy name we bless, O risen Lord,
   and sing today with one accord
   the life laid down, the life restored: Alleluia!

C.A.Alington (1872–1955)

487 Good Lady Poverty

Sebastian Temple

1 Good Lady Poverty,
  come to be my bride;
  forever you and me,
  walk side by side.
  Teach me your wisdom,
  lead me your way.
  Show me the path you take
  and walk with Christ each day.

2 Good Lady Poverty,
  so filled with grace;
  such sweet humility
  shines from your face.
  You have no pride
  or vanity.
  Great daughter of the Lord,
  his love has made you free.

3 Good Lady Poverty,
  I sing your praise.
  St. Francis, blessed one,
  has walked your ways.
  He sang your virtues;
  you were his prize.
  Good Lady Poverty,
  an angel in disguise.

Sebastian Temple

488 Grant us thy peace

ELLENBOROUGH (10 10 10 10)   John Ainslie

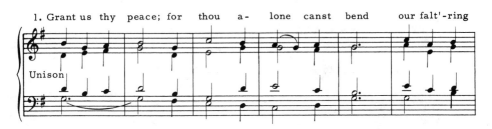

1. Grant us thy peace; for thou a-lone canst bend our falt'-ring

pur-pose to a no-bler end; thy love a-lone can teach our

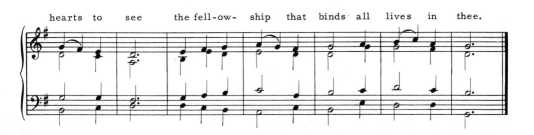

hearts to see the fell-ow-ship that binds all lives in thee.

2 Grant us thy peace; for men have filled the years
  with greed and envy and with foolish fears,
  with squandered treasures and ignoble gain,
  and fruitless harvests that we reap in vain.

3 Grant us thy peace; till all our strife shall seem
  the hateful memory of some evil dream;
  till that new song ring out that shall not cease,
  'In heaven thy glory and on earth thy peace'.

J.H.B.Masterman (1867–1933)

709

489 Greater love has no man

José Weber

*The keyboard harmonisation and guitar chords should **not** be used together.*

2 You will be my friends
   if you follow my precept:
   Love one another
   as I myself have loved you.

3 As the Father loves me always,
   so also have I loved you:
   Love on another
   as I myself have loved you.

4 Be constant in my love
   and follow my commandment.
   Love one another
   as I myself have loved you.

5 And approaching my Passover
   I have loved you to the end.
   Love one another
   as I myself have loved you.

6 By this shall men know
   that you are my disciples.
   Love one another
   as I myself have loved you.

From John 13,14 and 15,
arr by Helen Scott

490 Hail Mary (i)

Carey Landry

Hail Ma — ry, —— full of

grace, —————— the Lord ————— is with you. ———

—— blessed are you a — mong wo — men, and blest is the fruit
of your

womb. Je - sus. ——————— Ho-ly

D

Ma - ry, Mo-ther of God, ——————— pray for us sin-ners

G   D   G

now   and at the hour of death.   A - men.

D   C G   D

Refrain

Gen-tle wo-man, ——————— qui-et light,

D 713   G   D

You were cho-sen ———— from all wo-men ———— and for

G   D

D.S. Verse 2.

wo-man, ———— shining one.———— 2 Blessed are you ——

mp mf

E   A   A7   G

———— among wo-men. ———————— Blest in turn ———— all women

D   A

too. ———— Blessed they ———— with peaceful spirits.

D   G   D

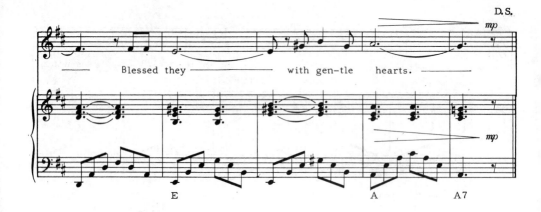

Blessed they ———————— with gen-tle hearts. —————

Hail Mary, full of grace,
the Lord is with you.
Blessed are you among women,
and blest is the fruit of your womb, Jesus.
Holy Mary, Mother of God,
pray for us sinners
now and at the hour of death.
Amen.

Gentle woman, quiet light,
morning star, so strong and bright,
gentle mother, peaceful dove,
teach us wisdom; teach us love.

1 You were chosen by the Father;
you were chosen for the Son.
You were chosen from all women,
and for women, shining one.

2 Blessed are you, among women.
Blest in turn all women too.
Blessed they with gentle spirits.
Blessed they with gentle hearts.

Based on Luke 1:28ff
Carey Landry

491 Hail Mary (ii)

Mary Lu Walker
Harmony by Eric Welch

1 Hail Mary, full of grace.
  The Lord is with thee.
  Blessed art thou among women,
  and blessed is the fruit of thy womb, Jesus.

2 Holy Mary, Mother of God,
  pray for us, sinners,
  now and at the hour of death;
  pray for us sinners now. Amen.

Based on Luke 1:28ff
adapted by Mary Lu Walker

492 Hail Mary, mother of our God

IN DER WIEGEN (86 866)

Melody from
Corner's *Geistliche Nachtigall* (1649)

*Chords should **not** be played with this arrangement

1 Hail Mary, mother of our God,
  a lamp that always burns;
  for you the angels keep a feast,
  from you all evil turns,
  from you all evil turns.

2 It's thanks to you God's only Son
  in darkness shed his light;
  it's thanks to you that sinful man
  rejoiced to know what's right,
  rejoiced to know what's right.

3 You gave a place within your womb
  to him who knows no bound;
  a virgin yet a mother too,
  in you his home he found,
  in you his home he found.

4 It's thanks to you creation came
  to know what's good and true;
  God calls his servant 'mother' now –
  no other maid but you,
  no other maid but you!

Willard F. Jabusch

493   He is Lord

Source Unknown
Arranged by Rosalind Pitcher

2 He is King, he is King.
   He is risen from the dead and he is King.
   Ev'ry knee shall bow, ev'ry tongue confess
   that Jesus Christ is King.

3 He is love, he is love.
   He is risen from the dead and he is love.
   Ev'ry knee shall bow, ev'ry tongue confess
   that Jesus Christ is love.

Anonymous

494   He is risen, alleluia

Sebastian Temple
Harmony by Stephen Dean

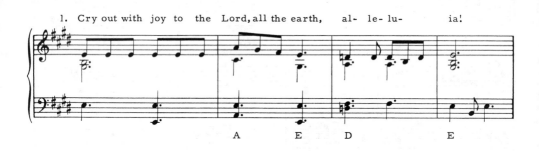

Come be-fore him, sing-ing for joy,   al- le- lu-   ia!

2 Know that he, the Lord, is God, *alleluia.*
   He made us, we belong to him, *alleluia.*
   We are his people, the sheep of his flock, *alleluia.*

3 Go within his gates giving thanks, *alleluia.*
   Enter his courts with songs of praise, *alleluia.*
   Give thanks to him and bless his name, *alleluia.*

4 Indeed, how good is the Lord, *alleluia.*
   Eternal his merciful love, *alleluia.*
   He is faithful from age to age, *alleluia.*

5 Glory to the Father and Son, *alleluia.*
   And to the Spirit with them one, *alleluia.*
   As it was and ever shall be one God for eternity.

Psalm 99(100) The Grail

495 He is risen, tell the story

Polish Traditional Melody
Arranged by Willard F. Jabusch

1 He is risen, tell the story
  to the nations of the night;
  from their sin and from their blindness,
  let them walk in Easter light.
  Now begins a new creation,
  now has come our true salvation.
  Jesus Christ, the Son of God!

2 Mary goes to tell the others
  of the wonders she has seen;
  John and Peter come a running
  what can all this truly mean?
  O Rabboni, Master holy,
  to appear to one so lowly!
  Jesus Christ, the Son of God!

3 He has cut down death and evil,
  he has conquered all despair;
  he has lifted from our shoulders,
  all the weight of anxious care.
  Risen Brother, now before you,
  we will worship and adore you.
  Jesus Christ, the Son of God!

4 Now get busy, bring the message,
  so that all may come to know
  there is hope for saint and sinner,
  for our God has loved us so.
  Ev'ry church bell is a'ringing,
  ev'ry Christian now is singing.
  Jesus Christ, the Son of God!

Willard F. Jabusch

496 He's a most unusual man

Christopher Willcock

At a moderate speed

He's a most un-us-u-al man, he makes the crowds all stop and stare, he tea-ches people how to care, he tea-ches peo-ple how to share. He has no place to lay his head, his home is ev'ry-

2 He's a most unusual man,
   he makes the stormy days turn fine,
   he changes water into wine,
   he gives his body as a sign.
   And he died that we might live,
   his life is yours and mine.

3 He's a most unusual man,
   as rich and poor as a man can be,
   he came to set the prisoners free,
   he came to make the blind men see.
   And he gave the world this message,
   'Come and follow me.'

Wendy Poussard

497 Help us accept each other

BARONITA (76 76D)   Doreen Potter

1 Help us accept each other
  as Christ accepted us;
  teach us as sister, brother,
  each person to embrace.
  Be present, Lord among us
  and bring us to believe
  we are ourselves accepted
  and meant to love and live.

2 Teach us, O Lord, your lessons,
  as in our daily life
  we struggle to be human
  and search for hope and faith.
  Teach us to care for people,
  for all not just for some,
  to love them as we find them
  or as they may become.

3 Let your acceptance change us,
  so that we may be moved
  in living situations
  to do the truth in love;
  to practise your acceptance
  until we know by heart
  the table of forgiveness
  and laughter's healing art.

4 Lord, for today's encounters
  with all who are in need,
  who hunger for acceptance,
  for righteousness and bread,
  we need new eyes for seeing,
  new hands for holding on:
  renew us with your Spirit;
  Lord, free us, make us one!

Fred Kaan

498　Hills of the North, rejoice

LITTLE CORNARD (66 66 88)　　　　　　　　　　　　Martin Shaw (1875–1958)

1. Hills of the north re- joice; riv- er and moun-tain-spring, hark to the ad- vent voice; val- ley and low- land, sing: though ab- sent long, your Lord is nigh; he judge-ment brings and vic- tor- y.

2 Isles of the southern seas,
  deep in your coral caves
  pent be each warring breeze,
  lulled be your restless waves:
  he comes to reign with boundless sway,
  and makes your wastes his great highway.

3 Lands of the east, awake,
  soon shall your sons be free;
  the sleep of ages break,
  and rise to liberty.
  On your far hills, long cold and grey,
  has dawned the everlasting day.

4 Shores of the utmost west,
  ye that have waited long,
  unvisited, unblest,
  break forth to swelling song;
  high raise the note, that Jesus died,
  yet lives and reigns, the Crucified.

5 Shout, while ye journey home;
  songs be in every mouth;
  lo, from the north we come,
  from east and west and south.
  City of God, the bonds are free,
  we come to live and reign in thee!

C.E. Oakley (1832–65)

499　His light now shines

Gonja Folk Melody
Adapted by Tom Colvin

1. His light now shines in the darkness a – bout us, his light now shines and the
Refrain. His name is love and he gives himself to us, his name is love and he

Verse ending　　　Refrain ending　　Fine

dark–ness has gone.　His　makes us his own.

This song should not have any harmonic accompaniment. Please resist the temptation to add 'Western' harmonies. Instead it should be accompanied by untuned percussion and spontaneous vocal harmony.

1 His light now shines in the darkness about us,
   his light now shines and the darkness has gone.

   His name is love and he gives himself to us;
   his name is love, and he makes us his own.

2 His love is warm like the sun of the morning,
   his love is warm like the promise of dawn.

3 His love surrounds like a mother's devotion,
   he meets our needs when awake and asleep.

4 How can we answer the love that he shows us,
   what can we do to respond to his care?

5 Receive his love and reflect it to others,
   do all for them as he does all for you.

6 For when we know him, we give ourselves to them,
   and when we love him, we give them our all.

Tom Colvin

500 Our God reigns

Leonard E. Smith Jr.

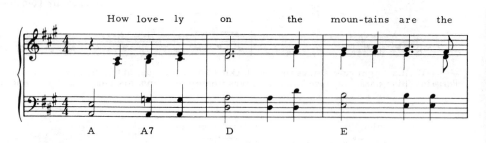

reigns,   our God   reigns,   our God   reigns,

A   A7   D   A

our God   reigns,   our God   reigns!

A7   D   E   A

2 You watchmen, lift your voices joyfully as one,
shout for your king, your king!
See eye to eye, the Lord restoring Sion:
Our God reigns . . .

3 Wasteplaces of Jerusalem, break forth with joy!
We are redeemed, redeemed,
the Lord has saved and comforted his people.
Our God reigns . . .

4 Ends of the earth, see the salvation of our God!
Jesus is Lord, is Lord!
Before the nations, he has bared his holy arm.
Our God reigns . . .

Based on Isaiah 52,
Leonard J. Smith

501   I am the bread of life

Suzanne Toolan

1. I am the Bread of life. He who comes to me shall not

hun - ger, he who be - lieves in me shall not thirst.

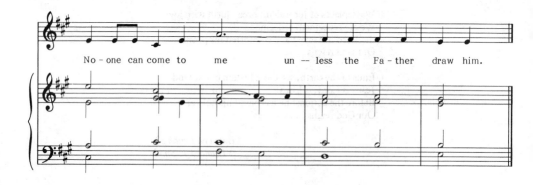

No - one can come to me un -- less the Fa - ther draw him.

Chorus

And I will raise him up, and I will raise him up, and I will raise him up on the last day.

2 The bread that I will give
  is my flesh for the life of the world,
  and he who eats of this bread,
  he shall live for ever,
  he shall live for ever.

  (Jn 6:50–51)

3 Unless you eat
  of the flesh of the Son of Man,
  and drink of his blood,
  and drink of his blood,
  you shall not have life within you.

  (Jn 6:53)

4 For my flesh is food indeed,
  and my blood is drink indeed.
  He who eats of my flesh
  and drinks of my blood
  abides in me.

  (Jn 6:55–56)

5 Yes, Lord, I/we believe,
  that you are the Christ,
  the Son of God,
  who have come
  into the world.

  (Jn 11:27)

Words arr by Suzanne Toolan

502   I am the vine

John Glynn
Harmony by Eric Welch

1 I am the vine, you are the branches:
no one can live apart from me.
Cut off from me you can do nothing:
yet joined with me, all things are yours.

2 You are the fruit borne by my Father,
who tends and cares for every limb.
Be not afraid: he will not harm you.
Your fear he'll prune, and set you free.

3 Remain in me: keep my commandments.
My love for you led me to die.
Hold fast to me: I'll never leave you,
in life, in death, I'll love you still.

Paraphrased from John 15
by John Glynn

503   I heard the Lord call my name

Jacob Krieger
Harmony by F. and R. Kelly

1 I heard the Lord call my name;
listen close, you'll hear the same! (3)
Take his hand, we are glory bound!

2 His Word is love, love's his word,
that's the message that I heard! (3)
Take his hand; we are glory bound!

Place your hand in his and you will know;
he will show you where to go.

3 I felt his love from above
settle on me like a dove. (3)
Take his hand; we are glory bound!

4 And to the Father all your days
with the Son and Spirit praise! (3)
Take his hand, we are glory bound!

Place your hand in his and you will know;
he will show you where to go.

5 *Repeat verse 1.*

Jacob Krieger

504   I lift my eyes

Gregory Norbet

I lift my eyes to the moun - tains; from

Verse 1

Capo 3   Em   B7   Em

where shall come my help? My help shall

Am   Em   B7   Am

come from the Lord, Yah-weh; it is he who made hea-ven and earth.

Em   Am   B7   Em

May he ne - ver al - low you to stum -

Verse 2

B7   Em

- ble, let him sleep not, your guard. No, he

Am   Em   B7   Am

sleeps not nor slum - bers, the Lord, Is - ra-el's guard.

Em   Am   B7   Em

The Lord is your guard and your shade,

Verse 3

B7   Em

at your right side he stands. By

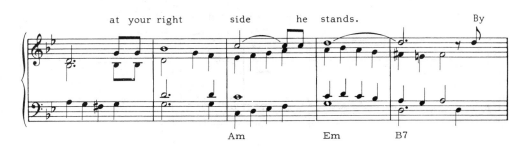

Am   Em   B7

day the sun shall not smite you, nor the moon in the

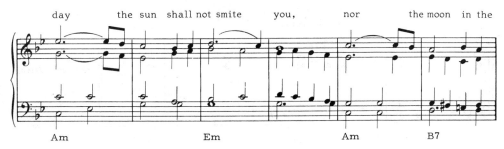

Am   Em   Am   B7

505　I lift up my eyes

Bernard Huijbers

737

* n.b. *After verse 3 and its Response, the Psalm ends with
the Antiphon and Response once more.*

Psalm 120(121) arr by Huub Oosterhuis,
tr by Tony Barr

506 I met you at the cross

Roger Jones

I met you at the
cross, Jes-us my Lord;
I heard you from that cross: my name you

called – asked me to fol-low you all of my days,

B(sus4)   B   A   E

asked me for ev – er more your name to praise.

A   Am   E   B(sus4)   E   (D♯

last time only

C♯   B Bass)   E

2 I saw you on the cross
  dying for me;
  I put you on that cross:
  but your one plea –
  would I now follow you all of my days
  and would I evermore your great name praise?

3 Jesus, my Lord and King,
  Saviour of all,
  Jesus the King of kings,
  you heard my call –
  that I would follow you all of my days,
  and that for evermore your name I'd praise.

Eric A. Thorn

507   I saw a star

Roger Whittaker

2 I saw the star shine down upon the stable.
  I watched the kings with gifts go riding by.
  I crept up close and looked into the manger
  and it was then I heard a baby cry.
  But . . .

  No one there would listen to my story,
  and no one seemed to care about the child;
  but he was beautiful,
  the baby born to save us,
  as in his mother's arms he gently lay.

3 I hurried home and there I met the townsfolk.
  I wandered in the hills and all around.
  I tried to tell my friends about the story
  of angels, shepherds, kings and babe I'd found.
  But . . .

  All alone I knelt before that manger,
  the sheep and cows and oxen standing by;
  and he was beautiful -
  the baby born to save us,
  as in his mother's arms he gently lay.
  Yes, he was beautiful,
  the baby Jesus born on Christmas Day.

  Joan McCrimmon

508   Here I am, Lord

Daniel L.Schutte
Arranged by Michael Pope

2 I, the Lord of snow and rain,
  I have borne my people's pain.
  I have wept for love of them.
  They turn away.
  I will break their hearts of stone,
  give them hearts for love alone.
  I will speak my word to them.
  Whom shall I send?

3 I, the Lord of wind and flame,
  I will send the poor and lame.
  I will set a feast for them.
  My hand will save.
  Finest bread I will provide
  till their hearts be satisfied.
  I will give my life to them.
  Whom shall I send?

Dan Schutte, SJ

509 I am Wisdom

John Glynn
Harmony by John Rombaut

1 I was born before creation,
  when the world was yet to be.
  From the dawn of time uncounted
  I have sung God's melody.

  I am Wisdom, his companion,
  ever at his side to be;
  I delight in his creating,
  never ending, ever free.

2 Ev'ry sea and ev'ry river
  I have seen them come to birth;
  for the hills and for the mountains
  seen him raise the virgin earth.

3 There were stars hung in the heavens,
  and the clouds were in his plan;
  but the time I'll ever cherish
  was the day he formed a man.

4 Never has he ceased creating,
  and I'm with him to this day;
  so I'm glad to see his image
  in the people of today.

Based on Proverbs 8:22–31
by John Glynn

510 I will be with you

Gerald Markland

748

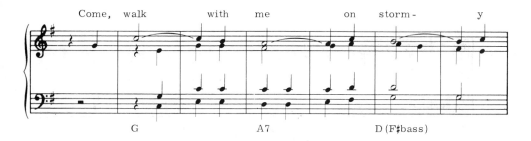

Come, walk with me on storm- y

G   A7   D (F♯bass)

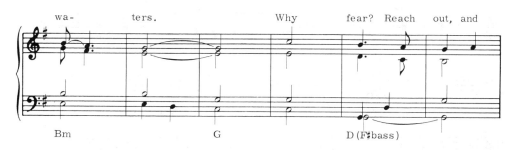

wa- ters. Why fear? Reach out, and

Bm   G   D (F♯bass)

I'll be there.

C9   Em7   A7   A7sus 4

2 And you, my friend, will you now leave me,
   or do you know me as your Lord?

3 Your life will be transformed with power
   by living truly in my name.

4 And if you say: 'Yes, Lord I love you,'
   then feed my lambs and feed my sheep.

Gerald Markland

749

511   I will never forget you

Carey Landry

1 I will never forget you, my people,
   I have carved you on the palm of my hand.
   I will never forget you;
   I will not leave your orphaned.
   I will never forget my own.

2 Does a mother forget her baby?
   Or a woman the child within her womb?
   Yet, even if these forget,
   yes, even if these forget,
   I will never forget my own.

Repeat Verse 1

Based on Isaiah 49:15–16a
by Carey Landry, SJ.

512   I will sing, I will sing

Max Dyer
Harmony by Stephen Dean

Allelu, alleluia, glory to the Lord, (3)
alleluia, glory to the Lord.

2 We will come, we will come as one
   before the Lord. (3)
  Alleluia, glory to the Lord.

3 If the Son, if the Son shall make
   you free, (3)
  you shall be free indeed.

4 They that sow in tears shall reap in joy. (3)
  Alleluia, glory to the Lord.

5 Ev'ry knee shall bow and ev'ry tongue
   confess (3)
  that Jesus Christ is Lord.

6 In his name, in his name we have
   the victory. (3)
  Alleluia, glory to the Lord.

Max Dyer

513　I will tell of your love

Sr Marie Lydia Pereira
Arranged by John Rombaut

752

I will tell of your love for me always, Lord;
I will tell of your goodness to me.

1 Ev'ry morning the sun comes shining through
to tell me a new day is born;
and I feel a joy rising in my heart,
the joy of life that comes from you.

2 Ev'ry mountain and hill that you have made
tells me how strong you are;
and I feel a pow'r rising in my heart,
the pow'r of strength that comes from you.

3 Ev'ry flower that lifts its head to me
tells me how gentle you are;
and I feel a joy rising in my heart,
the joy of love that comes from you.

4 As the darkness comes on at close of day
it tells me you watch through the night;
and I feel a longing rising in my heart,
a longing to be one with you.

Sister Marie Lydia Pereira

514 I'll sing God's praises

Aniceto Nazareth

I'll sing God's praises,
now and evermore.
I'll sing God's praises,
now and evermore.

1 He is my guide and my shepherd,
now and evermore.
He gives me rest in green pastures,
now and evermore.

2 Near restful waters he leads me,
now and evermore.
Along the right path he keeps me,
now and evermore.

3 His rod and crook are my comfort,
now and evermore.
With oil my head is anointed,
now and evermore.

4 His loving favours pursue me,
now and evermore.
His house, my dwelling for ever,
now and evermore.

Based on Psalm 22(23)
by Aniceto Nazareth

515   If God is for us

John B.Foley SJ

The chorus is sung rhythmically, not too fast. The verses should be sung faster by a leader or small group.
The melody is the middle notes of the top stave. Chords in brackets should be played on Capo C.

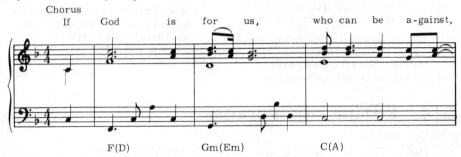

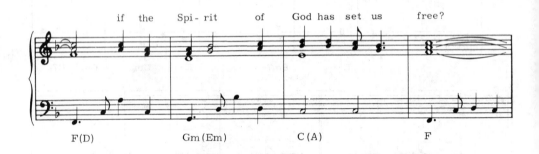

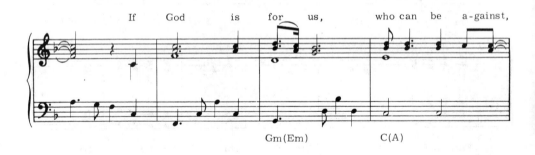

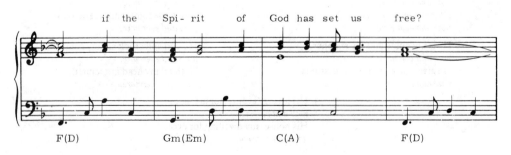

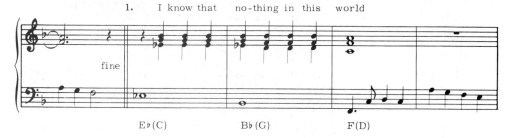

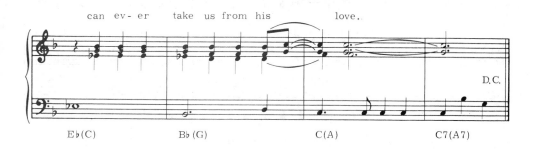

2 Nothing can take us from his love,
poured out in Jesus, the Lord.

3 And nothing present or to come
can ever take us from his love.

4 I know that neither death nor life
can ever take us from his love.

Based on Romans 8:31–39
by John Foley, SJ

516 If God is our defender

AURELIA (76 76D)

S.S.Wesley (1810–76)

1 If God is our defender,
   who will th'accuser be?
   His only Son he spared not,
   but gave him graciously.
   When God himself grants pardon,
   who ventures to condemn?
   Will Jesus Christ, the Saviour,
   who died and rose for men?

2 Can anything divide us
   from that most loving Lord?
   Can pain, or tribulation?
   Can famine, peril, sword?
   No, none of these can cause us
   from his great love to fall;
   for by the strength he gave us,
   we triumph over all.

3 Of this we can be certain,
   and sing with every breath:
   that nought that is, or will be,
   and neither life nor death,
   and nothing in creation,
   below us or above,
   can tear us from Christ Jesus,
   and from his Father's love.

Based on Romans 8:31–39 by Denis E. Hurley

517 In God alone

Douglas Rowe
Harmony by John Rombaut

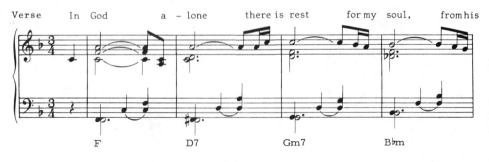

care comes my safe-ty in life. With him a—lone for my rock and my for-tress, this I know I will ne-ver fall down. So rest in God a-lone my soul, he is the source of my hope.

Dm G7 Csus4 C7 F

D7 Gm7 B♭m F C6 C7

Refrain

F Am E7 Am G

C G7 C C+

2 In God I find my shelter, my strength
all you people do rely on him.
Unburden your hearts to the Lord your God,
at all times he will listen to you.

3 Beware of those who will scoff at our God;
their intent is to misguide your way.
We trust alone in the rock of our safety
and we know we will never lose hope.

Based on Psalm 70(71)
by Douglas Rowe

518   In the beginning

Gregory Norbet

In the beginning all was empty and void;
God's spirit moved above the water.
Out of the darkness came a word that brought new life:
'This is so good, let there be light.'

1 Then in the stillness of the night your Word
  leapt into our city of turmoil;
  a man was born, a man of peace and not of war,
  revealing hopes yet unfulfilled.

2 Jesus, his name and what a gift he was,
  inspired to know the Father's vision.
  And he so loved us more than his own life.
  What greater gift could he have shared?

3 So we are called to give flesh to our word
  and be creators with the Spirit.
  Wonder will be the sign that we are on the way,
  sharing our hope, alive our word.

Gregory Norbet

519   It's a long hard journey

Nick Hodson
Harmony by Erik Routley

*The metre of this song is irregular; the note values in the melody
apply to verse 1. However, it is not difficult to fit the other verses.*

1 It's a long hard journey,
   and the road keeps turning
   and we just keep travelling on;
   the signs aren't clear enough,
   the ends aren't near enough,
   and half our time is gone.

   O, the Lord sends troubles,
   the Lord sends trials,
   the Lord sends a heavy load.
   But he'll keep on leading us,
   and keep on guiding us,
   as long as we're trav'ling his road,
   as long as we're trav'ling his road.

2 With so many days to live,
   it's hard for life to give
   a meaning mile after mile.
   The roads keep crossing,
   and the coins we're tossing
   choose the path in a visionless style.

3 Though we walk as brothers,
   still we hurt each other,
   and our love turns acid and stone.
   Though we're hand in hand
   we don't understand
   that no one's walking alone.

4 Well, he never told us
   that the road before us
   would be smooth or simple or clear.
   But he sets us singing
   and our hope keeps springing
   and we're raised from hating and fear.

5 Well, the road is ours
   with its rocks and flowers
   and mica gleams in the stone.
   Well, there's joy awaiting
   in the celebrating
   that we're never walking alone.

Nick Hodson

520 It's good to give thanks to the Lord

John Ylvisaker
Harmony by John Rombaut

Verse

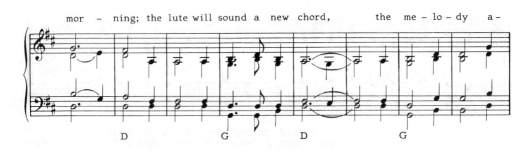

Refrain

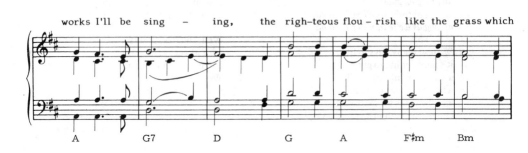

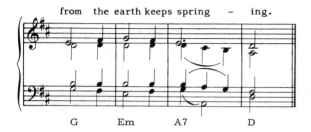

from the earth keeps spring - ing.

G   Em   A7   D

2 They're planted in God's own abode,
in God's own house they will flourish;
they'll still bear fruit when they're old,
for God will tend and nourish!

3 Sing glory to God up above,
the Son of God, our dear Saviour,
and to the Spirit of Love,
whose care will never waver!

Psalm 91(92)
paraphrased by John Ylvisaker

521 Lord, to whom shall we go?

Stephen Dean

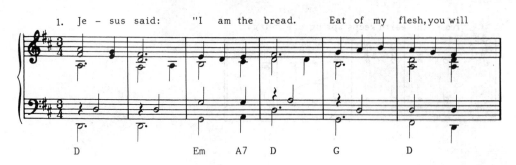

1. Je - sus said: "I am the bread. Eat of my flesh, you will

D   Em   A7   D   G   D

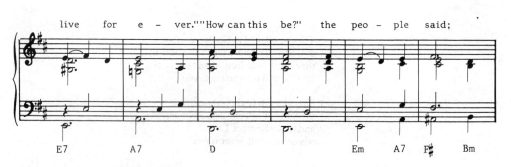

live   for   e - ver." "How can this be?" the peo - ple said;

E7   A7   D   Em   A7   F#   Bm

most of them went a - way.   So he said to the twelve "What of

Em   A7   D   A

Chorus

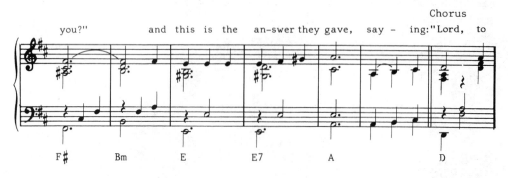

you?"   and this is the an - swer they gave, say - ing: "Lord, to

F#   Bm   E   E7   A   D

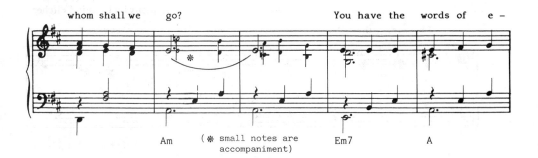

whom shall we go? You have the words of e-

Am (* small notes are accompaniment) Em7 A

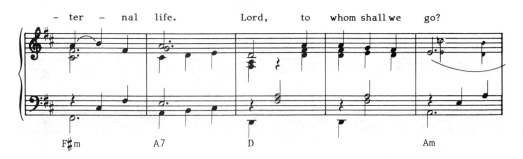

-ter - nal life. Lord, to whom shall we go?

F♯m A7 D Am

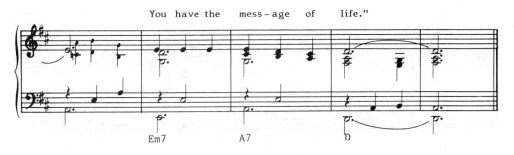

You have the mess-age of life."

Em7 A7 D

2 Jesus said: 'I came from heaven.
  I give my flesh for the life of the world.'
  'This man is mad!' the people said;
  slowly they went away.
  So he said to the twelve, 'What of you?'
  And this is the answer they gave, saying:

3 Jesus said: 'I have seen God.
  Eat of my body and you too will see him.'
  'This is not true!' the people said;
  angry they went away.
  So he said to the twelve, 'What of you?'
  And this is the answer they gave, saying:

Stephen Dean

763

522   Jesus, the holy lamb of God

Briege O'Hare
Harmony by Rosalind Pitcher

Refrain

Je-sus, the ho- ly lamb of God, car-ried the

cross for me. Je-sus, the ho- ly

Lamb of God, died that I might be | 1st time free.

Last time | Verse
free. | 1.He who is God made himself low: a

ser- vant and hum-bler yet. He bowed his

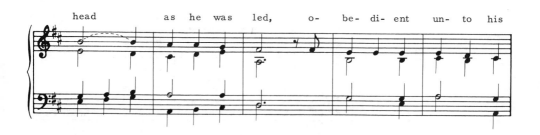

head as he was led, o- be- di- ent un- to his

death.

2 Therefore has God raised him on high
and named him our Saviour and Lord:
all knees will bend
in praise without end
to Jesus for ever adored.

Based on Philippians 2:6–11
by Briege O'Hare

523   Jesus the Lord said: I am the bread

YISU NE KAHA

Urdu melody
Harmony by Francis Westbrook (1903–75)

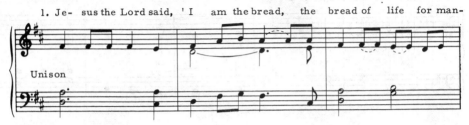

1. Je- sus the Lord said, 'I am the bread, the bread of life for man-

kind am I, the bread of life for man- kind am I, the

bread of life for man- kind am I.' Je- sus the Lord said,

'I am the bread, the bread of life for man- kind am I.'

2 Jesus the Lord said, 'I am the door,
   the way and the door for the poor *am I.' (3)*
   Jesus the Lord said, 'I am the door,
   the way and the door for the poor an I.'

3 Jesus the Lord said, 'I am the light,
   the one true light of the world *am I.' (3)*
   Jesus the Lord said, 'I am the light,
   the one true light of the world am I.'

4 Jesus the Lord said, 'I am the shepherd,
   the one good shepherd of the sheep *am I.' (3)*
   Jesus the Lord said, 'I am the shepherd,
   the one good shepherd of the sheep am I.'

5 Jesus the Lord said, 'I am the life,
   the resurrection and the life *am I.' (3)*
   Jesus the Lord said, 'I am the life,
   the resurrection and the life am I.'

Anon. Urdu
tr Dermott Monahan (1906–57)

524   Jesus the Word has lived among us

FRAGRANCE (BERGERS) (98 98 98)

Traditional French carol
Harmony by Martin Shaw (1875–1958)

1 Jesus the Word has lived among us,
   sharing his fullness, truth and grace,
   God's only Son, the Father's loved one
   reveals him to the human race.
   Jesus the Word has lived among us
   sharing his fullness, truth and grace.

2 He was with God from the beginning
   and through him all things came to be.
   He lightens darkness, conquers evil,
   gives life for living, glad and free.
   He was with God from the beginning
   and through him all things came to be.

3 Sing praise to God who sent Christ Jesus
   to be his sign of endless love;
   sent him to live his life among us,
   lifting our hearts to things above.
   Sing praise to God who sent Christ Jesus
   to be his sign of endless love!

John 1 and 3
paraphrased by Keith D. Pearson

525 Jesus, you are Lord

Mary Barrett and Eileen Binding

Because of their irregular metre, the four verses should be sung by a soloist. Everyone responds in the chorus.

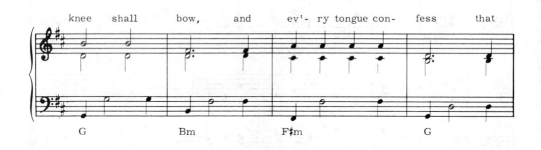

2 I am the Truth.
And I set my spirit deep within your hearts,
and you will know me, and love me,
and the truth I give to you will set you free.

3 I am the Life.
The living waters I pour out for you.
Anyone who drinks of the waters that I give
will have eternal life.

4 I am the Word,
the true light that shines brightly in the dark,
a light that darkness could not overpower,
the Word made flesh, risen among you.

Based on St John: Mary Barrett

526　Keep in mind

Lucien Deiss

Response

Keep in mind that Je-sus Christ has died for us and is ri-sen from the

dead.　He is our sa-ving Lord, he is joy for all a - ges.

Fine

Repeat the response after each verse, or after verses 2, 4, 6.

Verses 1 and 2

D.C.

1.　　If we die with the Lord, we shall live with the Lord.
2.　If we en - dure with the Lord, we shall reign with the Lord.

Verses 3-6

D.C.

3.　In him all our sor - row, in him all our joy.
4.　In him hope of glo - ry, in him all our love.
5.　In him our re - demp - tion, in him all our grace.
6.　In him our sal - va - tion, in him all our peace.

Response for mixed voices

Keep in mind that Je–sus Christ has died for us and is ri–sen from the

dead. He is our sa–ving Lord, he is joy for all a – ges.

Lucien Deiss

527 Laudato sii

Of unknown origin (Italian)
Arranged by Michael Irwin

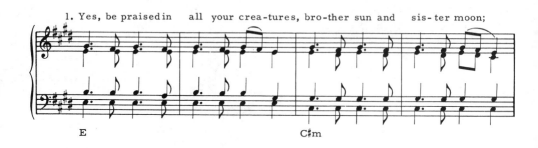

2 For our sister, mother earth,
   she who feeds us and sustains us;
   for her fruits, her grass, her flowers,
   for the mountains and the oceans.

3 Praise for those who spread forgiveness,
   those who share your peace with others,
   bearing trials and sickness bravely!
   Even sister death won't harm them.

4 For our life is but a song,
   and the reason for our singing
   is to praise you for the music;
   join the dance of your creation.

5 Praise to you, Father most holy,
   praise and thanks to you, Lord Jesus,
   praise to you, most Holy Spirit,
   life and joy of all creation!

Based on St Francis of Assisi
Damian Lundy

528   Lay your hands gently upon us

Carey Landry

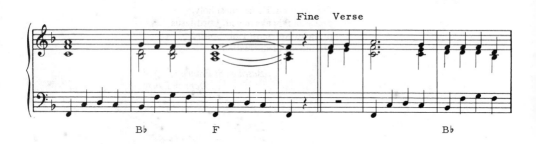

D.C.

Bb   F   Dm   F   Bb   F

Lay you hands gently upon us,
let their touch render your peace;
let them bring your forgiveness and healing,
lay your hands, gently lay your hands.

1 You were sent to free
the broken hearted.
You were sent to give sight
to the blind.
You desire to heal
all our illness.
Lay your hands,
gently lay your hands.

2 Lord, we come to you
through one another.
Lord, we come to you
in all our need.
Lord, we come to you
seeking wholeness.
Lay your hands,
gently lay your hands.

Carey Landry

529 Lead me, guide me

Peter Skinner
Harmony by Roger Humphrey

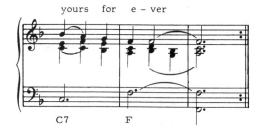

yours for e – ver

C7 F

Peter Skinner

530 Leave your country and your people

Willard F. Jabusch
Harmony by John Rombaut

Leave your country and your people,
leave your fam'ly and your friends.
Travel to the land he'll show you;
God will bless the ones he sends.

1 Go like Abraham before you,
  when he heard the Father's call,
  walking forth in faith and trusting;
  God is master of us all.

2 Sometimes God's Word is demanding,
  leave security you know,
  breaking ties and bonds that hold you,
  when the voice of God says: 'Go'.

3 Take the path into the desert,
  barren seems the rock and sand.
  God will lead you through the desert
  when you follow his command.

4 Go with courage up the mountain,
  climb the narrow, rocky ledge,
  leave behind all things that hinder,
  go with only God as pledge.

Based on Genesis 12:1ff
by Willard F. Jabusch

777

531 Lest he be too far from us

Bernard Huijbers

Verse
CANTOR

1. Lest he be too far from us, he prepared his com-ing.
2. He is ev-ery-where at hand, ev-ery de-tail hu-man.

p

Alternative accompaniment:-

He who longed to share our fate made with us his dwell-ing.
Yet he is not re-cog-nized, si-lent, ne-ver spo-ken.

Or:-

3 God from God and light from light,
all creation's keeper,
has a human face and talks,
man to man as brother.

4 So with patience as your guide,
show all kinds of goodness:
owe each other, for his sake,
only love and kindness.

5 Now be carefree, full of joy:
God, whom we do worship,
brushes past us day by day,
shares our home and kinship.

Huub Oosterhuis, tr Tony Barr

778

779

532   Let all who share one bread and cup

DAS SOLLT IHR (11 11 11 5)   Johann Cruger (1598–1662)

1 Let all who share one bread and cup remember
the oneness of that host of countless number
of those who are, as children of one Father,
part of each other.

2. If only we would live as sisters, brothers,
put faith to practice, truly care for others,
then we would do the will of him who sends us,
whose love attends us.

3 Use for yourself our highest and profoundest,
so that, O Lord, with all men who surround us,
we may enjoy a world in Christ united,
so long awaited.

J.A. Cramer
tr by Fred Kaan

533 Let it breathe on me

William E. Booth-Clibborn
Harmony by Eric Welch

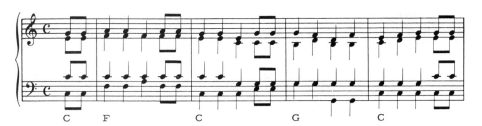

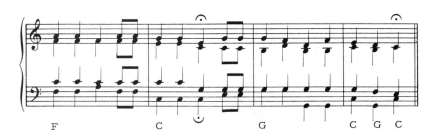

Let it breathe on me, let it breathe on me,
let this breath of God now breathe on me.
Let it breathe on me, let it breathe on me.
Let this breath of God now breathe on me.

William E. Booth-Clibborn

534   Let us praise our sov'reign Saviour

SOVEREIGN (887 887)

Philip Duffy

1 Let us praise our sovereign Saviour,
Christ, our shepherd, and our leader,
till the ending of our days.
Though we praise him all we're able,
all our praise is all too feeble,
he is far beyond all praise.

2 He, before he gave to others,
gave his little band of brothers
both his body and his blood –
not a mere symbolic token,
blood outpoured and body broken –
as an everlasting food.

3 What a theme to baffle study –
that mere bread becomes his body,
wine his blood! The king of kings
comes down on this altar duly
to repeat the wonder daily,
quite outside the run of things.

Repeat Verse 1

J. Gordon Nichols

535 Let us talents and tongues employ

LINSTEAD (88 88 and refrain)

Jamaican Traditional
Adapted by Doreen Potter

1 Let us talents and tongues employ,
reaching out with a shout of joy:
bread is broken, the wine is poured,
Christ is spoken and seen and heard.

Jesus lives again, earth can breath again,
pass the Word around: loaves abound!

2 Christ is able to make us one,
at his table he sets the tone,
teaching people to live to bless,
love in word and in deed express.

3 Jesus calls us in, sends us out
bearing fruit in a world of doubt,
gives us love to tell, bread to share:
God-Immanuel everywhere!

Fred Kaan

536 Light the Advent candle one

Mary Lu Walker

1 Light the Advent candle one.
  Now the waiting has begun,
  we have started on our way:
  time to think of Christmas day.

  Candle, candle, burning bright,
  shining in the cold winter night.
  Candle, candle, burning bright,
  fill our hearts with Christmas light.

2 Light the Advent candle two.
  Think of humble shepherds who
  filled with wonder at the sight
  of the child on Christmas night.

3 Light the Advent candle three.
  Think of heav'nly harmony:
  angels singing 'Peace on earth'
  at the blessed Saviour's birth.

4 Light the Christmas candles now!
  Sing of donkey, sheep and cow.
  Birthday candles for the King –
  let the 'Alleluias' ring!

Mary Lu Walker

537   Like a sea without a shore

Estelle White

1. Like a sea with-out a shore love di-vine is bound-less.

G   C   D7   G   C   D7

Time is now and ev-er-more and his love sur-rounds us.

G   C   D7   G   C   D7

Chorus

Ma - ra - na - tha!   Ma - ra - na - tha!

G   Em   Am   D7

Ma - ra - na - tha!   Come, Lord Je - sus, come!

G   Em   C   D7   G

2 So that mankind could be free
   he appeared among us,
   blest are those who have not seen,
   yet believed his promise.

3 All our visions, all our dreams,
   are but ghostly shadows
   of the radiant clarity
   waiting at life's close.

4 Death where is your victory?
   Death where is your sting?
   Closer than the air we breathe
   is our risen King.

Estelle White

538 Like the deer that thirsts for water

Kevin Mayhew

ANTIPHON

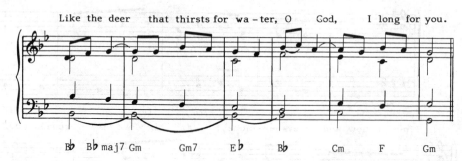

1 Like the deer that thirsts for water,
  O God, I long for you.
  Weeping, I have heard them taunt me:
  'What help is in your God?'

2 Gladly I would lead your people
  rejoicing to your house.
  Trust in God, my soul, and praise him,
  and he will dry your tears.

3 Grief and pain, like roaring torrents,
  had swept my soul away.
  But his mercy is my rescue,
  I will praise him all my days.

4 Weeping, I have heard them taunt me:
  'What help is your God?'
  Rock of strength, do not forget me;
  in you alone I trust.

5 To the Father, praise and honour;
  all glory to the Son;
  honour to the Holy Spirit;
  let God be glorified.

Paraphrased from Psalm 41(42)
by Luke Connaughton

539   Look around

Ronald Gokool
Harmony by James O'Donnell

1 Look around, look around you and you will see,
all the sunshine, the sky so blue and feel the breeze;
they are saying: God's love is real.

2 Take a walk thru' the countryside and watch
    the trees,
hear the birds singing sweetly and you will feel
    peace
and joy you've never known.

If you doubt your Father loves you,
stop and think for just a while:
is it need or greed that drives you
to be crying all the time?

3 Cleanse your mind, open wide your heart,
    and call to him,
and he'll fill you with wisdom so that you'll begin
to realise God's love is real.

Ronald Gokool

540 Look around you (Kyrie eleison)

Jodi Page Clark

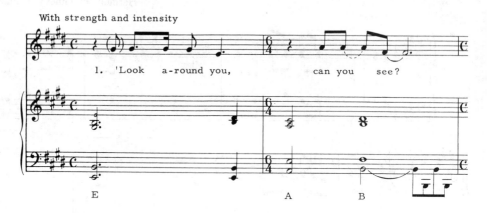

1. 'Look a-round you, can you see?

Times are troubled, peo-ple grieve. See the vio-lence,

feel the hardness; all my peo- ple, weep with me.'

Refrain

Ky- ri- e e- lei- son, Chris-te e-
lei- son, Ky- ri- e e- le-
i- son.

Final ending

2 'Walk among them, I'll go with you.
Reach out to them with my hands.
Suffer with me, and together we will serve them,
help them stand.'

3 Forgive us, Father; hear our prayer.
We would walk with you anywhere,
through your suff'ring, with forgiveness;
take your life into the world.

Jodi Page Clark

541 Looking at the sunrise

Ronald Gokool
Harmony by Eric Welch

1 Looking at the sunrise
heralding the dawn;
list'ning to the birds sing
hearing ev'ry sound.
I'm at peace with nature,
because, I suppose,
all my cares and troubles
are resting with the Lord.

2 Children playing round me,
laughter's in my heart.
People toiling sadly,
comfort I impart.
Joy is with me daily
and it's all I know,
because Jesus loves me,
for he told me so.

3 Listen to me, brothers,
heed to what I say;
place your trust in Jesus,
let him guide your way.
He will not forsake or
from you turn away;
peace is your, my brothers,
Jesus is the way.

Ronald Gokool

542 Lord, confronted with your might

DUNN'S RIVER (77 76)

Doreen Potter

1 Lord, confronted with your might,
  with your purity and light
  we are made with shame to see
  all that we fail to be.

2 Conscious of our feeble will,
  wanting good, but choosing ill,
  we are sorry for our sin:
  Lord, make us clean within.

3 Steady, Lord, our stumbling feet,
  free our spirits from deceit.
  Give us openness for pride;
  we have no place to hide.

4 Lift us from despair and grief,
  help us in our unbelief.
  As we spread our hands to you,
  fill us with life anew.

5 For the sake of Christ, forgive,
  speak the Word, and we shall live.
  Send us forward on our way,
  Lord, with our heads held high.

Fred Kaan

543   Lord enthroned in heavenly splendour

REGENT SQUARE (87 87 87)   Henry Smart (1813–79)

1. Lord en-throned in heav'n-ly splendour, first be-got-ten from the dead,

thou a-lone, our strong de-fend-er, lift-est up thy peo-ple's head.

Al-le-lu-ia, al-le-lu-ia, Je-sus, true and liv-ing bread!

2 Prince of life, for us thou livest,
    by thy body souls are healed;
    Prince of peace, thy peace thou givest,
    by thy blood is pardon sealed;
    alleluia, alleluia,
    Word of God, in flesh revealed.

3 Paschal Lamb! Thine offering finished,
    once for all, when thou wast slain,
    in its fullness undiminished
    shall for evermore remain,
    alleluia, alleluia,
    cleansing souls from every stain.

4 Great high priest of our profession,
    through the veil thou enterest in;
    by thy mighty intercession
    grace and mercy thou canst win:
    alleluia, alleluia,
    only sacrifice for sin.

5 Life-imparting heavenly manna,
    stricken rock, with streaming side,
    heaven and earth, with loud hosanna,
    worship thee, the Lamb who died;
    alleluia, alleluia,
    risen, ascended, glorified!

G.H. Bourne (1840–1925)

544 Lord, graciously hear us

Anne Conway

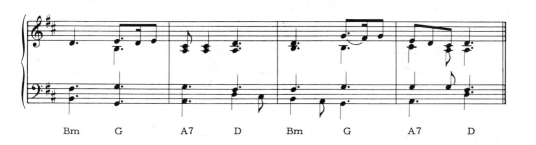

1 Lord, graciously hear us,
   hear us as we call on you,
   we tried to be faithful, Lord,
   but we have sinned against you.

2 You gave us your message,
   you showed us the way to live;
   we tried to be faithful, Lord,
   but we have not understood.

3 Lord, show us your mercy,
   heal those we have wounded here;
   we wanted to love like you,
   but we have forgotten the way.

4 Speak, Lord, to your people,
   speak, now, in a million ways;
   we want to be true to you,
   help, Lord, and forgive us, we pray.

Anne Conway

545 Lord, in everything I do

CHARLTON (77 77D)

Alan Wilson

1. Lord, in ev-ery-thing I do let me al-ways follow you; let the mo-ments of my days ov-er-flow with end-less praise; take my hands and let them move at the im-pulse of your love; ev-ery move that I shall make Lord, di-rect the steps I

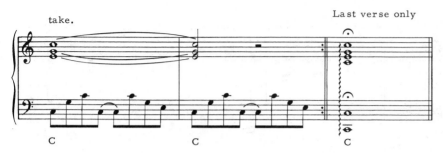

take.   Last verse only

C   C   C

2 Lord, with all your people here
  you invite me to draw near;
  Lord, accept the gifts I bring,
  Lord, accept the praise I sing.
  Take my lips and let them speak
  of your goodness through the week;
  let me echo this refrain
  till I come to you again.

3 As I listen to your call,
  Lord, I want to give my all;
  take my heart and mind and use
  every power you shall choose;
  all I have has come from you
  and I offer back to you
  only what was yours before:
  take my life for evermore.

Patrick Appleford

Choir Accompaniment to verse 2

546 Lord Jesus Christ, be present now

HERR JESU CHRIST (88 88)

Cantionale Germanicum (1681)

1 Lord Jesus Christ, be present now,
   and let your Holy Spirit bow
   all hearts in love and truth today
   to hear your Word and keep your way.

2 May your glad tidings always bring
   good news to men that they may sing
   of how you came to save all men.
   Instruct us till you come again.

3 To God the Father and the Son
   and Holy Spirit three in one,
   to you, O blessed Trinity,
   be praise throughout eternity.

Author unknown

547 Lord of Creation

SLANE (10 11 11 11)

Irish Traditional Melody

1. Lord of Cre - a - tion, to you be all praise!
Most migh - ty your work - ing, most wond - rous your ways.
Your glo - ry and might are be - yond us to tell,
and yet in the heart of the hum - ble you dwell.

2 Lord of all power, I give you my will,
in joyful obedience your tasks to fulfil.
Your bondage is freedom, your service is song,
and, held in your keeping, my weakness is strong.

3 Lord of all wisdom, I give you my mind,
rich truth that surpasses man's knowledge to find.
What eye has not seen and what ear has not heard
is taught by your Spirit and shines from your
Word.

4 Lord of all bounty, I give you my heart;
I praise and adore you for all you impart:
your love to inspire me, your counsel to guide,
your presence to cheer me, whatever betide.

5 Lord of all being, I give you my all;
if e'er I disown you I stumble and fall;
but, sworn in glad service your word to obey,
I walk in your freedom to the end of the way.

This hymn may also start at Verse 2

Jack C. Winslow

797

548   Lord, this paschal time reminds us

HYMN TO JOY (87 87D)　　　　　　　　　　　　　L. van Beethoven (1770–1827)

1 Lord, this paschal time reminds us
　how you came back from the dead.
　Firm and true the faith that binds us
　to our glorious, risen Head.
　Alleluia, alleluia,
　you have risen as you said,
　alleluia, alleluia,
　you have risen as you said.

2 'Neath the burden of our labour,
　'mid our joy and pain and strife,
　in our trying to be neighbour,
　to be parent, husband, wife;
　alleluia, alleluia,
　be to us the source of life
　alleluia, alleluia,
　be to us the source of life.

3 Make us true to our vocation
　with the strength that comes from you;
　make our life a dedication
　with the love that you imbue.
　Alleluia, alleluia,
　grace and peace in us renew,
　alleluia, alleluia,
　grace and peace in us renew.

4 Hold this vision, Lord, before us;
　in this hope our faith sustain:
　that to life you will restore us
　when at last you come again.
　Alleluia, alleluia,
　make us worthy of your reign,
　alleluia, alleluia,
　make us worthy of your reign.

Denis E. Hurley

549 Lord, thy word abideth

RAVENSHAW (66 66)

Adapted by W.H.Monk (1823–89)
from a melody in M.Weisse's *Neu Gesangbuchlein* (1531)

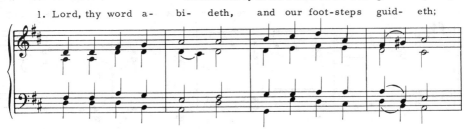

2 When our foes are near us,
   then thy word doth cheer us,
   word of consolation,
   message of salvation.

3 When the storms are o'er us,
   and dark clouds before us,
   then its light directeth,
   and our way protecteth.

4 Word of mercy, giving
   courage to the living;
   word of life, supplying
   comfort to the dying!

5 O that we discerning
   its most holy learning,
   Lord, may love and fear thee,
   evermore be near thee.

H.W. Baker (1875–1959)

550 Lord, you have come to the lakeside

C.Gabarain
accpt. by Stephen Dean

1. Lord, you have come to the lake-side, see-king
nei – ther wealthy or wise men, you on-ly
ask, Lord, that I should love you.

Chorus

With love you have looked in my eyes, Lord, smi-ling gent – ly

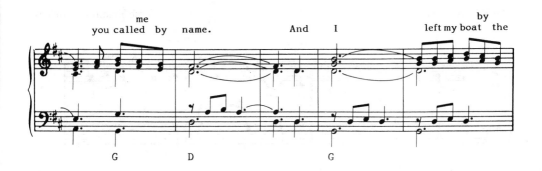

2 Lord, you well know that I carry
   in my boat no treasure nor weapon.
   I bring you only my willing labour.

3 Lord, you have need of my hands;
   I shall labour that others may rest;
   and from my love, Lord, may others love you.

4 Lord, other seas call me onward;
   hope eternal for hearts that are searching;
   and love will bind us as friends for ever.

C.Gabarain
tr. Fr. Edmund O'Shea

551 Love came down at Christmas

GARTAN (67 67)

Irish Traditional Melody

1 Love came down at Christmas,
  love all lovely, love divine:
  love was born at Christmas,
  star and angels gave the sign.

2 Worship we the Godhead,
  love incarnate, love divine;
  worship we our Jesus:
  but wherewith for sacred sign?

3 Love shall be our token,
  love be yours and love be mine,
  love to God and all men,
  love for plea and gift and sign.

Christina Rossetti (1830–94)

552   Lumen Christi

Jean-Paul Lecot

Refrain

Lu – men Chri – sti, al – le – lu – ia!   A – men!

Choir

Verse

1. I am the   light of the   world:
2. You are the   light of the   world:
3. Tell the wonderful deeds of the   Lord:

*whoever follows me will never   walk in   darkness.
*in the same way your light must   shine before   all!
 he called you from   darkness to   light.

alternative version:
* he who follows me will not walk in darkness.
* let your light shine before men.

Jean Paul Lecot

553 May the peace of the Lord be with you

Gary Ault
Harmony by Eric Welch

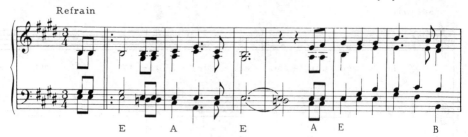

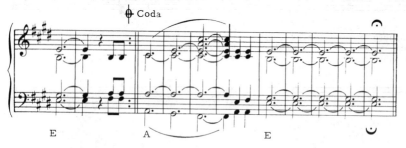

May the peace of the Lord be with you,
with your friends and your family too.
Let it be, let it grow, and everywhere you go
may the peace of the Lord follow you.

1 I leave you peace, now it's my peace I give to you:
  not as the world gives do I give to you.

2 Don't be afraid, let your hearts be untroubled:
  have faith in God and have faith in me.

Gary Ault

554 Modern man has the city for his home

J.W.Faustini

B7 Em Am D7 Em Am B Am F♯ Bm B Am

F F7 Am Bsus4 B7 C Em A7 B7 Em

1 Modern man has the city for his home
where his life is walled by want and dread,
pained by nights without sleep and days of grinding work,
in the struggle to earn his daily bread.

2 In our cities, immense and growing out,
there are millions from faith and love estranged,
who need to recapture hope of better things,
and whose hearts, by the grace of Christ, can change.

3 In the dark of our noisy city life,
men and women are groping for the light,
human beings who hunger to see right prevail,
unaware of the liberating Christ.

4 In the great giant cities of our globe,
hollowed out by the ways of greed and crime,
we are set to reflect the likeness of our God
and to act our renewal's great design.

5 Grow, then, cities to house the world of man,
with your skyscrapers blotting out the sun.
Let Christ be the light to shine from human homes
in the high-rising blocks of steel and stone.

Words by Joao Dias de Araujo,
tr by Fred Kaan

555   Mother of Jesus

John Glynn

Mother of Jesus, and mother of lowliness,
bearing the light of the world.
Radiant with glory, the glory of Jesus,
conceived by the Spirit of God.

1 In the beginning of time
   God's Holy Spirit did shine,
   breathed on the deep
   and the darkness of night,
   bringing the promise of light.

2 Then in the fullness of time
   came the same Spirit sublime
   breathed on the womb
   of the Virgin of grace,
   called her the chosen of God.

3 Wond'rous the moment that heard
   you say 'Amen' to the Word;
   Son of the Father,
   and Light of his light,
   face of the Godhead unveiled.

4 Mary, our Lady of light,
   you are the Father's delight:
   pray for us sinners
   to Jesus, your Son,
   show us the light of the world.

John Glynn

556 My God, don't ever desert me

Ronald Gokool
Harmony by Roger Humphrey

Fine Verse

com - fort me.———— 1. In this cold, forbid-ding world where

D   D7

on-ly
man seeks him-self,   I can find no-one who'll love   or who'll help.—

G   A7   D   D7   G   Em

—— There is on - ly you. ——————

D.C.

A7   D

My God, my God, don't ever desert me,
my God, my God, I need you beside me.
My life is so lonely, my heart is so empty,
my God, only you can comfort me.

1 In this cold, forbidding world
   where man seeks only himself,
   I can find no one who'll love
   or who'll help. There is only you.

2 In my joy I look for laughter,
   in my sorrow I seek a friend;
   but I see only fleeting shadows,
   and then I turn and find you there.

3 None but you know how I'm aching,
   you alone give the solace I seek.
   You alone give me kindness and care
   whenever I despair.

Ronald Gokool

557 My God, you fathom my heart (Psalm 138)

Bernard Huijbers

CANTOR

My God, you fa- thom my heart and you know me.

ALL

My God, you fa- thom my heart and you know me.

CANTOR

Noth-ing in me lies con- cealed from your eyes;

ALL

ev- ery thing I do, you al- rea- dy know it. You

CANTOR

al- rea- dy know it. How could I ev- er flee

from your spi- rit, or where could I take re- fuge, you

ALL   CANTOR

see me ev- ery- where. You see me ev- ery- where. I

climb to the hea- vens, you are in the hea- vens:

in the depths of the earth I find you ev- en there.

ALL

CANTOR

I find you ev- en there. And should I flee a-

way with the dawn or to the furth- er- most shores of the

sea; yes, ev- en there shall your hand

ALL

be to help me. Yes, ev- en there shall your hand

CANTOR

be to help me. How wond' rous are your

plans for me. My God how com- plete your de- signs.

ALL

My God how com- plete your de- signs.

CANTOR

How can I count

them, they are too plen- ty, as the sands of the sea ev- en then . . . . Then I shall know still noth-

ALL

thing of you. Then I shall know still noth-

thing of you.

From Psalm 138(139) arr. by Huub Oosterhuis,
tr by Tony Barr

558 My soul is longing for your peace

Lucien Deiss

Response

My soul is long-ing for your peace, near to you, my God. *Fine*

F Am Gm Dm Gm F

Verse

Lord, you know that my heart *is* not proud, and my eyes are not lif-ted from the earth. *D.C.*

F Gm Am Dm Am C Gm

Response for mixed voices

S A

T B

2 Lofty thoughts
   have never filled my mind,
   far beyond my sight
   all ambitious deeds.

3 In your peace
   I have maintained my soul,
   I have kept my heart
   in your quiet peace.

4 As a child
   rests on his mother's knee,
   so I place my soul
   in your loving care.

5 Israel,
   put all your hope in God,
   place your trust in him,
   now and evermore.

Based on Psalm 130(131)
by Lucien Deiss

559 New life!

Carey Landrey

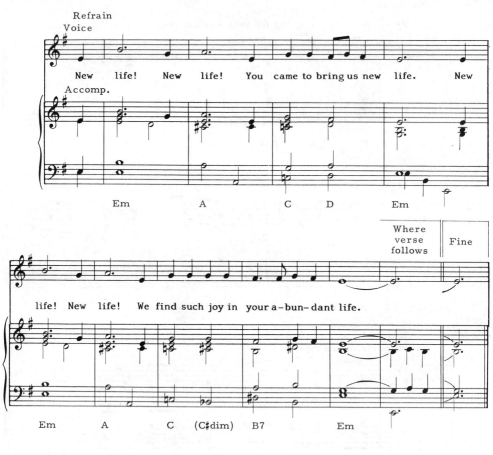

Refrain

New life! New life! You came to bring us new life. New
life! New life! We find such joy in your a-bun-dant life.

Em A C D Em

Em A C (C♯dim) B7 Em

Where verse follows — Fine

Verse

1. You are the source of our great joy, the foun-tain of all life. You give us li-ving
2. You are the source of our new life; in your light we see light. You show to us your

Em A C D Em Em

wa - ter you bid us come and drink. We come to you, we bless you, Lord. We glori - fy your
good-ness; you bid us taste and see.

A   C   D   B7   Em   A   Em   B   C

D.C.

name! We praise you, Lord, we worship you, we thank you for your gift   of new life.

B7   Em   A   C (C♯dim) B7   Em

Carey Landry

560 No one can give to me that peace

Douglas Rowe
Harmony by John Rombaut

Refrain

No one can give to me that peace which my ri-sen Lord, my ri-sen King can give.

D   C   Adim   Em F#m A7 D   Bm   G   A7

No one can give to me that peace which my ri-sen Lord, my ri-sen King can give.

D B7 Bb7 A7 D   C   Adim   Em F#m A7 D   Bm

Fine   *Verse*

1. When I look a-round and see all the things that trou-bl

G   A7   D G D   A7 that's   Em A7   D   A7

me and I seem to lose my peace in a world not at ease.

D.C.

D   Bm   E7   A   A7

2 For I take Christ's word as true:
'My true peace I give to you,
but not as the world might give,
is my peace that makes you live.'

3 His true peace in me will stay,
as I live from day to day
and his joy will never end,
and in Heaven it will extend.

4 All the world's in search of peace,
but from sin they'll never cease
how can they expect to find
inner joys and peace of mind?

5 All injustice, hate and strife,
sin of malice, sex and pride,
stem from those who've never known,
where the seeds of peace were sown.

6 Christ has risen from the dead,
triumphed over sin and death
and he'll never die again,
but as Lord he'll live and reign.

Douglas Rowe

561 Now let your people depart in peace

John Ylvisaker
Harmony by John Rombaut

2 Sing glory to the Creator Lord,
and to the Spirit the comforter,
and unto Jesus the blessed Son,
forever three and ever one.

From the Nunc Dimittis (Luke 2:29–32)
by John C. Ylvisaker

562   Now the tasks and toils are over

Kevin Nichols
Harmony by Rosalind Pitcher

1. Now the tasks and toils are over and an-

oth- er day at its end, dear Lord, our drow- sy

spi- rits in- to your hands we com- mend. The

day's fam- il- i- ar brightness is lost in the path- less

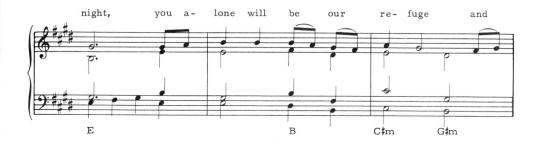

night,   you a- lone will   be   our   re- fuge   and

E   B   C#m   G#m

on- ly you our   light.

A   B7   E

2 The moonlight through the branches
  by the evening wind is stirred,
  the stars stand in their places
  as faithful as your word:
  although we shall not hear it,
  though our eyes are held in sleep,
  yet our wakeful hearts turn to you
  their promises to keep.

3 Protect us from all evil,
  from the terrors darkness brings
  that we may rest securely
  in the shadow of your wings.
  O watchful Father, guide us,
  our strength and life restore,
  that we may wake at morning
  to hear your voice once more.

563 Now watch for God's coming

Traditional Catalan carol
Harmony by Stephen Dean

N.B. The guitar chords should not be used with this harmony.

2 Man's steps are directed, God watches his path;
 he guides him and holds him and saves him from
  wrath,
 and though he may fall he will not go headlong,
 for God gives sound footing and keeps him from
  wrong.

3 So wait for his coming, be patient till then;
 the wicked are armed and would kill honest men.
 Their arms shall be broken, no refuge they'll see,
 but saved are the needy by God's own decree.

4 Now those who do evil will wither like grass,
 like green of the springtime they fade and they pass,
 so trust in the Lord and to him give your life,
 he'll bring heart's desires and peace in our strife.

Willard F. Jabusch

564　Now with the fading light of day

(88 88)

Alternative tunes: see Metrical Index

Anthony Milner

Em　　　Am　　Bm7 Em　　　　G　Em　Dsus4 D7　G

Em　　Am7 G　Am　　D　　　G　　C　　G　　Am7 D/A Em

1　Now with the fading light of day
　　Maker of all, to Thee we pray
　　that with Thy wonted care and love,
　　Thou guard and protect us from above.

2　Take far away each hideous dream,
　　things in the night that monstrous seem,
　　wiles of our old arch-foe restrain
　　lest faltering flesh contract a stain.

3　Father almighty, grace afford,
　　grant it through Jesus Christ our Lord,
　　who with the Holy Ghost and Thee
　　is reigning for all eternity.

Te lucis ante terminum,
tr by Sebastian Bullough

565 O be joyful in the Lord

Jonathan Asprey

O be joyful in the Lord!
O be joyful in the Lord!
Let us make a joyful noise,
let the whole earth rejoice!
O be joyful in the Lord,
all ye lands!

Psalm 99 (100)
paraphrased by
Jonathan Asprey

1 Know that the Lord he is God;
he has made us, we are his.
We are the sheep of his pasture,
the people of his hand.

2 Enter his gates with thanksgiving:
come into his courts with praise.
Be thankful unto him,
and speak good of his name.

3 Know that the Lord, he is good:
his love lasts for ever.
He's faithful and true,
through ev'ry generation.

566   O comfort my people

BI IOSA AM CHROISE (11 11 11 11)

Irish Traditional Melody
Harmony by Stephen Dean

2 Proclaim to the cities
   of Juda my word:
   that gentle yet strong is
   the hand of the Lord.
   I rescue the captives
   my people defend
   and bring them to justice
   and joy without end.

3 All mountains and hills shall
   become as a plain
   for vanished are mourning
   and hunger and pain.
   And never again shall
   these war against you.
   Behold I come quickly
   to make all things new.

Isaiah 40,
paraphrased by Chrysogonus Waddell

567 O food of travellers

EISENACH (88 88)

Melody by J.H.Schein (1586–1630)
Harmony by J.S.Bach (1685–1750)

1. O food of travellers, an-gels' bread, man-na wherewith the

blest are fed, come nigh, and with thy sweet-ness fill the

hun-gry hearts that seek thee still.

2 O fount of love, O well unpriced,
   outpouring from the heart of Christ,
   give us to drink of very thee,
   and all we pray shall answered be.

3 O Jesus Christ, we pray to thee
   that this presence which we see,
   though now in form of bread concealed,
   to us may be in heaven revealed.

Maintzisch Gesangbuch, 1661,
tr by Walter H. Shewring and others

568 O lady full of God's own grace

Estelle White

O la-dy, full of God's own grace, whose caring hands the child em-

braced, who listened to the Spi-rit's word, believed and trus- ted in the

D   Em   A   G

Lord. O vir-gin fair, star of the sea, my dearest moth- er, pray for

Chorus

D   G   D   Em   A7

me. O virgin fair, star of the sea, my dearest moth- er, pray for me.

D   G   D   Em   A7   D

2 O lady, who felt daily joy
  in caring for the holy boy,
  whose home was plain and shorn of wealth,
  yet was enriched by God's own breath.

3 O lady, who bore living's pain
  but still believed that love would reign,
  who on a hill watched Jesus die
  as on a cross they raised him high.

4 O lady, who, on Easter day,
  had all your sorrow wiped away
  as God the Father's will was done
  when from death's hold he freed your Son.

Estelle White

827

569   O light forever dawning

PASSION CHORALE (76 76D)

Melody by H.L.Hassler (1564–1612)
Adapted and harmonised by J.S.Bach (1685–1750)

1 O light forever dawning
  beyond the darkest night;
  O comfort of the mourning,
  our strength and our delight;
  receive our humble pleading
  for those whose course is run,
  lest pardon they be needing
  for any evil done.

2 To him who like the eagle
  arose on conqu'ring wing,
  the cross his banner regal,
  O death, where is your sting?
  There's surely no rejection
  for those who share his strife,
  but hope and resurrection
  and everlasting life.

Denis E. Hurley

570 O raise your eyes on high

ST MAGNUS (86 86)

Attributed to
Jeremiah Clarke (c.1659–1707)

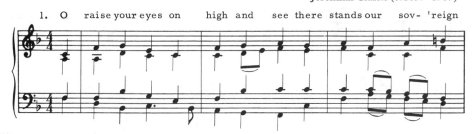

1. O raise your eyes on high and see there stands our sov-'reign

Lord, his glo-ry is this day revealed, his word a two-edged sword.

2 We glimpse the splendour and the power
   of him who conquered death,
   the Christ in whom the universe
   knows God's creating breath.

3 Of every creed and nation King
   in him all strife is stilled;
   the promise made to Abraham
   in him has been fulfilled.

4 The prophets stand and with great joy
   give witness as they gaze;
   the Father with a sign has sealed
   our trust, our hope, our praise.

5 This glory that today our eyes
   have glimpsed of God's own Son
   will help us ever sing with love
   of Three who are but One.

Ralph Wright, OSB

571 O what a gift

Pat Uhl

Refrain

O what a gift what a won-der – ful gift; who can

tell the won-ders of the Lord? Let us o – pen our eyes, our

ears, and our hearts; it is Christ the Lord, it is he! 1. In the

Fine.

stillness of the night, when the world was a-sleep the Lord made his mes-sage

known. It was then that his word came down from on high from the

Fa-ther's ro-yal   throne: Christ our Lord and our King!

D.C.

G   F#m   Bm   F#m   Bm

2 His mighty Word cuts quick and clean,
   far sharper than a two-edged sword:
   open your eyes, your ears, and your hearts,
   and hear the Word of the Lord:
   Christ our Lord and our King!

3 He came to his people, the chosen race,
   that his Father's will would be known;
   Lion of Judah, Light of the Word,
   our Redeemer came to his own,
   Christ our Lord and our King!

4 He lived here among us, he worked here among us,
   morning, night, and day;
   showed us his glory, gave us a promise,
   and then we turned away.
   Christ our Lord and our King!

5 At the Passover meal on the night before he died,
   he lifted up his eyes and prayed.
   Then he broke the bread, then he shared the wine
   the gift that God had made:
   Christ our Lord and our King!

6 On the hill of Calvary, the world held its breath;
   and there for the world to see,
   the Father gave his Son, his very own Son
   for the love of you and me.
   Christ our Lord and our King!

7 Early on that morning when the guards were asleep,
   the Father revealed his might;
   Christ in his glory arose from the dead,
   the Lord of Life and Light:
   Christ our Lord and our King!

8 On the road to Emmaus, the glory that is his,
   the disciples could never see.
   Then he broke the bread, then he shared the wine;
   it is the Lord, it is he:
   Christ our Lord and our King!

9 Now look around you and open your eyes;
   remember the Spirit is here.
   Here within his Church, his people are one.
   Look, the Lord is near:
   Christ our Lord and our King!

Pat Uhl and Michael Gilligan

572 Of one that is so fair and bright

Estelle White

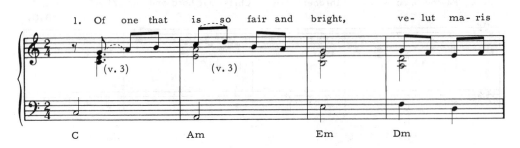

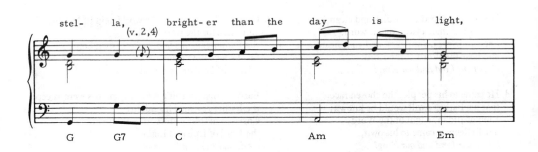

*in v. 3 these three quavers carry separate syllables

2 In sorrow, counsel thou art best,
   felix fecundata:
   for all the weary thou art rest,
   mater honorata:
   beseech him in thy mildest mood,
   who for us did shed his blood
   in cruce,
   that we may come to him
   in luce.

3 All this world was forlorn,
   Eva peccatrice,
   till our Saviour Lord was born
   de te genetrice;
   with thy ave sin went away,
   dark night went and in came day
   salutis.
   The well of healing sprang from thee,
   virtutis.

4 Lady, flower of everything,
   rosa sine spina,
   thou borest Jesus, heaven's king,
   gratia divina.
   Of all I say thou bore the prize,
   lady, queen of paradise,
   electa;
   maiden mild, mother
   es effecta.

Anon: medieval

573 Of the Father's love begotten

CORDE NATUS (87 87 877)

13th Century melody
as in *Piae Cantiones* (1582)
Harmony by Redmund Shaw

1. Of the Fa- ther's love be- got- ten, ere the

worlds be- gan to be, he is Al- pha and O-

me- ga, he the source, the end- ing he,

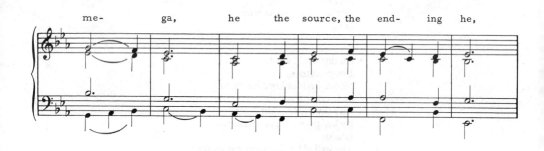

of all things that are and have been

and that fu- ture years shall see: Ev- er- more and

ev- er- more.

2 By his word was all created;
   He commanded, it was done:
   heaven and earth and depth of ocean,
   universe of three in one,
   all that grows beneath the shining
   of the light of moon and sun:

3 Blessed was the day for ever
   when the virgin, full of grace,
   by the Holy Ghost conceiving,
   bore the Saviour of our race,
   and the child, the world's Redeemer,
   first revealed his sacred face:

4 O, ye heights of heaven, adore him,
   angels and archangels sing!
   Every creature bow before him
   singing praise to God our King;
   let no earthly tongue be silent,
   all the world with homage ring:

5 He, by prophets sung, is here now,
   promised since the world began,
   now on earth in flesh descended
   to atone for sins of man.
   All creation praise its Master,
   see fulfilment of his plan:

6 Glory be to God the Father,
   glory be to God the Son,
   glory to the Holy Spirit,
   persons three, yet Godhead one.
   Glory be from all creation
   while eternal ages run:

Aurelius C. Prudentius (348–413)
tr by J.M. Neale (1818–66), H.W. Baker (1823–77)
and others

574 Song of a young prophet

Damian Lundy

The chorus is sung by the leader and repeated by all at the beginning, and after each verse. The leader sings the verses alone. The final chorus ends on D – all the others ending on F#.

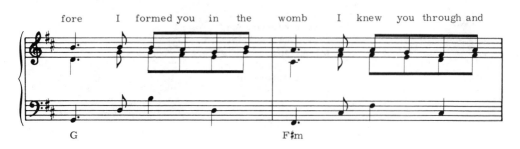

through, I chose you to be mine. Be - fore you left your mother's

Em   A7   D   D7   G

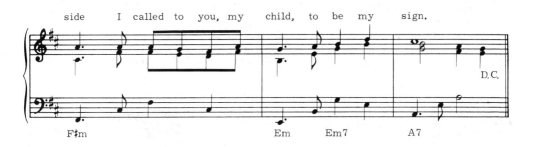

side I called to you, my child, to be my sign.

D.C.

F♯m   Em   Em7   A7

2 I know that you are very young,
   but I will make you strong
   - I'll fill you with my word;
   and you will travel through the land,
   fulfilling my command which you have heard.

3 And ev'rywhere you are to go
   my hand will follow you;
   you will not be alone.
   In all the danger that you fear
   you'll find me very near, your words my own.

4 With all my strength you will be filled:
   you will destroy and build,
   for that is my design.
   You will create and overthrow,
   reap harvests I will sow – your word is mine.

Based on Jeremiah 1,
Damian Lundy

837

575 The old rugged cross

George Bennard (1873–1960)

1 On a hill far away
   stood an old rugged cross,
   the emblem of suff'ring and shame;
   and I loved that old cross
   where the dearest and best
   for a world of lost sinners was slain.

   So I'll cherish the old rugged cross
   'till my trophies at last I lay down;
   I will cling to the old rugged cross
   and exchange it someday for a crown.

2 Oh that old rugged cross,
   so despised by the world,
   has a wondrous attraction for me:
   for the dear Lamb of God
   left his glory above
   to bear it to dark Calvary.

3 In the old rugged cross,
  stained with blood so divine,
  a wondrous beauty I see.
  For 'twas on that old cross
  Jesus suffered and died
  to pardon and sanctify me.

4 To the old rugged cross
  I will ever be true,
  its shame and reproach gladly bear.
  Then he'll call me some day
  to my home far away
  there his glory for ever I'll share.

George Bennar (1873–1960)

576 One day will come

Ronald Gokool
Harmony by Eric Welch

One day will come when this world which we roam will cease to pro-
duce sor-rows seeds which we have sown, that day there'll such rejoic-ing,
joy will banish tears. One day when love conquers all of our fears.
Some day we'll learn how to control our lives. It's on-ly

839

Ronald Gokool

577 Our Father, we have wandered

FIRST TUNE

PASSION CHORALE (76 76D)

Melody by H.L.Hassler (1564–1612)
Adapted and harmonised by J.S.Bach (1685–1750)

1 Our Father, we have wandered
and hidden from your face,
in foolishness have squandered
your legacy of grace.
But now, in exile dwelling,
we rise with fear and shame,
as distant but compelling,
we hear you call our name.

2 And now at length discerning
the evil that we do,
behold us Lord, returning
with hope and trust to you.
In haste you come to meet us
and home rejoicing bring.
In gladness there to greet us
with calf and robe and ring.

3 O Lord of all the living,
both banished and restored,
compassionate, forgiving
and ever caring Lord,
grant now that our transgressing,
our faithlessness may cease.
Stretch out your hand in blessing
in pardon and in peace.

Kevin Nichols

NESHANIC (76 76D)   Erik Routley

1. Our Father we have wandered and hidden from your face; in foolishness have squandered your legacy of grace. But now in exile dwelling, we rise with fear and shame, as distant but compelling, we hear you call our name.

578 Our help is the name of the Lord

Bernard Huijbers

Verses
CANTOR

1. He calls my life from out of the grave, he fills my days with
2. This God of ours does not con- demn us, ne- ver re- pays us
3. As a- ny man shows mer- cy to his sons, he is a most mer- ci- ful

Response overleaf ♢

CHOIR

Our

1. hap- pi- ness, and like an ea- gle my youth is re- stored.
   (Response)
2. e- vil for e- vil for he is great- er than our sins.
   (Response)
3. fa- ther to us. He knows us through for he made us.
   (Antiphon)

After verse 3, dal 𝄌

845

Response

help is the name of the Lord and his faith-ful-ness

ALL

has no end. Our help is the name of the Lord

To verses 2 & 3

and his faith-ful-ness has no end.

From Psalm 102(103):3–5. 8–10. 13–14.
Antiphon based on Psalm 120(121):2.
Versified by Huub Oosterhuis, tr by Tony Barr

579 Our Saviour Jesus Christ proclaimed

Estelle White

Slowly

1. Our Saviour Jesus Christ proclaimed that when we
gather in his name he would be there to love and
guide, lead us towards the Father's side. Our hearts are
longing for you, Lord, give us the faith to trust your word.

Chorus

2 He told us, 'Ask, you will receive,
seek and you'll find if you believe.
Knock at the door of love and truth
and we shall open it for you.'

3 His hands brought healing to the blind,
his words brought ease to troubled minds.
He said his friends could do the same
by invocation of his name.

4 He came to earth in form of man
to give to us his Father's plan.
We are the branches, he the vine,
we too can share his life divine.

Estelle White

580 Out of deep unordered water

Verse

Ron Klusmeier

1. Out of deep, un-or-dered wa-ter God cre-a-ted land and life; world of bird and beast and la-ter twosome peo-ple, man and wife.

Refrain

There is wa-ter in the

848

ri- ver bring-ing life to tree and plant.

F♯m   F♯m / B   B7   E

Let cre- a- tion praise its gi -ver: there is

G♯m   F♯m

wa- ter in the font.

F♯m / B   B7   E

1 Out of deep unordered water
God created land and life;
world of beast and bird and later
twosome people, man and wife.

There is water in the river
bringing life to tree and plant.
Let creation praise its giver:
there is water in the font.

2 Water on the human forehead,
birthmark of the love of God,
in the sign of death and rising,
through the sea there runs a road.

3 Standing round the font reminds us
of the Hebrew's climb ashore.
Life is hallowed by the knowledge
God has been this way before.

Fred Kaan

849

581 Peace is my parting gift to you

Sister Gabriel

'*Peace is my parting gift to you,*
my own peace.
Peace is my parting gift to you,'
says the Lord.

(Jn. 14:27)

1 Set your troubled hearts at rest,
and banish all your fears, for . . .

(Jn. 14:27)

2 I will give you peace such as the world,
it cannot give, for . . .

(Jn. 14:27)

3 Come to me all who are weary
and in need of rest, for . . .

(Mk. 11:28)

4 You will find my yoke is easy,
and my burden light, for . . .

(Mk. 11:30)

5 As the Father sent me, so now
I am sending you, for . . .

(Jn. 20:21)

6 In my Spirit's power
all your sins will be forgiven, for . . .

(Jn. 20:22–23)

7 Go and take my gift of peace
to all throughout the world, for . . .

(Mk. 16:15 and Mt. 18:18)

Paraphrased from Scripture by Sr Gabriel
(verse 1 and response)
and Robert B. Kelly (verses 2–7)

582 Peace, perfect peace, in this dark world

SONG 46   Orlando Gibbons (1583–1625)

1 Peace, perfect peace, in this dark world of sin?
  The blood of Jesus whispers peace within.

2 Peace, perfect peace, by thronging duties pressed?
  To do the will of Jesus, this is rest.

3 Peace, perfect peace, with sorrows surging round?
  On Jesus' bosom nought but calm is found.

4 Peace, perfect peace, with loved ones far away?
  In Jesus' keeping we are safe, and they.

5 Peace, perfect peace, our future all unknown?
  Jesus we know, and he is on the throne.

6 Peace, perfect peace, death shadowing us and ours?
  Jesus has vanquished death and all its powers.

7 It is enough; earth's troubles soon shall cease,
  and Jesus call us to heaven's perfect peace.

E.H. Bickersteth (1823–1906)

583 Peacetime

Carey Landrey

Peacetime, peacetime,
time for making peace.
Peacetime, peacetime,
time to say I forgive you,
time for saying 'I love you',
time to live as friends.

1 Happy are they
who are makers of peace;
happy are they
who forgive;
happy are they
who know how to love;
they're the sons
and daughters of God.

2 Happy are they
who are gentle of heart;
happy are those
who care;
happy are they
who seek the good of all;
they're the ones
so close to God's heart.

Carey Landry

584   Praise the Lord for the Heavens above!

Douglas Rowe
Harmony by John Rombaut

1 Praise the Lord for the heavens above!
Praise the Lord for the sun and the moon!
Praise the Lord for the stars shining bright!
Yes praise, O praise the Lord!

2 Praise the Lord for the breezes and the winds!
Praise the Lord for the cold and heat!
Praise the Lord for the showers so cool!
Yes praise, O praise the Lord!

3 Praise the Lord for the nights and the days!
Praise the Lord for the weeks and the months!
Praise the Lord for the years as they pass!
Yes praise, O praise the Lord!

4 Praise the Lord for redemption from sin!
Praise the Lord for salvation is ours!
Praise the Lord for that glorious day!
Yes praise, O praise the Lord!

5 Praise the Lord for his passion and death!
Praise the Lord for his sufferings so cruel!
Praise the Lord for arising from death!
Yes praise, O praise the Lord!

Douglas Rowe, SJ

585   Praise the Lord! Ye heavens, adore him

AUSTRIA (87 87D)   Croatian folk tune, adapted by F.J.Haydn (1732–1809)

in the height; sun and moon, re- joice be- fore him, praise him, all ye stars and light. Praise the Lord! For he hath spo- ken; worlds his migh- ty voice o- beyed: Laws, which nev- er shall be bro- ken, for their guid- ance he hath made.

2 Praise the Lord! for he is glorious;
  never shall his promise fail:
  God hath made his saints victorious;
  sin and death shall not prevail.
  Praise the God of our salvation;
  hosts on high, his power proclaim;
  heaven and earth and all creation,
  laud and magnify his name!

3 Worship, honour, glory, blessing,
  Lord, we offer to thy name;
  young and old, thy praise expressing,
  join their Saviour to proclaim.
  As the saints in heaven adore thee,
  we would bow before thy throne;
  as thine angels serve before thee,
  so on earth thy will be done.

Verses 1–2 from the Foundling Hospital Collection
(1796);
verse 3 by E. Osler (1798–1863)

586 Praise to the Lord!

Paschal Jordan
Harmony by Eric Welch

Praise to the Lord! Praise him!
Praise to the Lord!

1 Shout to God, all you heavens,
and clap your hands you on earth.
Enter into his presence
exulting and singing for joy!

2 Know that God is our Father;
he made us, we are his own.
Come to him with thanksgiving
extolling and blessing his name.

3 Merciful to us, sinners,
compassionate to his sons,
he has sent his beloved
to guide us in justice and peace!

4 Praise him, then, with full voices
and sing to him from the heart!
Gather, Christians, together,
together, to joyfully sing.

5 Praise the Lord with trumpet.
O praise his name with the dance;
celebrate with the cymbal,
exalt him with drum, pipe and string!

Paschal Jordan

587 Rain down justice

Tony Barr

Refrain

Rain down jus-tice you heavens from a-bove; let the earth bring forth for us

the one who is to come.

the one who is to come. Be not an-gry, O Lord, and re-

mem-ber no lon-ger our sin-ful-ness. Our ci-ty, the ci-ty of your

A   C   Bm   Em   Am   D

Ho-ly One,   has be - come a   de-sert.

Em   A   C   Bm   Em   A

Si - on is ly-ing   in ru-ins;   Je - ru-sa - lem, hav-ing fallen   lies

Bm7   C   Am   D   Em   Bm

de-so-late. Is this the House of your glory and your ho-li-ness, where our

E   C   Am   Em   C

fa-thers came to praise you?

Refrain

Bm   C   Am   D

Em   C   Em   Bm

2. We have sinned and stand be - fore you un - clean; we have

A   C   Bm   Em

cho - sen to walk   our   own   ways.   We have

Am   D   Em   A

fal - len   as   the   leaves   of   the   au - tumn,   scattered

C   Bm   Em   A   Bm7

by   the   wind.   Just   as   the   ra - vage   of

859

earth by the win-ter storms we have blot-ted your

memory from our sight. You have hid-den your

face a — way from us, you have crushed us with the

weight of our e-vil.

3. See the sorrow of your peo-ple, O Lord; send the

Sa-viour, the one who is to come. Send us the

Lamb to take a-way the sins of the world, to take a-

way our burdens. Send us a Lord to rule the

earth, to this ci-ty built on your ho-ly

mountain. Then he shall free us from all that has en-

slaved us the day he takes a – way the yoke of our cap –
ti – vi – ty.
4. Be com – for – ted, be com – for – ted my peo – ple, your sal –
va – tion is ve – ry close at hand. Why are your hearts so full of
sor – row, why does such grief so es – trange you?
Do not be a – fraid any more I am the
Promised One, the hope of the ages. You are my
peo – ple and soon I come to res – cue you; I am the
Ho – ly One, the Lord your Re – dee – mer.

Based on the Rorate Caeli by Tony Barr

861

588 Rejoice and shout for joy

Anne Seymour
Harmony by John Rombaut

Rejoice, and shout for joy
sing out in praise for what the Lord has done.
It's right to praise him and sing a new song.
Play it loudly. Sing so joyfully.
For his love it fills the earth.

1 O the words of the Lord are true
and his works are worthy of trust.
He loves what we do that's righteous
and what we do that's just.
He merely spoke and the world began
the heav'ns were formed with moons and stars.
He made the oceans by pouring them
into vast reservoirs.

2 With one breath he can scatter
the plans of a whole nation.
His intentions are the same
for ev'ry generation.
Happy is the nation
whose God is the Lord.
Not the king whose army
can boast a powerful sword.

3 O the Lord looks down from heaven
and he knows ev'ry thing we do.
He watches over those who obey him
and trust in his love so true.
O the Lord he saves and helps us
and protects us like a shield.
We depend on him. He is our hope.
To him alone we yield.

From Psalm 32(33)
by Anne Seymour

589 Rejoice, rejoice, rejoice

Norbert Farrell
Harmony by Eric Welch

Rejoice, rejoice, rejoice!
Come, let us praise the Lord! (3)
Praise the Lord! Praise the Lord! Praise the Lord!

1 Holy, holy, holy! (3)
   O, holy is the Lord!

2 Glory, glory, glory! (3)
   O, glory to the Lord!

Norbert Farrell

590 Remember man that you are dust

John Glynn

clay, that we should dare to call you 'Lord'?

Flute

Organ

Am   C   G   Dm

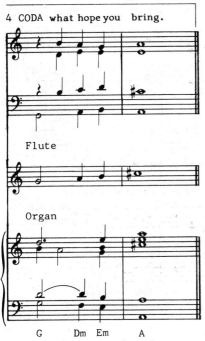

4 CODA what hope you bring.

Flute

Organ

G   Dm   Em   A

2 'Fear not, my child, I am your God.
For you I came; for you I died.'
What gift is this — a creature God!
- And in return, what can we give?

3 'O lift your heart, your heart of stone:
no longer lost, you are my own.'
O, we have sinned, deserve to die:
how can our pride admit your love?

3 O Lord of love, we turn to you:
forgive, and heal, and make us new.
No eye can see, no ear can hear,
no mind conceive what hope you bring,
what hope you bring.

John Glynn

591 Return to the Lord

Paschal Jordan
Harmony by Eric Welch

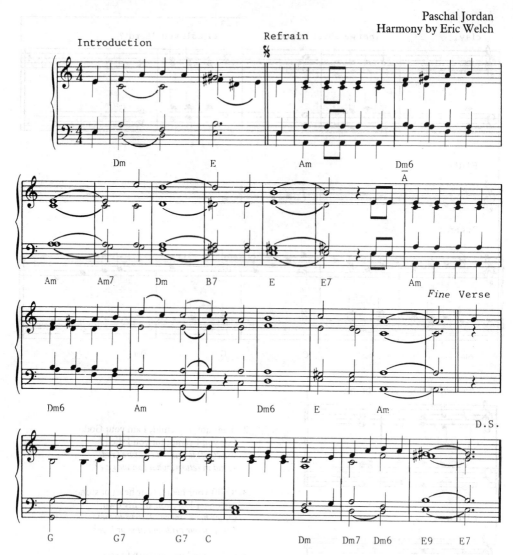

Return to the Lord, return O Israel!
He calls to you.
For the Lord is full of love and tender mercy;
he waits for your heart.

1 What shall I do with you, O my people?
  This love of yours so quickly disappears.
  (Hosea 6:4)

2 When will you share your bread with the hungry?
  When will you welcome in the homeless poor?
  (Isaiah 58:7)

3 I do not take delight in burnt off'ring.
  Give me yourself, your crushed and broken heart.
  (Psalm 51:17)

4 And I will plant my law deep within you.
  Deep in your heart will I inscribe my name.
  (Jeremiah 31:31)

5 I love you with a love everlasting;
  I hold you constantly close to my heart.
  (Jeremiah 31:31)

Paschal Jordan

868

592 Rock of Ages

PETRA (77 77 77)   Richard Redhead (1820–1901)

1. Rock of a-ges, cleft for me, let me hide my-self in thee;

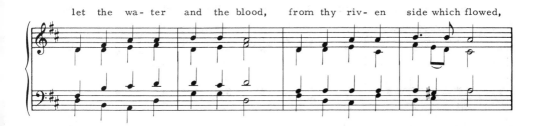

let the wa-ter and the blood, from thy riv-en side which flowed,

be of sin the doub-le cure: cleanse me from its guilt and power.

2 Not the labours of my hands
can fulfil thy law's demands;
could my zeal no respite know,
could my tears for ever flow,
all for sin could not atone:
thou must save, and thou alone.

3 Nothing in my hand I bring,
simply to thy Cross I cling;
naked, come to thee for dress;
helpless, look to thee for grace;
foul, I to the fountain fly;
wash me, Saviour, or I die.

4 While I draw this fleeting breath,
when my eyelids close in death,
when I soar through tracts unknown,
see thee on thy judgement throne;
rock of ages, cleft for me,
let me hide myself in thee.

A.M. Toplady (1740–1778)

593 Seek ye first

Karen Lafferty

This may be sung as a round.

2 Ask and it shall be given unto you,
   seek and ye shall find;
   knock and it shall be opened unto you;
   allelu, alleluia.

Karen Lafferty

594   Send forth your Spirit, God our Father

ST CLEMENT (98 98)   Clement C. Scholefield (1839–1904)

1 Send forth your Spirit, God our Father,
  as you have sent him in the past:
  at Gabriel's word, by Jordan's water,
  as Jesus went to pray and fast.

2 In this same Spirit he proclaimed you
  on Juda's hills, by Galilee,
  he called us to your heav'nly kingdom,
  he died and rose triumphantly.

3 And now though seen by us no longer
  he rests not from the task begun,
  but breathes the Spirit of his sonship,
  on men of ev'ry race and tongue.

4 May he be with us at this moment
  and give us of your Spirit still,
  that we may do the work that waits us
  and strive your purpose to fulfil.

At confirmation:

5 May all who come for confirmation
  be richly with your Spirit sealed:
  to love and serve you in their brothers,
  until your glory is revealed.

Denis E. Hurley

595 Send forth your Spirit, O Lord

Garfield Rochard
Harmony by Eric Welch

Send forth your Spirit, O Lord.
Send forth your Spirit
on these your chosen ones.
Send forth your Spirit of love.

1 To show the love of the Father,
  to show the love of the Son.
  To show the love of Jesus for all men;
  this is his new commandment.

Send forth your Spirit, O Lord.
Send forth your Spirit
on these your chosen ones.
Send forth your Spirit of truth.

2 To know the will of the Father,
  to know the will of the Son,
  to know the Gospel of Jesus the Lord,
  to proclaim to everyone.

Send forth your Spirit, O Lord.
Send forth your Spirit
on these your chosen ones.
Send them to cast your fire on earth.

Verse 3   *Sung by Confirmation Candidates*

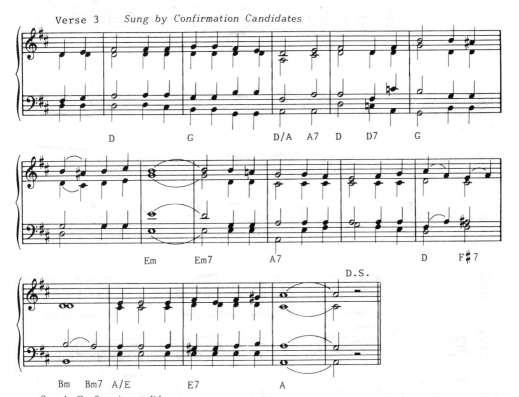

Sung by Confirmation candidates:

3 Come upon us, O Spirit of the living God!
  Come upon us, O Spirit of truth!
  Come upon us, O Spirit of love and life!
  Send us to cast your fire on earth!

Send forth your Spirit, O Lord.
Send forth your Spirit
on these your chosen ones.
Send them to cast your fire on earth.

Send forth your Spirit, O Lord.
Send forth your Spirit
on these your chosen ones.
Send forth your Spirit of love.

Garfield Rochard

596 Send forth your Spirit (Deiss)

Lucien Deiss

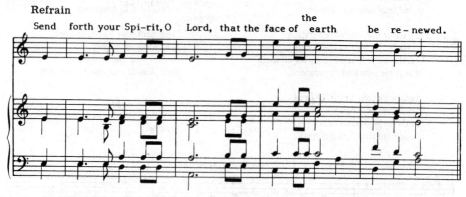

Refrain

Send forth your Spi-rit, O Lord, that the face of the earth be re-newed.

Verse

1. O my soul, a-rise and bless the Lord God, O

Lord, in ma-jesty, en-robed with pow'r and e-ter-nal might.

2 You are clothed with splendour and with beauty,
O God, and heav'nly light
is like a cloud that conceals your face.

3 You have built your palace on the waters;
on wings of winds and fire
you reign in heav'n, rule supreme on earth.

4 Like the winds your angels fly before you;
   as fire and flaming light,
   your ministers stand before your throne.

5 For the earth you fixed on its foundations;
   indeed, it shall stand firm,
   and not be moved for unending years.

6 On the earth the waters spread their mantle;
   and seas filled all the land;
   above the earth stood the rising flood.

7 When they heard on high your voice of thunder,
   in fear they took to flight;
   at your reproach, they dispersed and fled.

8 By your word, there sprang up hills and mountains;
   on earth the dry land rose,
   and in their place, rested glens and vales.

9 Your command sets bounds on all the waters,
   and they shall not return;
   they may not pass limits you have set.

10 Torrents fill the valleys at your order;
   while streams and rivers flow,
   refresh the beasts, slake the thirst of man.

11 From their nests, the birds give praise and glory
   to you, O Lord of hosts,
   from ev'ry branch, join in songs of praise.

12 In green fields you feed your sheep and cattle,
   and all your creatures, Lord;
   and yet to men, you have given more.

13 There is wine to cheer the heart of mankind;
   the wheat for man makes bread;
   and oil is used to anoint his head.

14 While I live, I sing the praise of Yahweh,
   O Lord, your glorious praise,
   my lips proclaim: Blessed be the Lord.

15 Praise to God, the author of these marvels,
   to God, the mighty One,
   who made the earth, glory to his name.

16 Praise to God, the Father, Son and Spirit,
   to God who gives us life,
   our thanks return, now and evermore.

Words from Psalm 103(104)
by Lucien Deiss

597   Shepherd of souls

NEUMARK (98 98 88)

Georg Neumark (1621–1681)
Harmony by J.S.Bach (1685–1750)

Alternative tune: Fragrance (545)

1 Shepherd of souls, in love come feed us
Life-giving bread for hungry hearts.
To those refreshing waters lead us
where dwells that grace your peace imparts.
May we, the wayward in your fold,
by your forgiveness rest consoled.

2 Life-giving vine, come, feed and nourish,
strengthen each branch with life divine.
Ever in you O may we flourish,
fruitful the branches of the vine.
Lord, may our souls be purified
so that in Christ we may abide.

3 Sinful are we who stand before you
worthy of you is Christ alone.
So in Christ's name we do implore you;
rich are mercies you have shown.
Say but the word, O Lord divine,
then are our hearts made pure like thine.

4 Following you, O Lord, who led them,
multitudes thronged the mountainside;
filled with compassion, Lord, you fed them,
fed them with loaves you multiplied.
Come, feed us now, O Lord, we pray:
lifegiving bread give us this day.

5 Help us, dear Lord, prepare a dwelling
worthy of you who made us all;
cleanse thou our hearts, our guilt dispelling,
purify us who heed your call.
'Take this and eat' were words you said,
so we have gathered for this bread.

J. Clifford Evers

598 Show me your ways

Sebastian Temple
Harmony by Stephen Dean

1. Show me your ways that I may follow you,

lead me, O master, on my way.

Guide me in all the things that I must do, di-

rect my steps that I don't go astray.

Chorus
In

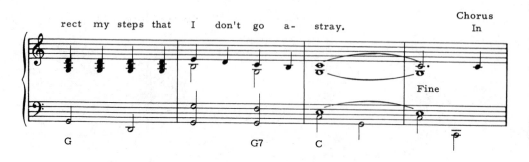

you I place my con- fi- dence and trust, O Lord,

have your way with me for I am yours.

2 Guard me when temptation calls on me to sin.
Protect me when the enemy is near.
Strengthen me to turn to you that I may win,
and bless me, Jesus, that I persevere.

Alternative Response:

The spirit's willing but the flesh is weak, O Lord.
But your support is all I'll ever need.

3 Show me your ways that I may follow you,
lead me, O Master, on my way.
Guide me in all the things that I must do,
direct my steps that I don't go astray.

Sebastian Temple

599 Sing a simple song

Carey Landry

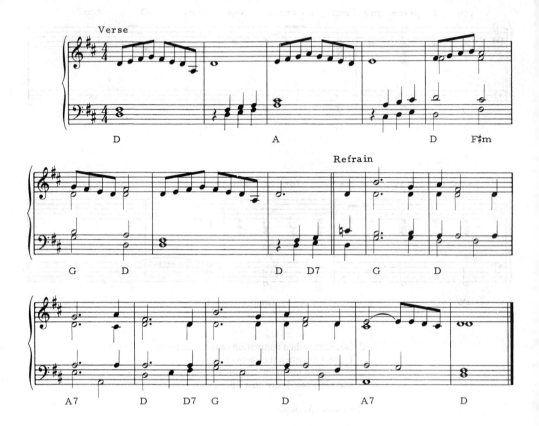

1 Sing a simple song unto the Lord;
  sing a simple song unto the Lord,
  sing it with your heart,
  sing it with your soul,
  sing a simple song unto the Lord.

  Oh Lord, I love you;
  Oh Lord, I see;
  Oh Lord, I love you,
  I see that you love me.

2 Say a simple prayer . . .

3 Give a simple gift . . .

Carey Landry

600 Sing everyone a song to the Lord

Anne Conway
Harmony by Eric Welch

1 Sing everyone a song to the Lord,
a song to the Lord of all our hearts.
He made us, we're the work of his hands,
the work of his hands in all we are.
Lord, we offer you
everything we do,
sing everyone a song to the Lord,
a song to the Lord of all our hearts.

2 Come everyone who works for his life,
who works for his life on this fair earth.
He worked for us and left us himself,
the gift of his life in bread and in wine.
Take our work and play,
it's yours every day.
Sing everyone a song to the Lord,
a song to the Lord who makes us live.

3 Sing softly, for the Lord is around,
he's there in the smallest summer breeze.
Sing sweetly, for the Lord isn't harsh,
he's gentle in voice, in giving, free.
Lord, we love with you
all those you give us now.
Sing loudly, for the love of the Lord,
the love of the Lord is all our joy.

Anne Conway

601 Sing praises to the Lord

Derick Clouden
Harmony by Eric Welch

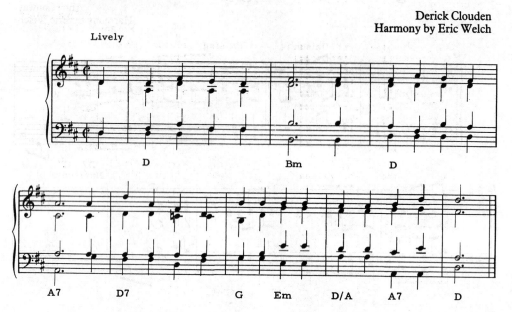

1 Sing praises to the Lord; (3)
  alleluia, alleluia!

2 And holy be his Name; (3)
  alleluia, alleluia!

3 For he is kind and good, (3)
  alleluia, alleluia!

4 He died that we might live;
  he rose again to life;
  he lives no more to die,
  alleluia, alleluia!

Derick Clouden

602 Sing to the Lord a song

Helena Warner
Harmony by Eric Welch

Refrain

Sing to the Lord a song, sing to the Lord a psalm.

Sing to the Lord, you na – tions! Praise his name!

Fine

Verse

He made hea-ven, he made the earth; the sea, the sky and all there is. He made A-dam out of naught and told him these were his.

D.C.

2 Now, Adam was a lonely man,
and God decided he would give
a helping-mate to this new man:
created the woman Eve.

3 Then God told Adam what to do:
'Go forth, good man, into the world,
multiply and fill the earth
and bless thy holy name.'

Helena Warner

883

603 Sing to the Lord, alleluia

John B. Foley SJ
Harmony by Rosalind Pitcher

2 Give to him,
you families of peoples,
glory and praise,
alleluia.

3 Great is he,
and worthy of praises
day after day,
alleluia.

4 He it is
who gave us the heavens,
glory to God,
alleluia.

5 Tell his glories,
tell all the nations,
day after day,
alleluia.

6 Bring your gifts
and enter his temple,
worship the Lord,
alleluia.

Psalm 95(96)
arr by John Foley, SJ.

604   Sing to the mountains

Bob Dufford SJ

Chorus

Sing to the moun-tains, sing to the sea. Raise your

voi - ces, lift your hearts. This is the day the

Lord has made. Let all the earth re - joice.

1. I will give thanks to you, my Lord. You have

an-swered my plea. You have saved my soul from

G7   C   E   E7   Am

death. You are my strength and my song.

D.C.

Am7   Dm   G   G7

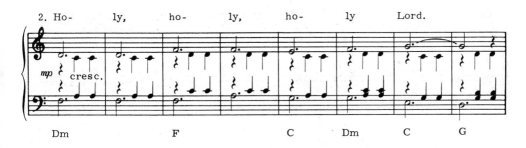

2. Ho-   ly,   ho-   ly,   ho-   ly   Lord.

mp   cresc.

Dm   F   C   Dm   C   G

Hea-   ven and earth are full of your glo-   ry.

ff   D.C.

E   E7   Am   Am7   Dm   Dm7   G   G7

3 This is the day that the Lord has made.
   Let us be glad and rejoice.
   He has turned all death to life.
   Sing of the glory of God.

Based on verses from Psalm 117(118),
Bob Dufford, SJ.

605 Sing to the world of Christ

Ernest Sands
Harmony by Paul Inwood

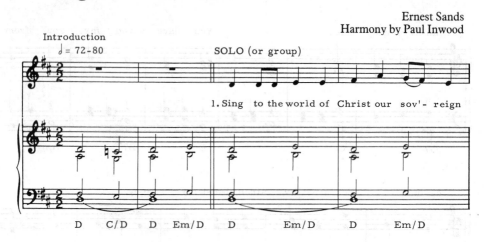

1. Sing to the world of Christ our sov'-reign
Lord;

tell of his birth which brought new life to all.

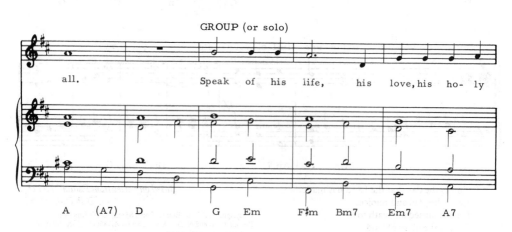

Speak of his life, his love, his ho-ly

word; let ev'-ry na- tion hear and know his call.

D G A7 D G/F♯ A7 D G A

Vss. 1 - 4

Sing to the world of Christ our sov'- reign Lord.

Bm C Bm7 Am7 D Em/D D Em/D

Last Time

(hand.)

D Em/D D Em/D D

2 Sing to the world of Christ the Prince of peace,
   showing to me the Father's loving care,
   pleading that love should reign and wars might cease,
   teaching we need the love of God to share.
   Sing to the world of Christ the Prince of peace.

3 Sing to the world of Christ our steadfast friend,
   off'ring himself to live the constant sign;
   food for our souls until we meet life's end,
   gives us his flesh for bread, his blood for wine.
   Sing to the world of Christ our steadfast friend.

4 Sing to the world of Christ our Saviour King,
   born that his death mankind's release should win;
   hung from a cross, forgiveness he could bring;
   buried, he rose to conquer death and sin.
   Sing to the world of Christ our Saviour King.

5 Sing to the world of Christ at God's right hand,
   praise to the Spirit both have sent to men,
   living in us till earth shall reach its span,
   time be no more, and Christ shall come again.
   Sing to the world of Christ at God's right hand.

Patrick Lee

606 Son of God and Son of David

Ton Van Erp

Son of God and
Son of Da-vid, priest de-void of dig-ni-ty, slave to ran-som
the en-sla-ved, butt of jibes jea-lou-sy: you were like us

2 Every creature should, with gladness,
kneel before your majesty;
every man, through joy and sadness,
witness to your sanctity,
bring you a rich credit balance
from his talents
and activity.

3 Jesus' name in condemnation
nailed to that torturing tree,
'King of Jews' that provocation
you forgave in agony.
Hear, Lord, this sinner's petition
for remission,
life eternally.

Ds Willem Barnard,
tr by Bonaventure Hinwood

607 Son of the Father

Melody from Sri Lanka
Harmony by F. and R. Kelly

1 Son of the Father, Jesus, Lord and slave,
born among the cattle in the squalor of a cave,
one with God, you made yourself
one with man, shunning wealth;
Lord, we worship you with hand and mind.

2 Son of the Father, Jesus, workers' friend,
you whom Joseph taught the skills of working with your hands,
man, at home in builder's yard,
one with man, toiling hard;
Lord, we worship you with hand and mind.

3 Son of the Father, author of our faith,
choosing men to follow you from every walk of life,
who with them, in boats, on shore,
troubles shared, burdens bore;
Lord, we worship you with hand and mind.

4 Seed of the Father, from life's furrow born,
teaching men in parables from agriculture drawn,
Jesus, lover of the soil,
man of earth, son of toil;
Lord, we worship you with hand and mind.

5 Father and Spirit, Jesus, Lord and Man,
bless us in the work you have appointed to be done.
Lift our spirits, guide our wills,
steer our hands, use our skills;
Lord, we worship you with hand and mind.

Fred Kaan

892

608 Take my life

HEINLEIN (77 77)

Melody attr. to M.Herbst (1654–1681)
Harmony by A.Gregory Murray

2 Take my hands, and let them move
   at the impulse of thy love.
   Take my feet, and let them be
   swift and purposeful for thee.

3 Take my voice, and let me sing
   always, only, for my King.
   Take my intellect, and use
   every power as thou shalt choose.

4 Take my will, and make it thine:
   it shall be no longer mine.
   Take my heart; it is thine own:
   it shall be thy royal throne.

5 Take my love; my Lord, I pour
   at thy feet its treasure-store.
   Take myself, and I will be
   ever, only, all for thee.

Frances R. Havergal (1836–79)

609   Tell out, my soul

WOODLANDS (10 10 10 10)   Walter Greatorex (1877–1949)

2 Tell out, my soul, the greatness of his name!
  Make known his might, the deeds his arm has
    done;
  his mercy sure, from age to age the same;
  his holy name – the Lord, the Mighty One.

3 Tell out, my soul, the greatness of his might!
  Powers and dominions lay their glory by.
  Proud hearts and stubborn wills are put to flight,
  the hungry fed, the humble lifted high.

4 Tell out, my soul, the glories of his word!
  Firm is his promise, and his mercy sure.
  Tell out, my soul, the greatness of the Lord
  to children's children and for evermore!

Timothy Dudley-Smith

610   The Word who is life

Carey Landry

all ho-nour and praise.   To him be glo - ry: Je - sus, our

C   F   C   F   C

Fine   Verses 2 and 3

Sav - iour and Lord.   2. He is the Light of Lights

Fine

Bb   C   Dm   G

to Refrain

our Re - deem-er King,   he is the Lord of Lords:

Dm   G   Dm   G

3 He is the bread of life;
    wonder-counsellor;
    he is Prince of peace.

Based on 1 John 1:1 by Carey Landry.

611   The angel Gabriel

GABRIEL'S MESSAGE

Basque Carol Melody
Arranged by C.Edgar Pettman (1865–1943)

1 The angel Gabriel from heaven came,
his wings as drifted snow, his eyes as flame;
'All hail,' he said, 'thou lowly maiden Mary,
most highly favoured lady.' *Gloria!*

2 'For know, a blessed Mother thou shalt be,
all generations laud and honour thee,
thy Son shall be Emmanuel, by seers foretold;
most highly favoured lady.' *Gloria!*

3 Then gently Mary meekly bowed her head,
'To me be as it pleaseth God,' she said.
'My soul shall laud and magnify his holy name';
most highly favoured lady. *Gloria!*

4 Of her, Emmanuel, the Christ was born
in Bethlehem, all on a Christmas morn,
and Christian folk throughout the world will ever say
'most highly favoured lady.' *Gloria!*

*Basque carol paraphrased by
Sabine Baring-Gould (1834–1924)*

612 The Church is wherever

A.Gregory Murray

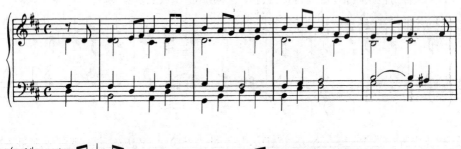

1 The Church is wherever God's people are easing
   burdens of others in love and good will.
   The Church is wherever the cross of the Saviour
   is borne by believers who follow him still.

2 The Church is wherever God's people are trusting;
   facing hard trials with hope, not despair.
   The Church is wherever a miracle follows
   beyond human power, in answer to prayer.

3 The Church is wherever his own come to Jesus,
   stirred by a longing and need to be whole.
   The Church is wherever God's people adore him
   in worship that rises from heart, mind and soul.

4 The Church is wherever disciples of Jesus
   turn to their Master each step of the way.
   The Church is wherever the love of the Saviour
   is seen in his followers' lives day by day.

Pat Regher

613 The King shall come when morning dawns

CONSOLATION (86 86)

Melody from *Kentucky Harmony* (1816
Harmony by Paul Inwood

1. The King shall come when morn-ing dawns and light tri-umph-ant

breaks, when beau-ty gilds the east-ern hills and

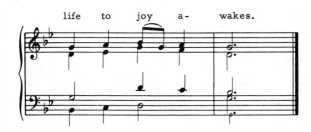

life to joy a-wakes.

2 Not as of old a little child,
to bear and fight and die,
but crowned with glory like the sun
that lights the morning sky.

3 O brighter than the rising morn
when he, victorious, rose,
and left the lonesome place of death,
despite the rage of foes.

4 O brighter than the glorious morn
shall this fair morning be,
when Christ our King in beauty comes,
and we his face shall see!

5 The King shall come when morning dawns
and light and beauty brings;
'Hail, Christ the Lord!' your people pray,
'Come quickly, King of kings!'

John Brownlie (1859–1925)

614 The Light of Christ

Donald Fishel

1. We must all be born a-gain to see the kingdom of God; the

water and the Spi-rit bring new life in God's love.

F   C   F G   C

Fz   G   C   Dm   G

D.C.

2 God gave up his only Son
  out of love for the world
  so that ev'ryone who believes in him
  will live for ever.

3 The Light of God has come to us
  so that we might have salvation,
  from the darkness of our sins, we walk
  into glory with Christ Jesus.

Donald Fishel

615 The Lord is my shepherd

Hubert Richards

1 The Lord is my shepherd.
He provides all I need
in the rich grassland,
where he lets me feed.
He brings me to water
my life to renew.
He guides me on true paths
because he is true.

2 I walk through the darkness,
with nothing to fear;
his right hand protects me
when danger is near.
He lays me a table
in spite of my foes.
He fills me with gladness,
my cup overflows.

3 Each day he is goodness,
each day he's my song.
I live in his household
the whole of life long.
The Lord is my shepherd.
He provides all I need
in the rich grassland,
where he lets me feed.

Based on Psalm 22(23)
by Hubert Richards

616 The seed is Christ's

Sean O Riada

The seed is Christ's, the har-vest his: may we be stored wi-thin God's barn. The sea is Christ's, the fish are his: may we be caught wi-thin God's net. From birth to age, from age to death, en-fold us, Christ, wi-thin your arms. Un-til the end, the

great re-birth, Christ be our joy in Pa-ra-dise.

Traditional Irish,
tr by James Quinn, SJ

617 The Spirit is moving

Carey Landry

Refrain
The Spi-rit is mo-ving all o - ver, all o - ver this land.

Verse

The Spirit is moving all over,
all over this land.

1 People are gathering, the Church is born;
the Spirit is blowing on a world reborn.

2 Doors are opening as the Spirit comes;
his fire is burning in his people now.

3 Filled with his Spirit we are sent to serve;
we are called out as brothers, we are called to work.

4 The world, born once, is born again;
we recreate it in love and joy.

5 Old men are dreaming dreams;
and young men see the light.

6 Old walls are falling down;
and people are speaking with each other.

7 The Spirit fills us with his power
to be his witnesses to all we meet.

8 The Spirit urges us to travel light
to be people of courage who spread his fire.

9 God has poured out his Spirit
on all; on all creation.

Carey Landry

618 Walk in the light

Source unknown
Arranged by Michael Irwin

1. The Spirit lives to set us free, walk, walk in the light. He binds us all in unity, walk, walk in the light.

Chorus

Walk in the light, walk in the light, walk in the light, walk in the light of the Lord.

2 Jesus promised life to all,
the dead were wakened by his call.

3 He died in pain on Calvary,
to save the lost like you and me.

4 We know his death was not the end,
He gave his Spirit to be our friend.

5 By Jesus' love our wounds are healed,
the Father's kindness is revealed.

6 The Spirit lives in you and me,
His light will shine for all to see.

Damian Lundy

619 The Spirit of God rests upon me

Lucien Deiss

Refrain

The Spi-rit of God rests up-on me, the Spi-rit of God consecrates

Gm   Dm E♭   B♭ Gm   Dm Gm   Cm

Verse

me   the Spi-rit of God bids me go forth to pro-claim his peace, his joy.   1. The

Dm   Gm E♭ B♭   Gm   E♭ B♭ Cm   G

Spirit of God sends me forth, called to   witness the kingdom of Christ among all the

Gm   Dm   E♭   B♭   F Cm E♭7   B♭ Gm F

na-tions; called to pro-claim the good news of Christ to the poor.   My

Cm Gm   Dm   F   Cm   Gm   B♭

spi- rit re-joic- es in God, my Sa- viour.

Eb   Cm   Bb   Cm   Gm

2 The Spirit of God sends me forth,
  called to witness the kingdom of Christ
  among all the nations;
  called to console
  the hearts overcome with great sorrow.
  My spirit rejoices in God, my Saviour.

3 The Spirit of God sends me forth,
  called to witness the kingdom of Christ
  among all the nations;
  called to comfort
  the poor who mourn and who weep.
  My spirit rejoices in God, my Saviour.

4 The Spirit of God sends me forth,
  called to witness the kingdom of Christ
  among all the nations;
  called to announce
  the grace of salvation to men.
  My spirit rejoices in God, my Saviour.

5 The Spirit of God sends me forth,
  called to witness the kingdom of Christ
  among all the nations;
  called to reveal
  his glory among all the people.
  My spirit rejoices in God, my Saviour.

Based on Isaiah 61:1–2 and Luke 4:18–19
by Lucien Deiss

620 There is a river

Origin unknown
Harmony by Stephen Dean

2 Wash me with water, and then I shall be clean;
white as the new snow, if you remove my sin.
(Psalm 50)

3 Plunged in the water, the tomb of our rebirth,
so may we rise up to share in Christ's new life.

4 All who are thirsty, now hear God as he calls;
come to the Lord's side, his life pours out for all.
(Jn. 19:33–35)

5 Safe in the new Ark, the Church of Christ our Lord,
praise God for water, his sign to save the world.

Verse 1 trad;
verses 2–5 Robert B. Kelly

621 There is one Lord

Lucien Deiss

There is one Lord,
there is one faith,
there is one baptism,
one God, who is Father.

1 We were called to be one in the Spirit of God,
in the bond of peace, we sing and proclaim.

2 We were called to form one body in one spirit,
we sing and proclaim.

3 We were called in the same hope in Christ the Lord,
we sing and proclaim.

Based on Ephesians 4:5 by Lucien Deiss

622 Thine be the glory

MACCABEUS

Adapted from G.F.Handel (1685–1759)

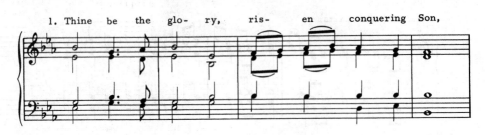

1. Thine be the glo- ry, ris- en conquering Son,

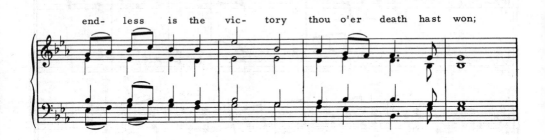

end- less is the vic- tory thou o'er death hast won;

an- gels in bright rai- ment rolled the stone a- way,

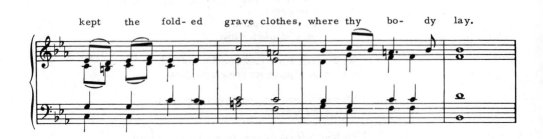

kept the fold- ed grave clothes, where thy bo- dy lay.

Refrain

Refrain
Thine be the glo- ry, ris- en, conquering Son,

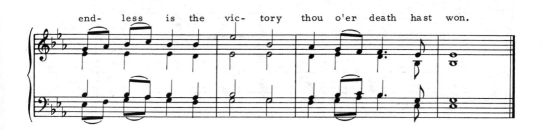

end- less is the vic- tory thou o'er death hast won.

2 Lo, Jesus meets us risen from the tomb;
   lovingly he greets us, scatters fear and gloom;
   let the church with gladness, hymn of triumph sing,
   for her Lord is living, death has lost its sting.

3 No more we doubt thee, glorious Prince of life;
   life is nought without thee; aid us in our strife;
   make us more than conquerors, through thy deathless love;
   bring us safe through Jordan to thy home above.

Edmond Louis Budry (1854–1932),
tr by Richard Birch Hoyle (1875–1939)

623 This is my body

Jimmy Owens

2 This is my blood poured out for you,
bringing forgiveness, making you free.
Take it and drink it, and when you do,
do it in love for me.

3 Back to my Father soon I shall go.
Do not forget me; then you will see
I am still with you, and you will know
you're very close to me.

4 Filled with my Spirit, how you will grow!
You are my branches; I am the tree.
If you are faithful, others will know
you are alive in me.

5 Love one another – I have loved you,
and I have shown you how to be free;
serve one another, and when you do,
do it in love for me.

Verse 1 and 2 Jimmy Owens;
verses 3–5 Damian Lundy

624 This is the day (i)

Anne Conway
Harmony by F. and R. Kelly

This is the day
that the Lord has made,
let us rejoice and shout
'Alleluia!'

1 We were asleep,
it seemed like death
but now the morning's broken.

2 The winter's past,
the grass is green
and Spring is life in our land.

3 The Lord of life
has passed through death
and still he lives among us.

Based on Psalm 117(118)
by Anne Conway

625   This is the day (ii)

Fiji folk song

1 This is the day (2)
   that the Lord has made. (2)
   We will rejoice, (2)
   and be glad in it. (2)
   This is the day
   that the Lord has made.
   We will rejoice
   and be glad in it.
   This is the day
   that the Lord has made.

2 This is the day
   when he rose again . . .

3 This is the day
   when the Spirit came . . .

Author unknown

626   This is the feast of victory

John Ylvisaker
Harmony by F. and R. Kelly

This is the feast of vict'ry for our God
for the Lamb who was slain
has begun his reign, alleluia!
This is the feast of vict'ry for our God
for the Lamb who was slain
has begun his reign, alleluia!

Verse

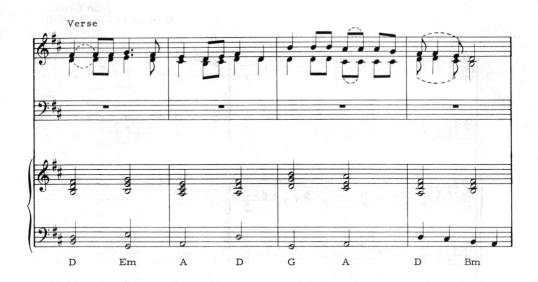

D   Em   A   D   G   A   D   Bm

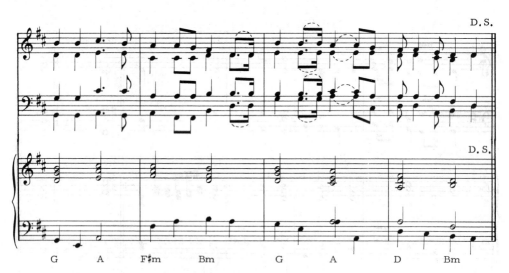

G   A   F♯m   Bm   G   A   D   Bm

1 Worthy is Christ, the Lamb who was slain,
   whose blood set us free to be people of God.
   Power, riches, wisdom and strength
   and honour, blessing and glory are his.

2 Sing with all the people of God
   and join in the hymn of all creation:
   blessing, honour, glory and might
   be to God and the Lamb for ever. Amen.

Based on Revelations 4:9–14
by John Ylvisaker

627   This is the night

Miriam Therese Winter

1. This is the night when God de — li — vered our fore-
2. This is the night the pillar of fire be-comes a

fa - thers from their chains, led them dry - shod through the sea,
bea - con of be — lief to lead the peo - ple on, when

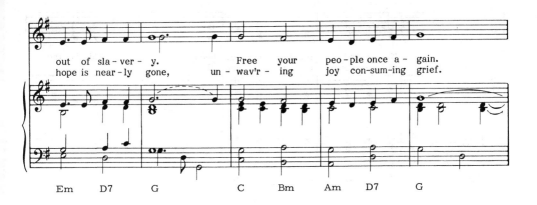

out of sla - ver - y. Free your peo - ple once a - gain.
hope is near - ly gone, un - wav'r - ing joy con-sum-ing grief.

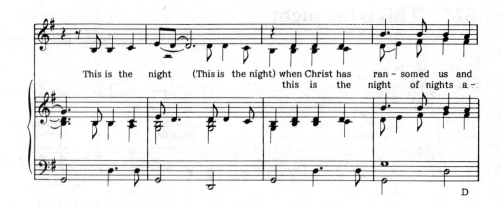

This is the night (This is the night) when Christ has ran - somed us and
this is the night of nights a -

paid the price of sin. The Pas-chal Lamb was slain, bring - ing peace through
wait - ed since the Fall, when death is our re - birth, with heav - en wed to

C G C G Am D7

pain. We will fol - low where he's been. This is the
earth, re — con - cil - ing one and all.

Em C D C D7 C D7 G

night this is the night he rose tri - um - phant from the
(This is the night) this is the night of joy, of sol - emn songs of

D G   D7   G   Bm7   C   D7

grave, o - pened what was sealed, for - gave and blessed and healed
praise, wash-ing guilt a - way. The night shall be as day,

G   C   G   Am   D7   G

those he suf-fered death to save. O hap - py fault!
mourning turned to danc-ing all our days. O hap-py

O hap - py fault.

Bm   Am   D7 G
919

Based on the Exsultet
by Miriam Therese Winter

920

628   This is what Yahweh asks of you

Mary McGann RSCJ
Harmony by Rosalind Pitcher

This is what Yah-weh asks of you, on-ly

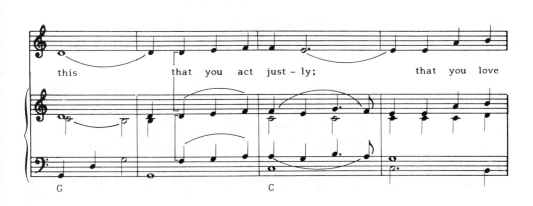

this that you act just-ly; that you love

ten-der-ly, that you walk hum-bly

with your God.

G C Am

FINE

1. "My

Dm G

Verses

(V3 ♩. ♪ ♩)

1. chil – dren I am with you such a lit–tle while,
2. "Do not let your hearts be trou – bled:
3. "Peace is the gift I leave with you,

G F C

(V2 ♩ ♩)

  and where I go now you can – not
  trust in God now, and trust in
a peace the world can ne – ver

Dm G

come.
Me.
give.

A new com-
I go to pre-
If you keep my word my

- mand — ment I give to you:
pa — re a place for you,
Fa — ther will love you,

as I have
and I shall
and we will

C

Am

F

C

Am

(V1)

(V1) (V1)

loved you, so love each o-ther."
come a-gain to take you home."
come to you to make our home."

F

G

C

D.C.

Mary McGann, RSCJ

923

629 Thou whose almighty Word

MOSCOW (664 6664)

Adapted from
Felice de Giardini (1716–96

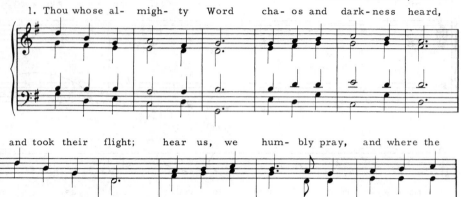

2 Thou who didst come to bring
on thy redeeming wing
healing and sight,
health to the sick in mind,
sight to the inly blind,
ah! now to all mankind
let there be light.

3 Spirit of truth and love,
life-giving, holy dove,
speed forth thy flight!
Move on the water's face,
bearing the lamp of grace,
and in earth's darkest place
let there be light!

4 Blessed and holy Thee,
glorious Trinity,
wisdom, love, might;
boundless as ocean tide
rolling in fullest pride,
through the world far and wide
let there be light!

J Marriott (1780–1825)

630 Though the mountains may fall

Daniel L. Schutte

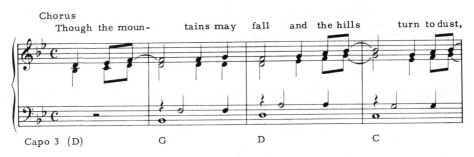

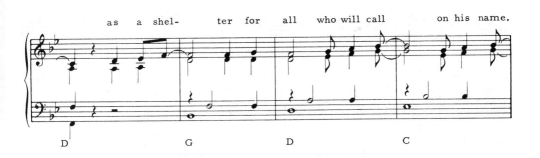

Verses

More gently

1. Could the Lord ev-er leave you? Could the Lord for-get his love?

Though the mo-ther for-sake her child, he will not a-ban-don you.

C   F#m   Bm   C   Am7   G   C   F#m   Bm   C   Am7   D

D.C.

2 Should you turn and forsake him,
  he will gently call your name.
  Should you wander away from him,
  he will always take you back.

3 Go to him when you're weary;
  he will give you eagle's wings.
  You will run, never tire,
  for your God will be your strength.

4 As he swore to your Fathers,
  when the flood destroyed the land.
  He will never forsake you;
  he will swear to you again.

Daniel L. Schutte, SJ

631 Through all the changing scenes of life

WILTSHIRE (86 86)   George T.Smart (1776–1867)

1 Through all the changing scenes of life,
  in trouble and in joy,
  the praises of my God shall still
  my heart and tongue employ.

2 Of his deliverance I will boast,
  till all that are distressed,
  when learning this, will comfort take
  and calm their griefs to rest.

3 O magnify the Lord with me,
  with me exalt his name;
  when in distress to him I called
  he to my rescue came.

4 The hosts of God encamp around
  the dwellings of the just;
  deliverance he affords to all
  who on his succour trust.

5 O make but trial of his love;
  experience will decide
  how blest are they, and only they,
  who in his truth confide.

6 Fear him, ye saints, and you will then
  having nothing else to fear;
  make you his service your delight,
  your wants shall be his care.

Psalm 33(34) 1–9,
Nahum Tate (1625–1715)
and Nicholas Brady (1659–1726) alt

927

632　To be the body of the Lord

Clyde Harvey
Harmony by Eric Welch

To be the body of the Lord in this world,
to have his Spirit coursing through my soul,
to know the passion of my Jesus
in his love for every man,
to show his mercy in the shadows of this land.

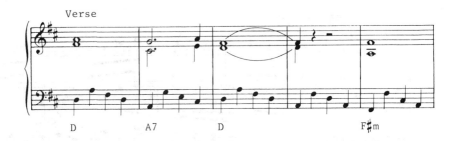

Verse

1 Come, walk with me; come, share my life,
  you must know the shadows
  if you would know the light.

2 No eyes have I, no ears to hear,
  you must be my Body and show
  my Father's care.

3 Open your eyes, see what I see.
  For this world how I suffer.
  Share my destiny.

4 I am the vine, branches are you.
  Life from me eternal to make
  your world anew.

5 One bread, one cup; one heart and mind.
  One great human people
  in fellowship divine.

Clyde Harvey

633 To God our Father be the praise

Bill Tamblyn

1 To God our Father be the praise,
  be glory ever given,
  for to this world he sent his Son
  that we might be forgiven.

2 The world in sin and darkness lay;
  goodness was put to flight;
  and in the fulness of his time
  God sent his Son, the Light.

3 'In him was life' the Gospel says,
  'this life was light of men.'
  The darkness has been overcome,
  the Light of God shines on.

4 The Light of God is in the world,
  but shines not everywhere;
  he shines alone in human lives
  when he's invited there.

5 'Behold at the door of your life I stand
  the Light, the Life, the Love;
  I will come in,' he says, 'and will
  illuminate your soul.'

6 Rejoice then, you who sing this hymn;
  real life, real joy and light
  shall be for you eternally,
  if you will welcome him.

William Armitage

634 Together we journey

John Glynn
Harmony by John Rombaut

Together we journey on the highway of God,
to the mountain of glory of glory and grace;
and together we'll seek for the pearl of great price
till we meet with the Lord face to face.

1 There's one on that journey who's burdened
    with sorrow,
  bitterness hidden by grief:
  yet we shall bear it, together we'll share it,
  united in heart and in mind.

2 Another who travels is joyful and trusting,
  clothed with the garment of peace:
  so we shall wear it, together we'll share it,
  united in heart and mind.

3 And all we who journey have gladness and sorrow
  somewhere on God's holy way:
  so we shall bear them, together we'll share them,
  united in heart and in mind.

John Glynn

931

635 Trust in the Lord

Robert F. O'Connor

Introduction ♩ = 105   Antiphon

Trust in the Lord; you shall not tire. Serve you the Lord; you shall not weak-en. For the Lord's own strength will up-hold you. You shall re-new your life and live. (Verse 1)

2. 3.　　　　　　　　　　　　　　Last time
　　　　　　　　　　　　　　　　　　　　Fine

live.　　　(Verse 2)　live.
　　　　　　(Verse 3)

F　　　　　　　　　　　Bb　　　F
　　　　　　　　　　　　　　　　Fine

Verse 1

1. The Lord is our e- ter- nal God. He nei-ther faints

Bb　　　　　　F　　　　　　　　C

nor grows wea-ry.　　Our hearts　　he probes from a-

F　　　　　　　　Bb

far,　　know-ing our ways,　　know-ing our ways.　　(Antiphon)
　　　　　　　　　　　　　　　　　　　　　　rit.

F　　　　Gm　　C　　　　F

933

Verse 2

2. Young hearts may grow faint and weak. Youths may col- lapse, stum-ble and fall. They that hope in the Lord will re-new their cour-age. They'll soar with ea-gle's might. *(Antiphon)*

Bb   F   C   F   Bb   F   Gm   C   F

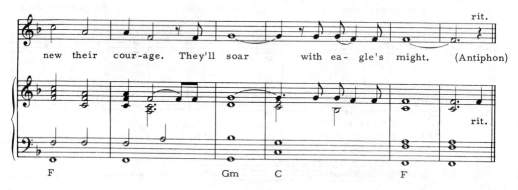

3 Old men shall dream new dreams;
   young men will find wisdom in visions.
   The Lord will speak in our lifetime,
   show his face to those who wait.

Based on Isaiah 40:28–31
by Robert F. O'Connor, SJ.

636 Unite us, Lord, in peace

Dominique Ombrie

2 You are our expectation
  in loneliness and pain;
  your healing and your pardon
  are greater than our sin.

3 Lord, look upon the starving
  and set the captive free.
  Share out among our brothers
  the bread of unity.

4 How happy are the people
  who strive to be at one,
  who learn to live as brothers,
  who lay their hatred down.

5 O Lord, whose silent spirit
  enlightens and endows,
  make us in faith receptive
  and help us love your house.

6 Your cross will draw together
  the circle of mankind;
  in you shall all the people
  their true communion find.

7 Death can no longer hurt us,
  triumphant is your word.
  Let life now grow and blossom,
  O Jesus, risen Lord!

Dominque Ombrie, tr by Fred Kaan

637   Upon thy table, Lord

Traditional English Melody
Harmony by Stephen Dean

DANBY (88.88)

1. Up- on thy ta- ble, Lord, we place these sym-bols

of our work and thine, life's food won on- ly by thy

grace, who giv'st to all the bread and wine.

2 Within these simple things there lie
  the height and depth of human life,
  the thought of man, his tears and toil,
  his hopes and fears, his joy and strife.

3 Accept them, Lord; from thee they come;
  we take them humbly at thy hand.
  These gifts of thine for higher use
  we offer, as thou dost command.

M.F.C. Willson (1884–1944)

638   Veni Sancte Spiritus

Christopher Walker

This was sung as the Entrance and Confirmation chants for the Papal Mass at Coventry Airport on Pentecost Sunday, May 30th 1982.

Establish the congregational refrain firmly before adding the solo part.* The refrain continues under each of the five verses and may be repeated at the end softly.

The congregation should sing quietly and prayerfully while the soloist sings according to the natural stresses of the words in the verses.

If desired a pleasing variation is to perform it with guitar accompaniment with the solo part taken by a flute. If desired the whole could be transposed into D with no capo.

height.   Come   thou   Fa-   ther   of   the   poor, come now with

Ve-   ni,   Ve-   ni San- cte Spi- ri-   tus;

Bm   D   Em7   F#m

trea- sures   that en- dure: Light of   all   who   live.

Ve-   ni   San-   cte Spi- ri-   tus.

Gmaj7   A   D   Gmaj7 A7   D

Verses 2 - 5 over

2. Thou of all con- so- lers the best. Thou the

soul's de- light- ful guest; re- fresh- ing peace be- stow. Thou in

toil my com- fort sweet; thou cool- ness in the heat.

Thou my so- lace in time of woe.

3. Light im- mor- tal, light di- vine; fire of

love our hearts re- fine, our in- most be- ing

fill. Take thy grace a- way and no- thing pure in man will stay,

all his good is turned to ill.

4. Heal our wounds our strength re-new, on our dry-ness pour thy dew; wash guilt a-way, bend the stub-born heart, melt the fro-zen, warm the chill and guide the steps that go a-stray.

5. Seven-fold gifts on us be pleased to pour, who thee con-fess and thee a-dore; bring us thy com-fort when we die; give us life with thee on high; give us joys, give us joys that ne-ver end.

Attr. to Stephen Langton (c1160–1228), altered by Christopher Walker
from the translation by Edward Caswall (1814–1878)

941

639 Wake, awake! For night is dying

WACHET AUF

Melody by P.Nicolai (1556–1608)
adapted and harmonized by J.S.Bach (1685–1750)

1st time · 2nd time

1 'Wake, awake! For night is dying,'
   the watchmen on the heights are crying,
   'Awake, Jerusalem, at last!'
   Midnight hears the welcome voices,
   and at the thrilling cry rejoices:
   'Come forth, you virgins, night is past;
   the bridegroom comes; awake,
   your lamps with gladness take,
   alleluia!
   And for his marriage feast prepare,
   for you must go to meet him there.'

2 Sion hears the watchmen singing,
   and all her heart with joy is springing;
   she wakes, she rises from her gloom:
   for her Lord comes down all-glorious,
   the strong in grace, in truth victorious;
   her star is risen, her light is come.
   Now come, O blessed one,
   God's own beloved Son;
   alleluia!
   We follow to the festal hall
   to sup with you, the Lord of all.

3 Now let earth and heaven adore you,
   as men and angels sing before you
   with harp and cymbal's joyful tone;
   of one pearl each shining portal,
   where we join with the choirs immortal
   of angels round your dazzling throne.
   No eye has seen, nor ear
   is yet attuned to hear,
   such great glory;
   alleluia, as here we sing
   our praise to you, eternal King!

Philipp Nicolai (1556–1608)
tr Catherine Winkworth (1827–78) alt

640 Wake up! The dawn is near

Eric Welch

Wake up! the dawn is near;
no time for sleeping, this:
our God is sending us his gift,
his Son, the Lord of bliss.

1 Come, Lord of all the world,
   creation's source and sum;
   break through these barren wintry skies
   and show your mercy – come!

2 Our sins are multiplied,
   yet yours alone we stand –
   you shaped us as the clay is shaped
   beneath the potter's hand.

3 See how we stray from you,
   so deeply have we sinned,
   swept on by wickedness; like leaves
   before the autumn wind.

4 Yet still we trust your word,
   your pardon precious-priced,
   your wisdom sweetly ruling all,
   the chosen one, your Christ.

Luke Connaughton (1919–79)

641 We are bound for the promised land

John C. Ylvisaker
Harmony by John Rombaut

We are bound for the promised land,
we're bound for the promised land;
Oh, who will come and go with us?
We are bound for the promised land.

1 We seek you, Lord, and all your strength
  your presence constantly,
  rememb'ring all your marv'lous works,
  and all that you can be:

2 You are the Lord, you are the God
  whose judgements fill this earth;
  you're mindful of your covenant;
  we can trust you at your Word.

3 To Abraham you made a vow,
  a promise to his son:
  'I'll give to you the promised land!
  Your inheritance is won.'

4 Give glory to the Father, Son,
  and Spirit, One in Three;
  as it was in the beginning,
  it shall forever be.

From Psalm 104(105)
paraphrased by John C. Ylvisaker

945

642 We cry 'Hosanna, Lord'

Mimi Farra

We cry 'Hosanna, Lord,' yes, 'Hosanna, Lord,'
yes, 'Hosanna, Lord' to you.
We cry, 'Hosanna, Lord,' yes 'Hosanna, Lord,'
yes, 'Hosanna, Lord,' to you.

2 Children wave their palms
as the King of all kings rides by.
Should we forget to praise our God,
the very stones would sing.

3 He comes to set us free.
He gives us liberty.
His vict'ry over death is
th'eternal sign of God's love for us,

Mimi Farra

643   We form one Church, one Christian folk

American Traditional Melody
Harmony by John Rombaut

1 We form one Church, one Christian folk,
  redeemed by God's own Son;
  refreshed by clear and saving streams,
  we share in graces won.
  We break the Bread of heaven
  to feed us on our way,
  we take the cup that holds blood
  to celebrate his day.

2 We know the kindness of his love;
  we know his will to save;
  we know he's won the victory
  o'er sin and o'er the grave.
  To each of us is given
  the fullness of his grace,
  to live in joy a life of love
  until we see his face.

3 Our hope is based on Jesus Christ,
  our faith is in his name;
  we know he seeks the sinful one,
  for that is why he came;
  he cares for those who suffer,
  he loves both young and old,
  a man of sorrows, risen now,
  as he himself foretold!

Willard F. Jabusch

947

644 We gather together to ask the Lord's blessing

KREMSER (12 11 12 12)

Netherlands Folk Melody (c.17)
Arr. Eduard Kremser

1. We gather together to ask the Lord's blessing, he chastens and hastens his will to make known; the wicked oppressing now cease from distressing, sing praises to his Name; he forgets not his own.

* these notes are tied in vv 2-3, in v 2 on 'all', in v 3 on 'O'.

2 Beside us to guide us, our God with us joining,
  ordaining, maintaining his kingdom divine;
  so from the beginning the fight we were winning:
  thou, Lord, wast at our side: all glory be thine!

3 We all do extol thee, thou leader triumphant.
  And pray that thou still our defender wilt be.
  Let thy congregation escape tribulation:
  thy Name be ever praised! O Lord, make us free!

Theodore Baker (1851–1934)

645 We praise you and thank you

ST PATRICK (11 11 11 11)   Irish Traditional Melody

1 We praise you and thank you our Father above,
who offer us peace in your kingdom of love.
Your people are saved by the death of your Son
who leads us to glory where all will be one.
Accepting this Gospel we honour Saint Patrick,
who taught in our land what your kindness has done.

2 Your Word has revealed what our future will be,
'Raised up from earth I draw all men to me.'
May we, like Saint Patrick, bear witness to you,
reflecting your love in whatever we do.
He came to our country which once had enslaved him,
to preach the good news that God makes all things new.

Donal Murray

949

646 We praise you, God (Te Deum)

SONG 1 (10 10.10 10.10 10)

Orlando Gibbons (1583–1625)

1 We praise you, God, confessing you as Lord!
  Eternal Father, all earth worships you!
  Angelic choirs, high heavens, celestial powers,
  cherubs and seraphs praise you ceaselessly:
  'All-holy Lord, O God of heavenly hosts,
  your glorious majesty fills heaven and earth.'

2 Blessed apostles join in praise of you
  with prophets famed and martyrs clothed in white,
  singing with holy Church throughout the earth:
  'Father, we praise your boundless majesty!
  We praise your glorious, true and only Son!
  We praise you, Holy Spirit, Paraclete!'

3 You are the King of glory, Jesus Christ!
  You are the Father's everlasting Son!
  Born for mankind from lowly Virgin's womb,
  death you have conquered, opening heaven to faith;
  throned now in glory at the Father's side
  you shall return in glory as our judge.

4 We pray you, therefore, give your servants aid,
  whom you have ransomed with your precious blood,
  let them be ranked in glory with your saints;
  save, Lord, the people who are wholly yours,
  bless them, for they are your inheritance,
  and, as their ruler, ever raise them up.

5 Throughout each single day, we bless you Lord,
  for all eternity we praise your name.
  Keep us this day, Lord, free from every sin;
  have mercy on us, Lord; have mercy, Lord;
  show us your love, as we have hoped in you!
  You are my hope, Lord; you shall fail me not!

Te Deum laudamus,
tr by James Quinn, SJ

647   We thank you, Father

Gregory Norbet and
Mary David Callahan OSB

Intro - Moderately

Refrain - a tempo
We thank you,

rit.

Fa- ther,   for the gift of faith   through Je- sus

Christ your   Son   and for the gift of life   with each

oth- er,   in this   our fam- i- ly.

May your Good- News   be a   constant source   of strength

and joy, for all of us who share in

G7   Am   C

Last time to Coda

your won-der-ful love each day.   1.   Verse
harmony To live in the

mel.

Spi-rit is to grow in lib-er-ty.   With-out love our free-dom

Em   F   G7   C   Em

can-not be real.   We thank you, day.   Final Ending
rit.

F   G7   C   Ped. sus to end.

Gregory Norbet, OSB,
and Mary David Callahan, OSB

648 Welcome all ye noble saints

Robert J. Stamps

1. Wel-come all ye no-ble saints of old,_____ as

Em　　　　　Bm　　　　Em

now be-fore your ve-ry eyes un-fold_____ the

D　　　　　A　　　　D

won-ders all so long a-go fore-told._____

Em　　　　Bm　　　　Em

Chorus

God and man at ta-ble are sat down,_____

Am　　　　Bm　　　　Em

God and man at ta-ble are sat down._____

Am　　　　Bm　　　　Em

954

2 Elders, martyrs, all are falling down,
  prophets, patriarchs are gath'ring round;
  what angels longed to see, now man has found.

3 Who is this who spreads the vict'ry feast?
  Who is this who makes our warning cease?
  Jesus risen, Saviour, Prince of Peace.

4 Beggars lame, and harlots also here;
  repentant publicans are drawing near;
  wayward sons come home without a fear.

5 Worship in the presence of the Lord
  with joyful songs, and hearts in one accord,
  and let our host at table be adored.

6 When at last this earth shall pass away,
  when Jesus and his bride are one to stay,
  the feast of love is just begun that day.

Robert J. Stamp

649   What child is this

GREENSLEEVES

Traditional English Melody
Harmony by Steven Foster

1 What child is this, who, laid to rest, on Mary's lap is sleeping?
  Whom angels greet with anthems sweet, while shepherds watch are keeping?
  This, this is Christ the King,
  whom shepherds guard and angels sing:
  come, greet the infant Lord, the Babe, the Son of Mary!

2 Why lies he in such mean estate, where ox and ass are feeding?
  Good Christians, fear: for sinners here the silent Word is pleading.
  Nails, spear, shall pierce him through,
  the cross be born for me, for you:
  hail, hail the Word made flesh, the Babe, the Son of Mary!

3 So bring him incense, gold and myrrh, come peasant, king, to own him.
  The King of kings salvation brings, let loving hearts enthrone him.
  Raise, raise the song on high,
  the Virgin sings her lullaby:
  joy, joy for Christ is born, the Babe, the Son of Mary!   *W.C. Dix*

650 What do you ask of me?

Miriam Therese Winter
Harmony by John Rombaut

1 What do you ask of me?
  What would you have me do?
  I give myself
  within these gifts I offer you.
  This bread is food for life.
  This wine is spirit of love for you.

2 What can I offer you?
  You've given life to me.
  You're part of all I am.
  What would you have me be?
  This bread is food for life.
  This wine is spirit of love for me.

Miriam Therese Winter

957

651 When Jesus comes to be baptized

ST VENANTIUS (88 88)

Rouen Church Melody
Harmony by Stephen Dean

1. When Je- sus comes to be bap- tized, he leaves the

hid- den years be- hind, the years of safe- ty

and of peace, to bear the sins of all man- kind.

2 The Spirit of the Lord comes down,
    anoints the Christ to suffering,
    to preach the word, to free the bound,
    and to the mourner, comfort bring.

3 He will not quench the dying flame,
    and what is bruised he will not break,
    but heal the wound injustice dealt,
    and out of death his triumph make.

4 Our everlasting Father, praise,
    with Christ, his well-beloved Son,
    who with the Spirit reigns serene,
    untroubled Trinity in One.

The Benedictines of Stanbrook

652 When morning gilds the skies

LAUDES DOMINI (666 666)   Joseph Barnby (1838–1896)

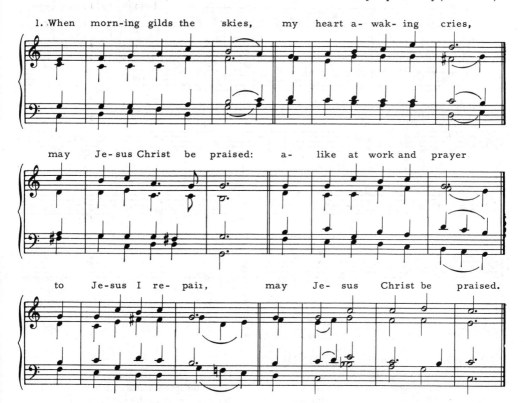

1. When morning gilds the skies, my heart awaking cries,
may Jesus Christ be praised: alike at work and prayer
to Jesus I repair, may Jesus Christ be praised.

2 To God, the word on high
the hosts of angels cry:
may Jesus Christ be praised!
Let mortals, too, upraise!
their voice in hymns of praise!
May Jesus Christ be praised!

3 Let earth's wide circle round
in joyful notes resound:
May Jesus Christ be praised!
Let air, and sea, and sky,
from depth to height, reply:
May Jesus Christ be praised!

4 Does sadness fill my mind?
A solace here I find,
may Jesus Christ be praised:
or fades my earthly bliss?
My comfort still is this,
may Jesus Christ be praised.

5 The night becomes as day,
when from the heart we say,
may Jesus Christ be praised:
the powers of darkness fear,
when this sweet chant they hear,
may Jesus Christ be praised.

6 Be this, while life is mine,
my canticle divine,
may Jesus Christ be praised:
be this the eternal song
through ages all along,
may Jesus Christ be praised.

19th Century,
tr E. Caswall (1814–78)

653   When the time came

Jo Akepsimas

1 When the time came to stretch out his arms,
and to lay down his life for his friends
God's only Son in the breaking of bread,
gave his own flesh as food for mankind,
gave his own flesh as food for mankind.

2 This is my flesh, O take it and eat.
This is my blood, O take it and drink
and to proclaim my death for mankind,
this must you do, until I return,
this must you do, until I return.

3 Hunger and thirst no longer we fear,
Christ's holy flesh becomes now our food.
And when we raise his chalice to drink,
joy overflows, our hope is renewed,
joy overflows, our hope is renewed.

4 O bread of life, O Banquet Divine,
sing of the love that makes us all one,
We who now share this gift from above,
surely have seen the goodness of God,
surely have seen the goodness of God.

5 Through Jesus Christ, the perfect high Priest,
and in the Spirit source of our peace.
For this great feast which you have prepared,
Father above, O praised be your name,
Father above, O praised be your name.

Michael Scouarnec, tr Margaret Daly

654   Whey he day?

Anthony Pierre
Harmony by Eric Welch

Whey he day? Whey he day?
Whey he day, mi Lard?
Whey he day? Whey he day?
Whey he day, mi Lard?
Whey he day? Whey he day?
Whey he day, mi Lard?
Ah cyant fine he, fine he at all.

1 Ah want to see de man from Galalee,
  Ah want to see de man who set me free,
  Ah want to see de man who died for me,
  Ay cyant fine he, fine he at all.

2 Ah want to see de man who bleed for me,
  Ay want to see de man dey scourge for me,
  Ah want to see dis man from Galalee,
  Ay cyant fine he, fine he at all.

3 Whey de man who make de bline to see?
  Whey de man who set de captive free?
  Whey de man who make de lame to walk?
  An de li'l dumb boy to talk?

Anthony Pierre

655 Who is she that stands triumphant

ECCLESIA

Richard R. Terry (1865–1938)

1 Who is she that stands triumphant,
  rock in strength, upon the rock,
  like some city crowned with turrets,
  braving storm and earthquake shock?
  Who is she her arms extending,
  blessing thus a world restored,
  all the anthems of creation
  lifting to creation's Lord?

  Hers the kingdom, hers the sceptre;
  fall, ye nations, at her feet;
  hers that truth whose fruit is freedom;
  light her yoke, her burden sweet.

2 As the moon its splendour borrows
  from a sun unseen at night,
  so from Christ, the sun of justice,
  evermore she draws her light.
  Touch'd by his, her hands have healing,
  bread of life, absolving key:
  Christ incarnate is her bridegroom,
  God is hers, his temple she.

3 Empires rise and sink like billows,
  vanish, and are seen no more;
  glorious as the star of morning
  she o'erlooks the wild uproar.
  Hers the household all-embracing,
  hers the vine that shadows earth:
  blest thy children, mighty mother;
  safe the stranger at thy hearth.

  Aubrey de Vere (1814–1902)

656   Who wants to live as God

Bernard Huijbers

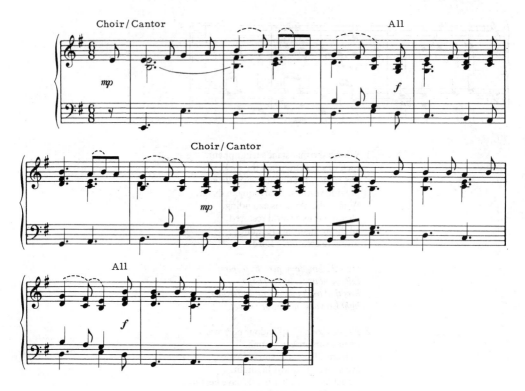

1 Who wants to live as God here on this earth (2)
   must go the way of all seed,
   in doing so find mercy. (2)

2 Must go the way of all things born of earth, (2)
   must share the fate, with heart and soul,
   of all things bound for dying. (2)

3 Both sun and rain will touch each of his days: (2)
   the smallest seed, come rain or shine,
   must die so as to live. (2)

4 So people live to die for one another, (2)
   the smallest seed, as living bread,
   to feed, sustain each other. (2)

5 And that is how our Lord and God has shown himself, (2)
   and so becomes his living self
   for each of us on earth. (2)

Huub Oosterhuis

657 Wind and fire, the signs of power

Bill Tamblyn

A Wind and fire, the signs of pow'r
giv'n by God at Pentecost,
to Apostles, full of joy,
when their waiting days were passed.

1 Wind, which at creation's start
stirred dark waters into life;
living Spirit, vital breath,
breathing life through man and wife.

Repeat Refrain A

2 Out they burst into the streets;
stirred the people with their news;
set explosive in men's minds
then God's Spirit lit the fuse.

B Wind and fire, the signs of pow'r
giv'n by God to us today;
fire, to set our hearts ablaze;
wind, to blow our fears away.

3 Hearts ablaze and free from fear,
we'll amaze the world again,
and God's wind and fire will still
surge into the minds of men.

Repeat Refrain B

*Alan Gaunt and
John Marsh*

658 Would you like to be happy?

Source Unknown

Would you like to be happy?
Would you like to be good?
Then obey God's law of love,
obey as children should.

1 You should love the Lord your God,
   with your head and hand and heart;
   you should love the Lord your God,
   body, soul and ev'ry part.

2 When your head thinks, think with love;
   when your hand works, work with love;
   when your heart beats, beat with love;
   ev'ry part must work with love.

3 You should love the Lord your God,
   you should love him best of all.
   Love all people as yourself
   for he made and loves them all.

Source unknown

659   Yahweh, I know you are near

Daniel L. Schutte

Chorus

Yah-weh, I know you are near, stand-ing al- ways at my side.

G   C9   G   D (F♯bass)

You guard me from the foe and you lead me in ways ev- er last- ing.

C9   Am7   G   D (F♯bass)   C9

fine

1. Lord, you have searched my heart, and you know when I sit and when I stand.

Bm   C   C (B bass) Am7 Am7(G bass) G

Your hand is up- on me, pro-

C9   D (F♯bass)   Em

Am   Bm   Em

tect- ing me from death, keep-ing me from harm.

Am   Bm   Am7   Am7 (G bass)   D (F♯bass)

2 When can I run from your love?
If I climb to the heavens, you are there.
If I fly to the sunrise or sail beyond the sea
still I'd find you there.

3 You know my heart and its ways,
you who formed me before I was born,
in secret of darkness, before I saw the sun,
in my mother's womb.

4 Marvellous to me are your works;
how profound are your thoughts my Lord!
Even if I could count them, they number as the
stars,
you would still be there.

Daniel L. Schutte, SJ.

660 You, Israel, return now

Melody from Northern Malawi
Collected by Tom Colvin

*This song should not have any harmonic accompaniment. Please resist the temptation to add 'Western'
harmonies. Instead it should be accompanied by untuned percussion and spontaneous vocal harmony.*

1. You, Is- ra- el re- turn now; re- turn to
God, your Fa- ther, your on- ly great cre-
a- tor; re- turn to God, your Fa- ther.

© 1976 Agapé

2 You won't be disappointed;

3 Although you have offended;

4 Although your sins are many;

5 He's sure to listen to you;

6 For he is calling to you;

7 Now seek your Lord's forgiveness;

8 He calls you all to hear him;

9 And gives yourselves to him now;

10 For he is your redeemer;

11 The people's liberator;

12 Return now, O return now;

13 You lonely and you lost ones;

14 Now pray to him his people;

15 And he will quickly answer;

16 So come now all your people;

*Tom Colvin,
based on a Tumbuka hymn by N.Z. Tembo*

661 You must cry out the Word of the Lord

Carol Gordon
Harmony by Eric Welch

Calypso

1 You must cry out the Word of the Lord!
   You must cry out the Word of the Lord!
   For you can heal a wounded man, or make a poor man rich,
   if you sing out the Word of the Lord!

2 You are called to the Word of the Lord!
   You are called to the Word of the Lord!
   For the Lord has come in power; if you believe, he lives in you,
   you must breathe out the Word of the Lord!

3 O my people, don't wait any longer!
   O my people, don't wait any longer!
   For my children are starving for my living water,
   you must cry our the Word of the Lord!

4 You must cry out the Word of the Lord!
   You must cry out the Word of the Lord!
   For you can heal a wounded man, or make a poor man rich,
   if you give out the Word of the Lord!

Carol Gordon

662 You servants of God (Psalm 113)

Paul Décha

1. You ser-vants of God, now give him praise: al-le-lu - ia! Sing
2. His name let us praise e-ter-nal - ly: al-le-lu - ia! Sing

out, for his goodness fills our days: al-le-lu - ia! His
praise, night and day, on land and sea: al-le-lu - ia! The

name let us praise now and al - ways: al-le-lu - ia!
Lord's name for ev-er blest will be: al-le-lu - ia!

3 Above all creation is the Lord: alleluia!
By all may he ever be adored: alleluia!
For God has our fallen life restored: alleluia!

4 The weak, and the poor, and all in need: alleluia!
The Lord without fail their pray'r will heed: alleluia!
Above others they are blest indeed: alleluia!

5 Give praise to the Father, and the Son: alleluia!
Give praise to the Spirit, three in one: alleluia!
Whose reign is for evermore: alleluia!

Based on Psalm 112(113)
by Jean-Paul Lecot, R.W. Lawrence,
R.B. Kelly

663 Be not afraid

Robert J. Dufford SJ

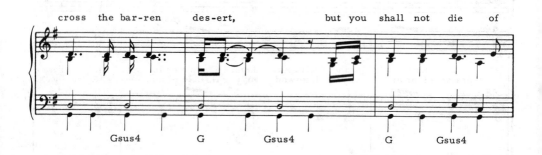

they will un- der- stand. You shall see the face of God and

C F D G E A A7

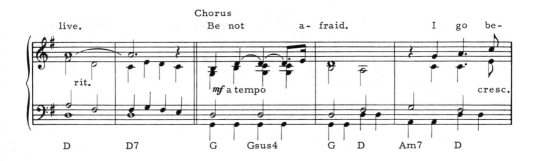

live. Chorus Be not a- fraid. I go be-

rit. *mf* a tempo cresc.

D D7 G Gsus4 G D Am7 D

fore you al- ways. Come, fol-low me, and I will give you

f cresc. decresc.

G6 C G/B Bm Em Am D

rest. 2. If you

mp fine

G Gsus4 G Gsus4 G C/G G

pass through ra- ging wa- ters in the sea, you shall not

G   Gsus4   G   Gsus4   G   Gsus4

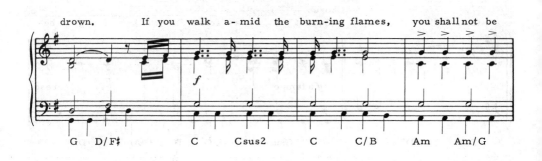

drown.   If you walk a- mid the burn-ing flames, you shall not be

G D/F♯   C   Csus2   C   C/B   Am   Am/G

harmed.   If you stand be-fore the pow'r of hell and death is at your

D/F♯   G   B7   Em   Am   C   F

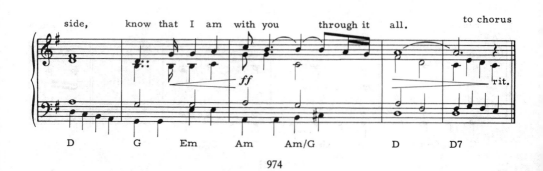

side,   know that I am with you through it all.   to chorus

D   G   Em   Am   Am/G   D   D7

3. Bless-ed are your poor, for the king-dom shall be theirs.

G Gsus4 G Gsus4 G Gsus4 G D/F♯

Blest are you that weep and mourn, for one day you shall laugh. And if

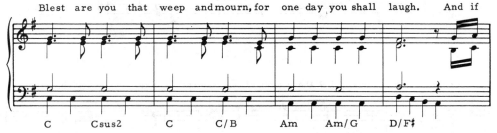

C Csus2 C C/B Am Am/G D/F♯

wick-ed men in-sult and hate you all be-cause of me,

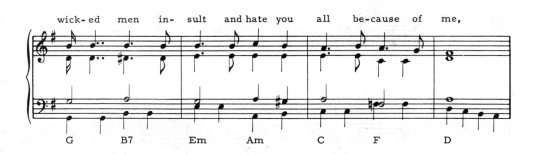

G B7 Em Am C F D

bless-ed, bless-ed are you!   to chorus

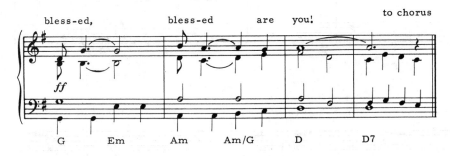

ff

G Em Am Am/G D D7

Based on Isaiah 43 and Luke 6
by Robert J. Dufford, SJ.

664 Your kingdom come

Tim Whipple

Your king-dom come, your will be done, now that we have be-

-come your sons. Let the prayer of our hearts dai – ly be:

'God, make us your fa – mi-ly.' Last time to Coda The

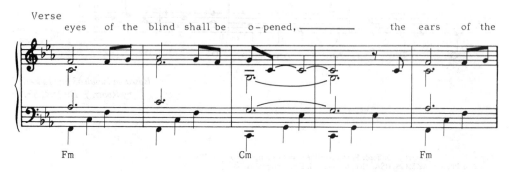

Verse
eyes of the blind shall be o-pened, ———— the ears of the

976

2 The ransomed of the Lord shall return,
   the islands will sing his songs at last.
   The chaff from the wheat shall be burned,
   his kingdom on earth it shall come to pass.

3 The nations will see their shame,
   the one true God will be adored.
   They turn from their fortune and shame,
   his holy mountain shall be restored.

Based on Isaiah 35 by Tim Whipple

665   Psalm 8

Response 1

How great is your name, O Lord our God   through all the earth!

Joseph Gelineau

Response 2

What is mor-tal man that you   care for him?

A.Gregory Murray

A.Gregory Murray

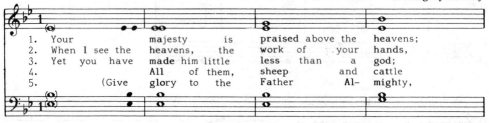

1. Your   majesty   is   praised above the   heavens;
2. When I see the   heavens,   the   work of   your   hands,
3. Yet you have   made him little   less   than   a   god;
4.   All   of them,   sheep   and   cattle
5.   (Give   glory to   the   Father   Al-   mighty,

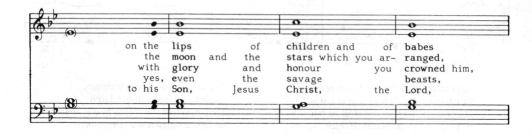

on the lips   of   children and   of babes
the   moon   and   the   stars which you ar- ranged,
with   glory   and   honour   you   crowned him,
yes,   even   the   savage   beasts,
to his Son,   Jesus   Christ,   the Lord,

you have found praise to foil your enemy,
what is man that you should keep him in mind,
gave him power over the works of your hand,
birds of the air and fish
to the Spirit who dwells in our hearts

to silence the foe and the rebel.
mortal man that you care for him?
put all things under his feet.
that make their way through the waters.*
both now and for ever./ A- men.)

Psalm 8
The Grail

666 Psalm 18(19):8–15

Response 1

Joseph Gelineau

You, O Lord, have the message of e-ter-nal life.

Response 2

Stephen Dean

Your words are spi-rit, Lord, and they are life.

1. The **law** of the **Lord** is **perfect,**
2. The **precepts** of the **Lord** are **right,**
3. The **fear** of the **Lord** is **holy,**
4. They are **more** to be de-**sired** than **gold;**

it re-**vives** the **soul.**
they **gladden** the **heart.**
a-**biding** for **ever.**
than the **purest** of **gold.**

The **rule** of the **Lord** is to be **trusted,**
The com-**mand** of the **Lord** is **clear,**
The de-**crees** of the **Lord** are **truth,**
and **sweeter** are **they** than **honey,**

980

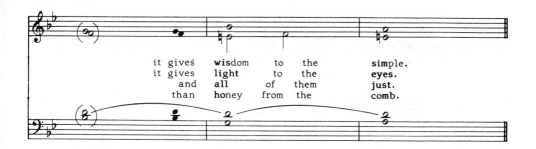

it gives	**wis**dom	to	the	**simple.**
it gives	**light**	to	the	**eyes.**
and	**all**	of	them	**just.**
than	**honey**	from	the	**comb.**

5 So in thém your sérvant finds instrúction,
  great rewárd is in their kéeping.
  But whó can detéct all his érrors?
  From hídden faults acquít me.

6 From presúmption restráin your sérvant,
  and lét it not rúle me.
  Thén shall Í be blámeless,
  cléan from grave sín.

7 May the spóken wórds of my móuth,
  the thóughts of my héart,
  win fávour in your síght, O Lórd,
  my Réscuer, my Róck!

8 (Praise the Fáther, the Són and holy Spírit
  both nów and for éver,
  the God who ís, who wás and who wíll be,
  wórld without énd.)

Psalm 18(19):8–15
The Grail

667 Psalm 22(23)

Response 1 — Joseph Gelineau

My shep- -herd is the Lord, no-thing in - deed shall I want.

Response 2 — A. Gregory Murray

His good-ness shall fol-low me al -ways to the end of my days.

Response 3 — Robert B. Kelly

The Lord him-self will give me re- pose.

PSALM — Joseph Gelineau

1. The Lord is my shepherd;
2. He guides me a- long the right path;
3. You have pre- pared a banquet for me
4. Surely goodness and kindness shall follow me
5. To the Father and Son give glory,

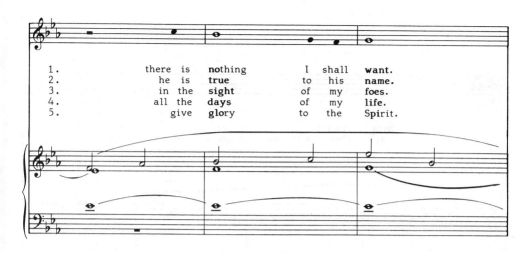

1.		there is	**no**thing		I shall	**want.**
2.		he is	**true**		to his	**name.**
3.		in the	**sight**		of my	**foes.**
4.		all the	**days**		of my	**life.**
5.		give	**glory**		to the	**Spirit.**

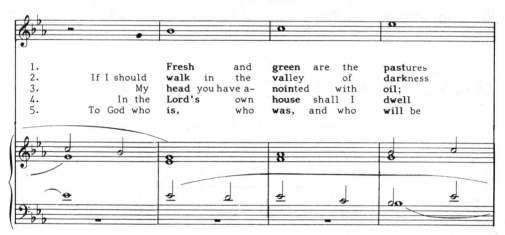

1.		**Fresh**	and	**green**	are the	**pastures**
2.	If I should	**walk**	in the	**valley**	of	**darkness**
3.	My	**head**	you have a-	**noin**ted	with	**oil;**
4.	In the	**Lord's**	own	**house**	shall I	**dwell**
5.	To God who	**is,**	who	**was,**	and who	**will** be

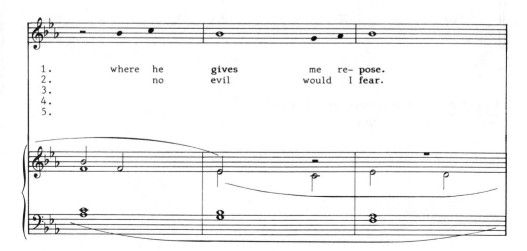

1.	where he	**gives**	me re-	**pose.**
2.	no	evil	would I	**fear.**
3.				
4.				
5.				

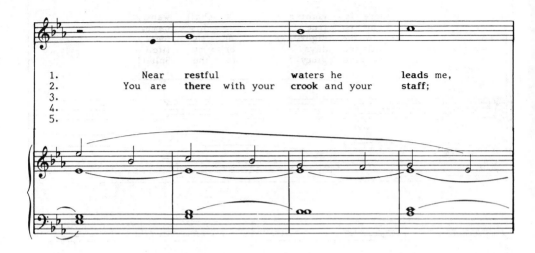

1. Near restful waters he leads me,
2. You are there with your crook and your staff;
3.
4.
5.

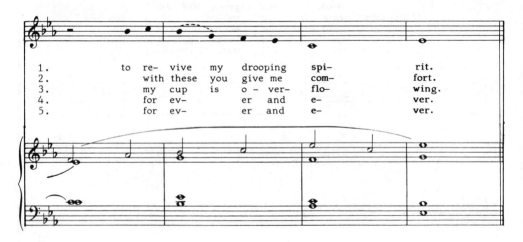

1. to re-vive my drooping spi- rit.
2. with these you give me com- fort.
3. my cup is o - ver- flo- wing.
4. for ev- er and e- ver.
5. for ev- er and e- ver.

Psalm 22(23)
The Grail

668   Psalm 23(24)

Response 1

Joseph Gelineau

Seek the face of the Lord and yearn for him.

Response 2

A. Gregory Murray

O-pen wide, O you gates e - ter - nal, and

let the King of glo - ry en - ter.

Response 3

Robert B. Kelly

Ho - san - na   to the Son of Da - vid!
Ho - san - na   in the highest hea - ven!

1. The **Lord's** is the **earth** and its **fullness,**
2. Who shall **climb** the **mountain** of the **Lord?**
3. He shall re-**ceive** **bless**ings from the **Lord.**

the **world** and **all** its **peoples.**
Who shall **stand** in his **ho** - ly **place?**
and re-**ward** from the **God** who **saves** him.

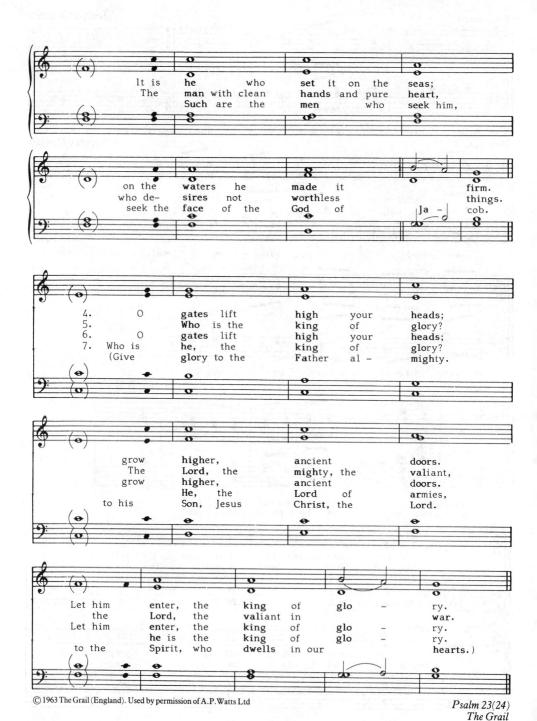

It is   he   who   set   it   on   the   seas;
The   man with clean   hands and pure   heart,
Such   are   the   men   who   seek him,

on the   waters   he   made   it   firm.
who de- sires   not   worthless   things.
seek the   face   of   the   God   of   Ja - cob.

4.   O   gates   lift   high   your   heads;
5.   Who   is   the   king   of   glory?
6.   O   gates   lift   high   your   heads;
7. Who is   he,   the   king   of   glory?
(Give   glory to the   Father   al –   mighty.

grow   higher,   ancient   doors.
The   Lord,   the   mighty, the   valiant,
grow   higher,   ancient   doors.
He,   the   Lord   of   armies,
to his   Son,   Jesus   Christ, the   Lord.

Let him   enter,   the   king   of   glo - ry.
the   Lord,   the   valiant   in   war.
Let him   enter,   the   king   of   glo - ry.
he   is   the   king   of   glo - ry.
to the   Spirit, who   dwells   in our   hearts.)

Psalm 23(24)
The Grail

669 Psalm 24(25)

Response   A. Gregory Murray

To you, O Lord,   I lift   up my   soul.

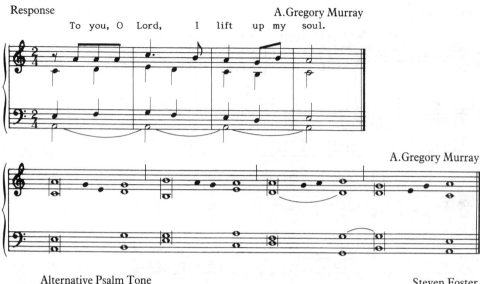

A. Gregory Murray

Alternative Psalm Tone   Steven Foster

1 Lord, make me knów your ways.
Lord, teach mé your paths.
Make me walk in your trúth, and teach me:
for you are Gód my saviour.

2 Remember your mércy, Lord,
and the love you have shown fróm of old.
In your love remémber me,
because of your goodnéss, O Lord.

3 The Lord is góod and upright.
He shows the path to thóse who stray,
he guides the humble in thé right path;
he teaches his way tó the poor.

4 His ways are faithfulnéss and love
for those who keep his covenánt and will.
The Lord's friendship is for those whó revere him;
to them he revéals his covenant.

5 (Glory be to the Father, and tó the Son,
and to the Hóly Spirit,
as it was in the beginning, is now,
and éver shall be,
world without énd. Amen.)

Psalm 24(25)
The Grail

670 Psalm 26(27)

Response 1 — Stephen Dean

The Lord is my light and my help. *Fine*

Response 2 — Stephen Dean

One thing I ask of the Lord, for this I long, to

slow

live in the house of the Lord all the days of my life. *Fine*

Response 3 — Stephen Dean

I am sure I shall see the Lord's good - ness

in the land of the liv - ing. *Fine.*

1. The Lord is my light and my help. Whom shall I fear? The
2. Though arm-ies do bat — tle a-gainst me, my heart will not fear. Though
3. For there in his house I am safe, in e — vil's dark hour. He
5. O Lord hear my voice when I call; have mer - cy and answer; of
6. Your face __ in - deed ___ I seek it; hide it not from me. Dis -
7. I know I shall see the Lord's goodness in his pro-mised land. Take

* vv.2,7 :

Lord is the stronghold of my life, be - fore whom shall I shrink.
war and de - struc - tion break * forth, e - ven then would I trust.
hides me and shel - ters my soul, my de - fen - der, my rock.
you __ my heart ___ has spo — ken; 'Seek ___ his face.'
-miss not your ser — vant in an — ger, for you are my help.
heart and stand firm, O my * soul, put your hope in the Lord!

(V.4 see over)

Alternative (simple) setting

4. There is one thing I ask of the Lord, for this I long; to live in the house of the Lord all the days of my life: to sa-vour the sweet-ness of the Lord; to be-hold his temple.

The Grail (slightly adapted)

© Stephen Dean

671 Psalm 41(42):1–6

Response 1
Joseph Gelineau

♩ = o of psalm
My soul is thirsting for the Lord: when shall I see him face to face?

Response 2
Joseph Gelineau

I will pour clean wa- ter o- ver you, and

cleanse you from all your sin.

Psalm
Joseph Gelineau

1.	Like	the	deer	that	yearns
2.	My	soul	is	thirsting for	God,
3.	My	tears	have be-	come my	bread,
4.	These things will	I	re-	member
5.	Why	are you cast	down,	my	soul,

for	running		streams,
the	God of my		life;
by	night,/	by	day,	as I
as I	pour out	my	soul;	how I would
why	groan	wi-	thin me?	Hope in

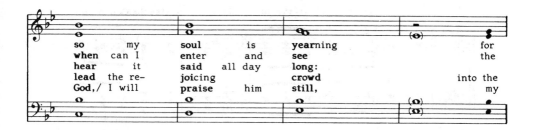

so   my   soul   is   yearning   for
when   can I   enter   and   see   the
hear   it   said   all day long:
lead   the re- joicing   crowd   into the
God,/   I will praise him   still,   my

you,   my   God.
face   of   God?
'Where is your God?'
house   of   God.
Saviour and my God.

6 (Praise the Fáther, the Són and Holy Spírit,
  both nów and for éver,
  the God who ís, who wás and who wíll be,
  wórld without énd.)

Psalm 41(42):1–6
The Grail

© The Grail (England). Used by permission of A.P.Watts Ltd

672 Psalm 42(43)

Response 1   Joseph Gelineau

I will go to the al-tar of God: praise the God of my joy.

Response 2   A. Gregory Murray

Hope in God. I will praise him still, my Sa-viour and my God.

Psalm 42

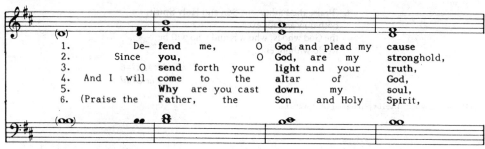

1.		De-	**fend**	me,	O	**God** and plead my	**cause**
2.		Since	**you,**	O	**God,**	are my	**strong**hold,
3.		O	**send**	forth	your	**light** and your	**truth,**
4.	And I will	**come**	to	the	**altar**	of	**God,**
5.			**Why**	are you cast	**down,**	my	**soul,**
6.	(Praise the	**Father,**	the	**Son**	and Holy	**Spirit,**

against a **godless** nation: from de-
why have you re- **jected** me?
let **these** by my **guide;** let them
the **God** of my **joy.** My Re-
why **groan** wi- **thin** me? Hope in
both **now** and for **ever,** the God who

994

ceitful and cunning men
Why do **I** go **mourning,** op-
bring me to your **ho**-ly **mountain,** to the
deemer, I will **thank** you on the **harp,** O
God, I will **praise** him **still,** my
is, who **was** and who **will be,**

rescue me, O **God.**
pressed by the **foe?**
place where you **dwell.**
God, my **God.**
Saviour and my **God.**
world without **end.**)

Psalm 42(43)
The Grail

673 Psalm 50(51)

Response 1   Joseph Gelineau

Have mer-cy, Lord, cleanse us from all our sin.

Response 2   Stephen Dean

Have mer-cy on us, O Lord for we have sinned.

Response 3   Stephen Dean

A pure heart cre- ate for me, O God.

1. Have mercy on me, God, in your kindness.
2. My of-fences truly I know them;
3. That you may be justified when you give sentence
4. In-deed you love truth in the heart;
5. Make me hear re-joicing and gladness,

In your com-passion blot out my of-fence.
my sin is always be-fore me.
and be with-out re-proach when you judge,
then in the secret of my heart teach me wisdom.
that the bones you have crushed may thrill.

	1.	O	**wash** me	more	and	**more**	from my	**guilt**
	2.	Against	**you,**	you	a–	**lone**	have I	**sinned;**
	3.	O	**see,**	in	**guilt**	I was	**born,**
	4.	O	**purify**	me,	**then I**	shall be	**clean;**
	5.	From my	**sins** turn	a–	**way**	your	**face**

and	**cleanse**	me	**from**	my	**sin.**
what is	**evil**	in your	**sight** I	have	**done.**
a	**sinner**	was	**I**	con–	**ceived.**
O	**wash** me, I	shall be	**whiter**	than	**snow.**
and	**blot**	out	**all**	my	**guilt.**

6 A púre heart creáte for me, O Gód,
   put a stéadfast spírit withín me.
   Do not cást me awáy from your présence,
   nor depríve me of your hóly spírit.

7 Give me agáin the jóy of your hélp;
   with a spírit of férvour sustáin me,
   that I may téach transgréssors your wáys,
   and sínners may retúrn to yóu.

8 O réscue me, Gód, my hélper,
   and my tóngue shall ríng out your góodness.
   O Lórd, ópen my líps,
   and my móuth shall decláre your práise.

9 For in sácrifice you táke no delíght,
   burnt óffering from mé you would refúse,
   my sácrifice, a cóntrite spírit.
   A húmbled, contrite héart you will not spúrn.

10 (Give glóry to the Fáther almíghty,
   to his Són, Jesus Chríst, the Lórd,
   to the Spírit who dwélls in our héarts,
   both nów and for éver. Amén.)

Psalm 50(51)
The Grail

674 Psalm 62(63)

Response   A. Gregory Murray

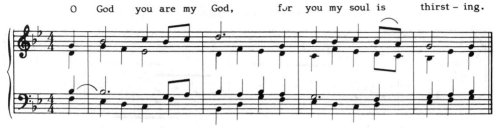

O God you are my God, for you my soul is thirst – ing.

Psalm Tone   A. Gregory Murray

Alternative Psalm Tone   Ian Forrester

1 O God, you are my God, for yóu I long;
  for you my soul is thírsting.
  My body pínes for you
  like a dry, weary land wíthout water. (R)

2 So I gaze on you ín the sanctuary
  to see your strength ánd your glory.
  For your love is bettér than life,
  my lips will spéak your praise. (R)

3 So I will bless you áll my life,
  in your name I will lift úp my hands.
  My mouth shall be filled as wíth a banquet,
  my mouth shall praise yóu with joy. (R)

4 For you have béen my help;
  in the shadow of your wings Í rejoice.
  My soul clíngs to you:
  your right hand hólds me fast. (R)

5 (Glory be to the Father, and tó the Son,
  and to the Hóly Spirit,
  as it was in the beginning, is now, and éver shall be,
  world without énd. Amen.

Psalm 62(63):1–6,8–9
The Grail

675 Psalm 83(84)

Response 1

A.Gregory Murray

Response 2

A.Gregory Murray

PSALM

Joseph Gelineau

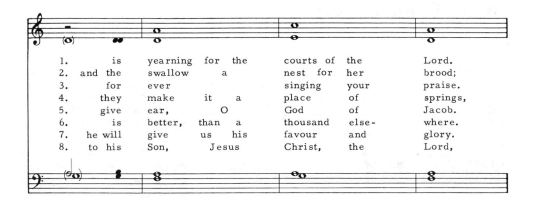

1.	is	yearning	for	the	courts of	the	Lord.
2.	and the	swallow	a		nest for	her	brood;
3.	for	ever			singing	your	praise.
4.	they	make	it	a	place	of	springs,
5.	give	ear,	O		God	of	Jacob.
6.	is	better,	than	a	thousand	else-	where.
7.	he will	give	us	his	favour	and	glory.
8.	to his	Son,	Jesus		Christ,	the	Lord,

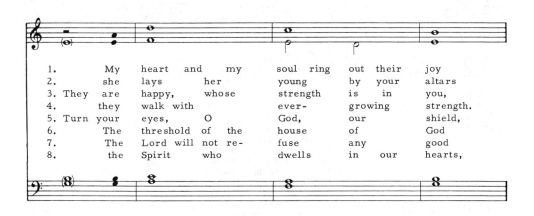

1.	My	heart and	my	soul ring	out	their	joy
2.	she	lays	her	young	by	your	altars
3. They	are	happy,	whose	strength	is	in	you,
4.	they	walk with		ever-	growing		strength.
5. Turn your	eyes,	O		God,	our		shield,
6.	The	threshold	of the	house	of		God
7.	The	Lord will	not re-	fuse	any		good
8.	the	Spirit	who	dwells	in	our	hearts,

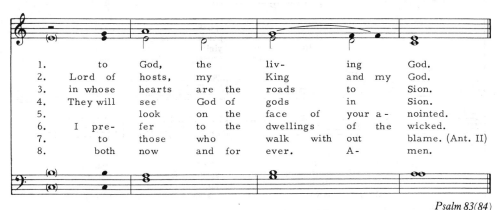

1.	to	God,	the	liv-	ing		God.
2.	Lord of	hosts,	my	King	and	my	God.
3.	in whose	hearts	are the	roads	to		Sion.
4.	They will	see	God of	gods	in		Sion.
5.		look	on the	face	of	your a-	nointed.
6.	I pre-	fer	to the	dwellings	of	the	wicked.
7.	to	those	who	walk	with	out	blame. (Ant. II)
8.	both	now	and for	ever.	A-		men.

Psalm 83(84)
The Grail

676 Psalm 84(85)

Response 1 — Joseph Gelineau

Let us see, O Lord your mer-cy; and give us your sa-ving help.

Response 2 — Stephen Dean

Come, Lord, and save us; come, Lord, and save us.

Psalm — Joseph Gelineau

1. I will **hear** what the Lord **God** has to **say,**
2. **Mercy** and **faithfulness** have **met;**
3. The **Lord,** will **make** us **prosper**
(4. Give **glory** to the **Father** al -- **mighty,**

a **voice** that **speaks** of **peace.**
justice and **peace** have em - **braced.**
and our **earth** shall **yield** its **fruit.**
to his **Son,** Jesus **Christ,** the **Lord,**

His help is **near** for **those** who **fear** him
Faithfulness shall **spring** from the **earth**
Justice shall **march** be --- **fore** him
to the **Spirit** who **dwells** in our **hearts**

and his **glory** will **dwell** in our **land.**
and **justice** look **down** from **heaven.**
and **peace** shall **follow** his **steps.**
both **now** and for **ever.** A — **men.)**

Psalm 84(85):9–14
The Grail

Music © J. Gelieau
Harmon to Response 1 © Stephen Dean
Response 2 © Stephen Dean

677 Psalm 90(91)

Response 1   Joseph Gelineau

Call u-pon the Lord and he will hear you.

Response 2   A. Gregory Murray

Be with me, Lord, in my dis- tress!

PSALM   Joseph Gelineau

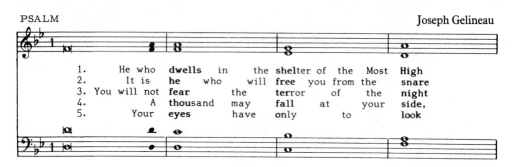

1. He who **dwells** in the **shelter** of the Most **High**
2. It is **he** who will **free** you from the **snare**
3. You will not **fear** the **terror** of the **night**
4. A **thousand** may **fall** at your **side**,
5. Your **eyes** have only to **look**

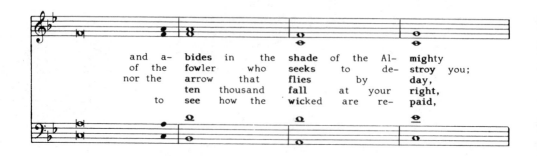

and a- **bides** in the **shade** of the Al- **mighty**
of the **fowler** who **seeks** to de- **stroy** you;
nor the **arrow** that **flies** by **day**,
ten thousand **fall** at your **right**,
to **see** how the **wicked** are re- **paid**,

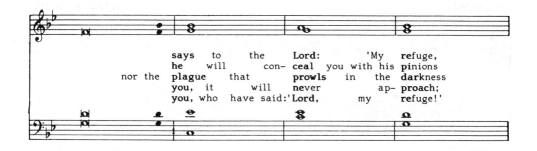

says to the Lord: 'My refuge,
he will con- ceal you with his pinions
nor the plague that prowls in the darkness
you, it will never ap- proach;
you, who have said:'Lord, my refuge!'

my stronghold, my God, in whom I trust!'
and under his wings you will find refuge
nor the scourge that lays waste at noon,
his faithfulness is buckler and shield.
and have made the Most High your dwelling.

6 Upon yóu no évil shall fáll,
   no plágue appróach where you dwéll.
   For yóu has he commánded his ángels,
   to kéep you in áll your wáys.

7 They shall béar you upón their hánds
   lest you stríke your fóot against a stóne.
   On the líon and the víper you will tréad
   and trámple the young líon and the drágon.

8 His lóve he set on mé, so I will réscue him;
   protéct him for he knóws my náme.
   When he cálls I shall ánswer: 'I am wíth you'.
   I will sáve him in distréss and give him glóry.

9 With léngth of lífe I will contént him;
   I will lét him see my sáving pówer.
   (To the Fáther, the Són and Holy Spírit
   give práise for éver./Amén.)

Psalm 90(91)
The Grail

678 Psalm 92(93)

Joseph Gelineau

A.Gregory Murray

Response 1

The Lord is King for e-ver more!

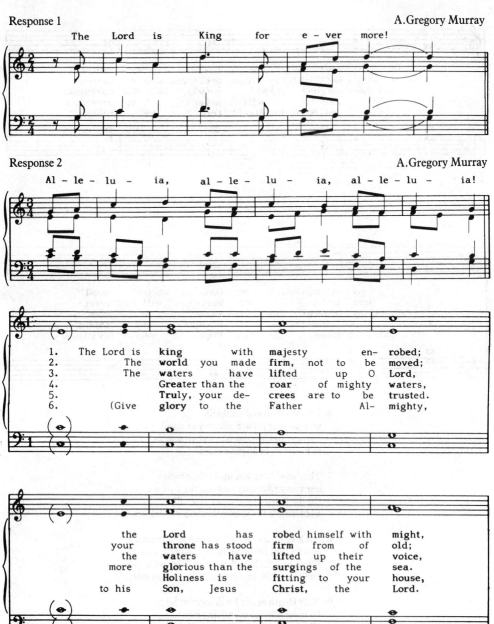

Response 2

A.Gregory Murray

Al-le-lu-ia, al-le-lu-ia, al-le-lu-ia!

1. The Lord is **king** with **majesty** en- **robed;**
2. The **world** you made **firm,** not to be **moved;**
3. The **waters** have **lifted** up O **Lord.**
4. **Greater** than the **roar** of mighty **waters,**
5. **Truly,** your de- **crees** are to be **trusted.**
6. (Give **glory** to the **Father** Al- **mighty,**

the **Lord** has **robed** himself with **might,**
your **throne** has stood **firm** from of **old;**
the **waters** have **lifted** up their **voice,**
more **glorious** than the **surgings** of the **sea.**
Holiness is **fitting** to your **house,**
to his **Son,** Jesus **Christ,** the **Lord.**

he has **gir**ded him **self** with **power.**
from all e- **ternity,** O **Lord,** you **are.**
the **waters** have **lifted** up their **thunder.**
the **Lord** is **glorious** on **high.**
O **Lord,** until the **end** of **time.**
to the **Spirit** who **dwells** in our **hearts.**)

Psalm 92(93)
The Grail

679 Psalm 94(95)

Response 1   Joseph Gelineau

O come let us wor - ship the Lord!

Response 2   Joseph Gelineau

O that to-day you would lis-ten to his voice, har-den not your hearts.

PSALM

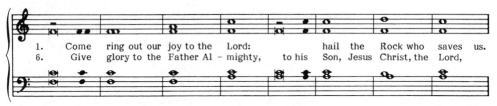

1. Come ring out our joy to the Lord: hail the Rock who saves us.
6. Give glory to the Father Al - mighty, to his Son, Jesus Christ, the Lord,

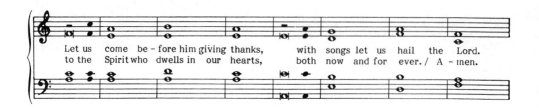

Let us come be - fore him giving thanks, with songs let us hail the Lord.
to the Spirit who dwells in our hearts, both now and for ever. / A - men.

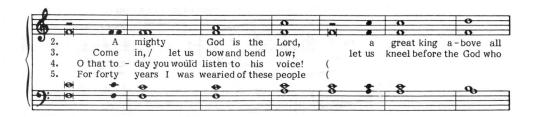

2. A mighty God is the Lord, a great king a-bove all
3. Come in, / let us bow and bend low; let us kneel before the God who
4. O that to - day you would listen to his voice! (
5. For forty years I was wearied of these people (

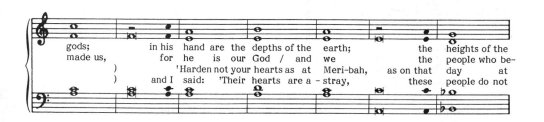

gods; in his hand are the depths of the earth; the heights of the
made us, for he is our God / and we the people who be-
) 'Harden not your hearts as at Meri-bah, as on that day at
) and I said: 'Their hearts are a - stray, these people do not

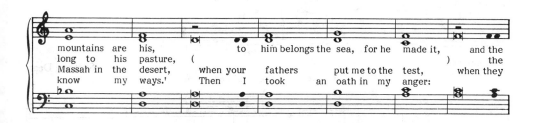

mountains are his, to him belongs the sea, for he made it, and the
long to his pasture, ( ) the
Massah in the desert, when your fathers put me to the test, when they
know my ways.' Then I took an oath in my anger:

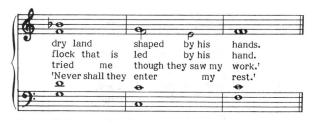

dry land shaped by his hands.
flock that is led by his hand.
tried me though they saw my work.'
'Never shall they enter my rest.'

Psalm 94(95)
The Grail

680 Psalm 99(100)

Response 1 — Joseph Gelineau

A-rise, come to your God, sing him your songs of re-joi-cing.

Response 2 — Joseph Gelineau

Glo-ry to you, O God.

Response 3 — A. Gregory Murray

Al-le-lu-ia, al-le-lu-ia, al-le-lu-ia.

Response 4 — Stephen Dean

We are his peo-ple, the sheep of his flock.

1. Cry out with joy to the Lord, all the earth.
2. Know that he, the Lord, is God.
3. Go within his gates giving thanks.
4. In-deed how good is the Lord,
5. (Give glory to the Father Al-mighty,

|Serve the Lord with gladness.
He made us, we be- long to him.
Enter his courts with songs of praise.
e- ternal his merciful love;
to his Son, Jesus Christ, the Lord,

1. Come be- fore him, singing for joy.
2. we are his people, the sheep of his flock.
3. Give thanks to him and bless his name.
4. he is faithful from age to age.
5. to the Spirit who dwells in our hearts.)

Psalm 99(100)
The Grail

681　Psalm 102(103):1–4.8.10.12–13

Joseph Gelineau

Responses

Harmony

1. The Lord is compas – sion and love: alle – lu – ia, al – le – lu – ia!
2. The Lord has set his sway in heaven:

Psalm 102

Joseph Gelineau

1.　My soul, give thanks to the Lord,
2.　It is he who for – gives all your guilt,
3.　The Lord is com – passion and love,
4.　As far as the east is from the west

all my being bless his ho – ly name.
who heals every one of your ills.
slow to anger and rich in mercy.
so far does he re – move our sins.

My soul, give thanks to the Lord,
who re – deems your life from the grave,
He does not treat us ac – cording to our sins
as a father has com – passion on his sons.

and   never   for   **get** all his **blessings.**
who   **crowns** you with **love** and com - **passion.**
nor re — **pay** us ac — **cor**ding to our **faults.**
the Lord has **pity**   on **those** who **fear** him.

5 (Give glóry to the Fáther almíghty,
to his Són, Jesus Chríst, the Lórd,
to the Spírit who dwélls in our héarts
both nów and for éver./Amén.)

Psalm 102(103)
The Grail

682 Psalm 103(104):1–2.5–6.10–14.24.27–30

Joseph Gelineau

Response

Send forth your Spi - rit, O Lord and re - new the face of the earth.

1. **Bless** the **Lord,** my **soul!**
2. You **founded** the **earth** on its **base,**
3. You make **springs** gush **forth** in the **valleys:**
4. From your **dwelling** you **water** the **hills;**

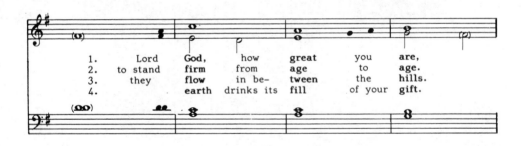

1. Lord **God,** how **great** you **are,**
2. to stand **firm** from **age** to **age.**
3. they **flow** in be- **tween** the **hills.**
4. **earth** drinks its **fill** of your **gift.**

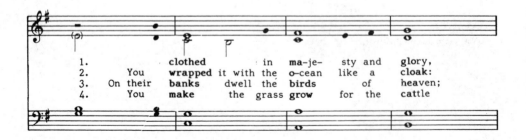

1. **clothed** in **ma-je-** sty and **glory,**
2. You **wrapped** it with the **o-cean** like a **cloak:**
3. On their **banks** dwell the **birds** of **heaven;**
4. You **make** the grass **grow** for the **cattle**

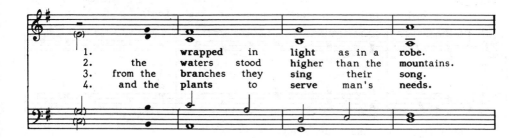

```
1.                  wrapped   in     light    as in a   robe.
2.         the      waters    stood  higher   than the  mountains.
3.         from the branches  they   sing     their     song.
4.         and the  plants    to     serve    man's     needs.
```

5 How mány are your wórks, O Lórd!
   In wísdom you have máde them áll.
   The eárth is fúll of your ríches.
   Bléss the Lórd, my sóul!

6 All créatures lóok to yóu
   to gíve them their fóod in due séason.
   You gíve it, they gáther it úp:
   you ópen your hánd, they have their fíll.

7 You táke back your spírit, they díe,
   retúrning to the dúst from which they cáme.
   You sénd forth your spírit, they are creáted;
   and you renéw the fáce of the éarth.

8 May the glóry of the Lórd last for éver!
   May the Lórd rejóice in his wórks!
   May my thóughts be pléasing to hím.
   I fínd my jóy in the Lórd.

9 (Give glóry to the Fáther almíghty,
   to his Són, Jesus Chríst, the Lórd,
   to the Spírit who dwélls in our héarts
   both nów and for éver./Amén.)

Psalm 103(104)
The Grail

683 & 684   Psalms 114–5(116)

Response 1 — A.Gregory Murray

I will walk in the presence of the Lord in the land of the liv-ing.

Response 2 — Stephen Dean

How can I re-pay the Lord for his good – ness to me?

A.Gregory Murray

Alternative Psalm Tone — Roger Humphrey

1 I love the Lord for hé has heard
the cry of mý appeal;
for he turned his éar to me
in the day whén I called him.

2 They surrounded me, the snáres of death,
with the anguish óf the tomb;
I called on thé Lord's name.
O Lord my Gód deliver me!

3 How gracious is the Lórd, and just;
our God hás compassion.
The Lord protects the símple hearts:
I was helpless só he saved me.

4 He has kept my sóul from death
my eyes from tears and my féet from stumbling.
I will walk in the presence óf the Lord
in the land óf the living.

5 (Glory be to the Father, and tó the Son,
and to the Hóly Spirit,
as it was in the beginning, is now,
    and éver shall be,
world without énd. Amen.)

1 My vows to the Lord I wíll fulfill
before áll his people.
O precious in the eyes óf the Lord
is the death óf his faithful.

2 Your servant, Lord, your servánt am I;
you have looséned my bonds.
A thanksgiving sacrifíce I make:
I will call on thé Lord's name.

3 My vows to the Lord I wíll fulfill
before áll his people,
in the courts of the house óf the Lord,
in your midst, Ó Jerusalem.

4 I trusted, even whén I said:
'I am sorelý afflicted,'
and when I said in mý alarm:
'No man cán be trusted.'

5 How can I repáy the Lord
for his goodnéss to me?
The cup of salvation Í will raise;
I will call on thé Lord's name.

6 (Glory be to the Father, and tó the Son,
and to the Hóly Spirit,
as it was in the beginning, is now,
    and éver shall be,
world without end. Amén.)

Psalms 114/115(116)
The Grail

Psalm 115
The Grail

685 Psalm 116(117)

Christopher Walker

Strong is his love for us he is faithful for e – ver.

Am   G   D

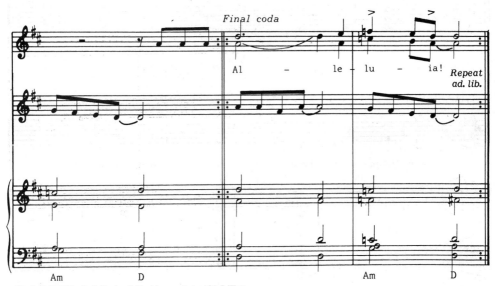

Final coda

Al – le – lu – ia! *Repeat ad. lib.*

Am   D   Am   D

Psalm 116(117)
The Grail

686   Psalm 117(118)

Christopher Walker

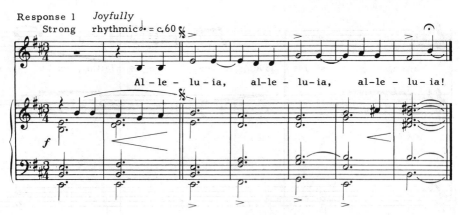

Response 1   *Joyfully*
Strong   rhythmic

Al – le – lu – ia,   al-le – lu-ia,   al-le – lu – ia!

Response 2   *Joyfully*

Strong

day   by
This was made the Lord;   we re-joice   and are glad.

Verse

Give thanks to the Lord   for   he   is   good, for his love

has no end. Let the sons of Is-ra-el say: 'His love

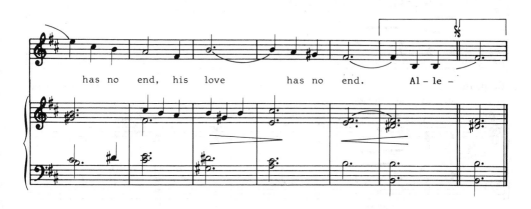

has no end, his love has no end. Al-le-

2 The Lord's right hand has triumphed;
   his right hand raised me up.
   I shall not die, I shall live
   and recount his deeds,
   recount his deeds.

3 The stone which the builders rejected
   has become the corner stone.
   This is the work of the Lord,
   a marvel in our eyes,
   a marvel in our eyes.

Psalm 117(118):1–2,16–17,22–23
The Grail

687 Psalm 121(122)

Response 1
Joseph Gelineau
Give your peace, O Lord, to those who count on you.

Response 2
Stephen Dean
I re-joiced when I heard them say: Let us go to God's house!

Response 3
Stephen Dean
Let us go to God's house, re— joic— ing.

Psalm 121
Joseph Gelineau

1.   I re- joic'd when I heard them say:
2.   Je- rusalem is built as a city
3.   For Israel's law it is
4. For the peace of Je- rusalem, pray:

    'Let us go to God's house.   And
    strongly com- pact.   It is
there to praise the Lord's name
    'Peace be to your homes!'   May

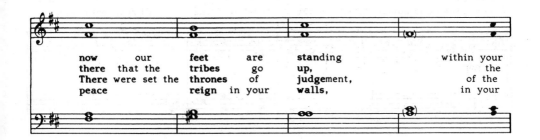

now	our	feet	are	standing	within your
there	that the	tribes	go	up,	the
There	were set the	thrones	of	judgement,	of the
peace		reign	in your	walls,	in your

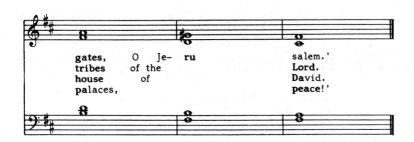

gates,	O Je- ru	salem.'
tribes	of the	Lord.
house	of	David.
palaces,		peace!'

5 (Praise the Fáther, the Són and Holy Spírit,
  both nów and foréver:
  the God who ís, who wás and who wíll be,
  wórld without énd.

Psalm 121
The Grail

688 Psalm 125(126)

Response 1
Joseph Gelineau

Those who sow in tears and sor-row, one day will reap with joy.

Unison only

Response 2
Stephen Dean

What mar-vels the Lord worked for us! In-deed we were glad.

PSALM
Joseph Gelineau

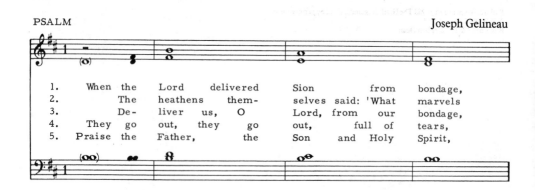

1. When the Lord delivered Sion from bondage,
2. The heathens them-selves said: 'What marvels
3. De-liver us, O Lord, from our bondage,
4. They go out, they go out, full of tears,
5. Praise the Father, the Son and Holy Spirit,

it seemed like a dream.   Then was our
the Lord worked for them!'   What marvels the
as streams in dry land.   Those who
carrying seed for the sowing; they come back, they come
both now and for ever, the God who is, who

mouth filled with laughter, on our lips there were songs.
Lord worked for us!   In- deed, we were glad.
sow in tears   will sing when they reap.
back, full of song,   carrying their sheaves.
was and who will be,   world without end.

Psalm 125(126)
The Grail

689 Psalm 129(130)

Response 1

Joseph Gelineau

I place all my trust in you my God, all my hope is in your sa-ving Word.

Response 2

Stephen Dean

With the Lord there is mer-cy and full-ness of re-demption.

Joseph Gelineau

1. Out of the depths   I   cry to you, O   Lord,
2. If you, O Lord should   mark   our   guilt,
3.   My soul   is   waiting for the   Lord,
4.   Be-cause with the   Lord there is   mercy
5. (To the Father Al-   Mighty   give   glory,

Lord, hear my **voice!**
Lord, who would sur– **vive?**
I **count** on his **word:**
and **fullness** of re– **demption,**
give **glory** to his **Son.**

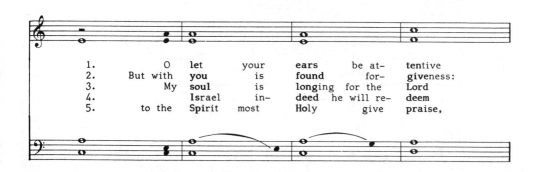

1. O **let** your **ears** be at– **ten**tive
2. But with **you** is **found** for– **giveness:**
3. My **soul** is **longing** for the **Lord**
4. Israel in– **deed** he will re– **deem**
5. to the **Spirit** most **Holy** give **praise,**

to the **voice** of my **plea**– **ding.**
 for **this** we re– **vere** **you.**
more than **watch**– man for **day**– **break.**
 from **all** its i– **ni**– **quity.**
 whose **reign** is for e– **ver.)**

Psalm 129(130)
The Grail

690   Psalm 135(136)

Joseph Gelineau

Voice

1. O give thanks to the Lord for he is good,
2. Who a- lone has wrought mar - vell - ous works,
3. It was he who made the great lights,
4. The first- born of the E - gyp - tians he smote
5. He di- vided the Red Sea in two,
6. Through the desert his peo - ple he led
7. He let Israel in - her - it their land,
8. And he snatched us a- way from our foes,

Great is his love,   love wi - thout end.

1. give thanks to the God of gods,
2. whose wisdom it was made the skies,
3. the sun to rule in the day,
4. he brought Israel out from their midst,
5. he made Israel pass through the midst,
6. nations in their great - ness he struck,
7. on his servant their land he be - stowed,
8. he gives food to all liv- ing things,

1028

Great is his love, love wi-thout end.

1.   give thanks to the **Lord** of **Lords.**
2.   who **spread** the **earth** on the **seas.**
3.   the **moon** and **stars** in the **night.**
4. arm out-**stretched,** with **power** in his **hand.**
5.   flung **Pharaoh** and his **force** in the **sea.**
6.   **kings** in their **splen**-dour he **slew.**
7. he re-**membered** **us** in our dis-**tress.**
8. to the **God** of **hea** – ven **give** **thanks.**

Great is his love, love wi-thout end.

Psalm 135(136)
The Grail

691   Psalm 144(145)

Response 1

A. Gregory Murray

I will bless your name for e – ver, O God my King.

or

Response 2

Eric Welch

You o-pen wide your hand; O Lord, you grant our de – sires.

Psalm Tone

A. Gregory Murray

Alternative Psalm Tone

John Harper

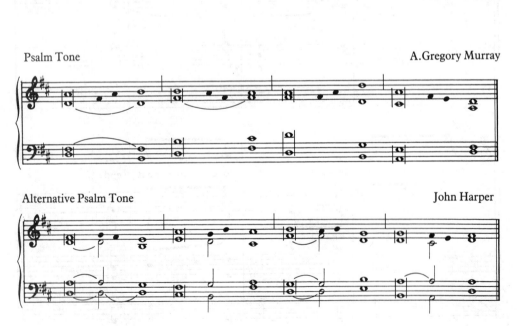

1 I will give you glory, O Gód my King.
   I will bless your náme for ever.
   I will bless you day áfter day
   and praise your náme for ever.

2 The Lord is kind and full óf compassion,
   slow to anger, abounding in love.
   How good is the Lórd to all,
   compassionate to áll his creatures.

3 All your creatures shall thank yóu, O Lord,
   and your friends shall repéat their blessing.
   They shall speak of the glory óf your reign
   and declare your míght, O God.

4 To make known to men your míghty deeds
   and the glorious splendour óf your reign.
   Yours is an everlásting kingdom;
   your rule lasts from áge to age.

5 The Lord is faithful in áll his words
   and loving in áll his deeds.
   The Lord supports áll who fall
   and raises all who áre bowed down.

6 The eyes of all creatures lóok to you
   and give them their food ín due time.
   You open wíde your hand,
   grant the desires of áll who live.

7 The Lord is just in áll his ways
   and loving in áll his deeds.
   He is close to áll who call him,
   who call on him fróm their hearts.

8 (Glory be to the Father, and tó the Son,
   and to the Hóly Spirit,
   as it was in the beginning, is now,
     and éver shall be,
   world without énd. Amen.)

Psalm 144(145):1–2,8–18
The Grail

692 Psalm 150

Jan Vermulst

al‑le‑lu – ia.

2 Praise him with the blast of trumpet;
   praise him now with lyre and harps;
   praise him with the timbrel and dance;
   praise him with the sound of string and reed.

3 Praise him with resounding cymbals;
   with cymbals that crash give praise;
   O let everything that has breath,
   let all living creatures praise the Lord.

4 Praise God the almighty Father;
   praise Christ his beloved Son;
   give praise to the Spirit of love,
   for ever the triune God be praised.

Psalm 150,
paraphrased by Omer Westendorf

693 The Benedictus (Luke 1:68–79)

Tone 1   John Harper

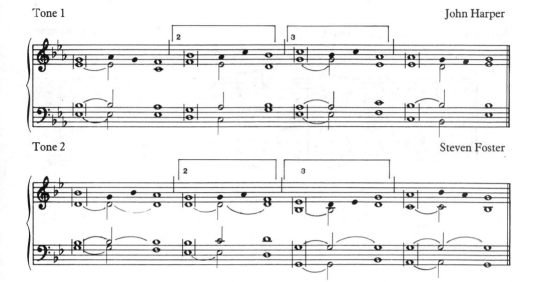

Tone 2   Steven Foster

Blessed be the Lord, the Gód of Israel!
      (omit sections 2 & 3 of chant)
He has visited his people and redeemed them.

He has raised up for us a míghty saviour
in the house of Davíd his servant,
as he promised by the lips of hóly men,
those who were his prophets fróm of old.

A saviour who would free us fróm our foes,
from the hands of āll who hate us.
So his love for our fathers ís fulfilled
and his holy covenānt remembered.

He swore to Abraham our fathér to grant us,
that free from fear, and saved from the hands
    óf our foes,
we might serve him in holinéss and justice
all the days of our life ín his presence.

As for you, líttle child,
you shall be called a prophet of God, thē Most High.
You shall go ahead óf the Lord
to prepare his wǎys before him.

To make known to his people their salvation
through forgiveness of āll their sins,
the loving-kindness of the heart óf our God
who visits us like the dawn fróm on high.

He will give light to thóse in darkness
those who dwell in the shadów of death,
    (omit section 3 of chant)
and guide us into the wǎy of peace.

Glory be to the Father, and tó the Son,
and to the Hóly Spirit,
as it was in the beginning, is now and ěver shall be,
world without énd, Amen.

The Grail

694   The Magnificat (Luke 1:46–55)

Joseph Gelineau

A. Gregory Murray

Response   ♩ = o of canticle

The   Lord has done mar-vels for me: ho-ly   is his   name.

is his

```
1.                My   soul        glorifies     the   Lord,
2.                He  looks  on his servant  in  her  nothingness;
9.                the mer-    cy   promised to  our  fathers,
10.   Praise the  Father,  the    Son  and   Holy Spirit,
```

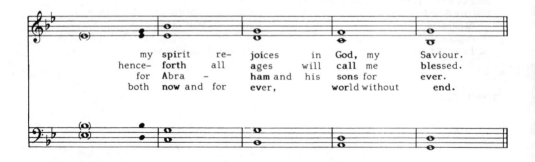

```
         my   spirit  re-   joices    in  God,  my   Saviour.
hence-   forth  all   ages  will  call me   blessed.
for   Abra  –   ham and  his  sons for  ever.
both  now and for  ever,     world without  end.
```

1036

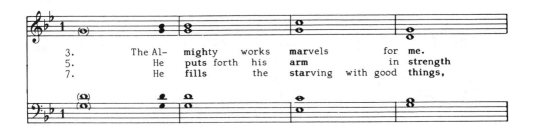

3. The Al- mighty works marvels for me.
5. He puts forth his arm in strength
7. He fills the starving with good things,

Holy his name!
and scatters the proud- hearted.
sends the rich away empty.

4. His mercy is from age to
6. He casts the mighty from their
8. He pro- tects Israel his

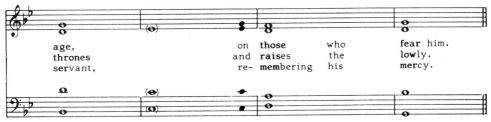

age, on those who fear him.
thrones and raises the lowly.
servant, re- membering his mercy.

The Grail

695 The Nunc Dimittis (Luke 2:29–32)

Response 1

Joseph Gelineau

Guard us O Lord, while we sleep and keep us in peace.

Response 2

Guy Wetz

My eyes have seen your sal-va-tion: the light of all peo-ples.

Canticle

Joseph Gelineau

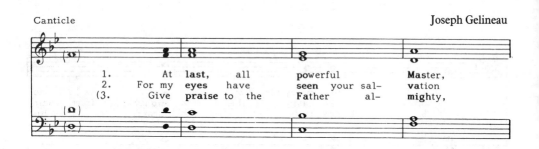

1.   At last, all powerful Master,
2. For my eyes have seen your sal-vation
(3.   Give praise to the Father al-mighty,

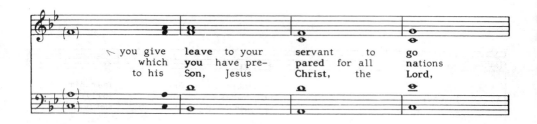

you give leave to your servant to go
which you have pre-pared for all nations
to his Son, Jesus Christ, the Lord,

the light to en- lighten the Gentiles
to the Spirit who dwells in our hearts,

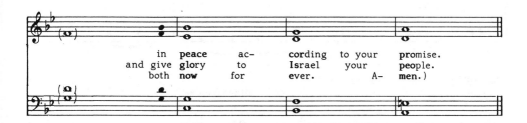

in peace ac- cording to your promise.
and give glory to Israel your people.
both now for ever. A- men.)

The Grail

Another setting of the Nunc Dimittis is number 561

696 Adoramus te, Domine

Jacques Berthier

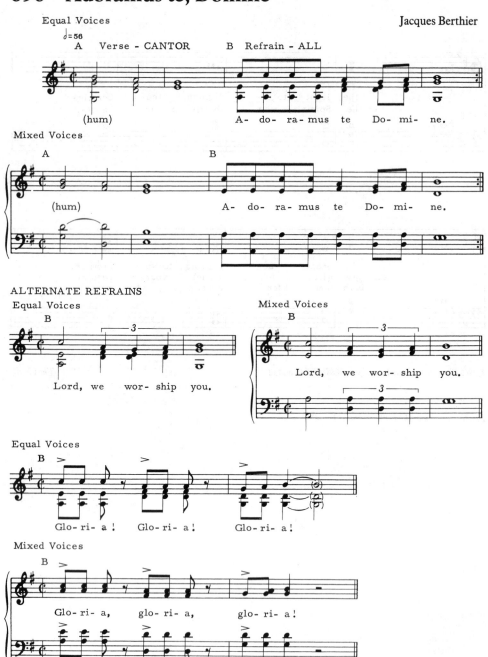

ALTERNATE REFRAINS

Verses

CANTOR

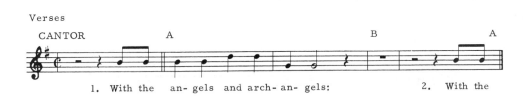

1. With the an- gels and arch- an- gels: 2. With the

pa- tri-archs and pro-phets: 3. With the Vir- gin Ma- ry

moth-er of God: 4. With the A- pos-tles and e- van-gel-ists:

5. With all the martyrs of Christ: 6. With all who

wit-ness to the Gos- pel of the Lord: 7. With all your

peo- ple of the Church through-out the world:

* Choose either part.

697 Praemananda Alleluia

Christopher Walker

698　Alleluia Round

William Boyce (1707–79)

699 The Beatitudes

Stephen Dean

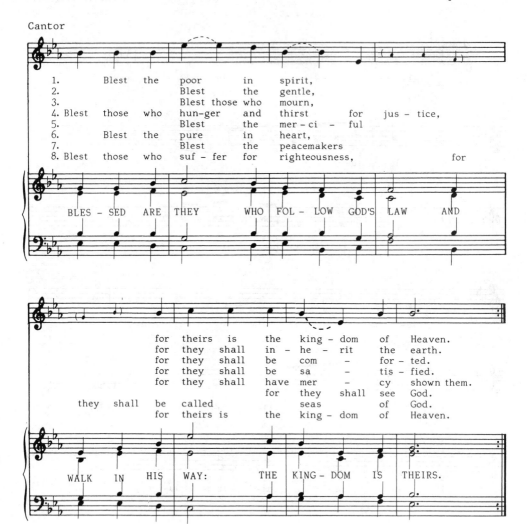

1. Blest the poor in spirit,
2. Blest the gentle,
3. Blest those who mourn,
4. Blest those who hun-ger and thirst for jus-tice,
5. Blest the mer-ci-ful
6. Blest the pure in heart,
7. Blest the peacemakers
8. Blest those who suf-fer for righteousness, for

BLES-SED ARE THEY WHO FOL-LOW GOD'S LAW AND

for theirs is the king-dom of Heaven.
for they shall in-he-rit the earth.
for they shall be com-for-ted.
for they shall be sa-tis-fied.
for they shall have mer-cy shown them.
for they shall see God.
they shall be called seas of God.
for theirs is the king-dom of Heaven.

WALK IN HIS WAY: THE KING-DOM IS THEIRS.

Music © Stephen Dean

The chorus is sung continuously. The cantor sings verses as required. When the cantor is singing, the people hum with closed lips.

700 Breath of Life

Bernard Huijbers

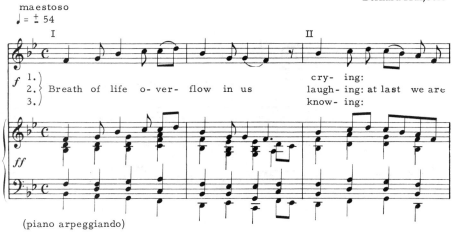

maestoso
♩ = ± 54

1.)
2.) Breath of life o-ver- flow in us   laugh- ing: at last we are
3.)

ff

(piano arpeggiando)

cry- ing:
laugh- ing:
know- ing:

born a- gain.

*Performance: the three verses could be sung throughout in
unison before they are sung as a canon.*

Huub Oosterhuis, English arr. by Tony Barr

701 Dona nobis pacem

Anonymous

1 Do- na no- bis pa- cem, pa- cem,

2 Do- na no- bis pa- cem,

3 Do- na no- bis pa- cem,

Do- na no- bis pa- cem.

Do- na no- bis pa- cem.

Do- na no- bis pa- cem.

702   Glory be to God the Father

Anonymous

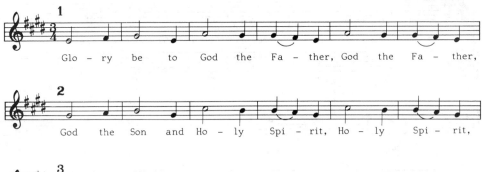

Glo – ry be to God the Fa – ther, God the Fa – ther,

God the Son and Ho – ly Spi – rit, Ho – ly Spi – rit,

as it was and shall be e – ver – more.

Music © Faber Music Ltd

703   Go out to the whole world

Bill Tamblyn

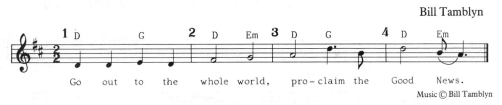

Go out to the whole world, pro – claim the Good News.

Music © Bill Tamblyn

704   I rejoiced

Bill Tamblyn

I re – joiced when I heard them say, 'Let us go to God's

house.' Al – le – lu – ia!

Music © Bill Tamblyn

705 Jesus Christ, little Lord

Roger Humphrey

This is a simple Christmas song suitable for children. It can be sung as a round: the second voice entering when the first voice has reached the asterisk ❋.

© McCrimmon Publishing Co Ltd

Roger Humphrey

706 Jubilate Deo (i)

Michael Praetorius (1571–1621)
Accompaniments by Jacques Berthier

Canon (Praetorius)

Ju – bi – la – te De – o, Ju – bi – la – te De – o, Al – le – lu – ia.

Accompaniments (Jaques Berthier)

Guitar

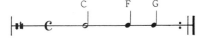

Choir

Ju – bi – la – te De – o,

Ju – bi – la – te, Ju – bi – la – te, Ju – bi – la – te,
Ju – bi – la – te De – o, Ju – bi – la – te,

Ju – bi – la – te, A – men.

707 Jubilate Deo (ii)

Jacques Berthier

Canon – (2 Voices)

Ju-bi-la-te De-o omnis ter-ra. Ser-vi-te

Do-mi-no in lae-ti-ti-a. Al-le-lu-ia, al-le-lu-ia, on lae-ti-ti-

a. Al-le-lu-ia, al-le-lu-ia, in lae-ti-ti-a!

in lae-ti-ti-

Accompaniments

Keyboard or Instruments

Guitar

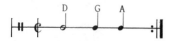

708 Let us go forth

Estelle White

Let us go forth in – to the world

with the good news, spread–ing his word, for we're

Eas – ter peo – ple, saved by Christ.

Estelle White

709 Misericordias Domini

Jacques Berthier

Verses
CANTOR

1. From age to age through all gen-er-a-tions, my mouth shall proclaim your

truth O Lord. 2. Who, O God, who in the u-ni-verse can compare with you?

3. Blest be the Lord for ev-er, through-out e-ter-ni-ty.

*
A- men! A- men!

* Choose either part.

From Psalm 88(89)
© Copyright Les Presses de Taizé.
All rights reserved.
Used by permission of Collins
Liturgical Publications

710 O Lord hear my prayer

Jacques Berthier

O Lord hear my pray'r, O Lord hear my pray'r; when I call,

an- swer me. O Lord hear my pray'r, O Lord hear my pray'r.

Come and li-sten to me. O

© Copyright Les Presses de Taizé.
All rights reserved.
Used by permission of Collins
Liturgical Publications

711 Ostende Nobis Domine

Jacques Berthier

Principal Canon

Os – ten – de no – bis Do – mi – ne, mi – se – ri – cor – di – am tu –

am. A – men! A – men! Ma – ra – na – tha! Ma – ra – na – tha! Os – ten – de. – tha.

Accompaniments

Keyboard

Guitar

Choral Accompaniment I

A men! A – men! A – men!

A – men! A – men! A – men!

Secondary Canon (or Choral Accompaniment II) Basses and Altos

Os – ten – de no – bis Do – mi – ne, mi – se – ri – cor – di – am tu – am Os –

Choral Accompaniment III

Os — ten — de no — bis, no — bis Do — mi — ne, mi — se — ri —

(mi-se-ri – cor-di – am)   1, 2, 3. . . .   (Fine)

cor-di –am tu – am,   tu – am,   tu   am. Os – am.

712   Sing alleluia to the Lord

Linda Stassen
Harmony by F. & R.Kelly

Linda Stassen

713 Sing and rejoice

(This song may be sung as a round: successive entries are numbered)

Herman Stern
Harmony by F. & R. Kelly

Herman Stern

714 Stand and stare not

Bernard Huijbers

1. Stand and stare not at what used to be
2. and re- main not in the past. . For
3. I, says he, make new be- gin- nings. Look,
4. all things are new now, do you not see?

(let each line play itself out)

Accompaniment

fine

Music © Berhard Huijbers
Words © Huub Oosterhuis
Tr © Tony Barr, from the original Dutch
Published by Jabulani Music Ltd, 9 Patmore Road, Colchester, Essex

Huub Oosterhuis, tr. Tony Barr

715 Christus Vincit

Plainchant
arr. Laurence Bévenot O.S.B.

CANTOR
Chri- stus vin- cit: Chri- stus re- gnat: Chri- stus im-

ALL
pe- rat. Chri- stus vin- cit: Chri- stus re- gnat:

Chri- stus im- pe- rat. Ex- au- di Chri- ste. Ex- au- di

CANTOR   ALL

CANTOR
Chri- ste. Sum- mo Pon- ti- fi- ci et u- ni- ver- sa- li Pa- pae

ALL   CANTOR   ALL
vi- ta.   Sal- va- tor mun- di: tu il- lum

CANTOR ad- ju- va. Sancta Ma- ri- a: ALL tu il lum

CANTOR ad- ju- va. Sancte Pe- tre: ALL tu il- lum

CANTOR ad- ju- va. Sancte Pau- le: ALL tu il- lum

CANTOR ad- ju- va. Sancte Gre- go- ri: ALL tu il- lum

ad- ju- va. Chri- stus vin- cit: Chri- stus re- gnat:

716 Pange Lingua

PANGE LINGUA

Plainchant
Harmony by A. Gregory Murray

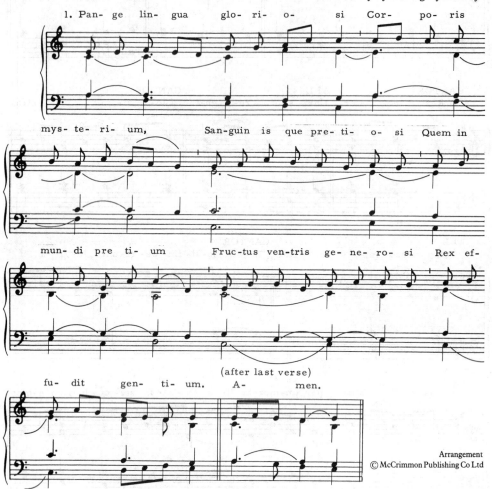

1. Pan- ge lin- gua glo- ri- o- si Cor- po- ris
mys- te- ri- um, San-guin is que pre- ti- o- si Quem in
mun- di pre ti- um Fruc-tus ven-tris ge- ne- ro- si Rex ef-
(after last verse)
fu- dit gen- ti- um. A- men.

2 Nobis datus, nobis natus
ex intactus Virgine;
et in mundo conversatus,
sparso verbi semine,
sui moras incolatus
miro clausit ordine.

3 In supremæ nocte cœnæ
recumbens cum fratribus,
observata lege plene
cibin in legalibus:
cibum turbæ duodenæ
se dat suis manibus.

4 Verbum caro, panem verum
Verbo carnem efficit:
fitque sanguis Christi merun;
et si sensus deficit,
ad firmandum cor sincerum
sola fides sufficit.

5 Tantum ergo Sacramentum
veneremur cernui:
et antiquum documentum
novo cedat ritui:
præstet fides supplementum
sensuum defectui.

6 Genitori, genitoque
laus, et jubilatio,
salus, honor, virtus quoque
sit et benedictio:
procedenti ab utroque
compar sit laudatio. Amen

St Thomas Aquinas (1227–74)

717 Regina Caeli

REGINA CAELI

Plainchant
Harmony by James O'Donnell

Anonymous

718 Salve Regina

REGINA CAELI

Plainchant
Harmony by James O'Donnell

Sal- ve Re- gi- na, Ma- ter mi- se- ri- cor- di- ae: Vi- ta, dul-

ce- do et spes nos- tra, sal- ve. Ad te cla- ma- mus,

ex- su- les fi- li- i He- vae. Ad te sus- pi- ra- mus, ge-

men- tes et flen- tes in hac la- cri- ma- rum val- le. E- ia er- go,

ad- vo- ca- ta nos- tra, il- los tu- os mi- se- ri- cor- des o- cu- los

Anonymous

719　Te Deum Laudamus

sti cre- den- ti- bus re- gna cæ- lo- rum. Tu ad dex- te- ram

De- i se- des, in glo- ri- a Pa- tris. Ju- dex cre- de

ris es- se ven- tu- rus. Te er- go quæ- su- mus, tu- is

fa- mu- lis sub- ve- ni, quos pre- ti- o- so san- gui- ne

re- de- mi- sti. Ae- ter—— na fac cum sanctis tu-

is in glo- ri- a nu- me- ra- ri. Sal- vum fac po- pu- lum

tu- um Do- mi- ne, et be- ne- dic hæ- re

di- ta- te tu- æ. Et re- ge e-

os, et ex- tol- le il- los us- que

in æ- ter- num. Per sin- gu- los di- es,

Anonymous

720   Veni Creator Spiritus

VENI CREATOR

Plainchant
Harmony by A.Gregory Murray

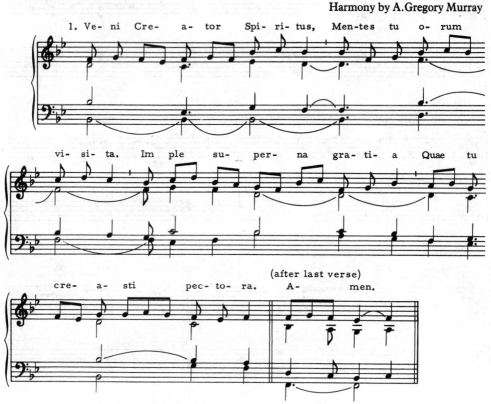

1. Ve- ni Cre- a- tor Spi- ri- tus, Men-tes tu o- rum

vi- si- ta. Im ple su- per- na gra-ti- a Quae tu

cre- a- sti pec- to- ra.   (after last verse)   A- men.

2   Qui diceris Paraclitus,
    altissimi donum Dei,
    fons vivus, ignis, caritas
    et spiritalis unctio.

3   Tu septiformis munere,
    digitus paternæ dexteræ,
    tu rite promissum Patris
    sermone ditans guttura.

4   Accende lumen sensibus,
    infunde amorem cordibus,
    infirma nostri corporis
    virtute firmans perpeti.

5   Hostem repellas longius
    pacemque dones protinus;
    ductore sic te prævio
    vitemus omne noxium.

6   Per te sciamus da Patrem
    noscamus atque Filium,
    teque utriusque Spiritum
    credamus omni tempore.
      Amen.

Anonymous, 9th century

721 Victimae Paschali

Plainchant
Harmony by James O'Donnell

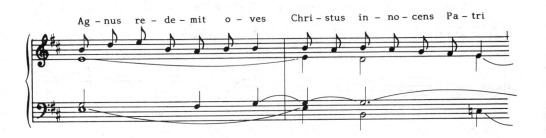

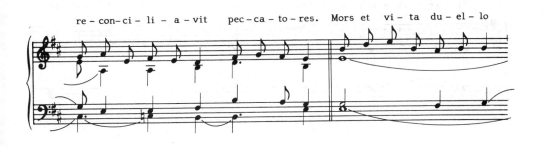

Dic no-bis Ma-ri-a, quid vi-di-sti in vi-a?

Se-pul-chrum Christi vi-ven-tis, et glo-ri-am vi-di re-sur-gen-tis:

An-ge-li-cos tes-tes, su-da-ri-um et ves-tes.

Sur-re-xit Christus spes me-a: prae-ce-det su-os in Ga-li-lae-am.

Sci – mus Chri – stum sur – re – xis – se   a   mor – tu – is   ve – re:

tu   no – bis, vi – ctor Rex, mi – se – re – re.   A   –   men.

(At Mass only:)

(Al – le – lu – ia.)

Attributed to Wipo of Burgundy, 10th century

722 I vow to thee, my country

THAXTED

Gustav Holst (1874–1934)

1 I vow to thee, my country, all earthly things above,
  entire and whole and perfect, the service of my love:
  the love that asks no questions, the love that stands the test,
  that lays upon the altar the dearest and the best;
  the love that never falters, the love that pays the price,
  the love that makes undaunted the final sacrifice.

2 And there's another country, I've heard of long ago,
  most dear to them that love her, most great to them that know;
  we may not count her armies, we may not see her King;
  her fortress is a faithful heart, her pride is suffering;
  and soul by soul and silently her shining bounds increase,
  and her ways are ways of gentleness and all her paths are peace.

Sir Cecil Spring-Rice

723 God Save the Queen

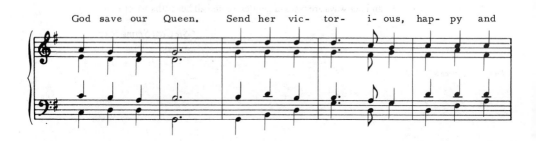

2   Thy choicest gifts in store
    On her be pleased to pour,
    Long may she reign.
    May she defend our laws,
    And ever give us cause
    To sing with heart and voice,
    God save the Queen.

NEW SONGS
OF CELEBRATION

724 All the ends of the earth

Marty Haugen and David Haas

VERSES·

(more lyrically)

1. Sing to the Lord a new song, for he has done wondrous deeds; his

2. The Lord has made his sal-va — tion known, his jus-tice re-vealed to all. Re-

3. All of the ends of earth have seen sal-va — tion by our God.

4. Sing to the Lord with harp and song, with trum — pet and with horn.

Bm   E   A   F♯m7   Bm   E7   F♯

f To refrain

1. right hand has won the vict'ry for him, his ho-ly arm.

2. membered his kindness and faith-ful-ness to Is-ra-el.

3. Joyful-ly sing out all you lands, break forth in song.

4. Sing in your joy be-fore the king, the king, our lord.

mp   *mp*   *f*

G   D/F♯   Em7   A   B   G   Em   G/A   A   G/A   A

1083

725   Awake, awake and greet the new morn

REJOICE, REJOICE

Marty Haugen

1. A—wake! A-wake, and greet the new morn, for an—gels her-ald its
dawn-ing, sing out your joy, for soon he is born, be—
—hold! the Child of our long——ing. Come as a ba—by

, weak and poor, to bring all hearts to-geth — er, he o — pens wide the

heav'n - ly door and lives now in-side us for e — ver. 1. 2.

2 To us, to all in sorrow and fear,
   Emmanuel comes a-singing,
   his humble song is quiet and near,
   yet fills the earth with its ringing;
   music to heal the broken soul
   and hymns of loving kindness,
   the thunder of his anthems roll
   to shatter all hatred and blindness.

3 In darkest night his coming shall be,
   when all the earth is despairing,
   as morning light so quiet and free,
   so warm and gentle and caring.
   Then shall the mute break forth in song,
   the lame shall leap in wonder,
   the weak be raised above the strong,
   and weapons be broken asunder.

4 Rejoice, rejoice, take heart in the night,
   though dark the winter and cheerless,
   the rising sun shall crown you with light,
   be strong and loving and fearless;
   love be our song and love our prayer,
   and love, our endless story,
   may God fill every day we share,
   and bring us at last into glory.

Marty Haugen

726 As a tree planted

Marty Haugen

As a tree plant – ed by streams of wat — er, is the one who de — lights in the word of the Lord.

Lord.

VERSES

Slower (rubato)

p 1. Bles - sed are the poor in spi — rit, theirs is the King — dom of
mp 2. Bles - sed are the meek and low — ly, they shall in - her — it the
mp 3. Bles - sed are the mer - ci - ful, for they shall have mer — cy
mf 4. Bles - ed are the peace-ful hearts, for they shall be called God's

hea — ven; bles — sed are the ones who mourn, for they shall be
earth; bles -sed are those who thirst for good, for they shall be
shown them; bles — sed are the pure in heart, for they shall —
chil — dren; bless's those suf - f'ring for right-eous-ness, the King — dom of

com — fort — ed.
sat — is — fied.
see — their God.
hea — ven is theirs.

(To Refrain)

As a

MUNDEN (SM)   FIRST TUNE   David Peacock

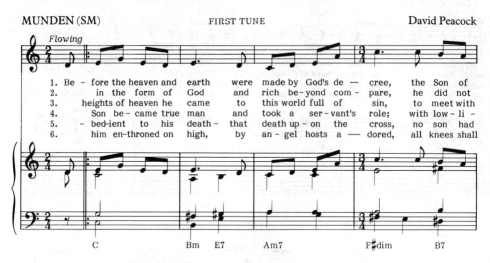

1. Be - fore the heaven and earth   were made by God's de — cree,   the Son of
2.   in the form of   God   and   rich be - yond com - pare,   he   did not
3.   heights of heaven he came to   this world full of   sin,   to meet with
4.   Son be - came true man   and   took a ser - vant's role;   with low - li -
5.   - bed-ient to his death – that death up - on the   cross,   no son had
6.   him en-throned on high,   by   an - gel hosts a — dored,   all knees shall

God   all glo - rious dwelt   in God's e — ter — ni — ty.   Though
stop   to grasp his prize;   nor did he lin — ger   there.   From
hun — ger, ha - tred, hell,   our life, our love to   win.   The
ness   and self - less love,   he came, to make us   whole.   O -
ev — er shown such love,   nor fa - ther known such   loss.   To

bow,   and tongues con - fess   that Je - sus   Christ is   Lord.

NARENZA (SM)

J. Leisentritt, *Catholicum*
Hymnologium Germanicum, 1584

Capo 3(G)

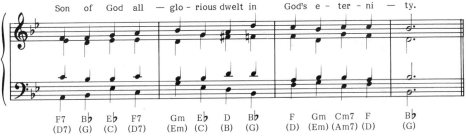

2 Though in the form of God
  and rich beyond compare,
  he did not stop to grasp his prize;
  nor did he linger there.

3 From heights of heaven he came
  to this world full of sin,
  to meet with hunger, hatred, hell,
  our life, our love to win.

4 The Son became true man
  and took a servant's role;
  with lowliness and selfless love,
  he came, to make us whole.

5 Obedient to his death
  that death upon the cross,
  no son had ever shown such love,
  nor father known such loss.

6 To him enthroned on high,
  by angel hosts adored,
  all knees shall bow, and tongues confess
  that Jesus Christ is Lord.

Brian Black, from Philippians 2:6-11

728 Bless the Lord, my soul

Jacques Berthier

VERSES From Psalm 102(103)

Cantor

1. It is he who forgives all your guilt, who heals ev-'ry one of your ills, who re-

-deems your life from the grave, who crowns you with love and com-pas-sion.

2. The Lord is com-pas-sion and love, slow to an-ger and rich in mer-cy. He does not

treat us ac-cording to our sins nor re —pay us ac-cording to our faults.

3. As a Fa-ther has compassion on his chil-dren, the Lord has pi-ty on those who

fear him; for he knows of what we are made, he re-members that we are dust.

EIN FESTE BURG

Martin Luther (1483-1546)
arr. J.S.Bach (1685-1750)

1 Christ's church shall glory in his power
   and grow to his perfection;
   He is our rock, our mighty tower,
   our life, our resurrection.
     So by his skilful hand
     the church of Christ shall stand;
     the master-builder's plan
     he works, as he began,
   and soon will crown with splendour.

2 Christ's people serve his wayward world
   to whom he seems a stranger;
   he knows its welcome from of old,
   he shares our joy, our danger.
     So strong, and yet so weak,
     the church of Christ shall speak;
     his cross our greatest need,
     his word the vital seed
   that brings a fruitful harvest.

3 Christ's living lamp shall brightly burn,
   and to our earthly city
   forgotten beauty shall return,
   and purity and pity.
     To give the oppressed their right
     the church of Christ shall fight;
     and though the years seem long
     God is our strength and song,
   and God is our salvation.

4 Christ's body triumphs in his name;
   one Father, sovereign giver,
   one Spirit, with his love aflame,
   one Lord, the same for ever.
     To you, O God our prize,
     the church of Christ shall rise
     beyond all measured height
     to that eternal light,
   where Christ shall reign all-holy.

Christopher Idle

730 Christ triumphant

Michael Baughen

Christ tri-um-phant ev — er reign — ing, Sav-iour, Mast-er, King,

F(D)   Gm7(Em7)

Lord of heav'n, our lives sus-tain-ing, hear us as we

C7(A7)   F(D)   F7(D7)   B♭(G)   Gm7(Em7)   C7(A7)

sing. Yours the glo-ry and the crown, the high

F(D)   C7(A7)   F(D)   F7(D7)   B♭(G)

re — nown, the e — ter — nal name.

D7(B7)   Gm(Em)   Fsus4(Dsus4)   C7(A7)   F(D)

2 Word incarnate, truth revealing,
  Son of Man on earth!
  Power and majesty concealing
  by your humble birth:

3 Suffering servant, scorned, illtreated,
  victim crucified!
  Death is through the cross defeated,
  sinners justified:

4 Priestly King, enthroned for ever
  high in heaven above!
  Sin and death and hell shall never
  stifle hymns of love:

5 So, our hearts and voices raising
  through the ages long,
  ceaselessly upon you gazing,
  this shall be our song:

Michael Saward

731 Come, rejoice before your maker

JUBILATE DEO (87 87)

Noel Tredinnick

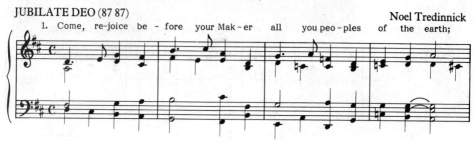

1. Come, re-joice be-fore your Mak-er all you peo-ples of the earth;

serve the Lord your God with glad-ness, come be-fore him with a song!

2 Know for certain, our Creator
is the true and only God;
we are his, for he has made us,
we are sheep within his fold.

3 Come with grateful hearts before him,
enter now his courts with praise;
show your thankfulness towards him,
give due honour to his name.

4 For the Lord our God is gracious
everlasting in his love,
and to every generation
his great faithfulness endures.

Michael Baughen (from Psalm 100)

732 Come, Saviour come

RORATE COELI

Plainchant, arr. Stephen Dean

Antiphon:

Come, Sa - viour, come like dew on the grass;   break through
the clouds like gen-tle rain.

1. Be ang-ry, Lord,   no more with us; re - mem-ber no long-er our trans-gres — sion.

See the ci - ty of God laid waste and des-o -late: Zi-on is turned   to wil — der-ness,

Je - ru - sa - lem, ra - vaged and ru - ined. Your dwelling place and the Ho-ly   of Ho-lies,

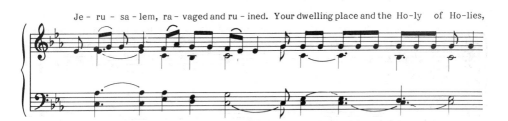

the house of your glo - ry: si - lent are those voic - es now that once pro-claimed
your praise.

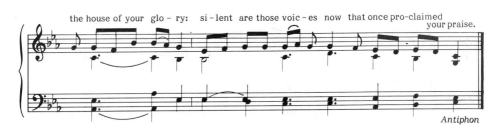

Antiphon

2. We have gone a-stray; in the mult-i-tude of our sins we have been made un-clean,

fall-en, fall-en, strick-en as the leaves of au-tumn. The stormwind carries us a-way,

the temp-est of our e-vil deeds; you have turned a-way from us the face of your mer-cy,

and our i-ni-qui-ty has crushed us like a pot — ter's ves — sel.

Antiphon

3. O Lord our God, look up-on your people in their aff-lic-tion: be mind-ful of your promises.

Send us the Lamb who will set up his do-min-i-on from the Rock of the Wil-der-ness to

Zi - on throned on her moun-tain. There is no other whose power can break the chains and set us free.

Antiphon

4. Be comfort-ed, be comfort-ed, take heart, my peo-ple: you shall quickly see your sal-va - tion.

Why do you waste your-self with grief, though you have walked so long with sor - row?

I am your Sav-iour, be a-fraid no more. For am I not God,

the Lord your God whom you worship, the Holy One of Is - ra - el, come to re-deem you?

Antiphon

10th C., tr. Luke Connaughton (1919-79)

733   Come to set us free

Bernadette Farrell

Last time only | *To verse*

1. You are light which shines in dark-ness, Morn-ing
2. You are hope which brings us cour-age, you are
3. You are pro-mise of sal-va-tion, you are

Dm Am Dm Dm Am Dm   Bb C F

Star which ne - ver sets.   O - pen our eyes which on - ly dim - ly
strength which ne - ver fails.   O - pen our minds to ways we do not
God in hu - man form.   Bring to our world of emp - ti - ness and

Gm7 C Dm G F/G G F/G

see the truth which sets us free.
know but where your Spi-rit grows.
fear the word we long to hear.

D.C.

G F/G G F/G Bb Gm7 C

734 Come, we that love the Lord

VINEYARD HAVEN

Richard Dirksen

1 Come, we that love the Lord,
and let our joys be known;
join in a song with sweet accord
and thus surround the throne.

Hosanna, hosanna,
Rejoice, give thanks and sing.

2 Sing till we feel our hearts
ascending with our tongues;
sing till the love of sin departs
and grace inspires our songs.

3 You pilgrims on the road
to Zion's city, sing;
rejoice now in the Lamb of God,
in Christ, the eternal King.

4 There shall each rapturous tongue
his endless praise proclaim,
and sing in sweeter notes the song
of Moses and the Lamb.

5 Then let our songs abound
and let our tears be dry;
We're marching through Emmanuel's
ground
to fairer worlds on high.

1 & 5, Isaac Watts (1674-1748)
2-4, William Hammond (1719-83)

Jacques Berthier

736 Early morning

ST BAVON

A.T.I.Jagger

When the tune is sung in harmony, in the last line the upper of the two tenor parts may be used.

1 Early morning. 'Come, prepare him,
to the tomb your spices bring;
death is cold and death decaying.
We must beautify our King.'

2 Early morning, women excited,
seeking Peter everywhere;
telling of a man who told them,
'He is risen; don't despair'.

3 Peter racing, early morning,
to the tomb and rushing in;
seeing shrouds of death dispensed with,
finding new-born faith begin.

4 Early morning, Mary weeping,
asking if the gardener knew;
knowing, as his voice says, 'Mary',
'Lord, Rabbuni, it is you'.

5 'Mary, you can live without me,
as I now to God ascend;
peace be with you; I am with you
early morning without end.'

6 Early morning, stay for ever,
early morning, never cease;
early morning, come to all men
for their good and power and peace.

John Gregory

737   Eye has not seen

Marty Haugen

Eye has not seen, ear has not heard, what

God has read-y for those who love him;

spi – rit of love, come give us the mind of Je – sus,

Last time to Coda

teach us the wis – dom of God. *(to Verse)*

(to Verse)

VERSES

Melody

Harmony

1. When pain and sor – row weigh us down, be near to us oh Lord, for y –
2. Our lives are but a sin – gle breath, we flow – er and we fade, yet
3. To those who see with eyes of faith, the Lord is ev – er near, re –

- give the weak-ness of our faith, and bear us up with - in your peace-ful
all our days are in your hands, so we re - turn in love what love has
- flec-ted in the fa — ces, of all the poor and low - ly of the

word.
made.
world.

(to Refrain)

VERSE 4

4. We sing a mys-t'ry from the past, in halls where saints have trod, yet

ev-er new the mu-sic rings, to Je-sus, liv-ing song of God.

(to Refrain)

Eye has not seen, ear has not heard, what

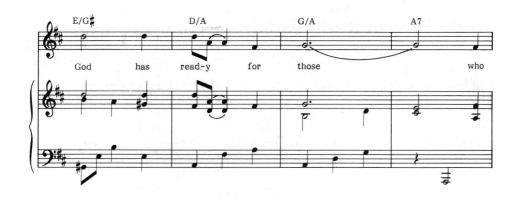

God   has   read-y   for   those   who

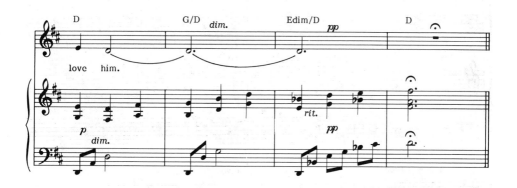

love   him.

738 Song of Ruth (Father, we come in prayer) 15

Anthony Sharpe

2 Jesus, we ask your help
  to conquer for all time
  the darkness in our land.
  Jesus, where we live you live too,
  unite our hearts with you in your love.

3 Spirit, we feel your pow'r
  your presence in our hearts:
  be with us in each day,
  Spirit, may we be one in you,
  make all we say and do give you praise.

Anthony Sharpe
(based on the book of Ruth)

739 Father, we come to you

James Walsh OSB

Strong! steady rhythm CANTOR(S) *mf*

Fa-ther, we come to you, God of all power and might. Show us your glo-ry: give us your life.

ALL *f*

Fa-ther, we come to you, God of all power and might. Show us your glo-ry: give us your life.

CANTOR(S) *mf*

You have u-ni-ted us, bound us in love and peace: God in the

ALL *f*

midst of us, ho - ly, un - seen. Bless-ed is he who comes pierc-ing our

night of sin. O - pen your hearts to him. Great is his name.

CANTOR(S) *mf*   *poco rall . . . .*

Bread of life shared with us, bo - dy of Christ the Lord, bro - ken and

ALL *f a tempo*

died for us: life for the world. Fa-ther, we come to you, God of all

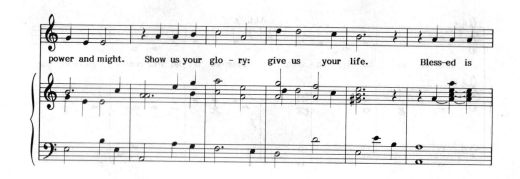

power and might. Show us your glo – ry: give us your life. Bless–ed is

he who comes pierc–ing our night of sin. O – pen our hearts to you:

great is your name. O – pen our hearts to you: great is your name!

TALBOT WOODS (446 D)   Michael Dawney

1. For call to faith, for gift of faith, thank God who calls, who gives; _____ for

C   F   G   Em Am Dm   Gm

call to life, for gift of life, thank God who e-ver lives. _____

Eb   Ab   C7   F   Dm   G7   C

2 For truth of God,
  for word of God,
  thank God that we can learn
  the ways of God,
  his law, his love,
  and love him in return,

3 For Son of God,
  for Son of Man,
  thank God for Christ his Son;
  For Jesus, Saviour,
  Saviour-King,
  and our salvation won.

4 For sacrifice,
  for sacrament,
  thank God with priestly prayer;
  for food of life,
  for bread of life,
  for Christ, our own to share.

5 Pray to the Father
  and the Son
  their Holy Spirit's praise,
  for faith professed,
  for love possessed
  in his confirming grace.

6 Pray praise, pray love,
  pray thanks to God,
  pray every kind of prayer;
  Pray, everyone,
  for everyone
  to praise God everywhere.

Brian Foley

Words by permission of Oxford University Press
Music © Michael Dawney

ENGLANDS LANE (77 77 77)

First Tune

English melody,
arr. Geoffrey Shaw (1879-1943)

Music by permission of Oxford University Press

1 For the beauty of the earth,
   for the beauty of the skies,
   for the love which from our birth
   over and around us lies,
   Christ our God, to you we raise
   this our sacrifice of praise.

2 For the beauty of each hour
   of the day and of the night,
   hill and vale, and tree and flower,
   sun and moon and stars of light.
   Christ our God, to you we raise
   this our sacrifice of praise.

3 For the joy of ear and eye,
   for the heart and mind's delight,
   for the mystic harmony
   linking sense to sound and sight.
   Christ our God, to you we raise
   this our sacrifice of praise.

4 For the joy of human love,
   brother, sister, parent, child,
   friends on earth and friends above,
   pleasures pure and undefiled,
   Christ our God, to you we raise
   this our sacrifice of praise.

5 For each perfect gift divine
   to our race so freely given,
   joys bestowed by love's design,
   flowers of earth and fruits of heaven,
   Christ our God, to you we raise
   this our sacrifice of praise.

F.S. Pierpoint (1835-1917)

LUCERNA LAUDONIAE (77 77 77)   David Evans (1874-1948)
Second Tune

Music by permission of Oxford University Press

Marty Haugen

shines in all who look to you, come, light the hearts of all in dark and
hearts are yearn-ing for Your Word, come, make us whole, be com-fort to our
ad — vent, draw us all to you, our hope re- born in dy - ing and in
seek, yet un – ful-filled re - main, o - pen to us the path-way of Your
heart be o-pened to the Lord, for we are all the peo- ple of His
of the moun-tains and the seas, Lord of the stars, and pres-ent to us

(to Refrain)

sha — dow.
hearts.
ri — sing.
peace.
hand.
now.

(to Refrain)

Marty Haugen
based on the 'O' Antiphons

743 Forgive our sins as we forgive

DETROIT (CM)

Kentucky Harmony, 1820,
harmonised by Gerald Knight (1908-79)

1 'Forgive our sins as we forgive,'
 you taught us, Lord, to pray,
 but you alone can grant us grace
 to live the words we say.

2 How can your pardon reach and bless
 the unforgiving heart
 that broods on wrongs and will not let
 old bitterness depart?

3 In blazing light your Cross reveals
 the truth we dimly knew:
 what trivial debts are owed to us,
 how great our debt to you!

4 Lord, cleanse the depths within our souls
 and bid resentment cease.
 Then, bound to all in bonds of love,
 our lives will spread your peace.

Rosalind Herklots

744 Forth in the peace of Christ

LLEDROD (LLANGOLLEN) (LM)

Caniadau y Cyssegr, 1837

1 Forth in the peace of Christ we go:
  Christ to the world with joy we bring;
  Christ in our minds, Christ on our lips,
  Christ in our hearts, the world's true
    King.

2 King of our hearts, Christ makes us kings;
  kingship with him his servants gain;
  with Christ, the Servant-Lord of all,
  Christ's world we serve to share Christ's
    reign.

3 Priests of the world, Christ sends us forth
  this world of time to consecrate,
  this world of sin by grace to heal,
  Christ's world in Christ to recreate.

4 Prophets of Christ, we hear his word:
  he claims our minds, to search his ways,
  he claims our lips, to speak his truth,
  he claims our hearts, to sing his praise.

5 We are his Church, he makes us one:
  here is one hearth for all to find,
  here is one flock, one Shepherd-King,
  here is one faith, one heart, one mind.

James Quinn SJ

Alternative tune ANGELS' SONG, Celebration Hymnal no. 78

RESURREXIT (77 77 and refrain)   Robert Sherlaw Johnson

2 One man for the people dies,
  Christ, the paschal lamb decreed,
  one man in whom all may rise;

3 We, like those who crossed dryshod
  Egypt's marches and the reed,
  praise in liberty our God;

4 God himself his people saves,
  harvest of the dying seed
  springing lively from the graves;
  Hamish F.G. Swanston

Words and music from New Catholic Hymnal, Faber Music, 3 Queen Square, London WC1N 3AV

746 God is my great desire

LEONI (6684 D)

From the *Yigdal*, transcribed
by Meyer Lyon, c.1751-97

1 God is my great desire,
  his face I seek the first;
  to him my heart and soul aspire,
  for him I thirst.
  As one in desert lands,
  whose very flesh is flame,
  in burning love I lift my hands
  and bless his name.

2 God is my true delight,
  my richest feast his praise,
  through silent watches of the night,
  through all my days.
  To him my spirit clings,
  on him my soul is cast;
  beneath the shadow of his wings
  he holds me fast.

3 God is my strong defence
  in ev'ry evil hour;
  in him I face with confidence
  the tempter's power.
  I trust his mercy sure,
  with truth and triumph crowned:
  my hope and joy for evermore
  in him are found.

Timothy Dudley-Smith

Words © Timothy Dudley-Smith

747 God who spoke in the beginning

KENSINGTON (87 87 87)

Herbert Howells

Words © Stainer & Bell Ltd, 82 High Road, London N2 9PW Music © Novello & Co

1 God who spoke in the beginning,
forming rock and shaping spar,
set all life and growth in motion,
earthly world and distant star;
he who calls the earth to order
is the ground of what we are.

2 God who spoke through men and nations,
through events long past and gone,
showing still today his purpose
speaks supremely through his Son;
he who calls the earth to order
gives his word and it is done.

3 God whose speech becomes incarnate,
Christ is servant, Christ is Lord!
calls us to a life of service,
heart and will to action stirred;
he who uses man's obedience
has the first and final word.

Fred Kaan

748 God, your glory we have seen

DIEU, NOUS AVONS VU (12 12 + refrain)

Jean Langlais

full of truth, full of heavenly grace; in Christ make us live, his love shine on our face,

and the na-tions will see in us the tri-umph you have won.

(pauses last time only)

VERSES

Harmony

1. In the fields of this world his good news he has sown, and
sends us out to reap till the har — vest is done.

back to Refrain

2 In his love like a fire
  that consumes he passed by:
  the flame has touched our lips;
  let us shout: 'Here am I!'

3 He was broken for us,
  God-forsaken his cry,
  and still the bread he breaks:
  to ourselves we must die:

4 He has trampled the grapes
  of new life on his Cross;
  now drink the cup and live:
  he has filled it for us:

5 He has founded a kingdom
  that none shall destroy;
  the corner-stone is laid:
  Go to work, build with joy!

Didier Rimaud, tr. Brian Wren

749   Great is the Lord

Paul Inwood

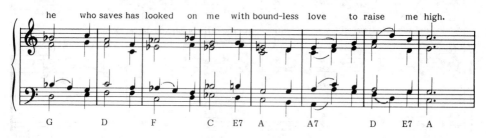

2 Ages to come shall know that I
am blessed and favoured by the Lord:
his name is holy, mighty God;
his wondrous power on me is poured.

3 All those who fear him find his love,
in every age, in every land.
His strong right arm puts down the proud,
disperses them like grains of sand.

4 Down from their thrones he casts the strong,
and raises up the meek of heart.
He gives the hungry choicest food;
in emptiness the rich depart.

5 Israel his servant knows his help,
in keeping with the promise sworn
to Abraham and all his race:
God's love will never be withdrawn.

6 Glory to God: the Father, Son,
and Spirit — Trinity sublime.
All honour, thanks and praise be theirs
across the spans of endless time.

The Magnificat (Lk 1:46-55)
versified by Paul Inwood

750 Who calls my life again

ANTIPHON   1 Choir   2 All

Plainchant, arr. Bernard Huijbers

Who calls my life a-gain from the grave? And, like an eag-le re-news my youth?

VERSE ONE

You are the forgiveness of our sins,   for you are greater than our sins.

antiphon

VERSE TWO

As pa — rents pro-tecting their child-ren, so are you for us   most ten-der and lov-ing.

antiphon

VERSE THREE

You know us well, you have not for-got-ten that we are made from the dust of the earth.

antiphon

Peo - ple, their days are just like the grass, they bloom as the flow-ers in the o - pen field.

The wind blows up, and they van-ish for good, but God's love shall have no end.

ANTIPHON

Who calls my life a-gain from the grave? and, like an eag-le re-news my youth?_____

Words and music by permission of Jabulani Music

751 Hear us, almighty Lord (Attende Domine) 28

ATTENDE DOMINE

Plainchant, arr. Richard Proulx

Hear us, al-might-y Lord, show us your mer-cy, sin-ners we stand here be-fore you.
At -ten-de Do-mi-ne, et mi-se-re -re, qui-a pec-ca-vi-mus ti — bi.

Alternative accpt.

Principal accpt.

1. Je - sus our Sa - viour, Lord of all the na — tions, Christ our Re-deem-er,
2. Word of the Fa - ther, key-stone of God's build - ing, source of our glad -ness,
3. God of com-pas-sion, Lord of might and splen - dour, gra -cious-ly lis — ten,
1. Ad te Rex sum-me, om - ni - um re - dem - ptor, o - cu-los no - stros
2. Dex-te - ra Pa-tris, la - pis an - gu - la — ris, vi - a sa-lu - tis
3. Ro - ga - mus, De- us, tu - am ma-je - sta — tem: au - ri-bus sa - cris

hear the prayers we of — fer, spare us and save us, com-fort us in sor — row.
gate-way to the King - dom, free us in mer-cy from the sins that bind us.
hear our cries of an — guish. Touch us and heal us where our sins have wound - ded.
sub - le va-mus flen - tes: ex - au - di, Chri-ste, sup - pli- can-tum pre - ces.
ja - nu - a cae-le — stis, ab - lu - e no - stri ma - cu - las de - li - cti.
ge - mi - tus ex-au — di: cri - mi - na no - stra pla - ci - dus in - dul - ge.

4 Humbly confessing that we have offended,
 stripped of illusions, naked in our sorrow,
 pardon, Lord Jesus, those your blood has
 ransomed.

5 Innocent captive, you were led to slaughter,
 sentenced by sinners when they brought
 false witness.
 Keep from damnation those your death
 has rescued.

Alternative response

**Attende Domine et miserere
quia peccavimus tibi.**

Attende Domine, *c.10,*
tr. Ralph Wright OSB

752 Gather us in (Here in this place)

Marty Haugen

1. Here in this place, new light is stream-ing, now is the dark-ness, vanished a-way, see, in this space, our fears and our dream-ings, brought here to you in the light of this day. Gath-er us in the lost and for-sak-en, gath-er us in the

blind and the lame; call to us now, and we shall a-wak-en,

we shall a-rise at the sound of our name.

2 We are the young — our lives are a mystery,
we are the old — who yearn for your face,
we have been sung throughout all of history
called to be light to the whole human race.
Gather us in the rich and the haughty,
gather us in the proud and the strong;
give us a heart so meek and so lowly,
give us the courage to enter the song.

3 Here we will take the wine and the water,
here we will take the bread of new birth,
here you shall call your sons and your
daughters,
call us anew to be salt for the earth.
Give us to drink the wine of compassion,
give us to eat the bread that is you;
nourish us well, and teach us to fashion,
lives that are holy and hearts that are true.

4 Not in the dark of buildings confining,
not in some heaven, light years away, but
here in this place, the new light is shining,
now is the Kingdom, now is the day.
Gather us in and hold us for ever,
gather us in and make us your own;
gather us in all peoples together,
fire of love in our flesh and our bone.

Marty Haugen

753   How shall they hear the word of God

Paul Inwood

How shall they hear the Word of God un-less his truth is told?

How shall the sin-ful be set free, the sor-row-ful con-soled?

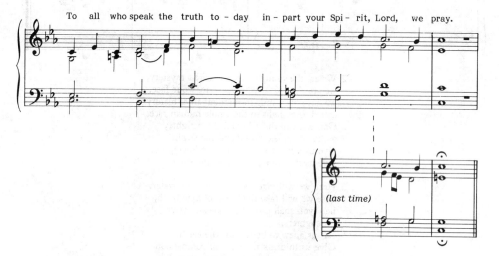

To all who speak the truth to-day in-part your Spi-rit, Lord, we pray.

(last time)

2 How shall they call to God for help
unless they have believed?
how shall the poor be given hope,
the prisoner reprieved?
  To those who help the blind to see
  give light and love and clarity.

3 How shall the gospel be proclaimed
if heralds are not sent?
how shall the world find peace at last
if we are negligent?
  So send us, Lord, for we rejoice
  to speak of Christ with life and voice.

Paul Inwood

754 I received the living God

Anonymous (US), arr. R.Proulx

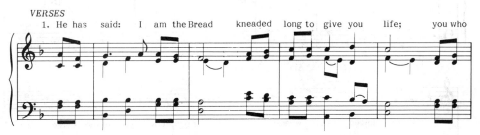

2 He has said: I am the Way,
and my Father longs for you;
so I come to bring you home
to be one with him anew.

3 He has said: I am the Truth;
if you follow close to me,
you will know me in your heart,
and my word shall make you free.

4 He has said: I am the Life
far from whom no thing can grow,
but receive this living bread,
and my Spirit you shall know.

Anonymous

755   I rejoiced when I heard them say

Stephen Dean

MELODY INSTRUMENTS

INTRODUCTION

RESPONSE

VERSES

Words from *The Psalms: A New Translation* published by Wm Collins Sons & Co. Reproduced by permission of A.P.Watt Ltd on behalf of The Grail, England. Music © 1983 Stephen Dean

756 If God should lead us

Bernard Huijbers

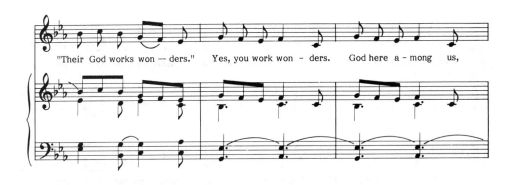

"Their God works won — ders." Yes, you work won - ders. God here a - mong us,

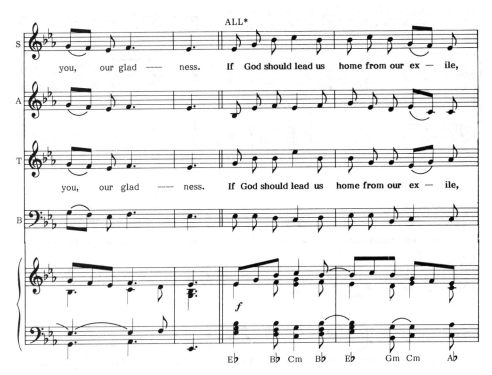

you, our glad ——— ness. If God should lead us home from our ex — ile,

you, our glad ——— ness. If God should lead us home from our ex — ile,

Eb   Bb Cm Bb   Eb   Gm Cm   Ab

* *The congregational melody is the soprano line*

1137

what wond'rous dream-world! If God should lead us home from our ex — ile,

what wond'rous dream-world! If God should lead us home from our ex — ile,

CHOIR

what wond'rous dream — world! Then lead us home, re — store us to life,

what wond'rous dream — world! Then lead us home, re — store us to life,

just as the ri — vers in the desert as the new rains fall start flowing a-gain.

CHOIR or ALL

sow-ing in sor — row, reap-ing in glad — ness, a man sets out in

tears for the sow -- ing, back he comes sing - ing, sheaves on his shoul — der.

Huub Oosterhuis, tr. Tony Barr   From Psalm 125 (126)

1140

757   In the abundance of your compassion

Owen Alstott
Accpt. by Randall DeBruyn

INTRODUCTION
Gently

REFRAIN

REFRAIN
In the a-bun-dance of your com-pas-sion wash my sins a-way.

Show me your mer-cy, O God, and cleansed in the wa-ter of

your sal — va-tion, I shall be whit-er than snow. *Fine*

VERSES

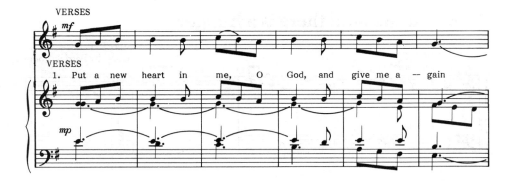

1. Put a new heart in me, O God, and give me a — gain

a con — stant spir — it.

2 We cannot live unless we die,
   unless we are born of water and spirit.

3 Trust in the Lord for He is good,
   His mercy endures, His love is unending.

Owen Alstott

758 In the land there is a hunger

Mike Lynch
Accpt. by Patrick Loomis

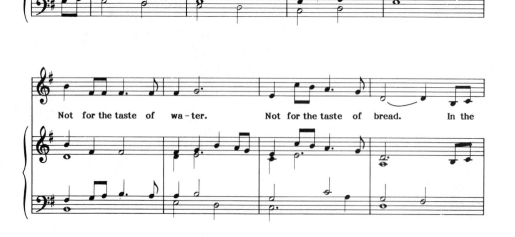

In the land there is a hun-ger. In the land there is a need

Not for the taste of wa-ter. Not for the taste of bread. In the

land there is a hun-ger. In the land there is a need.

For the sound of the word of God up - on ev'ry word we feed.

1-3 to Verses | Final

VERSE 1

1. Hear O Lord, my cry.   Day and night I call.

My soul is thirst-ing   for you my God.

D.S.

VERSE 2

2. Your word O Lord, is spir-it and life.

You have the words, Lord, of ev-er-last-ing life.

D.S.

VERSE 3

3. On-ly in God, is my soul at rest.

He is my rock and my sal-va —— tion.

D.S.

759 In the Lord I'll be ever thankful

Jacques Berthier

ALTERNATIVE TEXT

In the Lord is my true salvation,
in the Lord my lasting joy.
He became my strength and my song,
I trust in him and I shall not fear,
I trust in him and I shall not fear.

Paul Inwood

760 In your love remember me

Chris O'Hara

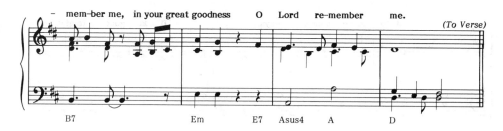

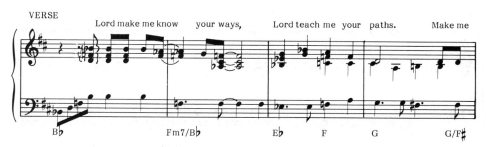

2 Remember your mercy, Lord,
your eternal love.
In your mercy I ask forgiveness:
in your love remember me.

3 His way is faithfulness,
faithfulness and love.
To the humble He shows the right path
teaches the way of poverty.

Psalm 24 (25)
adapted by Chris O'Hara

761 It is good to give thanks

Anthony Sharpe

REFRAIN

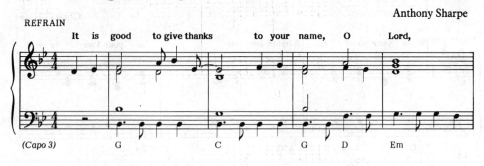

It is good to give thanks to your name, O Lord,

(Capo 3)   G   C   G   D   Em

and to ho — nour your ways. It is good to give glo-

C   D   G   Am7   D   G

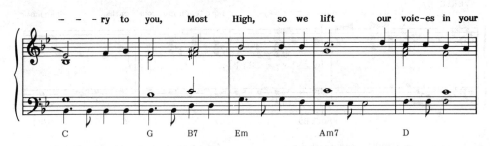

- - - ry to you, Most High, so we lift our voic-es in your

C   G   B7   Em   Am7   D

last time

praise.   praise.   *fine*   1. We pro — claim your love from

G   G   C   D   C

day - break, from the first light of the sun. Faith - ful -

G   Am7   D   G   G7   C

- ly you guard your peo - ple all through the night.   D.S.

F♯m   B7   Em   Am7   C   D

2 Praise your name for all creation,
  for your deeds we give you thanks.
  Great and true, your wondrous achievements
  by your own right hand.

3 All of our days we sing your praises
  your great wisdom we acclaim.
  Deep your thoughts, the fool cannot know
    them.
  Praise your Holy Name.

4 In your house, to give you glory,
  forever we will sing:
  To proclaim that Yahweh is faithful
  Our God, our King.

Ps 91 (92), versified by
Anthony Sharpe

762 Jesus is Lord!

D.J.Mansell

1 Jesus is Lord! creation's voice proclaims it,
  for by his power each tree and flower was
    planned and made.
Jesus is Lord! the universe declares it —
sun, moon and stars in heaven cry:
  'Jesus is Lord!'

Jesus is Lord, Jesus is Lord!
Praise him with alleluias,
  for Jesus is Lord.

2 Jesus is Lord! yet from his throne eternal
  in flesh he came to die in pain on Calvary's
    tree.
Jesus is Lord! from him all life proceeding —
yet gave his life a ransom thus setting us free.

3 Jesus is Lord! o'er sin the mighty conqueror;
  from death he rose and all his foes shall
    own his name.
Jesus is Lord! God sends his Holy Spirit
to show by works of power that Jesus is
Lord.

D.J. Mansell

763 Jesus, lead the way

SEELENBRAUTIGAM (55 88 55)   *Geistreiches Gesangbuch,* 1698 Attr. to A.Drese (1620-1701)

1. Je - sus, lead the way through our life's long day, when at times the way is

cheer — less, help us fol — low, calm and fear — less;

guide us by your hand to the pro — mised land.

2 Jesus be our light,
 in the midst of night,
 let not faithless fear o'er-take us,
 let not faith and hope forsake us;
 may we feel you near
 as we worship here.

3 When in deepest grief,
 strengthen our belief.
 When temptations come alluring,
 make us patient and enduring;
 Lord we seek your grace
 in this holy place.

4 Jesus, still lead on
 'til our rest be won:
 if you lead us through rough places,
 grant us your redeeming graces.
 When our course is o'er,
 open heaven's door.

Nicholas von Zinzendorf (1700-60)
tr. Jane Borthwick, 1813-97, alt.

Jesus, Lord of life and love

GREAT DIXTER (76 74) Christopher Walker

1 Jesus, Lord of life and love
   I greet your presence here
   in this holy sign of life
   your love is clear.

2 Jesus, Lord, your loving eyes
   a sinner's heart reveal,
   by this holy sign of faith
   my failure heal.

3 Jesus, Lord, who sorrow knew
   console all those who mourn;
   in this holy sign of Heaven
   may Joy be born.

4 Jesus, Lord, in teaching here
   man came to follow you;
   in this holy sign, my Lord
   inspire anew.

5 Jesus, Lord of all my heart,
   I pray that every day
   through this holy sign of love
   in peace I stay.

Christopher Walker

765 Bread, blessed and broken (Jesus, you're the one)

Mike Lynch
Accpt. by Patrick Loomis

INTRODUCTION

VERSES *(Melody is repeated except in v.3)*

1. Je - sus, you're the one I love; you're the one I know.

You're the one who makes me strong, Spi - rit in my soul.

Fine

REFRAIN

Bread, blessed and bro - ken for us all,

1 Jesus, you're the one I love;
  you're the one I know.
  You're the one who makes me strong,
  Spirit in my soul.
  From the clouds of yesterday,
  through the night of pain,
  teach me, Lord, to know your way,
  know it once again.

  Bread, blessed and broken for us all,
  symbol of your love from the grain
  ** so tall.**
  Bread, blessed and broken for us all,
  Bread of life you give to us,
  bread of life for all.

2 May the bread we break today,
  may the cup we share
  lift the burdens of our hearts,
  lift them ev'rywhere.
  Passing on to each of us
  a measure of your love,
  love to make us whole again,
  as we share your Word.

3 Jesus, you're the one I love;
  you're the one I know.
  You're the one who makes me strong,
  Spirit in my soul.

Michael Lynch

F.Dunn

767 World peace prayer (Lead us from death to life)

Marty Haugen

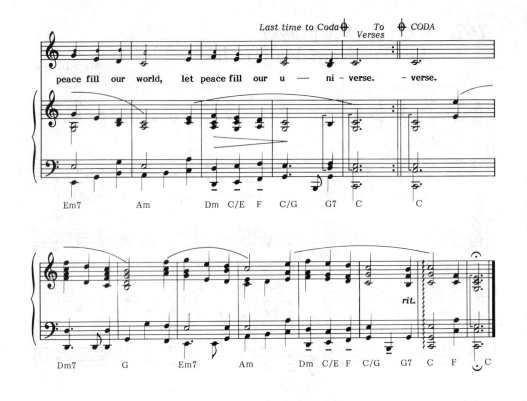

peace fill our world, let peace fill our u — ni - verse. - verse.

Em7 Am Dm C/E F C/G G7 C C

Dm7 G Em7 Am Dm C/E F C/G G7 C F C

rit.

VERSES

1. Still all the an-gry cries, still all the an-gry guns, still now your

C Dm7 G Em7 Am

peo-ple die, earth's sons and daugh-ters. Let jus-tice roll, let

Dm7 G C Am Dm7

mer - cy pour down,_____ come and teach us_____ your way of com - pas - sion.

E7   Am   F D7   C/G   G7   C

To refrain

2 So many lonely hearts,
  so many broken lives,
  longing for love to break
  into their darkness.
  Come, teach us love,
  come, teach us peace,
  come and teach us
  your way of compassion.

3 Let justice ever roll,
  let mercy fill the earth,
  let us begin to grow
  into your people.
  We can be love,
  we can bring peace,
  we can still be
  your way of compassion.

Verses: Marty Haugen
Refrain: Anonymous

768 Shine, Jesus, shine
(Lord, the light of your love)

INTRODUCTION   *Capo 2(G)*

Majestic and steady

A(G) D/A(C)   E(A/D) D/A(C)   A(G) D(A/C)   E(A/D) D(A/C)

VERSE

1. Lord, the light of Your love is shin — ing   in the midst of the

A(G)   Asus4(Gsus4)   A(G)   E/A(D)   A(G)   Asus4(Gsus4)

dark – ness, shin — ing;   Je – sus, Light of the World, shine up-on — us,

A(G)   E/A(D)   D(C)   E/D(D)   C♯m(Bm)   F♯m(Em)

set us free by the truth You now bring — us, shine on — me,

D(C)   E/D(D)   C♯m(Bm)   F♯m(Em)   G(F)   Esus4 E(D)
(Dsus4)

CHORUS

shine on — me.   **Shine, Je - sus, shine, —— fill this land with the**

G(F)   Esus4 E(D)   A(G) E/A(D) A(G) D(C)   A(G) Bm(Am) Bm/A(Am7)
(Dsus4)

2 Lord, I come to Your awesome presence,
from the shadows into Your radiance;
by the blood I may enter Your brightness,
search me, try me, consume all my darkness.
Shine on me, shine on me.

3 As we gaze on Your kingly brightness
so our faces display Your likeness,
ever changing from glory to glory,
mirrored here may our lives tell Your story.
Shine on me, shine on me.

Graham Kendrick

769 Majesty

Jack Hayford

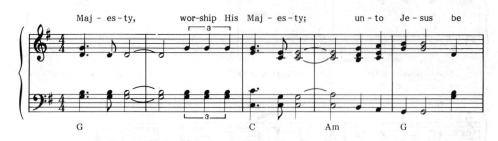

Maj - es - ty, wor-ship His Maj - es - ty; un - to Je - sus be

glo - ry, hon-our and praise. Maj - es - ty, kingdom, au - tho - ri - ty,

flows from His throne un - to His own, His an - them raise.

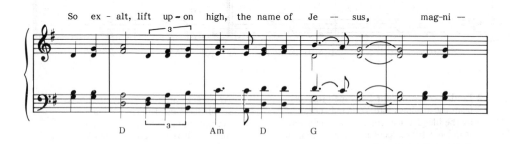

So ex - alt, lift up - on high, the name of Je — sus, mag-ni —

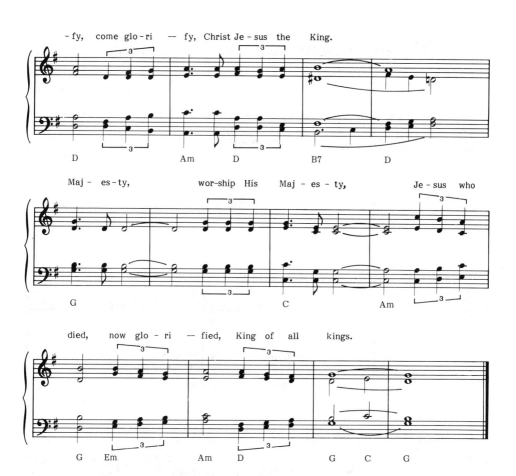

Words and Music © 1976 Rocksmith Music. Administered by Leo Song Copyright Service Ltd for UK and Eire, 4a Newman Passage, London W1

Jack W. Hayford

770 My love will set you free (My people)

Anthony Sharpe
Accpt. revised by Stephen Dean

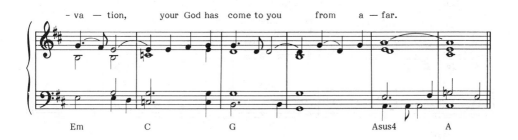

2 All of you who are blind and lame
  all who are my scattered sheep
  You, I will bring back to me,
  my hand will gather you, from every land.

3 You who once turned away from me
  you who show regret and shame,
  you will now rejoice again;
  you are forgiven, give thanks and praise!

Anthony Sharpe
adapted from Jeremiah 31

771 Song of repentance (My soul cannot be still)

Anthony Sharpe
arr. Chris O'Hara

Melody from *La Forme des Prières*, Strasbourg 1545
(2nd line as in *Genevan Psalter, 1551*

RENDEZ A DIEU (98 98 D)

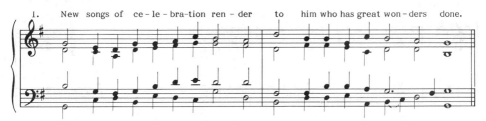

1. New songs of ce-le-bra-tion ren-der to him who has great won-ders done.

Awed by his power his foes sur-ren-der and fall be-fore the Migh-ty One.

He has made known his great sal-va — tion which all his friends with joy con-fess;

he has re-vealed to ev'-ry na — tion his ev - er-last-ing right-eous-ness.

* *For an alternative harmonisation see No.819*

2 Joyfully, heartily resounding,
   let every instrument and voice
   peal out the praise of grace abounding,
   calling the whole world to rejoice.
   Trumpets and organs set in motion
   such sounds as make the heavens ring:
   all things that live in earth and ocean
   make music for your mighty King.

3 Rivers and seas and torrents roaring,
   honour the Lord with wild acclaim;
   mountains and stones look up adoring
   and find a voice to praise his name.
   Righteous, commanding, ever glorious,
   praises be his that never cease:
   just is our God, whose truth victorious
   establishes the world in peace.

Erik Routley (1917-82)
Psalm 98 (97)

Words by permission of Oxford University Press

773   Nothing can ever take away

50

Hubert J. Richards
Accpt. by Stephen Dean

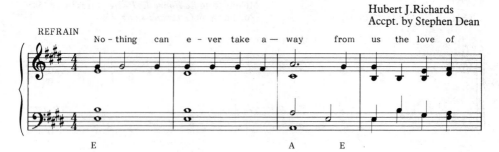

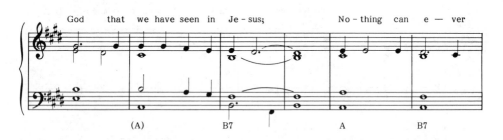

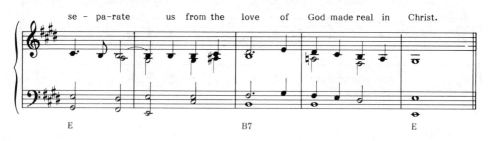

- gives us, who can still ac — cuse? If God has cleared us,

(A)   (F♯7)   B7   A

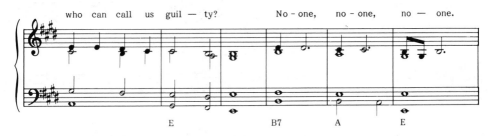

who can call us guil — ty? No - one, no - one, no — one.

E   B7   A   E

2 No hardship, no kind of deprivation,
   no persecution, suffering or pain,
   in peace or war, no trouble, threat or danger,
   nothing, nothing, nothing.

3 Nothing on the earth or in the heavens,
   nothing that exists or is still to come,
   nothing in our life, not even dying,
   nothing, nothing, nothing.

Hubert Richards
Based on Romans 8:31-39

51

774 Now in this banquet

Marty Haugen

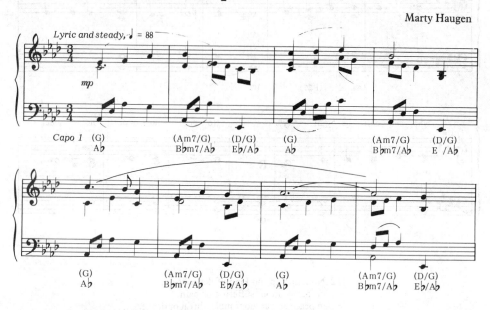

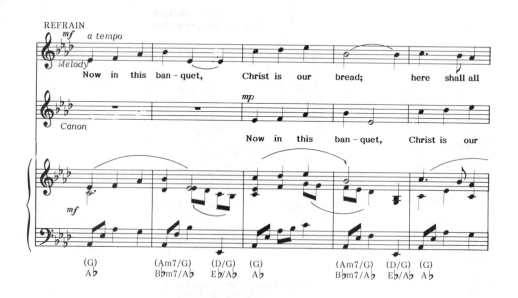

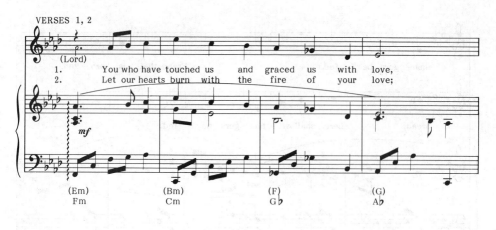

VERSES 1, 2

(Lord)
1. You who have touched us and graced us with love,
2. Let our hearts burn with the fire of your love;

(Em)   (Bm)   (F)   (G)
Fm   Cm   G♭   A♭

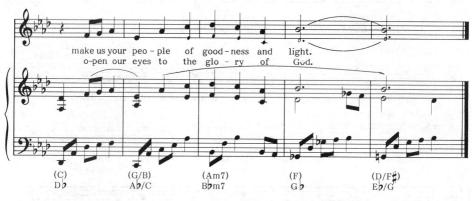

make us your peo - ple of good - ness and light.
o-pen our eyes to the glo - ry of God.

(C)   (G/B)   (Am7)   (F)   (D/F♯)
D♭   A♭/C   B♭m7   G♭   E♭/G

VERSE 3

(Lord)
3. God who makes the blind to see,   God who makes the lame to walk,

(Em)   (C)   (F)   (Em7)
Fm   D♭   G♭   Fm7

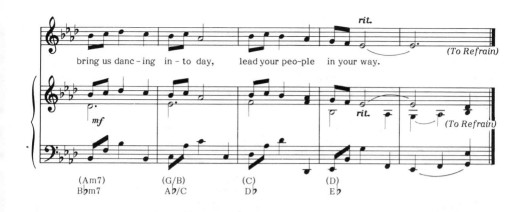

bring us danc-ing in-to day, lead your peo-ple in your way.

(To Refrain)

(Am7)   (G/B)   (C)   (D)
B♭m7   A♭/C   D♭   E♭

VERSE 4

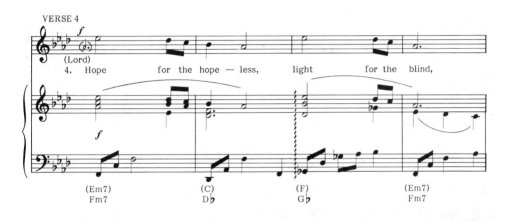

(Lord)
4. Hope for the hope — less, light for the blind,

(Em7)   (C)   (F)   (Em7)
Fm7   D♭   G♭   Fm7

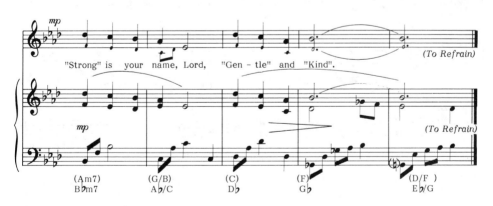

"Strong" is your name, Lord, "Gen - tle" and "Kind".

(To Refrain)

(Am7)   (G/B)   (C)   (F)   (D/F)
B♭m7   A♭/C   D♭   G♭   E♭/G

VERSE 5

5. Call us to be your light, call us to be your love,

make us your peo - ple a — gain. *(To Refrain)*

VERSE 6

6. Come, O Spi - rit! re — new our hearts!

We shall a — rise to be child - ren of light. *(To Refrain)*

ALTERNATIVE TEXTS FOR REFRAIN

1. God of our jour - neys, day - break to night; lead us to
2. Lord, you can o — pen hearts that are stone; live in our

1. God of our jour - neys, day - break to
2. Lord, you can o — pen hearts that are

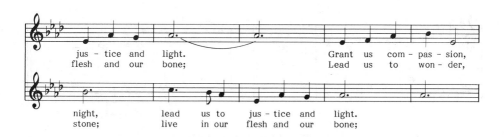

jus - tice and light. Grant us com - pas - sion,
flesh and our bone; Lead us to won - der,

night, lead us to jus - tice and light.
stone; live in our flesh and our bone;

Last time to Coda

strength for the day, wis — dom to walk in your way.
mys - t'ry and grace, one in your lov - ing em — brace.

Grant us com - pas - sion, strength for the day, wis — dom to
Lead us to won - der, mys - t'ry and grace, one in your

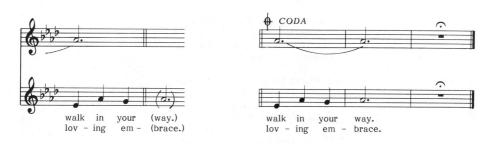

CODA

walk in your (way.)
lov - ing em - (brace.)

walk in your way.
lov - ing em - brace.

1179

775 O changeless Christ

F.H.Barthélémon (1741-1801)

1 O changeless Christ, for ever new,
who walked our earthly ways,
still draw our hearts as once you drew
the hearts of other days.

2 As once you spoke by plain and hill
or taught by shore and sea,
so be today our teacher still,
O Christ of Galilee.

3 As wind and storm their master heard
and his command fulfilled,
may troubled hearts receive your word;
the tempest-tossed be stilled.

4 And as of old to all who prayed
your healing hand was shown,
so be your touch upon us laid,
unseen but not unknown.

5 In broken bread, in wine out-poured,
your new and living way
proclaim to us, O risen Lord,
O Christ of this our day.

6 O changeless Christ, till life is past
your blessing still be given;
then bring us home, to taste at last
the timeless joys of heaven.

Timothy Dudley-Smith

776   O Christ the healer

ERHALT UNS, HERR (LM)

Klug's *Geistliche Lieder*, 1543
Harmonised by J.S.Bach (1685-1750)

1. O Christ, the heal—er, we have come to pray for health, to plead for friends. How can we fail to be re—stored, when reached by love that nev—er ends?

Alt. Tune: Rockingham

2 From every ailment flesh endures
our bodies clamour to be freed;
yet in our hearts we would confess
that wholeness is our deepest need.

3 How strong, O Lord, are our desires,
how weak our knowledge of ourselves!
Release in us those healing truths
unconscious pride resists or shelves.

4 In conflicts that destroy our health
we recognise the world's disease;
our common life declares our ills:
is there no cure, O Christ, for these?

5 Grant that we all, made one in faith,
in your community may find
the wholeness that, enriching us,
shall reach the whole of human kind.

Frederick Pratt Green

2. You are there with your rod and staff; with these you give me com - fort.

You have pre-pared a ban - quet for me in the sight of my foes.

My head you have a-nointed with oil; my cup is o - ver-flow-ing. Sure-ly

good - ness and kind - ness shall fol-low me all the days of my life.

In the Lord's own house shall I dwell for e - ver and e - ver.

Choose either part

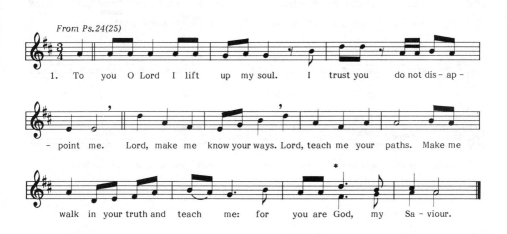

From Ps.24(25)

1. To you O Lord I lift up my soul. I trust you do not dis - ap -

- point me. Lord, make me know your ways. Lord, teach me your paths. Make me

walk in your truth and teach me: for you are God, my Sa - viour.

2. In you I hope all day long be-cause of your good-ness, O Lord. Re-

- mem-ber your mer-cy, Lord, and the love you have shown from of old. Do not re-

- mem-ber the sins of my youth. In your love re-mem-ber me.

From Ps.33(34)

Taste and see that the Lord is good. Hap-py are they who seek re-fuge in him.

From Ps.84(85)

I will hear what the Lord God has to say, a voice that speaks of peace.

Peace for his peo-ple and his friends, and those whose hearts turn to him.

From Ps.129(130)

My soul is wait-ing for the Lord, I count on his word. Be-

- cause with the Lord there is mer - cy and full-ness of re - demp-tion.

AMEN

A - men. A ———— men.

* *Choose either part*

Marty Haugen

VERSES

1. As a dry and wear-y des-ert land, so my

2. I think of You when at night I rest, I re-

3. I will bless Your name all the days I live, I will

1.-*mf* 2.-*p* 3.-*f*

F#m7(Em7)   B7/F#(A7/E)

soul is thirsting for my God, and my flesh is faint for the

- flect u-pon Your steadfast love. I will cling to You, Oh

raise my hands and call on You. My joy-ful lips shall

Bm7/F (Am7/E)   C#m7(Bm7)   F#(E)   F#m7(Em7)

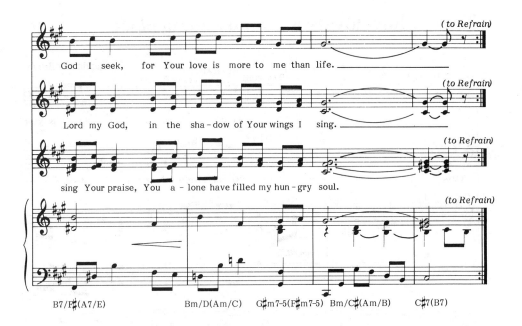

(to Refrain)

God I seek, for Your love is more to me than life. _____

(to Refrain)

Lord my God, in the sha-dow of Your wings I sing. _____

(to Refrain)

sing Your praise, You a-lone have filled my hun-gry soul.

(to Refrain)

B7/F♯(A7/E)   Bm/D(Am/C)   G♯m7-5(F♯m7-5) Bm/C♯(Am/B)   C♯7(B7)

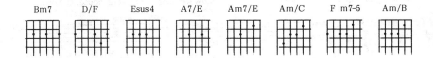

Bm7   D/F   Esus4   A7/E   Am7/E   Am/C   F m7-5   Am/B

Randall DeBruyn

1. Ev - en spar-rows find a home with you, and swal-lows lay their young to rest.
2. Bless'd are those who find their strength in you, whose hearts are high-ways for your will.
3. Hear our prayer, O Lord God of hosts; re - ceive our lives in - to your hands!
4. For one day with-in your house ex-ceeds a thou-sand spent a - way from you.
5. For our God pro-tects us from all harm; he gives his fa - vour and his love.

D.S.

1. Bless - ed are those who dwell in you and sing your praise, O God!
2. Bring-ing joy to those a - round them, they go from strength to strength.
3. Look in - to the hearts of those you love and grant us all we need!
4. We would rath - er serve with - in your house than wealth and pow'r re — ceive.
5. All good things will come to those who love the Lord, and walk with him.

Randall DeBruyn,
based on Psalm 83(84)

780 O Lord, be not mindful

Lucien Deiss

ANTIPHON

O Lord, be not mind-ful of our guilt and our sins; O Lord, do not judge us for our faults and of-fen-ces. May your mer-ci-ful love be up-on us.

VERSES

1. Help your peo-ple, Lord, O God our Sav — iour, de-liv-er us for the glo-ry of your name! 2. Par-don us, O Lord, all our sins, de-liv-er us for the glo-ry of your name! 3. Praise to you, O Lord, through all ag-es with-out end, de-liv-er us for the glo-ry of your name!

781 Centre of my life

Paul Inwood

O Lord, you are the cen-tre of my life:

I will al-ways praise you, I will al-ways serve you, I will al-ways keep you in my sight. O

sight. (3. And) sight. 1. Keep me safe, O God ___ I take re-fuge in you. ___ I
2. I will bless the Lord who gives me coun - sel, _____ who

say to the Lord, "You are my God. My hap - pi - ness
ev - en at night di-rects my heart. I keep the Lord

lies in you a - lone; my hap - pi - ness___ lies in you a - lone."___ O

ev - er in my sight: since he is at my right hand,___ I shall stand firm. O

VERSE 3

3. so my heart re - joic — es, my soul is glad;___ e — ven in safe-ty shall my

bod - y rest. For you will not leave my soul a - mong the dead, nor

let___ your be - lov - ed know de — cay.___ O

VERSE 4

4. You will show ___ me the path of life, _____ the full-ness of joy__ in your

pres-ence, ___ at your right hand, at your right hand

hap-pi-ness for ev-er. O

D.S.

782   In perfect charity

Randall DeBruyn

- in your ev-er ho-ly will. Lord, may your light with-in me burn, shin-ing

out in per-fect char-i — ty. ty.

2 O most high and glorious God,
   open wide the door that leads me to your
      love.
   Give me your firm, and gentle strength;
   may I live that perfect charity.
   Lord, may your peace be ever in me,
   that I may always seek to serve
   your children here on earth;
   that I may find my home in you,
   and live in perfect charity.

3 Then most high and thankful praise
   I will sing unto the glory of your name;
   to Father, Son and Spirit bright,
   Living Presence, Perfect Charity.
   Praise to the Love that shines in splendour,
   that lights the pathways of my heart,
   and brings me close to you.
   O Holy One, invite me in,
   where you live in perfect charity.

V.1 based on the 'Prayer of St Francis'
Vv. 2-3 by Randall DeBruyn

783   O that today

Chris O'Hara

2 Come in, let us bow and bend low;
let us kneel to the God who made us;
like a flock he leads us by his hand
to pasture he guides us on.

3 'At Meribah you harden your hearts
and at Massah you seek to test me.'
Let us trust our God and hope in him;
today let us seek his voice.

*Psalm 94 (95). Response
and v.1 from the Grail Psalter.
Vv 2-3 adapted by Chris O'Hara.*

OH HEALING RIVER

Capo 3

American Baptist Hymn,
arr. Michael Joncas

1. O heal-ing   ri - ver,   send   down   your
2. This land is   parch-ing,   this   land   is
3. Let the seed of free-dom,   a — wake and

1. O   heal — ing ri - ver,
2. This land   is parch-ing,
3. Let the seed of free-dom,

Eb(C)   Bb(G)   Eb(C)   Bb(G)   Eb(C)

wa - ters,   send   down   your wa - ters
burn- ing,   no   seed   is grow-ing
flour - ish,   let the deep   roots nour - ish

send   down   your wa - ters,   send   down   your
this   land   is burn - ing,   no   seed   is
a — wake and flour-ish   let the deep   roots

Bb(G)   Eb(C)   Bb(G)   Eb(C)   Bb(G)   Eb(C)

up — on this land.
in the bar — ren ground.
let the tall stalks rise.

wa – ters
grow- ing
nour – ish

up — on this
in the bar — ren
let the tall stalks

B♭(G)   C7(A7)   F(D)   C7(A7)

O heal — ing ri - ver   send down your
O heal — ing ri - ver   send down your
O heal — ing ri - ver   send down your

land.
ground.
rise.

O heal — ing ri - ver
O heal — ing ri - ver
O heal — ing ri - ver

F(D)   F7(D7)   B♭(G)   E♭(C)   B♭(G)   D7(B7)

785 One shall tell another

Graham Kendrick, arr. by Chris Rolinson

1. One shall tell a-no-ther, and he shall tell his friend; husbands, wives and child-ren shall come fol-low-ing on. From house to house in fam-i-lies shall more be gath-ered in; and lights will shine in ev-ery street, so warm and wel-com-ing.

2. -pass-ion of the Fa-ther is rea-dy now to flow; through acts of love and mer-cy we must let it show. He turns now from his an-ger to show a smil-ing face, and longs that we should stand be-neath the foun-tain of his grace.

3. longs to do much more than our faith has yet al-lowed, to thrill us and sur-prise us with his sove-reign power. Where dark-ness has been dark-est, the bright-est light will shine; his in-vi-ta-tion comes to us it's yours and it is mine.

Words and music © Thankyou Music

CHORUS

Come on in and taste the new wine, the wine of the king-dom, the wine of the king-dom of God: here is heal — ling and for-give-ness, the wine of the king-dom, the wine of the king-dom of God.

786   Peace I give   63

Anthony Sharpe, accpt. revised by Stephen Dean

Peace I give to you, my friends, peace the
world can ne — ver know, gi — ven now to
share with each o - ther, peace I give to you
my friends.

Last time to

2. Love I give . . .
3. Joy I give . . .

fine

Words and music © 1987 by Anthony Sharpe

787 Praise now your God

L.de Vocht,
accompaniment by Stephen Dean

1. Praise now your God, ev-'ry tongue, ev-'ry na — tion, tell the good news to the next ge-ne-ra — tion: Christ, the Re-dee — mer, who rose from the dead, ___ stays with his peo — ple as life — gi-ving Bread. ___ Al — le — lu — ia, God is great! Al — le — lu — ia, God is Good!

2 Christ gave his word at the multiplication.
Bread and sweet wine are now Christ our
  oblation.
Cross and last Supper are with us today.
Life now abounds, and God's will we obey.

3 Here is your Saviour, give deep adoration,
sing of his glory in glad celebration.
Come, for his manna is food for the road,
strength for the journey, our glory fore-
  showed.

C.J. Marivoet

788 Praise to you, O Christ

Bernadette Farrell,
accompaniment by Paul Inwood

REFRAIN

Praise___ to you, O Christ, our___ Sav-iour, Word of the Fa — ther,

call-ing us to life;___ Son___ of God who leads us to free — dom:

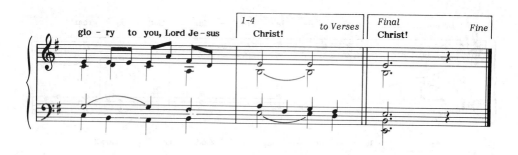

glo — ry to you, Lord Je-sus | *1-4* Christ! *to Verses* | *Final* Christ! *Fine*

VERSES

1. You are the Word who calls us out of dark — ness; you are the Word who

2 You are the one whom prophets hoped
    and longed for;
  you are the one who speaks to us today;
  you are the one who leads us to our future;
  glory to you, Lord Jesus Christ.

3 You are the Word who calls us to be
    servants;
  you are the Word whose only law is love;
  you are the Word-made-flesh who lives
  among us:
  glory to you, Lord Jesus Christ.

4 You are the Word who binds us and unites
    us;
  you are the Word who calls us to be one;
  you are the Word who teaches us forgiveness:
  glory to you, Lord Jesus Christ!

Bernadette Farrell

789 Prepare ye the way

Stephen Dean

Words and music © 1984 Stephen Dean

saving power of God. Pre- God.

first time only *before verse*

Last time to Coda

F#m   Bm   E7   A   E7   A   Em   F

VERSES

1. Re - pent, for the King-dom of God _____ is at hand;
2. Cry out with a voice that is strong _____ and sure;
3. Get up the high moun-tain and shout _____ the good News;
4. Like a shep- herd he shel-ters his flock _____ from harm;

C   F   C   G

the light which the dark - ness can ne _____ ver with - stand.
"The flo - wer will fade but my word _____ will en - dure."
"Fear not, for the Lord God Al - migh _____ ty rules." CHORUS
and ten - der - ly leads the young lambs _____ with his arm.

Gm   Dm   Bdim   E

CODA   Fine

Pre- of God.   ff   of God!

E7   C   A   Em   F   C   E7   A

1207

790 Psallite Domino

Jacques Berthier

1. Chorale *(for a small group, in unison or as a canon)*

3
Ex — sul — ta — te!   Ex — sul — ta — te!

4
Can - ta - te al-le - lu — ia!   Can-ta - te al-le-lu — ia!

2. Chorale II *(small group; unison or canon)*

1
Psal - li - te,   Psa - li - te   et   can — ta — te!

2
Psal - li - te,   Psal — li - te   et   can — ta — te!

3
Al - le-lu — ia,   al - le-lu - ia,   et   ex - sul - ta - te!

3. English text *(small group; unison or canon)* From Psalm 97(98)

1 *
Sing! Sing!   Sing   a   new song!   Sing! Sing!   Sing   to   the Lord!

2
Sing   al - le — lu — ia!   Al-le -lu — ia   praise the Lord!

3
All   the   ends   of   the   earth have seen   the   sal - va - tion   of   our God.

4 *
Shout   to   the Lord   all   the   earth, ring out your joy, al - le - lu — ai!

* *Choose either part*

1209

4. Mixed Voices

Psa-lli-te, Psa-lli — te! Al-le-lu – ia! Psa-lli-te, Psa-lli – te. Al-le-lu – ia!

Psa-lli-te, Psa-lli — te! Al-le-lu – ia! Psa-lli-te, Psa-lli – te! Al-le-lu – ia!

5. Two Sopranos (Soloists)

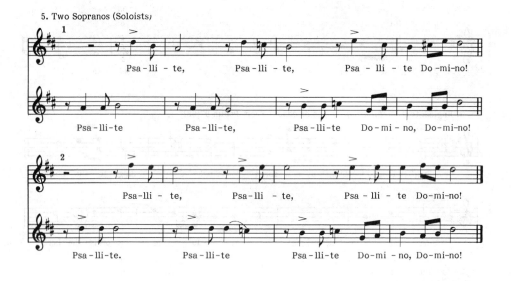

Psa-lli — te, Psa-lli — te, Psa-lli – te Do-mi-no!

Psa-lli-te Psa-lli-te, Psa-lli-te Do-mi – no, Do-mi-no!

Psa-lli — te, Psa-lli — te, Psa-lli – te Do-mi-no!

Psa-lli-te. Psa-lli-te Psa-lli-te Do-mi – no, Do-mi-no!

791   Safe in the shadow of the Lord

First Tune

Paul Inwood

Music © 1984 Paul Inwood.

CREATOR GOD

Second Tune

© Norman Warren (born 1934)

2 My hope is set on God alone
  though Satan spreads his snare;
   I trust in him, I trust in him
  to keep me in his care.

3 From fears and phantoms of the night,
  from foes about my way,
   I trust in him, I trust in him
  by darkness as by day.

4 His holy angels keep my feet
  secure from every stone;
   I trust in him, I trust in him
  and unafraid go on.

5 Strong in the everlasting name,
  and in my Father's care,
   I trust in him, I trust in him
  who hears and answers prayer.

6 Safe in the shadow of the Lord,
  possessed by love divine,
   I trust in him, I trust in him
  and meet his love with mine.

Words © Timothy Dudley-Smith

Timothy Dudley-Smith

792 Sing a new song

CANTATE DOMINO (Irreg.)

David Wilson

1. Sing a new song to the Lord, _____ he to whom wonders belong! _____ Re-joice _____ in his tri-umph and tell _____ of his
power. _____ O sing _____ to the Lord _____ a new

1, 2, 3.
song! _____

4.
song!

2 Now to the ends of the earth
see his salvation is shown;
and still he remembers his mercy and truth
unchanging in love to his own.

3 Sing a new song and rejoice,
publish his praises abroad!
Let voices in chorus, and trumpet and horn,
resound for the joy of the Lord!

4 Join with the hills and the sea
thunders of praise to prolong!
In judgement and justice he comes to the
earth,
O sing to the Lord a new song!

Psalm 98(97)
versified by Timothy Dudley-Smith

793 Sing all creation

ISTE CONFESSOR (Rouen) (11 11 11 5)

Melody from *Poitiers Antiphoner*, 1746

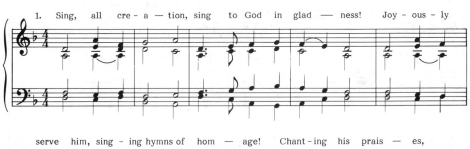

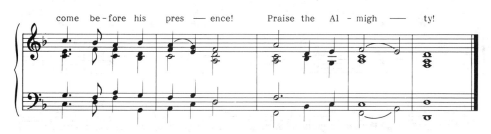

2 Know that our God is Lord of all the ages!
He is our maker, we are all his creatures,
people he fashioned, sheep he leads to
  pasture!
Praise the Almighty!

3 Enter his temple, ringing out his praises!
Sing in thanksgiving as you come before
  him!
Blessing his bountry, glorify his greatness!
Praise the Almighty!

4 Great in his goodness is the Lord we
  worship;
steadfast his kindness, love that knows no
  ending!
Faithful his word is, changeless, everlasting!
Praise the Almighty!

James Quinn SJ,
based on Psalm 100 (99)

794 Sing of the Lord's goodness

Ernest Sands, accpt. by Paul Inwood
Descant by Christopher Walker

God. Come and ring out the Lord's glo-ry, praise him with your mu-sic,

thanks to God. Ring out the Lord's glo-ry, praise him with your mu-sic.

Em   Am7   D   Gmaj7

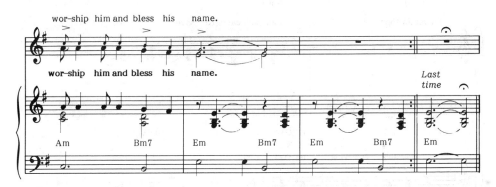

wor-ship him and bless his name.

wor-ship him and bless his name.

Last time

Am   Bm7   Em   Bm7   Em   Bm7   Em

2 Power he has wielded, honour is his
    garment,
  risen from the snares of death.
  His word he has spoken, one bread he has
    broken,
  new life he now gives to all.

3 Courage in our darkness, comfort in our
    sorrow,
  Spirit of our God most high;
  solace for the weary, pardon for the sinner,
  splendour of the living God.

4 Praise him with your singing, praise him
    with the trumpet,
  praise God with the lute and harp;
  praise him with the cymbals, praise him
    with your dancing,
  praise God till the end of days.

Ernest Sands

Another rhythm for the keyboard accompaniment:

etc. ...

The three less usual guitar chords in this piece:

Am7   Bm7   Gmaj7

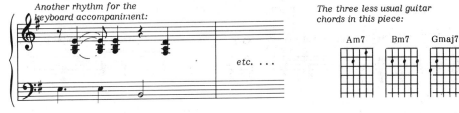

795   Sing it in the valleys

Michael J. Anderson, accpt. by Chris O'Hara

(Oh —) shout it from the mountain tops,

Fine

B (G) Gm(Em) E (C) F(D) B (G)

VERSES

1. Je — sus you are by my side, you take

E (C) F(D) Dm(Bm) Gm(Em) E (C)

all my fears. If i

F(D) Fm7(Dm7) B (G) Gm(Em)

on — ly come to you, you will

C(A) F(D) Dm(Bm) Gm(Em)

heal the pain of years.

D.S.

E (C) A (F) E (C) F(D)

2 You have not deserted me,
though I go astray.
Jesus take me in your arms,
help me walk with you today.

3 Jesus, you are living now,
Jesus, I believe.
Jesus, take me, heart and soul,
Yours alone I want to be.

Mike Anderson

796 Surrexit Christus

Jacques Berthier

MIXED VOICES

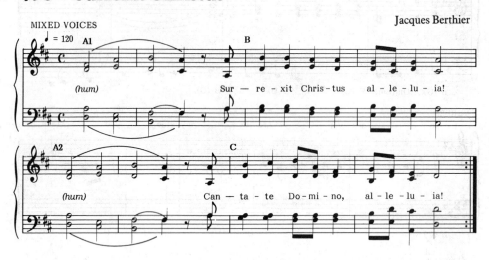

(hum)

Sur — re - xit Chris - tus al - le - lu - ia!

(hum)

Can — ta - te Do - mi - no, al - le - lu - ia!

Choir variation for **B** *and* **C**

Sur — re - xit Christ-us, al - le - lu - ia!

Can — ta - te Do - mi - no, al - le - lu - ia!

Keyboard or Guitar

D   A   Bm F♯m   G   F♯m7 Em   A   D   A   Bm F♯m   G   D   Em7   A   D

VERSES **A1** and **A2**

Cantor

From Daniel 3 (The praises of creation)

1. All you heav-ens, bless the Lord. Stars of the heav-ens

bless the Lord. 2. Sun and moon, bless the Lord.

And you, night and day, bless the Lord.

3. Frost and cold, bless the Lord.

Ice and snow, bless the Lord. 4. Fire and heat,

bless the Lord. And you, light and dark-ness,

bless the Lord. 5. Spir-its and souls of the just, bless the Lord

* *Choose either part*   Saints and the hum-ble heart-ed, bless the Lord.

From Psalm 117(118)

1. Give thanks to the Lord, for he is good, for his love

has no end. 2. The Lord is my strength, the Lord is my song,

he has been my Sa — viour. 3. I shall not die,

I shall live, I shall live and re - count his deeds.

1219

797 The gift of the Holy Spirit

Sr Katherine Boschetti

VENETIAN 87.87.99.11

1. The gift of the Ho-ly Spi — rit is the gift of God's great love. To us comes the touch of heal — ing from the God of heav'n a — bove; joy and strength for our dai-ly liv — ing, trust and love for the work of giv - ing, and the spi — rit of true for - giv — ing each one. - sign.

2 Anointed, we are Christ's witness
in the walk of life each day,
a comfort and light to others
whom we meet along the way.
We will cherish your life within us,
show the mercy you show to sinners,
by your suffering, you chose to win us
    from death.

3 Thanksgiving we bring, and honour,
to the Father and the Son
and, with them, the Holy Spirit,
God for ever, Three in One.
Praise and glory we give and blessing,
one faith, one in truth confessing,
one in love in your all-embracing design.

Kathleen Boschetti MSC

Simpler Version   Stephen Dean

The kingdom of God

HANOVER (10 10 11 11)

Attr. to William Croft (1678-1727)

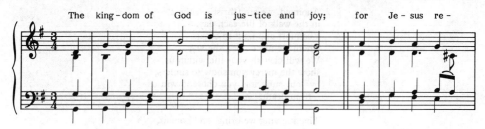

The king-dom of God is jus-tice and joy; for Je-sus re-

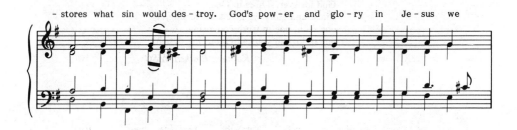

- stores what sin would des-troy. God's pow-er and glo-ry in Je-sus we

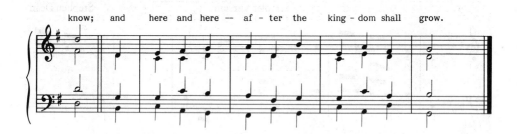

know; and here and here — af-ter the king-dom shall grow.

2 The kingdom of God is mercy and grace;
   the captives are freed, the sinners find
      place,
   the outcast are welcomed God's banquet
      to share;
   and hope is awakened in place of despair.

3 The kingdom of God is challenge and
      choice:
   believe the good news, repent and rejoice!
   His love for us sinners brought Christ to
      his cross:
   our crisis of judgement for gain or for loss.

4 God's kingdom is come, the gift and the
      goal;
   In Jesus begun, in heaven made whole.
   The heirs of the kingdom shall answer his
      call;
   and all things cry 'Glory!' to God all in all.

Bryn Rees

799 The master came to bring good news

ICH GLAUB AN GOTT (87 87 + refrain)
VERSES

Mainz Gesangbuch, 1870
Harmony by Richard Proulx

1. The Mas-ter came to bring good news, the news of love and free — dom, to

heal the sick and seek the poor, to build the peace-ful king — dom.

REFRAIN

Fa — ther, for - give us! Through Je - sus hear us!

As we for — give one a — noth — er!

2 The Law's fulfilled through Jesus Christ,
the man who lived for others,
the law of Christ is: Serve in love
our sisters and our brothers.

3 To seek the sinners Jesus came,
to live among the friendless,
to show them love that they might share
the kingdom that is endless.

4 Forgive us, Lord, as we forgive
and seek to help each other.
Forgive us, Lord, and we shall live
to pray and work together.

Ralph Finn

WOODLANDS (10 10 10 10)   Walter Greatorex (1877-1949)

1. The voice of God,   goes out through all the world: his   glo — ry

speaks a - cross the u — ni — verse. The great King's he —— rald cries from star to

star: with power, with ju - stice, he will   walk   his   way.

ALTERNATIVE ORGAN VERSION FROM *

2 Give glory to the mystery revealed,
the voice of God, his image and his Word:
his word of peace, the image of his grace:
with power, with justice, he will walk his way.

3 The Lord has said: Receive my messenger,
my promise to the world, my pledge made
flesh,
a lamp to every nation, light from light:
with power, with justice, he will walk his way.

4 The broken reed he will not trample
down,
nor set his heel upon the dying flame.
He binds the wounds, and health is in
his hand:
with power, with justice, he will walk his way.

5 Anointed with the Spirit and with power,
he comes to crown with comfort all the weak,
to show the face of justice to the poor:
with power, with justice, he will walk his way.

6 His touch will bless the eyes that darkness
held,
the lame shall run, the halting tongue
shall sing,
and prisoners laugh in light and liberty:
with power, with justice, he will walk his way.

Luke Connaughton (1919-79)

801 More desired than gold (The Word of God)

Chris O'Hara

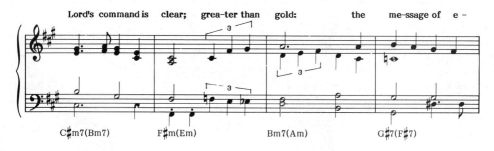

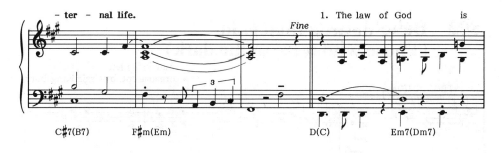

-ter - nal life.   1. The law of God   is

Fine

C♯7(B7)   F♯m(Em)   D(C)   Em7(Dm7)

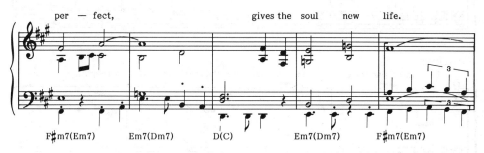

per — fect,   gives the soul   new   life.

F♯m7(Em7)   Em7(Dm7)   D(C)   Em7(Dm7)   F♯m7(Em7)

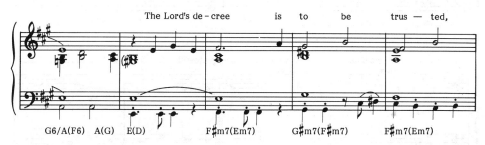

The Lord's de - cree   is   to   be   trus — ted,

G6/A(F6)   A(G)   E(D)   F♯m7(Em7)   G♯m7(F♯m7)   F♯m7(Em7)

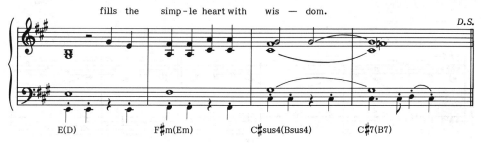

fills the   simp-le heart with   wis — dom.

D.S.

E(D)   F♯m(Em)   C♯sus4(Bsus4)   C♯7(B7)

2 The precepts of the Lord
   fill our hearts with joy.
   The Lord's command is clear and truthful;
   giving light for the eyes.

3 Much more desired than gold,
   more than finest gold;
   the word of God is so much sweeter,
   sweeter than the honeycomb.

Psalm 18(19) adapted by Chris O'Hara

802 Behold the Lamb of God
(Those who were in the dark)

Martin Willett,
organ accpt. by Craig Kingsbury

all,   all who dwell in God _____ shall

come to know _____ his glo-ry. _____

1-3

D.S.

Final

glo-ry. _____

Fine

2 Peaceful now those whose hearts
  are blessed with understanding.
  Of the wheat, of the wine
  united with his Word
  and the love we share.

3 Gentle one, Child of God,
  join with us at this table.
  Bless our lives, nourish all
  who hunger for this feast;
  shelter them with peace.

4 Lord of all, give us light;
  deliver us from evil.
  Make us one; be our shield.
  Make still the winds that blow;
  cradle us with love.

Martin Willett

TO GOD BE THE GLORY   W.H. Doane (1832-1916)

VERSES 1. To God be the glo-ry, great things he has done! So loved he the

world that he gave us his Son. Who yield — ed his life in a —

tone-ment for sin, and op-ened the life-gate that all may go in.

REFRAIN Praise the Lord! Praise the Lord! Let the earth hear his voice! Praise the

Lord! Praise the Lord! Let the peo-ple re-joice! O come to the Fa-ther, through

Je-sus his Son; and give him the glo-ry great things he has done!

2 O perfect redemption, the purchase of
    blood,
  to every believer the promise of God!
  And every offender who truly believes,
  that moment from Jesus a pardon receives.

3 Great things he has taught us, great things
    he has done,
  and great our rejoicing through Jesus the
    Son;
  but purer, and higher, and greater will be
  our wonder, our rapture, when Jesus we
    see.

Frances J. van Alstyne (1820-1915)

804 To Jesus Christ, our Soverign King

81

ICH GLAUB AN GOTT (87 87 + refrain)

Mainz Gesangbuch, 1870

2 Your reign extend, O King benign,
  to every land and nation;
  for in your Kingdom, Lord divine,
  alone we find salvation.

3 To you, and to your church, great king,
  we pledge our heart's oblation;
  until before your throne we sing
  in endless jubilation.

Martin B. Hellriegel (1891-1981) alt.

805   Wait for the Lord

Jacques Berthier

Wait for the Lord, his day is near. Wait for the Lord be strong take heart!

Equal Voices

Wait for the Lord, his day is near. Wait for the Lord, be strong, take heart.

ACCOMPANIMENT
Keyboard or Guitar

* *Either: the Response is sung as an ostinato without the verses,*

  or: *the Response and the verses are sung alternately.*

VERSES (optional)
Choir (humming) or Keyboard

heart. (hum)

Cantor

1. Pre-pare the way for the Lord. Make a straight path for Him. (Is.40)

2. The glo — ry of the Lord shall be re-vealed. (Is.40)

3. As the earth will see the Lord. (Is.40)

4. Re-joice in the Lord al - ways. He is at hand. (Phil.4)

5. Seek first the king-dom of God, seek and you shall find. (Mat.6-7)

6. Joy and glad-ness for all who seek the Lord. (Ps.69)

7. I wait-ed for the Lord; he heard my cry. (Ps.39)

8. Our eyes are fixed on the Lord our God. (Ps.122)

9. O Lord show us your way. Guide us in your truth. (Ps.118)

10. Pre - pare the way for the Lord.

806 Wake your power

Tom Lowenthal

ORGAN INTRODUCTION

ANTIPHON

Be here among us, word freely given,

* *accompaniment throughout as for 4 part choir*

that I may hear you with heart and soul.

** *to bridge*

REFRAIN
All (sung twice each time)

(fine)

Wake your pow'r, come, lead us to free — dom.

** ORGAN BRIDGE
To refrain

Before verses, and last time:
play chord in brackets (*)

VERSE ONE

VERSE TWO

(3 lady soloists) *mf*

2. And may our lives be not emp-ty and aim -

S
A

pp And may our lives be not emp-ty and aim ——— less.

T
B

- less. Keep us from fall ——— ing back to the

Keep us from fall ——— ing back to the dust.

dust. Send your Spi ——— rit that we be re-cre ——— a — ted.

to refrain

Send your Spi - rit that we be re-cre-a — ted.

to bridge *to refrain*

VERSE THREE

Huub Oosterhuis, tr. Tony Barr

1237

807 We are your people

WHITFIELD (54 557)   John Wilson

1. We are your peo - ple: Lord, by your grace, you dare to make us

First and last stanza | *Stanzas 2-5*

Christ to our neighbours, of ev-'ry na - tion and race.

2 How can we demonstrate
  your love and care?
  Speaking or listening?
  Battling or serving?
  Help us to know when and where.

3 Called to portray you,
  help us to live
  closer than neighbours,
  open to strangers,
  able to clash and forgive.

4 Glad of tradition,
  help us to see
  in all life's changing
  where you are leading,
  where our best efforts should be.

5 Joined in community,
  breaking your bread,
  May we discover
  gifts in each other,
  willing to lead and be led.

6 Lord, as we minister
  in diff'rent ways,
  may all we're doing
  show that you're living,
  meeting your love with our praise.

Words and music © Oxford University Press   *Brian Wren*

808 We give God thanks

MELCOMBE (LM)   Samuel Webbe (1740-1816)

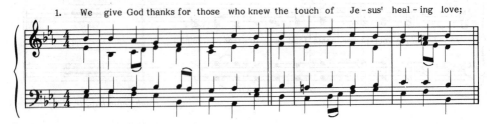

1. We give God thanks for those who knew the touch of Je - sus' heal - ing love;

they trust-ed him to make them whole, to give them peace, their guilt re-move.

2 We offer prayer for all who go
  relying on his grace and power,
  to help the anxious and the ill,
  to heal their wounds, their lives restore.

3 We dedicate our skills and time
  to those who suffer where we live,
  to bring such comfort as we can
  to meet their need, their pain relieve.

4 So Jesus' touch of healing grace
  lives on within our willing care;
  by thought and prayer and gift we prove
  his mercy still, his love we share.   *Michael Perry*

Words © Michael Perry/Jubilate Hymns

809   We have a Gospel to proclaim   86

FULDA (LM)   W. Gardiner's *Sacred Melodies*, 1815

1. We have a gos-pel to pro-claim, good news for men in all the earth;

the gos-pel of a sa-viour's name: we sing his glo — ry, tell his worth.

2 Tell of his birth at Bethlehem,
  not in a royal house or hall
  but in a stable dark and dim:
  the Word made flesh, a light for all.

3 Tell of his death at Calvary,
  hated by those he came to save;
  in lonely suffering on the cross
  for all he loved, his life he gave.

4 Tell of that glorious Easter morn:
  empty the tomb, for he was free;
  he broke the power of death and hell
  that we might share his victory.

5 Tell of his reign at God's right hand,
  by all creation glorified;
  he sends his Spirit on his church
  to live for him, the lamb who died.

6 Now we rejoice to name him king;
  Jesus is Lord of all the earth;
  the gospel-message we proclaim:
  we sing his glory, tell his worth.   *Edward J. Burns*

Words © Dr E.J.Burns

810 We have a King

Israeli Folk Song, arranged by C. Knoll

1. We have a King who comes in splen-dor, comes on clouds of glo —— ry!

Hold-ing in his hand the scep-tre, hold-ing all our lives.

His the might and his the pow-er strong-er than the moun —— tains!

1-3. Son of God and still the Son of Ma —— ry, Je-sus, ho —— ly Lord.

2 We call him King for so he is,
who sits beside the Father;
his to rule and his to judge
the living and the dead.
But his eyes are full of kindness,
mercy is his measure.

3 So listen to his words and heed them;
turn from sin and sorrow.
He will come and dwell among us,
finding here his home.
Live the life and taste the freedom,
share with him his glory!

Willard F. Jabusch

811 We have been told

David Haas

INTRODUCTION

Capo 1 Legato (♩ = 92)

D   G/D A/D   G/D A/D   D

D   G/D A/D   G/D A/D   D

ANTIPHON

Soprano/Bass (melody)

Alto:
We have been told,   we've seen His face, and

Tenor:
We have been told,   we've seen His face, and

D   G/D A/D   D   G/D A/D   D

heard His   voice   a — live in our   hearts;

heard His   voice   a — live in our   hearts;

Em7   D/F♯   G   G/A   A

Last time to CODA ✷

1243

VERSE 1

"I am the vine, you are the branch-es, and

G   D/F♯   Em   A7   D

D.S. 𝄋

all who live in me will bear great fruit."

C   G/B   F   A   A/G   D/F♯   A/E

VERSES 2,3

2. "You are my friends, if you keep my com -- mands,
3. "No great-er love is there than this: to

G   D/F♯   Em   A7   D

D.S. 𝄋

no long - er slaves, I call you friends."
lay down one's life, for a friend."

C   G/B   F   A   A/G   D/F♯   A/E

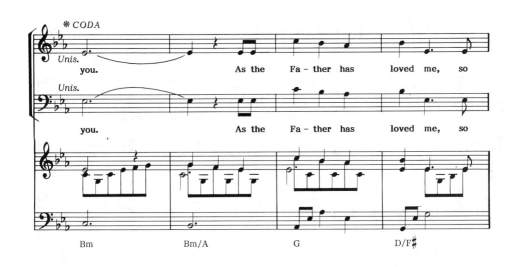

✻ *CODA*

Unis.
you. As the Fa – ther has loved me, so

Unis.
you. As the Fa – ther has loved me, so

Bm   Bm/A   G   D/F♯

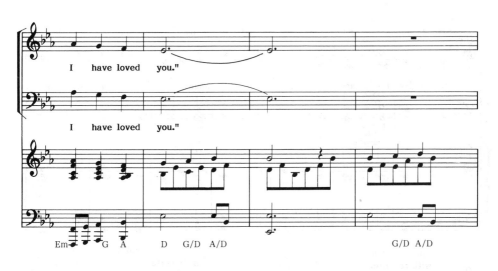

I have loved you."

I have loved you."

Em   G   A   D   G/D   A/D   G/D   A/D

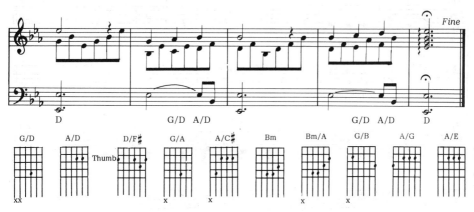

Fine

D   G/D   A/D   G/D   A/D   D

G/D   A/D   D/F♯   G/A   A/C♯   Bm   Bm/A   G/B   A/G   A/E

812 Unless a grain of wheat

1. If we have died with him, then we shall live with him; if we hold
2. an - y - one serves me, then they must fol - low me; where-ev - er
3. Make your home in me as I make mine in you; those who re -
4. If you re - main in me and my word lives in you; then you will
5. Those who love me are loved by my Fa —— ther; we shall be
6. Peace I leave with you, my peace I give to you; peace which the

firm we shall reign with him. Un -
I am my ser - vants will be. Un -
-main in me bear much fruit. Un -
be my dis - ci - ples. Un -
with them and dwell in them. Un -
world can - not give is my gift. Un -

Optional choral version

3. Make your home in me as I make mine in you; those who re -
5. Those who love me are loved by my Fa —— ther; we shall be

bear much fruit.
dwell with them.

-main in me bear much fruit.
with them and dwell in them.
Un -

bear much fruit.
dwell with them.

813 We're forgiven

Hubert J.Richards
Accpt. by Stephen Dean

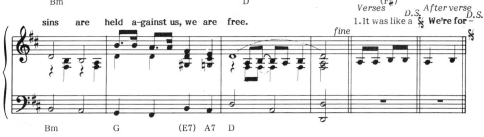

1 It was like a blindness,
darkness all around, (*three times*)
When he shone his light, I
Realised that I could see.

2 It was like a deafness,
couldn't hear a thing, (*three times*)
When he spoke his word, I
Heard he was addressing me.

3 It was like a dumbness,
my tongue was tied, (*three times*)
When he touched my mouth, I
Found that I was talking free.

4 It was like a prison,
chains around my feet, (*three times*)
When he took my chains off,
It was like a jubilee!

5 It was like a coffin,
couldn't move a limb, (*three times*)
When he took my hand, he
Raised me up and said, Be free!

Hubert Richards

814 We shall draw water joyfully

Paul Inwood

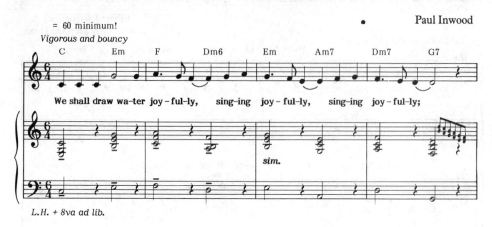

We shall draw wa-ter joy–ful-ly, sing-ing joy–ful-ly, sing-ing joy–ful-ly;

we shall draw wa – ter joy – ful-ly from the well springs of sal – va —— tion.

VERSES

1. Tru–ly God is our sal-va–tion; we trust, we shall not fear. For the

2. Give thanks, O give thanks to the Lord; give praise to his ho-ly name! Make his

Words and music © 1986, 1988 Paul Inwood

1. Lord is our strength, the Lord is our song; he be-came our sa-viour.

2. might-y deeds known to all of the na-tions; pro-claim his great-ness.

cresc.

VERSES

3. Sing a psalm, sing a psalm to the Lord for he has done glorious deeds.

smoother

3. Make known his works to all of the earth; peo-ple of Zi-on, sing for joy, for

cresc. sempre

3. great in your midst, great in your midst is the Ho-ly One of Is-rael.

815 We walk by faith SHANTI (CM)

Marty Haugen

INTRODUCTION

With quiet strength (♩ = ca.69.72)

mf

1. & 5. We walk by faith, and not by sight: no gra-cious words we

hear of him who spoke as none e'er spoke, but we be-lieve him

1-4 | Final | D.S. | rit. | Fine

1. & 5. near. 2. We may not 5. near.

mp *rit.* *pp*

2 We may not touch his hands and side,
nor follow where he trod;
yet in his promise we rejoice,
and cry 'My Lord and God!'

3 Help then, O Lord, our unbelief,
and may our faith abound;
to call on you when you are near,
and seek where you are found:

4 That when our life and faith is done
in realms of clearer light
we may behold you as you are
in full and endless sight.

Henry Alford (1810-71) alt.

816 Servant song (What do you want of me)   93

Sr Donna Marie McGargill, OSM
Accompaniment by Craig Kingsbury

VERSES

1. What do you want of me, Lord?
2. I hear you call my name, Lord,
3. A-bove, be-low and a-round me.
4. You are the light in my dark ness.
5. I am your song and ser vant,

Where do you want me to serve you?
and I am moved with-in me.
Be-fore, be-hind, and all through me,
You are my strength when I'm wea ry.
sing-ing your praise like Ma ry.

Where can I sing your prais es?
Your Spir-it stirs my deep est self.
Your Spir-it burns deep with-in me.
You give me sight when I'm blind ed.
Sur-ren-dered to your Spir it,

I am your song.
Sing your songs in me.
Fire my Life with your Love.
Come, see for me.
"Let it be done to me."

REFRAIN

1-5. Je — sus, Je — sus,

1. you are the Lord.
2. you are my Lord.
3. be warmth of my heart.
4. you are my Light.
5. "Let it be done to me."

1-5. Je — sus, Je — sus,

Words and music © 1984 OCP Publications. All rights reserved. Used with permission.

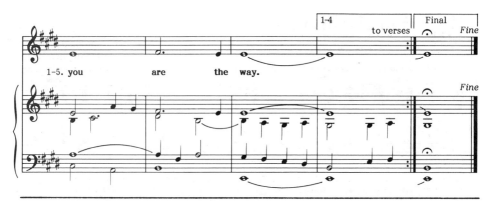

1-5. you are the way.

817 What does the Lord require

SHARPTHORNE (66 66 33 6)   Erik Routley (1917-1982)

1. What does the Lord re-quire for praise and of — fer-ing? What sac-ri-fice, de-sire or trib-ute bid you bring? Do just — ly; love mer — cy; walk hum-bly with your God.

2 Rulers of earth, give ear!
should you not justice know?
Will God your pleading hear,
while crime and cruelty grow?
    Do justly;
    love mercy;
walk humbly with your God.

3 Masters of wealth and trade,
all you for whom men toil,
Think not to win God's aid
if lies your commerce soil.
    Do justly;
    love mercy;
walk humbly with your God.

4 Still down the ages ring
the prophet's stern commands:
to merchant, worker, king,
he brings God's high demands:
    Do justly;
    love mercy;
walk humbly with your God.

5 How shall our life fulfil
God's law so hard and high?
Let Christ endue our will
with grace to fortify.
    Then justly,
    love mercy;
walk humbly with your God.

Albert F. Bayly (1901-84)
based on Micah 6:6-8

Words and music
© Oxford University Press

1255

818 What is this place?

Dutch traditional melody,
accompaniment by Stephen Dean

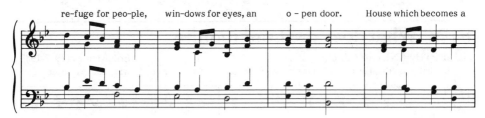

2 Word from the past, stars that are falling,
    sparks sown among us long ago.
    Names for our God, dreams, signs and
        wonders,
    voicing the world's relentless flow.
    We are but dust who see and who hear,
    who speak what we have heard:
    God's free resplendent word.

3 Table for one, bread that is broken,
    Cup to be shared, one bread, one wine.
    Wonder of God: peace among people,
    ancient yet new this hidden sign.
    Breaking and sharing, how can this be,
    impossible come true?
    From death comes life anew.

Huub Oosterhuis,
tr. Tony Barr (after David Smith)

819 When John baptised

RENDEZ A DIEU (98 98 D)

Melody from *La Forme des Prières*, Strasbourg 1545
(2nd line as in *Genevan Psalter*, 1551

1. When John baptized by Jor-dan's riv — ver in faith and hope the peo — ple came,

that John and Jor-dan might de - liv — er their trou - bled souls from sin and shame.

They came to seek a new be - gin — ning, the hu - man spi-rit's age — less quest,

re - pentance, and an end of sin — ning, re - nounc-ing ev -'ry wrong con-fessed.

2 There as the Lord, baptized and praying,
rose from the stream, the sinless one,
a voice was heard from heaven saying,
'This is my own beloved Son.'
There as the Father's word was spoken,
not in the power of wind and flame,
but of his love and peace the token,
seen as a dove, the Spirit came.

3 O Son of Man, our nature sharing,
in whose obedience all are blest,
Saviour, our sins and sorrows bearing,
hear us and grant us this request:
Daily to grow, by grace defended,
filled with the Spirit from above;
in Christ baptized, beloved,
   befriended,
children of God in peace and love.

Timothy Dudley-Smith

820   When the King shall come again

AVE VIRGO VIRGINUM (76 76 D)   Mediaeval melody as given by J. Horn, 1544

1. When the King shall come a-gain all his power re-veal - ing, splendour shall announce his reign,

life and joy and heal-ing: earth no long-er in de-cay, hope no more frust-ra - ted;

this is God's re-demp-tion day long - ing - ly a - wait - ed.

2 In the desert trees take root
fresh from his creation;
plants and flowers and sweetest fruit
join the celebration:
rivers spring up from the earth,
barren lands adorning; valleys,
this is your new birth,
mountains, greet the morning!

3 Strengthen feeble hands and knees,
fainting hearts, be cheerful!
God who comes for such as these
seeks and saves the fearful:
now the deaf can hear the dumb
sing away their weeping;
blind eyes see the injured come
walking, running, leaping.

4 There God's highway shall be seen
where no roaring lion,
nothing evil or unclean
walks the road to Zion:
ransomed people homeward bound
all your praises voicing,
see your Lord with glory crowned,
share in his rejoicing!

Christopher Idle

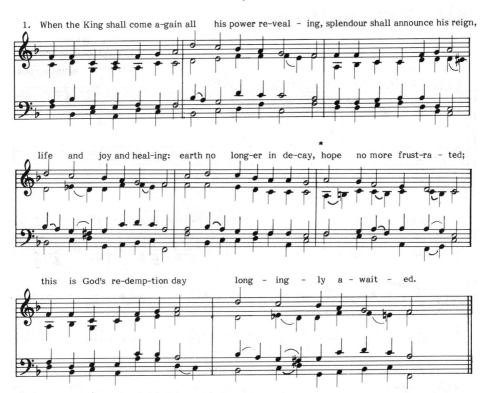

1. When the King shall come a-gain all his power re-veal - ing, splendour shall announce his reign,

life and joy and heal-ing: earth no long-er in de-cay, hope no more frust-ra - ted;

this is God's re-demp-tion day long - ing - ly a - wait - ed.

* alternative rhythm for this bar
  hope no more frus - tra - ted.

821 With open hands

Aidan Whelan,
accpt. by Stephen Dean

822　You are the Lord

Randall DeBruyn

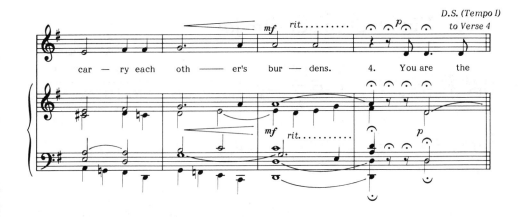

car — ry each oth — er's bur — dens. 4. You are the

823   You shall go out with joy

Stuart Dauermann

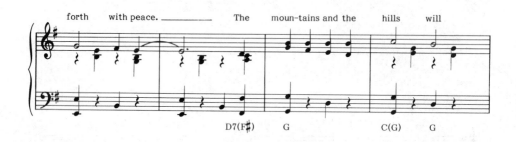

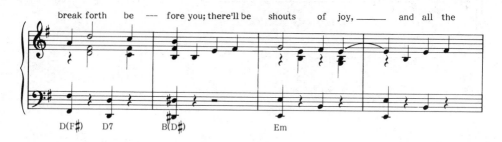

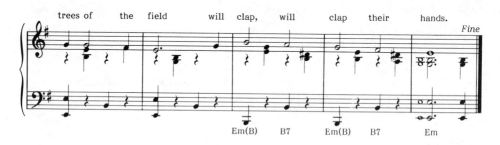

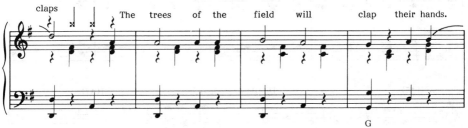

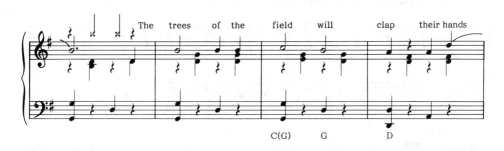

824 You are the King of glory

Mavis Ford

You are the King of Glo - ry, you are the Prince of Peace,

you are the Lord of heav'n and earth, you're the Son of right-eous - ness.

An - gels bow down be — fore You, wor — ship and a — dore, for

You have the words of e — ter - nal life; You are Je-sus Christ the Lord. Ho-

-san-na to the Son of Da-vid! Ho-san-na to the King of kings!

Glo-ry in the high-est hea — ven, for Je-sus the Mess-i - ah reigns.

1 You are the King of Glory,
you are the Prince of Peace,
you are the Lord of heav'n and earth,
you're the sun of righteousness.
Angels bow down before you,
worship and adore, for
you have the words of eternal life;
you are Jesus Christ, the Lord.

Hosanna to the Son of David!
Hosanna to the King of kings!
Glory in the highest heaven,
for Jesus the Messiah reigns.

2 You touched the broken hearted;
you made the blind to see;
you made the lame to walk again;
you set the prisoners free.
You bring us joy in sadness,
fill our hearts with hope, for
you give us joy and peace from heaven;
you are Jesus Christ the Lord.

3 You are the Lord who conquers;
yours is the victory;
triumphing over Satan's power
You rose to life again.
Now, Lord, you sit in heaven
reigning with the Father,
all knees shall bow in praise and worship;
you are Jesus Christ the Lord.

V.1 Mavis Ford.
Vv 2-3 by Julie Sharp

825 You are the vine

102

Chris O'Hara

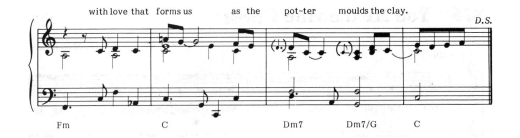

with love that forms us as the pot-ter moulds the clay.

D.S.

Fm   C   Dm7   Dm7/G   C

2 Together you stand,
  divided you fall,
  but those who listen
  receive my word and hear my call.
  Make your home here within me
  and you'll find I'll be with you,
  with you forever
  making life forever new.

Chris O'Hara

826 You have put on Christ

Stephen Dean

REFRAIN

You have put on Christ, in him you have been bap-tised, Al - le -
- lu - ia, al - le — lu - ia, al - le — lu ia!

VERSES

1. We who were dead are now re - born. We who were bu — ried now are
2. For though in A — dam all have sinned, in Je- sus Christ are all made
3. One Lord we serve who died for us; one faith we hold in life to
4. And this we know, that no-thing ill, No prince nor power, nor death nor

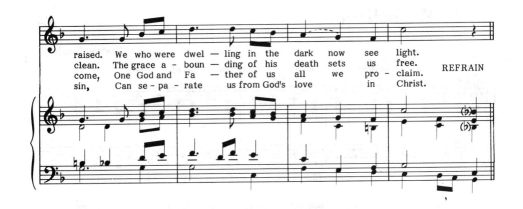

raised. We who were dwel — ling in the dark now see light.
clean. The grace a - boun — ding of his death sets us free.
come, One God and Fa — ther of us all we pro - claim.
sin, Can se - pa - rate us from God's love in Christ.

REFRAIN

827 We believe

Graham Kendrick

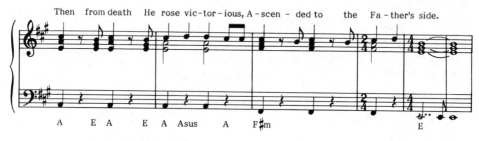

We believe He sends His Spirit,
on His church with gifts of power.
God His word of truth affirming,
sends us to the nations now.
He will come again in glory,
Judge the living and the dead,
every knee shall bow before Him,
then must every tongue confess.

Graham Kendrick

S1 God gives his people strength

Sister Miriam-Therese Winter
Harmonised by James O'Donnell

2 God gives his people hope.
  If we but trust in his word,
  our prayers are always heard.
  He warmly welcomes anyone who's erred.
  God gives his people hope.

3 God gives his people love.
  If we but open wide our heart,
  he's sure to do his part;
  he's always the first to make a start.
  God gives his people love.

4 God gives his people peace.
  When sorrow fills us to the brim,
  and courage grow dim,
  he lays to rest our restlessness in him.
  God gives his people peace.

Medical Mission Sisters

S2 I have counted the cost

Kevin Nichols

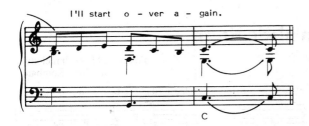
I'll start o - ver a - gain.

C

2 Lord, I thought that I knew all the question's you'd ask,
   what you'd want me to do ev'ry truth, ev'ry task;
   and your word seemed so near and your light seemed so
       strong
   and the road seemed so clear that you called me along.
   I will walk in your way, still in spite of it all,
   I will walk in your way.

3 I had mastered it all, all my answers were true,
   but when I heard your call all your questions were new;
   all the ways that you came, the disguises you wore,
   you were just not the same, not the same anymore.
   Still in spite of the loss and in spite of the pain,
   still in spite of it all I will find you again,
   still in spite of it all I will find you again.

Kevin Nichols

S3 Now the green blade riseth

Traditional French melody,
arr. John Rombaut

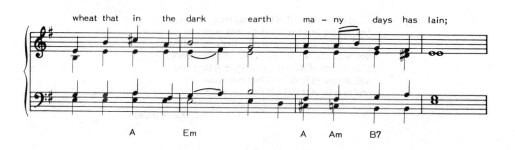

2 In the grave they laid him, Love whom men had slain,
  thinking that never he would wake again,
  laid in the earth like grain that sleeps unseen:
  love is come again like wheat that springeth green.

3 Forth he came at Easter, like the risen grain,
  he that for three days in the grave had lain,
  quick from the dead my risen Lord is seen:
  love is come again like wheat that springeth green.

4 When our hearts are wintry, grieving or in pain,
  thy touch can call us back to life again,
  fields of our heart that dead and bare have been:
  love is come again like wheat that springeth green.

J. M. C. Crum

S4 O great St David

Dom Gregory Murray O.S.B.

O great Saint David, still we hear thee call us,
Yea, down the ages, will thy words enthral us,
unto a life that knows no fear of death;
strong, happy words: "Be joyful, keep the faith."

On Cambria's sons stretch out thy hands in blessing;
for our dear land thy help we now implore.
Lead us to God, with humble hearts confessing

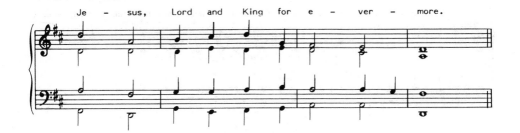

Je - sus, Lord and King for e - ver - more.

2 Christ was the centre rock of all thy teaching,
God's holy will – the splendour of its theme.
His grace informed, his love inflamed thy preaching
Christ's sway on earth, the substance of they dream.

Chorus: On Cambria's sons, etc.

3 In early childhood, choosing Jesus only,
Thy fervour showed his yoke was light and sweet
and thus for thee, life's journey was not lonely –
the path made plain by prints of wounded feet.

Chorus: On Cambria's sons, etc.

4 O glorious saint, we wander in the dark;
With thee we seek our trusted guide in Rome.
Help him to steer on earth Saint Peter's barque,
that we may safely reach our heavenly home.

Chorus: On Cambria's sons, etc.

Francis E. Mostyn (1860–1939)

S5 Saint Andrew called to follow Christ

Joan McCrimmon

Saint An - drew called to fol - low Christ, to learn to fish for men; sought
out his bro - ther Pe - ter first and brought him to the Lord.

2 Then with five thousand to be fed
in desert wild and drear;
'twas Andrew found a boy with bread
and brought him to the Lord.

3 And when the Greeks through Philip sought
that Jesus they might see;
'twas Andrew first whom Philip brought
to bring them to the Lord.

4 So may we, this St Andrew's-tide,
share Andrew's burning zeal;
and fish for men both far and wide,
to bring them to the Lord.

Frank Gibson

S6 Hail, holy Joseph, hail

Anonymous, harmonised by S.S.Wesley

Hail, ho - ly Jo - seph, hail! Hus - band of Ma - ry, hail!
Chaste as the li - ly flow'r in E - den's peace-ful vale.

2 Hail, holy Joseph, hail!
  Father of Christ esteemed,
  Father be thou to those
  thy foster Son redeemed.

3 Hail, holy Joseph, hail!
  Prince of the house of God,
  may his blest graces be
  by thy pure hands bestowed.

4 Hail, holy Joseph, hail!
  comrade of angels, hail:
  cheer thou the hearts that faint,
  and guide the steps that fail.

5 Hail, holy Joseph, hail!
  God's choice wert thou alone;
  to thee the Word made flesh
  was subject as a Son.

6 Mother of Jesus, bless,
  and bless, ye saints on high,
  all meek and simple souls
  that to Saint Joseph cry.

Frederick William Faber (1814–1863)

S7 Lord make me an instrument

Sister Briege O'Hare

Based on St Francis of Assisi

S8 Spirit of God

Sister Miriam-Therese Winter

1288

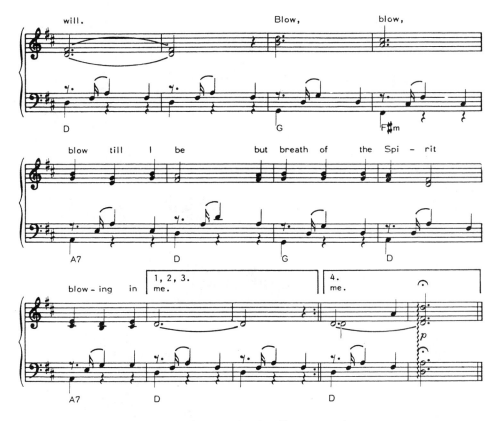

2 Down in the meadow the willows are moaning,
   sheep in the pasture-land cannot lie still.
   Spirit of God creation is groaning,
   fill the earth, bring it to birth and blow where you will.
   Blow, blow, blow till I be but breath of the Spirit
   blowing in me.

3 I saw the scar of a year that lay dying,
   heard the lament of a lone whip-poorwill.
   Spirit of God see that cloud crying,
   fill he earth, bring it to birth and blow where you will.
   Blow, blow, blow till I be but breath of the Spirit
   blowing in me.

4 Spirit of God, every man's heart is lonely.
   watching and waiting and hungry until,
   Spirit of God, man longs that you only,
   fulfil the earth, bring it to birth and blow where you will.
   Blow, blow, blow till I be but breath of the Spirit
   blowing in me.

Medical Missions Sisters

THE
DIVINE OFFICE

The Divine Office

The full texts will be found in the books containing the Divine Office. A selection is given here which will allow a parish or group to celebrate a form of morning, evening or night prayer according to their needs.

Invitatory

To begin the first office of the day

All make the sign of the cross on their lips.

Leader: O Lord, o-pen our lips. *All:* And we shall praise your name.

Psalm 94(95) *is sung, with optional refrain as follows:*

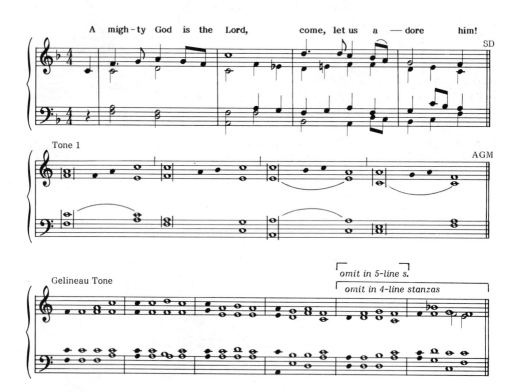

Come, ríng out your jóy to the Lórd;
háil the róck who sáves us.
Let us cóme befóre him, gíving thanks,
with sóngs let us háil the Lórd.

A míghty Gód is the Lórd,/
a gréat king abóve all góds.
In his hánd are the dépths of the éarth;/
the héights of the móuntains are hís.
To hím belongs the séa, for he máde it,
and the drý land sháped by his hánds.

1292

Come ín; let us bów and bend lów;
let us knéel before the God who máde us
for hé is our Gód and wé/
   the péople who belóng to his pásture,
the flóck that is léd by his hánd.

O that todáy you would lísten to his vóice !
   Hárden not your héarts as at Meríbah,/
as on that dáy at Mássah in the désert
when your fáthers pút me to the tést;
when they tríed me, thóugh they saw my wórk.

For forty yéars I was wéaried of these péople/
   and I sáid: 'Their héarts are astráy,
These péople do not knów my wáys.'
Thén I took an oáth in my ánger:
'Néver shall they énter my rést.'

Give glóry to the Fáther Almíghty,
to his Són, Jesus Chríst, the Lórd,
to the Spírit who dwélls in our héarts,
both nów and for éver. Ámén.

Alternative setting

DARWALL'S 148th (66 66 88)   J. Darwall (1731-89)

1 To God with gladness sing,
   your Rock and Saviour bless,
   within his temple bring
   your songs of thankfulness !
   O God of might,
   to you we sing
   enthroned as King
   on heaven's height !

2 He cradles in his hand
   the heights and depths of earth;
   he made the sea and land,
   he brought the land to birth !
   O God most high,
   we are your sheep
   on us you keep
   your Shepherd's eye !

3 Your heav'nly Father praise,
   Acclaim his only Son,
   your voice in homage raise
   to him who makes all one !
   O Dove of peace,
   on us descend
   that strife may end
   and joy increase !

James Quinn SJ

Words © 1966, 1987 by James Quinn SJ. By permission of Geoffrey Chapman, (a division of Cassell Ltd), Artillery House, Artillery Row, Westminster, London SW1P 1RT

Other settings of this psalm: Complete Celebration Hymnal 435, New Songs of Celebration 60 (783)

Alternative invitatories: Psalm 23(24) or 99(100), e.g. New Songs of Celebration 8 (731)

Morning Prayer

Introduction

Omitted if invitatory has been sung

O God, come to our aid. O Lord, make haste to help us.

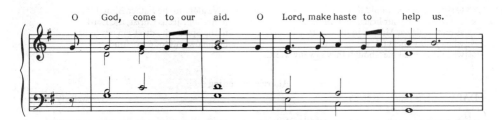

Glo – ry be to the Fa – ther, the Son and the Ho – ly Spi – rit,

as it was in the be – gin – ning, is now and e — ver shall be

(Except in Lent)

world with-out end, A — men. Al – le – lu — ia.

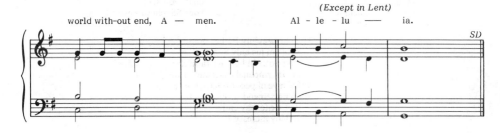

Hymn
from the Morning section, or ad libitum

Psalmody

*See Complete List of Psalms at the end of this section. Suitable psalms are nos. 42, 50, 62;
a Canticle (Daniel 3, no. 73 (796)), and a Praise psalm (150) or the following:*

Tone 1

Gelineau Tone

Psalm 148

Práise the Lórd from the héavens,
práise him in the héights.
práise him, all his ángels,
práise him, all his hósts.

Práise him, sún and móon,
praise him, shíning stárs.
práise him, híghest héavens
and the wáters abóve the héavens.

Let them práise the náme of the Lórd.
He commánded: they were máde.
He fíxed them for éver,
gave a láw which shall nót pass awáy.

Práise the Lórd from the éarth,
séa creatures and all óceans,
fire and háil, snow and míst,
stormy wínds that obéy his wórd;

áll móuntains and hílls,
all frúit trees and cédars,
béasts, wíld and táme,
réptiles and bírds on the wíng;

áll earth's kíngs and péoples,
earth's prínces and rúlers;
yóung men and máidens,
old men togéther with chíldren.

Let them práise the náme of the Lórd
for he alóne is exálted.
The spléndour of his náme
réaches beyond héaven and éarth.

He exálts the stréngth of his péople.
He is the práise of all his sáints,
of the sóns of Ísraël,
of the péople to whóm he comes clóse.

Give glóry to the Fáther almíghty,
To his Són, Jesus Chríst, the Lórd,
to the Spírit who dwélls in our héarts,
both nów and for éver, Amén.

Reading (optional)

Response to the Word of God

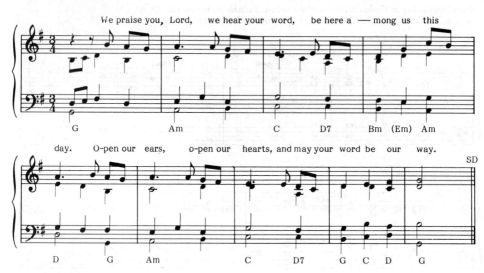

We praise you, Lord, we hear your word, be here a — mong us this day. O-pen our ears, o-pen our hearts, and may your word be our way.

VERSE (Cantor)

1.

Advent:	Let us see, O Lord, your mercy;	and give us your	sa - ving help.	R.
Christmas:	The Word was made flesh,	and	lived a - mong us.	R.
Lent:	A pure heart create for me, O Lord,	put a steadfast spi -	rit with in me.	R.
Easter:	This day was made by the Lord,	we rejoice	and are glad.	R.
General:	Your words are spirit, Lord, and they are life;	you have the message of	e - ter - nal life.	R.

2. Glory be to the Father, and to the Son; and to the Ho - ly Spirit. *R.*

Other suitable hymns and songs:

Bless the Lord, 5 (728), Confitemini Domino, 12 (735), O Christe Domine Jesu, 54 (777), Psallite Domino, 67 (790); or Complete Cel. Hymnal nos 696, 701, 702 or 709

Gospel Canticle – The Benedictus

Tone 1

John Harper

Tone 2

Steven Foster

Blessed be the Lord, the God of Israel !

                (omit sections 2 & 3 of chant)

He has visited his people and redeemed them.

He has raised up for us a mighty saviour
in the house of David his servant,
as he promised by the lips of holy men,
those who were his prophets from of old.

A saviour who would free us from our foes,
from the hands of all who hate us.
So his love for our fathers is fulfilled
and his holy covenant remembered.

He swore to Abraham our father to grant us,
that free from fear, and saved from the hands
   of our foes,
we might serve him in holiness and justice
all the days of our life in his presence.

As for you, little child,
you shall be called a prophet of God, the Most High.
You shall go ahead of the Lord
to prepare his ways before him,

To make known to his people their salvation
through forgiveness of all their sins,
the loving-kindness of the heart of our God
who visits us like the dawn from on high.

He will give light to those in darkness,
those who dwell in the shadow of death,

                (omit section 3 of chant)

and lead us into the way of peace.

Glory be to the Father, and to the Son,
and to the Holy Spirit,
as it was in the beginning, is now and ever shall be,
world without end, Amen.

Intercessions

A response such as the following is made: Alternative suggestion: O Lord hear my prayer (CCH 710)

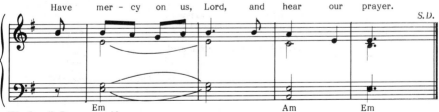

The Lord's Prayer *is said or sung.*

Concluding Prayer *by the leader.*

A priest or deacon uses the usual form of blessing; a layperson says:
The Lord bless us and keep us from all evil, and bring us to everlasting life.   Amen

Evening Prayer

Introduction *as at Morning Prayer*

Hymn *from the Evening section or ad libitum according to the season*

If Evening Prayer begins with a Service of Light (Lucernarium), the following or a similar greeting may be used:

Leader: Jesus Christ is the light of the world.
All: **A light the darkness cannot o — ver - power.**

Hymn
Another tune in this metre may be chosen. This tune may be sung in canon.

TALLIS' CANON 88.88 (LM)

Shortened form of melody by
Thomas Tallis c.1505-85

1 O gracious Light, Lord Jesus Christ,
in you the Father's glory shone.
Immortal, holy, blest is he,
and blest are you, his only Son.

2 Now sunset comes, but light shines forth,
the lamps are lit to pierce the night.
Praise Father, Son and Spirit: God
who dwells in the eternal light.

3 Worthy are you of endless praise,
O Son of God, Life-giving Lord;
wherefore you are through all the earth
and in the highest heaven adored.

2nd Century, tr. F. Bland Tucker

Evening Thanksgiving

Leader: Let us give thanks to God the Father always and for everything.
All: **In the name of our Lord Je - sus Christ.**

We give you thanks, O Lord,
through your Son Jesus Christ,
through whom you have enlightened us
and shown us the light which can never be extinguished.
Now we have come to the end of the day and night is falling.
Through the day you have shone on us the light
which you created for our need,
and now, through your grace, we do not lack the light of evening;
and so we praise you and glorify you
through your Son, Jesus Christ our Lord,
through whom, with the Holy Spirit,
are glory and power and honour
now and for ever and to endless ages.
Amen.

Incense Psalm

Incense may be used as a symbol of prayer. While this is going on Ps 140(141) is sung with refrain as follows:

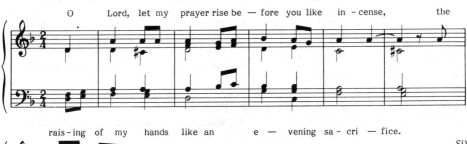

I have cálled to you, Lórd, hásten to hélp me !
Héar my vóice when I crý to yóu.
Let my práyer aríse befóre you like íncense,
the ráising of my hánds like an évening oblátion.

Sét, O Lórd, a guard óver my móuth;
keep wátch, O Lórd, at the dóor of my líps !
Do not túrn my héart to thíngs that are wróng,
to évil déeds with mén who are sínners.

Néver allów me to sháre in their féasting.
If a góod man stríkes or repróves me it is kíndness;
but let the óil of the wícked not anóint my héad.
Let my práyer be éver agáinst their málice.

To yóu, Lord Gód, my éyes are túrned:
in yóu I take réfuge; spáre my sóul !
From the tráp they have láid for me kéep me sáfe:
kéep me from the snáres of thóse who do évil.

(omit parts 1 & 2 of chant)

Give glóry to the Fáther, the Són and Holy Spírit,
both nów and for éver, wórld withóut énd.

Psalmody

Suitable psalms may be chosen from the complete list at the end of the Office section. The psalms that follow are those for Sunday Evening Prayer.

Psalm 109 (110)
Weeks 1-4

The Lord's revelation to my Màster:
'Sit ón my right:
your foes I will put beneàth your feet.'

The Lord will wield from Sìon
your sceptŕe of power:
rule in the midst of àll your foes.

A prince from the day of your bìrth
on the hóly mountains:
from the womb before the dawn Ì begot you.

The Lord has sworn an oath he will not chànge.
'You are a prìest for ever,
a priest like Melchizedèk of old.'

The master standing at yóur right hand
will shatter kings in the day òf his wrath.

He shall drink from the stream bý the wayside
and therefore he shall lift ùp his head.

Glory be to the Father and tó the Son
and to the Hòly Spirit.

As it was in the beginning, is now, and éver shall be
world without ènd. Amen.

Psalm 113a (114)
Week 1

When Israel came forth from Egypt,
Jacob's sons from an alien people,
Judah became the Lord's temple,
Israel became his kingdom.

The sea fled at the sight:
the Jordan turned back on its course,
the mountains leapt like rams
and the hills like yearling sheep.

Why was it, sea, that you fled,
that you turned back, Jordan, on your course ?
Mountains, that you leapt like rams,
hills, like yearling sheep ?

Tremble, O earth, before the Lord,
in the presence of the God of Jacob,
who turns the rock into a pool
and flint into a spring of water.

Glory be to the Father, and to the Son
and to the Holy Spirit,
as it was in the beginning, is now and ever shall be,
world without end, Amen.

Psalm 113b (115) Week 2

Ian Forrester

Not to us, Lord, not to us
but to your name give the glory
for the sake of your love and your truth,
lest the heathen say: 'Where is their God ?'

But our God is in the heavens;
he does whatever he wills.
Their idols are silver and gold,
the work of human hands.

They have mouths but they cannot speak:
they have eyes but they cannot see;
they have ears but they cannot hear:
they have nostrils but they cannot smell.

With their hands they cannot feel:/
with their feet they cannot walk.
No sound comes from their throats.
Their makers will come to be like them,
and so will all who trust in them.

Steven Foster

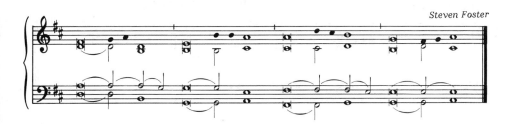

Sons of Israel, trust in the Lord;
he is their help and their shield.
Sons of Aaron, trust in the Lord;
he is their help and their shield.

You who fear him, trust in the Lord;
he is their help and their shield.
He remembers us, and he will bless us;
he will bless the sons of Israel./
    he will bless the sons of Aaron.

The Lord will bless those who fear him,
the little no less than the great:
to you may the Lord grant increase,
to you and all your children.

May you be blessed by the Lord
the maker of heaven and earth.
The heavens belong to the Lord
but the earth he has given to men.

The dead shall not praise the Lord,
nor those who go down into the silence.
But we who live bless the Lord
now and for ever. Amen.

Glory be to the Father, and to the Son
and to the Holy Spirit,
as it was in the beginning, is now and ever shall be,
world without end. Amen.

Psalm 110 (111) Week 3

Ian Forrester

I will thank the Lord with all my heart
in the meetings of the just and their assembly.
Great are the works of the Lord;
to be pondered by all who love them.

Majestic and glorious his work,
his justice stands firm for ever.
He makes us remember his wonders.
The Lord is compassion and love.

He gives food to those who fear him;
keeps his covenant ever in mind.
He has shown his might to his people
by giving them the lands of the nations.

His works are justice and truth;
his precepts are all of them sure,
standing firm for ever and ever:
they are made in uprightness and truth.

He has sent deliverance to his people/
    and established his covenant for ever.
Holy his name, to be feared.
To fear the Lord is the first stage of wisdom:/
    all who do so prove themselves wise.
His praise shall last for ever !

Glory be to the Father, and to the Son
and to the Holy Spirit,
as it was in the beginning, is now and ever shall be,
world without end. Amen.

Alternative Chant

Graham Elliott

Psalm 111 (112) Week 4

John Harper

Happy the man who fears the Lord,
who takes delight in all his commands.
His sons will be powerful on earth;
the children of the upright are blessed.

Riches and wealth are in his house;
his justice stands firm for ever.
He is a light in the darkness for the upright:
he is generous, merciful and just.

The good man takes pity and lends,
he conducts his affairs with honour.
The just man will never waver:
he will be remembered for ever.

He has no fear of evil news;
with a firm heart he trusts in the Lord.
With a steadfast heart he will not fear;
he will see the downfall of his foes.

Openhanded, he gives to the poor;/
    his justice stands firm for ever.
His head will be raised in glory.
The wicked man sees and is angry,/
    grinds his teeth and fades away;
the desire of the wicked leads to doom.

Glory be to the Father, and to the Son
and to the Holy Spirit,
as it was in the beginning, is now and ever shall be,
world without end. Amen.

Alternative Chant

John Harper

Reading (optional)

Response to the Word of God
See the Responsory for Morning Prayer; or as follows:

Texts of the Short Responsories for Sunday Evening Prayer:

Weeks 1 & 3

R. Bless - ed are you in the vault of heaven. *repeat*

Cantor: You are ex - alt - ed and glo - ri - fied a — bove all else for e — ver.
Repeat response

Cantor: Glo - ry be to the Fa - ther and to the Son, and to the Ho - ly Spi - rit.
Repeat response

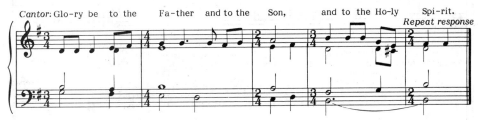

Weeks 2 & 4

Gospel Canticle: The Magnificat

Tone 1

Gelineau Tone

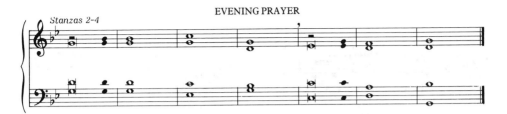

Stanzas 2-4

My sóul glórifies the Lórd,
my spírit rejóices in Gód, my Sáviour.
He lóoks on his sérvant in her lówliness;
hencefórth all áges will cáll me bléssed.

    The Almíghty works márvels for mé.
    Hóly his náme !
    His mércy is from áge to áge,
    on thóse who féar him.

    He púts forth his árm in stréngth
    and scátters the proud-héarted.
    He cásts the míghty from their thrónes
    and ráises the lówly.

He fílls the stárving with good thíngs,
sends the rích away émpty.
He protécts Ísrael, his sérvant,
remémbering his mércy,

the mércy prómised to our fáthers,
to Ábrahám and his sóns for éver.
Praise the Fáther, the Són and Holy Spírit,
both nów and for éver, wórld without énd.

Alternative Setting

Chris O'Hara

My sou-l mag-ni - fies the Lord,   my   spi-rit re-joi-ces in God my

Sa - viour,   he   looks on his ser-vant in her low-li - ness,   hence.-

- forth all a-ges will call me ble-ssed. The al — mi – ghty works marvels for me: ho – ly his name! His mer-cy is from age to age on those who fear him. He pu – ts forth his arm in strength and scatters the proud heart-ed. He casts the mi-ghty from their seat and

rai ——— ses the low-ly. He fills the star-ving with good things, sends the rich a-way em-pty. He pro-tec-ts Is-ra-el his ser-vant re-mem-be-ring his mer-cy; the mer-cy pro-mised to our Fathers, to A-bra-ham and his sons for e-ver. Glo-ry be to the

Music © 1984 Chris O'Hara. Reprinted with permission

Intercessions
The following or a similar response is made:

or see the response for Morning Prayer.

* optional descant in small notes

Or see the Intercessions for Morning Prayer.
Alternative response: O Lord, hear my prayer (CH710)

The Lord's Prayer *is said or sung.*

Concluding Prayer *by the leader.*

Blessing and Dismissal

A priest or deacon uses the usual form of blessing; a layperson says:
The Lord bless us and keep us from all evil, and bring us to everlasting life. **Amen.**

Night Prayer

Introduction *as at Morning Prayer*

*Here an examination of conscience is commended. In a common celebration this may be
included in a penitential act using the formulas given in the Missal.*

Hymn *from the Evening section or as appropriate.*

TE LUCIS ANTE TERMINUM (LM)   Plainchant, arr. Stephen Dean

1 We praise you, Father, for your gift
   of dusk and nightfall over earth.
   Foreshadowing the mystery
   of death that leads to endless day.

2 Within your hands we rest secure;
   in quiet sleep our strength renew;
   yet give your people hearts that wake
   in love to you, unsleeping Lord.

3 Your glory may we ever seek
   in rest, as in activity,
   until its fulness is revealed,
   O source of life, O Trinity.

The Benedictine Nuns of West Malling

Psalmody

The Psalms for Sunday Night Prayer follow. Also appropriate is Psalm 90 (91), (Celebration Hymnal 677).

Psalm 4

When I cáll, ánswer me, O Gód of jústice;
from ánguish you reléased me, have mércy and héar me.

O mén, how lóng will your héarts be clósed,
will you lóve what is fútile and séek what is fálse ?

It is the Lórd who grants fávours to thóse whom he lóves;
the Lórd hears me whenéver I cáll him.

Fear him; do not sín; pónder on your béd and be stíll;
Make jústice your sácrifice and trúst in the Lórd.

'Whát can bring us háppiness ?' mány sáy;
Let the líght of your fáce shíne on us, O Lórd.

You have pút into my héart a gréater jóy
than théy have from abúndance of córn and new wíne.

I will líe down in péace and sléep comes at ónce
for yóu alone, Lórd, make me dwéll in sáfety.

Glory bé to the Fáther, the Són and Holy Spírit
both nów and for éver, wórld without énd.

Psalm 133 (134)

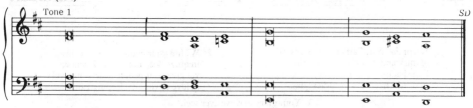

O come, bless the Lord,
all yóu who sérve the Lórd,
who stand in the house of the Lord,
in the cóurts of the hóuse of our Gód.

Lift up your hands to the holy place
and bléss the Lórd through the níght.
May the Lord bless you from Sion,
he who máde both héaven and éarth.

Give glory to the Father Almíghty,
to his Són, Jesus Chríst, our Lórd,
to the Spírit who dwélls in our hearts
both nów and for éver, Ámén.

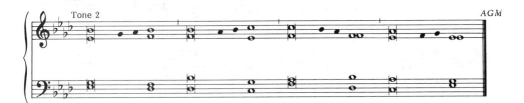

Scripture Reading *Deuteronomy 6:4-7*

Hear, O Israel: the Lord our God is one Lord; and you shall love the Lord your God
with all your heart, and with all your soul, and with all your might. And these words
which I command you this day shall be upon your heart; and you shall teach them
diligently to your children, and shall talk of them when you sit in your house, and
when you walk by the way, and when you lie down, and when you rise.

Response to the Word of God

(Paschaltide version overleaf)

THE DIVINE OFFICE

Response to the Word of God: Paschaltide

Cantor:

R. In – to your hands, O Lord, I com – mend my Spi — rit,

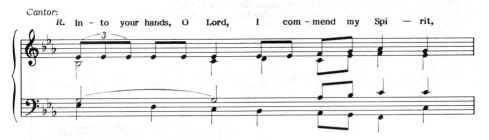

al – le – lu — ia, al – le – lu — ia!

All repeat R.

V. You have re – deem – ed us, Lord, God of truth.

All repeat R.

V. Glo – ry be to the Fa – ther, and to the Son, and to the Ho – ly Spi – rit.

All repeat R.

Gospel Canticle The Nunc Dimittis

Antiphon

Save us, Lord, while we are a — wake, pro — tect us

while   we   sleep,   that   we   may   keep   watch   with

Christ,   and   rest   here   in   peace.

Tone 1   omit in 1st stanza   JMcC

At lást, all pówerful Máster,
you give léave to your sérvant to gó
in péace, accórding to your prómise.

For my éyes have séen your salvátion
which yóu have prepáred for all nátions,
the líght to enlíghten the Géntiles,
and give glóry to Ísrael, your péople.

Give práise to the Fáther Almíghty,
to his Són, Jesus Chríst, the Lórd,
to the Spírit who dwélls in our héarts
both nów and for éver, Amén.

Gelineau Tone   omit in 1st stanza

Concluding Prayer *by the leader.*

Blessing   The Lord grant us a quiet night and a perfect end. **Amen.**

Anthem to Our Lady

As an alternative to the anthems given here, the Hail Holy Queen may be recited.

SALVE REGINA

Plainchant, arr. James O'Donnell

REGINA CAELI

Plainchant, arr. James O'Donnell

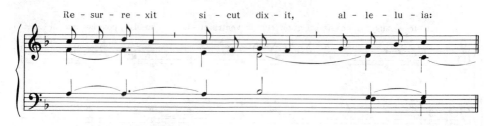

Plainchant, arr. James O'Donnell

Other psalm versions in The Complete Celebration Hymnal/ New Songs of Celebration

An asterisk * indicates a Grail Psalm

CANTICLES AND HYMNS BASED ON SCRIPTURE

Old Testament:

New Testament:

Acknowledgements – Divine Office

Psalms from THE PSALMS: A NEW TRANSLATION published by Wm Collins Sons & Co Ltd. Reproduced by permission of A.P.Watt Ltd on behalf of The Grail (England.) Other texts, unless otherwise stated, from The Divine Office © The Bishops' Conference of England and Wales. (BCEW) Items marked SD are © Stephen Dean. Items marked MPC © McCrimmon Publishing Co Ltd.

INVITATORY. Antiphon SD. Psalm tone 1 MPC. Psalm words and Gelineau tone © The Grail. Hymn © James Quinn SJ by permission of Geoffrey Chapman.

MORNING PRAYER. Introduction music SD, words BCEW. Response to the Word of God, text and music; Intercessions music SD. Blessing and dismissal BCEW.

EVENING PRAYER. O Gracious Light by F.Bland Tucker, © Church Pension Fund. Incense Psalm music SD. Thanksgiving tr. SD. Psalm Tones: Pss 109 and 113a SD; Ps 110, 111, 113b MPC. Short Responsories, texts BCEW, music SD. Magnificat tone I MCP, Gelineau tone The Grail. Through-setting © Chris O'Hara. Intercession response music SD.

NIGHT PRAYER. Hymn We praise you Father © The Benedictine Nuns of West Malling. Ps 4 Gelineau tone © The Grail. Ps 133 tone 1 SD, tone 2 MCP. Scripture Reading from the Jerusalem Bible. Response, text BCEW, music SD. Gospel Canticle: antiphon text BCEW, Music SD. Anthem to Our Lady accpt. MPC.

ACKNOWLEDGEMENTS

The publishers wish to express their gratitude to the following for permission to include copyright material in this book:

Agape, Carol Stream, Il 60188, USA for Break not the circle © 1975; Divided our pathways © 1974; Help us to accept each other © 1975; His light now shines in the darkness © 1969; Let us talents and tongues employ © 1975; Lord, confronted with your might © 1975; You, Israel, return now © 1976. International copyright secured. All rights reserved. Used with permission.
John Ainslie, 76 Great Bushey Drive, Totteridge, London N20 8QL for the tune 'Ellenborough' (Grant us thy peace). Used by permission.
Alba House Communications, Canfield, Ohio 44406, USA for What can we offer you © 1977.
Christopher Alston, for the words of Father most holy.
The American Catholic Press, 1223 Rossell Oak Park, Ill 60302, USA for the words and music of O what a gift © 1967, 1970. Used by permission. All rights reserved.
Ampleforth Abbey, York Y06 4EN for the words O raise your eye on high and see. Used by permission.
Mike Anderson, 11a Rampit Close, Penny Lane, Haydock, Merseyside WA11 OYH for the words and music of The Kingdom.
The Archdiocese of Durban, 408 Innes Road, Durban 4001, South Africa for the words of Across the years, God at creation's dawn; God our maker; if God is our defender; Lord, this paschaltide; O light forever dawning; Send forth your Spirit; and for the words and music of Firm is our Faith. All used with permission.
William Armitage, Canada, for the words of To God our Father © 1977.
Augsburg Publishing House, 426 South Fifth Street, Box 1209, Minneapolis, Mn 55440, USA for This is the feast, reprinted from Contemporary Worship 2; The Holy Communion © 1970; Christ has arisen, Alleluia! reprinted by permission from Lead us, Lord. ed. by Howard S Olson © 1977. Used by permission.
Tony Barr, 9 Patmore Road, Colchester, Essex for the words and music of Rain down justice. Tony Barr and Jabulani Music (same address) for My God you fathom my heart; The song of God among us (Lest he be too far from us); I lift up my eyes; Our help is in the name of the Lord; Who wants to live as God (The song of all seed); Breath of life and Stand and stare not. Music © Bernard Huijbers; text © Huub Oosterhuis; translation © Tony Barr. Used with permission.
Belwin Mills Music Ltd, for the words and music of Suffer little children. Reproduced by kind permission of the copyright owners, Belwin Mills Music Ltd, 250 Purley Way, Croydon CR9 4QD.
The Benedictine Foundation of the State of Vermont, Weston Priory, Weston, Vermont 05161, USA for A child is born for us today © 1971; I lift up my eyes to the mountains © 1975; In the beginning © 1974, 1975; We thank you, Father © 1971, 1980. All used with permission.
The Benedictines of Stanbrook, Stanbrook Abbey Press, Callow End, Worcester WR2 4TD for the words and music of When Jesus comes to be baptised. Used with permission.
Laurence Bevenot OSB (Executor: Ampleforth Abbey) for Christus Vincit. Used with permission.
Bmg. Music, Holland for the music of God's Spirit precedes us.
Mrs William Booth-Clibborn for the words and music of Let it breathe on me.
Bosworth & Co. Ltd of 14/18 Heddon Street, London W1R 8DP for the words and music of Thank you.
Breitkopf & Hartel, Buch und Musicverlag, Walkmuhlstrasse 52, Wiesbaden 1, West Germany for the music of Be still my soul. Used with permission.
Burckhardthaus Verlag GmbH, 6460 Gelnhausen 1, Germany, for the original words and music of Give us the will to listen. Used with permission.
Burns and Oates, Wellwood, North Farm Road, Tunbridge Wells, Kent TN2 3DR for the music of Take my life and let it be; Who is she that stands triumphant. Used with permission.
Celebration Services (International) Ltd, Cathedral of the Isles, Millport, Isle of Cumbrae, KA28 OHE, Scotland for the words and music of Alleluia! Sons of God arise © 1971, 1975; Be like your Father © 1979; Fear not, rejoice and be glad © 1971, 1975; Fear not, for I have redeemed you © 1975; I will sing, I will sing © 1974, 1975; We cry 'Hosanna, Lord' © 1975. All used with permission.
Geoffrey Chapman (A division of Cassell Ltd), 1 Vincent Square, London SW1P 2PN on behalf of James Quinn SJ, for the words of A sign is seen in heaven © 1980; Dear love of my heart © 1980; The seed is Christ's © 1980; We praise you God © 1969; for the words of Christ beside me; This is my will; Come, adore this wondrous presence; Come, praise the Lord, the Almighty; Day is done, but love unfailing; Forth in the presence of Christ we go; I believe in God the Father; Loving Father, from thy bounty; O Father take in sign of Love; O Priest and victim and This day God gives us. Used with permission.
Chevalier Press, PO Box 13, Kensington, NSW 2033, Australia for the words and music of Father in my life (Trinity Song). Reproduced from 'Eagles Wings' by Fr Frank Anderson MSC. Used with permission.
Christian Conference of Asia, 480 Lorong 2, Toa Payoh, Singapore 1231, on behalf of D P Niles and E G Maquiso for Father in heaven © 1961. Used with permission.
Collins Liturgical Publications, 187 Piccadilly, London W1V 9DA for the following Taizé material: Adoramus Te; Jubilato Deo; Jubilato Servite, Misericordias Domini and Ostende Nobis. © 1978, 1980, 1981 Les Presses de Taizé (France). International Copyright secured. All rights reserved. Used with permission.
Anne Conway, St Joseph's School, Upper Lindum Street, Lincoln LN2 5RW for the words and music of Be still and know I am with you; As earth that is dry; (Come to the waters) Lord graciously hear us; Sing everyone a song to the Lord; This is the day. Used with permission.

ACKNOWLEDGMENTS

J Curwen and Sons Ltd., Stockley Close, Stockley Road, West Drayton, Middx UB7 9BE for the words and music of Hills of the North Rejoice, from Curwen Edition no. 80634 and for the music of I vow to thee my country. Used with permission.
Stewart Cross, Ribchester Rd, Blackburn BB1 9EF for the words of Father, Lord of all creation. Used with permission.
Margaret Daly, Eire for the words of When the time came © 1978. Used with permission.
The trustees of the late Sir Walter Davies, for the words and music of God be in my head.
Dawntreader Music/Thank you Music, PO Box 75, Eastbourne, E Sussex BN 23 6NW for the words and music of God and man at table are sat down. © 1972
Stephen Dean for the words and music of Come let us sing out our joy, and Jesus said 'I am the bread'; and for part of the following Psalms: 666(18) 670(26) 673(50) 676(84) 680(99) 684(115) 687(121) 688(125) 689(129) and for the music of Round 699.
N & K Donnelly, 80 Cardross Rd, Dumbarton G82 4JQ for the words and music of Christ is coming © 1978. Used with permission.
Dove Communications Pty Ltd. Suite 1, 60–64 Railway Road, Blackburn, Victoria Box 316 Blackburn, Vic.3130, Australia for the words and music of He's a most unusual man © 1978.
Timothy Dudley-Smith, Bramerton, Norwich NR14 7DW for the words of Tell out my soul. Used with permission.
Ediciones Paulinas, Madrid, for the words and music of Lord you have come to the Lakeside. Translation Fr Edward O'Shea. Used with permission.
EMI Music Publishing Ltd. 138–140 Charing Cross Rd., London WC2H 0LD for The Angel Gabriel. Used with permission.
Ephpheta House, c/o Mary McGann, 3330 Adams Rd, Auburn Heights, Michigan 48057, USA for the words and music of This is what Yahweh asks (Walk humbly with your God) © 1974. Used with permission.
Faber Music Ltd, 3 Queen Square, London WC1N 3AU for the words of A noble flower of Juda and Glory be to God the Father. Reprinted from the New Catholic Hymnal. Used with permission.
Famous Music Corporation (Famous Chappell), 129 Park St., London W1Y 3FA for the words and music of Brother Sun and Sister Moon © 1973 from the film of the same title. Reproduced by kind permission of Chappell Music Ltd, London W1Y 3FA.
J W Faustini, Brazil for the music of Modern man © 1967.
B Feldman & Co, for the words and music of Fill my House.
FEL Publications for the words and music of Sons of God and We are one in the Spirit. Reprinted by permission of the copyright owner. Further reproduction (even words only) is not permitted without FEL's written permission.
Patrick G Fitzpatrick, St Joseph's College, Dumfries, Scotland for the music of A sign is seen in heaven © 1980, and for the words and music of Alleluia, Alleluia, salvation and glory © 1976. Used with permission.
Franciscan Communications Center, 1229 S. Santee St., Los Angeles, California 90015, USA for the words and music of: All that I am; Glorious God; Do not worry; Let's make peace in our hearts; Follow Christ; Lord we pray for golden peace; Sing, sing, sing; Happy the man; Make me a channel of your peace; The Mass is ended; Take my hands; Sign praises to the living God; Good Lady poverty © 1967. Used with permission. All rights reserved.
Enrico Garzilli, 33 Vermont St., Cranston, Rhode Island 02920 USA for the words and music of For those who love God (Romans VIII © 1970. Used with permission.
Alan Gaunt and John Marsh for the words of Wind and Fire.
C A Gibson, Department of English, University of Otago, Dunedin, New Zealand for the words of Sing praise and thanksgiving (part). Used with permission.
John Glynn, The Presbytery, Roman Road, Ingatestone, Essex CM4 9AA for the words of I watch the sunrise; for the words and music of Come Holy Lord © 1975; I am the vine © 1979; I was born before creation © 1978; Mother of Jesus © 1978; Remember, man © 1980; Together we journey © 1978. Used with permission.
Gospel Light Publications, Shirley House, 27 Camden Road, London NW1 9LN, on behalf of Manna Music, for How great thou art.
The Grail (England) Ltd, administered by A P Watt Ltd, London WC1R 4HL for the words of He is risen, alleluia! and for the words of Psalms 24, 62, 114, 115, 116, 117, 144, 109, 111, 110, 113a, 113b, for the words of the Benedictus, and for the music (in whole or in part) of the following: Psalms 8, 18, 22, 23, 41, 42, 50, 83, 84, 90, 92, 94, 99, 102, 103, 121, 125, 129, 135, The Magnificat and the Nunc Dimittis. Used with permission.
Gregorian Institute of America Publications Inc. (GIA), 7404 South Mason Avenue, Chicago, Illinois 60638, USA for the words and music of I am the bread of life © 1971. Used with permission.
Harmuse Publications 529 Spears Rd, Oakville, Ontario, Canada L6K 2G4 for the music of Out of deep unordered water © 1977. Used with permission.
The Executors of the late Dr B Harwood for the music of Let all the world and Thy hand O God.
Michael Hewlett, Poughill Vicarage, Nr Crediton, Devon for the words of Bartimaeus © 1980. Used with permission.
David Higham Assoc. Ltd., 5–8 Lower John Street, Golden Square London W1R 4HA for the words of Morning has broken by Eleanor Farjeon from The Children's Bells published by Oxford University Press.
Bonaventure Hinwood OFM, PO Box 17126 Groenkloof, Pretoria 0027, South Africa for Alleluia! Jesus is alive © 1974; May God's Spirit come © 1974; God's Spirit precedes us © 1974; Son of God and son of David © 1974. Used with permission.
Nick Hodson for the words of It's a long hard journey.
Rev Clifford Howell SJ, for the words of Glory to thee, O Lord; O God thy people gather; O God we give ourselves today and See us Lord about thine altar.
The Literary Estate of Eleanor Hull and Chatto and Windus Ltd., for the words of A Prayer (Be thou my vision) from the Poem Book of Gael.
Hymns Ancient and Modern Ltd., St. Mary's Plain, Norwich, Norfolk NR3 3BG for the words of Good Christian Men. Used by permission of Hymns Ancient and Modern.

01603 — 612914

ACKNOWLEDGMENTS

Interkerklijke Stichting voor Kerlied, Koningin Emmalaan 38, 2264 Sk Leidschendam, Holland for the music of This is my body © 1970. Used with permission.
International Commission on English in the Liturgy Inc. (ICEL), 1234 Massachusetts Avenue N W., Washington DC 20005 USA for the words and music of A child is born in Bethlehem © 1981 and Our Father we have wandered © 1981. Both from Resource Collection of Hymns and Service Music for the Liturgy. All rights reserved. Used with permission.
Paul Inwood for the harmonization of Awake, awake, fling off the night; Of the Father's love begotten; The King shall come when morning dawns. Used with permission.
The Executrix of the Estate of the late John Ireland, for the music of My song is love unknown.
Michael Iverson for the words and music of Spirit of the Living God.
Willard F Jabusch, Mundelein, Illinois 60060, USA for the words of All this world belongs to Jesus; Many times I have turned; The King of glory comes; We celebrate this festive day; We gather together; Whatsoever you do and Open your ears; for the words and music of From the depths © 1966; Leave your country and your people; and for the words of Hail Mary © 1966; He is risen; We form one church © 1976; Now watch for God's coming. Used with permission.
Francis Jackson, Nether Garth, Acklam, Malton, N Yorks YO17 9RG for the tune East Acklam. Used with permission.
Pastor James G Johnson, Joliet Lutheran Parish, Box 956, Red Lodge, Montana 59068, USA for the words and music of Servantsong (Called to be servants) © 1979. Used with permission.
Joint Board of Christian Education of Australia and New Zealand, 5th Floor, 117 Collins St., Melbourne, Vic. Australia 3000 for the words and music of Come, God's people © 1976; Jesus the word © 1976. Used with permission.
Roger Jones and Christian Music Ministries, 325 Bromford Road, Birmingham B36 8ET for the music of I met you at the cross.
Fred Kaan, Spencer St., Leamington Spa, Warks CV31 3NE for the words of Each Morning © 1972; Let all who share © 1972; Modern Man © 1972; Son of the Father © 1972; Unite us Lord in peace © 1972. All used with permission.
Kevin Mayhew Ltd., The Paddock, Rattlesden, Bury St. Edmunds, Suffolk IP30 0SZ for the words and music of Come, Lord Jesus, come; I am the bread of life; He was born like you and I; May the peace of Christ be with you; Peace, perfect peace; Seasons come, seasons go; Holy Virgin by God's decree; the words of My God loves me (vs.2–5) and for the music of Round me falls the night. For the words and music of As I kneel before you; © 1978; Follow me © 1978; Do not be afraid © 1978; Gifts of bread and wine © 1978; God gives us harvest © 1978; I will be with you © 1978; I am the way (Jesus you are Lord) © 1978; Laudato Sii © 1981; Oh the word of my Lord © 1978; The spirit lives to set us free (Walk in the light) © 1978. All rights reserved. Used with permission. Like a sea without a shore; O lady full of God's own grace. Used by agreement. You servants of God; Christ our Lord has come; God has gladdened my heart (The Lourdes Magnificat); I am the light (Lumen Christi); As one body we are wed. English language rights © assigned 1984 Kevin Mayhew Ltd.
Lexicon Music Inc. Administered by Word (UK) Ltd., Northbridge Rd, Berkhampstead, Herts HP4 1EH for the words of Holy, holy from Come Together by Jimmy and Carol Owens © 1972; for the words and music of God forgave my sin © 1972; for verse 1 and 2 of This is my body © 1978. All rights reserved. Used by permission.
The Rt.Rev Monsignor David McRoberts, for the words of Praise we now the Lord our God.
Magnificat Music for the music of Father I place into your hands © 1981; and for the music of Sing to the world of Christ our sovereign Lord, text © 1978, music © 1980; arr. © 1982 & 1984. All rights reserved. Used with permission.
Maranatha Music, PO Box 1396, Costa Mesa, California 92626, USA for the words and music of Seek ye first © 1972. All rights reserved. International copyright secured. Used with permission.
The Medical Mission Sisters, 92 Sherman St., Hartford, Conn. 06105, USA for the words and music of: What do you ask of me? This is the night; Spirit of God and God gives his people strength. © 1976, 1980. All rights reserved. Used with permission.
The Methodist Church Division of Education and Youth, 2 Chester House, Pages Lane, Muswell Hill, London N10 1PR for the words of Jesus, the Lord. Used with permission.
Anthony Milner for the music of Christ be my way © 1979; Now with the fading light of day © 1958, 1979.
The Missionary Society of St Paul the Apostle in the State of New York, 1865 Broadway, N.Y. USA for the words and music of A certain traveller © 1975; Hail Mary © 1975; Light the Advent Candle © 1975. All from 'Dandelions'. All rights reserved.
A.R. Mowbray & Co.Ltd for the words of This joyful Eastertide and Unto us a Son is born.
Donal Murray, Dublin, Eire for the words of We praise you. Used with permission.
A Gregory Murray, Stratton on the Fosse, Bath BA3 4RM for the words and music of This joyful Eastertide and Unto us a Son is born; for the music of O Great St David, Pangua Lingua and Veni Creator. Used with permission.
Anicito Nazareth St Pius College, Bombay 63 for Blest are you, Lord; © 1980; I'll sing God's praises © 1980; Faith in God can move the mountains. Words and music. All rights reserved. Used with permission.
J G Nichols, Wallasey, Merseyside L45 0JP for the words of Let us praise our Sovereign Saviour © 1980. Used with permission.
North American Liturgy Resources (NALR) 10802 North Twenty Third Avenue, Phoenix, Arizona 85029, USA for the words and music of Abba, abba, Father; Do you really love me? Lay your hands; Sing a simple song; I will never forget you; New Life! Peacetime; The word who is life; (That which we have heard); If God is for us; Sing to the Lord; Blest be the Lord; Here I am Lord; (I the Lord); Glory and praise to our God; Though the mountains may fall; Yahweh, I know you are near; Trust in the Lord; Sing to the mountains; Be not afraid; (You shall cross the barren desert); The peace of the Lord. All rights reserved. Used with permission.
Novello and Company Ltd., Borough Green, Sevenoaks, Kent TN15 8DT for the music Michael for All my hope on God is founded, and for the words of All for Jesus. Used with permission.
Edward O'Shea for the translation of Lord you have come to the Lakeside.
The trustees of the estate of Sean O'Riada, Co Chorcaighe, Eire, for the music of The Seed is Christ's.

ACKNOWLEDGMENTS

Oxford University Press, Ely House, 37 Dover Street, London W1X 4AH for the following: From the English Hymnal: The music LASST UNS ERFREUEN (All creatures of our God and King and Bring all ye dear bought nations); the words of The Pilgrim Song (He who would valiant be) with the music MONK'S GATE: the music CRANHAM (In the bleak midwinter); the music SINE NOMINE (For all the Saints); the music DOWN AMPNEY (Come down O love divine); the words of O God of earth and altar with the music KINGS LYNN; the words O Holy Lord by all adored; the music FOREST GREEN (O little town of Bethlehem). For the following from 'Enlarged Songs of Praise': the words of Lord of all hopefulness with the music SLANE, further use of the music SLANE (Be thou my vision); for the words of God is love. For the music God be in my head and for the words of Little Jesus, sweetly sleep with the melody ROCKING from 'The Oxford Book of Carols'. For the following tunes: FRAGRANCE(from the Oxford book of Carols); ABBOT'S LEIGH (from the BBC Hymn Book); RANDOLPH and SUSSEX (from the English Hymnal; GARTAN AND CHRISTE SANCTORUM (from the revised Church Hymnary 1927); PURPOSE (from Enlarged Songs of Praise); WOODLANDS, BRIDEGROOM, FOLKSONG, NETHERLANDS and YISU NE KAHA and for the words of Father we praise you and Praise (Glory) to God. All used with permission.

Mrs Mildred Peacey, Hurstpierpoint, West Sussex for the words of Awake, awake! Used with permission.

Robertson Publications (for J Curwen & Sons Ltd) for the words of All creatures of our God and King.

Rev. Roger Ruston, OP for the words of Attend and keep this happy fast and Promised Lord and Christ is he.

G Schirmer Ltd. London for the words of We gather together to ask God's blessing. Used with permission.

Helena Scott, 2 Chelsea Embankment, London SW3 4LG for the words of Greater love© 1973. Used with permission.

Sefim, 92240 L'Hay Les Roses, France on behalf of the French liturgical music copyright holders for By the Cross; Glory to God; God most high; Unite us Lord; When the time came. Used with permission.

Anne Seymour for the words and music of Rejoice and shout for joy.

Shalom Community, 1504 Polk, Wichita Falls, Texas, USA for the words and music of O living water and I'll sing a song to you, Lord, Abba Father, send your spirit© 1974 All rights reserved. Used with permission.

Anthony Sharpe, 13 Meadow Rise, High Crompton, Shaw, Oldham, Lancs for the words and music of A voice cries in the wilderness (Lord of Light).

Sheed and Ward Ltd, 2 Creechurch Lane, London EC3 for the words of As long as men. Used with permission.

Singspiration Inc., 1415 Lake Drive SE, Grand Rapids, Michigan 49506, USA for the words and music of Feed my lambs© 1969. Used with permission.

Stainer and Bell Ltd, 82 High Road, London N2 9PW for the words and music of Lord of the dance; When I needed a neighbour; for the words of: An Upper room did the Lord prepare;© By the cross©; For the fruit of His creation©; For the healing of the nations© 1968; Out of deep unordered water© 1968; and for the words and music of Gathered here© 1972. Used with permission.

Linda Stassen, New Song Ministries, PO Box 11662, Costa Mesa, California 92626, USA for the words and music of Sing Alleluia to the Lord© 1974 Linda Stassen. All rights reserved. International Copyright secured. Used with permission.

Pamela Stotter, 2 Fergus Drive, Shannon, Co Clare, Eire for the words of Christ is alive© 1978; Day and Night© 1978; for the translation of God most high© 1978. Used with permission.

Taizé Copyright Permission Department, Les Presses de Taizé, 71250 Taizé Community, France for the words and music of O Lord hear my prayer. Used with permission.

Bill Tamblyn, 28 Priory Street, Colchester, Essex for the music of Bartimaeus© 1980; To God our Father be the praise© 1980; Wind and Fire© 1980; Go out to the whole world© 1975; I rejoiced© 1975. Used with permission.

Tembo Music Ltd, 50 Regent's Park Road, Primrose Hill, London NW1 7SX for the music of I saw a star. Used with permission.

Thank you Music. PO Box 75, Eastbourne BN23 6NW for the words and music of Bind us together by Bob Gillman© 1977; Our God reigns by L E Smith Jnr. © 1974/78; Father, I place into your hands by J Hewer© 1975 and for Light up the Fire© 1973. Used with permission.

Eric A Thorn 17 Rowan Walk, Crawley Down, West Sussex for the words of I met you at the cross.

Honor Mary Thwaites for the words of A mighty stronghold. Used with permission.

Tro Essex Music Ltd, 85 Gower St, London WC1E 6HJ for We shall overcome© 1960, 1963 Ludlow Music Inc., assigned to Tro Essex Music Ltd.

Mrs J Tyrrell, 41 Minster Rd, Godalming, Surrey GU7 1SR for the words of Lord of all power. Used with permission.

United Reform Church, 86 Tavistock Place, London WC1H 9RT for the words of Almighty Father and for the music of Lord of all power. Used with permission.

Tom Van Erp, Wychen, Nederlands for the music of Son of God and Son of David.

Vanguard Music for the music of God's Spirit is in my heart; The Bakerwoman; Sing of the Bride; Where would we be without Christ our Lord.

Verlag Merseburger, Berlin GmbH, Buro Kassel, 35 Kassel, Motzstrasse 13, West Germany for the words and music of Sing and rejoice in the Lord.

Chrysogonus Waddell & St Joseph's Abbey, Mount St. Joseph's Abbey, Roscreen, Co. Tipperary, Eire for the words and music of O comfort my people.

Christopher Walker for the music of Alleluia (Premananda); Alleluia (Ps.116); Give thanks to the Lord (Ps.117; Veni Sancte Spiritus, and for the translation of Veni Sancte Spiritus. Used with permission.

Joseph Walshe OSCO, Mount Melleray Abbey, Cappoquin, Co. Waterford, Eire for By his wounds (Christ suffered for you). Words and music. Used with permission.

Jose Webber for the music of Greater love© 1970.

ACKNOWLEDGMENTS

Joseph Weinberger Ltd., 12–14 Mortimer St., London W1N 8EL for the words and music of All creation, bless the Lord; O Lord, all the world belongs to you; Lord, Jesus Christ and Lord, in everything I do © 1979. Used with permission.
The Trustees of the Diocese of Westminster, for the words and music of Battle is O'er and Maiden yet a Mother; for the music of Angels we have heard in heaven; Angels we have heard on high; Ave Maria; Crown him with many thorns; Draw nigh and take the body; Glory to thee; Lord for tomorrow; My God, I love thee not because; New praises be given; O Godhead hid; O Sacred heart; Praise to the holiest and for the words of Christ is king of earth and heaven; Keep we the fast; New praises be given; To Christ the Lord; Where is love and loving kindness and Star of Ocean.
The Word of God Music, PO Box 8617, Ann Arbor, Mi 48107, USA for the words and music of Alleluia! Give thanks © 1973; I heard the Lord call my name © 1973; The light of Christ © 1974. Used with permission.
World Council of Churches, Geneva for the use of the following harmonization from Cantate Domino (1980 edition); Let all who share one bread; Modern Man. Used with permission.
World Library Publications Inc., 5040 Ravenswood, Chicago, Illinois 60640, USA for the words and music of Take our bread; All the earth © 1965; All you nations © 1965; Keep in mind © 1965; My soul is longing © 1965; Send forth your spirit © 1965; The spirit of God © 1970; There is one Lord © 1965; Alleluia (Ps. 150) © 1964; Pasch of the New Law © 1965, 1966, 1973; Give praise to the Lord, and for the words of Shepherd of Souls © Used with permission.
World Student Christian Federation, Geneva for the words of Thine be the glory. Used with permission.
John C Ylvisaker, Minneapolis, Minnesota 55423, USA for the words and music of It's good to give thank to the Lord; Now let your people depart in peace © 1979; We are bound for the promised land © 1979. Used with permission.
All or part of the copyright of the following is vested in McCrimmon Publishing Company Ltd., 10–12 High Street, Great Wakering, Essex, SS3 OEQ:
S2, S3, S5, S6, 5, 6, 11, 12, 23, 32, 43, 47, 51, 54, 59, 61, 76, 81, 83, 85, 87, 92, 102, 114, 116, 125, 127, 129, 131, 135, 138, 139, 140, 145, 146, 148, 155, 173, 175, 185, 190, 194, 197, 208, 209, 210, 231, 237, 240, 252, 255, 256, 258, 261, 263, 267, 268, 278, 289, 298, 304, 307, 314, 317, 322, 324, 327, 336, 340, 343, 350, 356, 357, 361, 362, 366, 367, 368, 369, 370, 371, 375B, 388, 392, 393, 394, 403, 406a, 408, 414, 415, 418, 420, 422, 423, 425, 434, 436, 437, 438, 458, 464, 465, 466, 467, 471, 481, 484, 485, 491, 493, 494, 502, 503, 507, 509, 512, 513, 517, 520, 522, 529, 530, 533, 536, 538, 539, 541, 553, 555, 556, 559, 560, 561, 562, 563, 566, 572, 576, 579, 580, 581, 584, 586, 588, 589, 591, 595, 598, 600, 601, 602, 603, 612, 615, 620, 624, 626, 632, 634, 637, 640, 641, 643, 644, 650, 651, 654, 661.
Psalms: 667(22), 668(23), 669(24), 674(62), 676(84), 683(114), 691(144). The Benedictus 693. Rounds: 705, 708, 712, 716, 717, 718, 719, 720, 721.
The Divine Office is © The Grail, the Bishop's Conference of England and Wales, Stephen Dean and McCrimmon Publishing Co. Ltd. The arrangement of the following: 14, 19, 33, 39, 41, 52, 62, 66, 84, 89, 95, 96, 97, 100, 101, 105, 117, 133, 136, 144, 147, 159, 162, 167, 169, 174, 191, 195, 196, 205, 216, 217, 229, 230, 232, 242, 251, 254, 259, 269, 276, 277, 283, 291, 310, 321, 323, 329, 338, 344, 345, 347, 348, 354.

Every effort has been made to trace the owners of copyright material, and we hope that no copyright has been infringed. Pardon is sought and apology made if the contrary be the case, and a correction will be made in any reprint of this book.
McCrimmon Publishing Company Ltd take this opportunity to record their thanks to all involved in the research, secretarial work, compilation and technical production of this hymnal; may it be used with the same dedication with which it was produced.
It is unlawful to reproduce in any way any of the copyright material without the explicit written permission of the copyright holder.

INDEXES

INDEXES

ALPHABETICAL INDEX OF TUNES

METRICAL INDEX

66.66

Ave maris stella 290
Lisbon s6
Ravenshaw 151, 549

66.68 Short Metre, SM

Carlisle 37
Franconia 36
Narenza 333
Optatus 301
Southwell 180
Vineyard Haven (+ ref.) 734

77.77

Culbach 82
Heinlein 80, 608
Lubeck 187
Monkland 171
Orientis Partibus 339
Vienna 120

86.86 Common Metre, CM

Andreus s5
Amazing grace 19
Ballerma 775
Belmont 115, 201
Billing 262
Consolation 613
Crimond 312
Detroit 743
Dundee 315(ii)
Everlasting Love 204
Farrant 18
Horsley 218, 316
Irish 224
Jazer 153
Lindisfarne 408
McKee 136
Richmond 432
St Anne 222
St Bernard 15
St Columba (Erin) 385
St Fulbert 315(i), 363
St Flavian 183, 198
St Magnus 308, 570
Shanti 815
Song 5 454
Tallis' Ordinal 50

Unity 217
Westminster 203
Wiltshire 631
Winchester Old 360

87.87

Come, rejoice 731
Cross of Jesus 439 (i)
Dominus regit me 311
Laus Deo/Redhead no 46 42, 275
Love divine 184
Merton 112
Omni die 75
Stuttgart 34, 439 (ii)
Sussex 130, 449

88.88 Long Metre, LM

Angels' Song (Song 34) 78, 79
Breslau 2
Church Triumphant 386
Creator alme siderum 61
Danby 637
Deus tuorum militum 332, 405
Duguet 309
Duke Street 73
Eisenach 306, 318(ii)
Erhalt uns, Herr 756
Fulda 809
Grosser Gott 172, 212
Herr Jesu Christ 546
LLedrod/Llangollen 744
Lumen de lumine 459
Melcombe 245, 372/3, 808
Miles Lane 9
Old 100th 10
Rockingham 202, 355
Saxony 160
St Venantius 651
Suantrai 327
Tallis' Canon 17, 91
Truro 318 (i)
Winchester New 239, 271
Winscott, part 250

98 98

Folksong/O waly waly 399
Les commandemens de Dieu 402
St Clement 303, 594
Weisse 412

10 10.10 10

Eventide 1
Slane, modified 35
Gustate 65
Anima Christi 288
Ellenborough 488
Woodlands 609, 800

10 10.11 11

Laudate Dominum 244
Hanover 253, 798

11 10.11 10

St David s4
Liebster Immanuel 192
Strength and stay 243

11 11.11 11

Adoro te 95
St Patrick 105, 645
St Denio 134, 207
Aquinas 220
Maria zu lieben 246
They say I am wise 324
Duan Chroi Iosa 442
O comfort my people 566

11 11 11.5

Christe sanctorum 70, 94, 428, 455
Das sollt ihr 532
Rouen (Iste Confessor) 793

55 88 5

Romanis 272
Seelenbräutigam 763

66.66.88

Love Unknown 206
Gopsal 270
Little Cornard 448
Darwall's 148th Morning Prayer

77.77.77

Dix 24
England's Lane 741 (i)
Lucerna Laudoniae 741 (ii)
Petra 592

87.87.87

St Thomas 46, 177, 219,
  279, 372/3
Kensington 747
Mannheim 165
Picardy 166, 186
Praise my soul 260
Oriel 335
Regent Square 543

88.88.88

Surrey 71
St Catherine 213
Sunset 295

65.65D

Laudes 109
Une vraie crainte 188

66.86D Double Short Metre, DSM
Corona 56 (i)
Diademata 56 (ii)

76.76D

Aurelia 233, 300, 516

Ave Virgo Virginum 433, 820
Baronita 497
Cruger 110
Ellacombe 302
Ewing 149
Kings Lynn 221 (i)
Magnificat 142
Moville 429
Neshanic 577 (ii)
O King of might 234
Passion Chorale 247, 569, 577 (i)
Picardy 166, 186, 462
Royal Oak 13
St Theodulph 8
Thornbury 332
Turris Davidica 132
Vaughan 176
Westminster Abbey 427
Willsbridge 221 (ii)

77.77D

Salzburg 27
Westminster Old 40
St George 55
King divine 107
Aberystwyth 150
St Edmund 286
Charlton 545

86.86D Double Common Metre,
  DCM

Claudius 25
Ellacombe, modified 156
Come to me 208
Forest Green 235
Festive day 344

87.87D

Abbot's Leigh 453, 472
Austria 585
Hyfrydol 7
Daily, daily 57 (i)
Laudes Mariae 57 (ii)
Au sang qu'un Dieu 98
Contemplation 103
Swavesey 163
Pleading Saviour 281
Rex Gloriae 483

98.98D

Rendez á Dieu 772, 819

HYMNS BASED ON SCRIPTURE

GENESIS
12:1ff 530

I KINGS
17:11–16 314

ISAIAH
9:2–7 315
9:6 436, 464
12:2–6 814
35:5–6.10 664
40:28–31 635
40:1–2,4,9 566
40:3.5 805 vv.2–4
40:3–4.9–11 16
40:31–32 630
43:1–2 663

43:1–4 444
43:2,4,10,18–20 456
45:8 587, 732
49:15 630
49:15–16a 511
52:7–10 500
54:6–10 630
55:1–2 779
55:1–2,6,9,12 400
55:1.10–12 Water of Life
58:5–9 25
58:7 591 (v2)
61:1–2 319, 496 (v.3), 619

JEREMIAH
1:4–10 574
4:19.23–25; 17:12–13 771

31:2.3.8 etc. 770
31:31 591

DANIEL
3:52ff 3, 12, 796

HOSEA
6:4 591

JOEL
2:13 Water of Life (v.4)
2:21–23,27; 3:2; 4:18 457
3:1ff 617

MICAH
6:8 628
6:6–8 817

INDEX OF PSALM VERSIONS

Some psalms have two numbers. This is because of a discrepancy between the numbering in the Hebrew version of the Bible (used by Jews and the reformed churches) and the Greek version (used until now by the Catholic church.) This means for example that what in the Authorised Version is known as the Twenty-Third Psalm (The Lord's my shepherd) is Psalm 22 in Catholic liturgical books; and likewise the psalm with the tune known as The Old Hundredth is Psalm 99. Both numberings are given here but it is likely that the Hebrew numbering will eventually displace the Greek.

TOPICAL INDEX

Hymns for the Sacraments and Other Rites

Christian Initiation

(Numbers in brackets refer to paragraphs in the text of RCIA)

1. Rite of Acceptance into the Order of Catechumens

This takes place at a time to be decided by each community.

Gathering (48):
325 This day God gives me
508 Here I am, Lord
659 Yahweh, I know you are near
728 Bless the Lord, my soul
779 Oh how lovely is your dwelling place
794 Sing of the Lord's goodness

Greeting (49):
674 Psalm 62
746 God is my great desire
778 Oh God, I seek you
812 Unless a grain of wheat
AK22, 34

Signing (54):
444 Do not be afraid
557 My God, you fathom my heart
777 O Christe Domine Jesu
AK76

Intercessions
710 O Lord, hear my prayer

Closing Song
706/707 Jubilate Deo
749 Great is the Lord
AK86

2. The Rite of Election
This takes place on the 1st Sunday of Lent

Gathering
793 Sing all creation
752 Gather us in

Enrollment
550 Lord, you have come to the lakeside
781 Centre of my life

Psalms
18(19), 22(23), 23(24), 41(42), 62(63)
AK13, 22

Gospel Acc.
788 Praise to you, O Christ

After the Witness:
473 Glory and praise to our God
508 I the Lord of sea and sky

Signing of Names (132):
444 Do not be afraid
659 Yahweh, I know you are near

Closing song
815 We walk by faith

3. The Scrutinies

383, 400, 557, 659, 696, 710, 746, 758, 774, 777, 778, 788, 812

4. The Celebration of Initiation

Thirsting for God
671 Ps 41(42)
674 Ps 62(63)
728 Bless the Lord, my soul
746 God is my great desire
778 Oh God, I seek you

Faith
75 Firmly I believe and truly
130 I believe in God the Father

Acclamations and Refrains
430 Christ our Lord has come to save
559 New life
621 There is one Lord

784 Oh healing river
812 Unless a grain of wheat
826 You have put on Christ
     Water of Life
AK1

Psalms

667 Ps 22(23)
670 Ps 26(27)
673 Ps 50(51)
688 Psalm 125(126)
756 If God should lead us (Ps 125/126)
AK22, 34, 35

Prayer and Trust

383 Abba, Father
475 God at creation's dawn
659 Yahweh, I know you are near
700 Breath of life
710 O Lord, hear my prayer

Giving thanks

244 O praise ye the Lord
260 Praise, my soul, the King of heaven
384 Abba, Father, send your Spirit
394 Alleluia, sons of God, arise
405 Awake, awake
420 Called to be servants
456 Fear not, rejoice and be glad
463 For to those who love God
477 God forgave my sin
479 God has gladdened my heart
580 Out of deep unordered water
609 Tell out, my soul
614 The light of Christ
620 There is a river
779 Oh how lovely is your dwelling place
794 Sing of the Lord's goodness

Mission

78/744 Forth in the peace of Christ
444 Do not be afraid
508 Here I am, Lord

Infant Baptism

116 Here's a child for you
154 Jesus, gentlest Saviour
292 Suffer little children
312 The Lord's my shepherd
384 Abba, Father, send your Spirit
667 Psalm 22(23)
670 Psalm 26(27)

5. Confirmation

37   Breathe on me, breath of God
49   Come down, O love divine
50   Come, Holy Ghost, Creator, come
51   Come, Lord Jesus, come
78/744 Forth in the peace of Christ
93   God be in my head
99   God's Spirit is in my heart
289 Spirit of the living God
383/4 Abba, Father
460 Follow me
502 I am the vine
510 I will be with you
545 Lord, in everything I do
547 Lord of creation
574 Oh the word of my Lord
594-6 Send forth your Spirit
608 Take my life
617 The Spirit is moving
619 The Spirit of God
638 Veni Sancte Spiritus
657 Wind and fire
663 You shall cross the barren desert
700 Breath of life
744 see 78
781 Centre of my life
797 The gift of the Holy Spirit
806 Wake your power
809 We have a gospel to proclaim
811 We have been told
816 What do you want of me, Lord?
823 You shall go out with joy

Psalms

667 Psalm 22(23)
682 Psalm 103(104)
685 Psalm 116(117)
691 Psalm 144(145)

Reception of a baptized person into full communion with the Catholic Church

Choose from the Baptism and Confirmation sections. The following psalms are especially suitable:

670 Psalm 26(27)
671 Psalm 41(42)
674 Psalm 62(63)
504/5 Psalm 120(121)
AK34, 66

Worship of the Eucharist outside Mass

Adoration

95 Godhead here in hiding
157 Jesus, my Lord, my God, my All
213 O bread of heaven
220 O Godhead hid
294 Sweet Sacrament divine
696 Adoramus te, Domine
754 I received the living God
764 Jesus, Lord of life and love
777 O Christe Domine Jesu

Banquet

7 Alleluia! sing to Jesus
27 At the Lamb's high feast
774 Now in this banquet
802 Behold the Lamb of God

Bread of Life

412 Bread of the world
521 Jesus said: I am the bread
523 Jesus the Lord said

Food

166 Let all mortal flesh
438 Come, O Lord
567 O food of travellers
597 Shepherd of souls

Last Supper

185 Love is his word
399 An upper room

408 Before Christ died
501 I am the bread of life
623 This is my body
653 When the time came
812 Unless a grain of wheat

Sacrament of Unity

136 In Christ there is no east or west
139 Into one we all are gathered
249 O thou who at thy Eucharist
403 As one body

Praise

543 Lord, enthroned in heavenly splendour
605 Sing to the world of Christ
788 Praise now your God
794 Sing of the Lord's goodness

Hymns for the Rite
Verbum supernum/O Salutaris:

245 O salutaris (English)
372 O salutaris (Latin)
373 O salutaris (English, another version)
309 Complete in English

Pange Lingua/Tantum Ergo:

219 Complete in English
716 Complete in Latin
374 Tantum Ergo (Latin)
375 Tantum Ergo (English)

Penance and Reconciliation

Sorrow

81 From the deep I lift my voice
98 God of mercy and compassion
144 It's me, O Lord
165 Lead us, heavenly Father
180 Lord Jesus, think on me
191 Many times I have turned
221 O God of earth and altar
223 O God, thy people gather
247 O sacred head sore wounded

330 Thou wilt keep him in perfect peace
338 Vaster far than any ocean
385 Across the years
397 Almighty Father, who for us
400 As earth that is dry
443 Divided our pathways
454 Father of heaven, whose love profound
542 Lord, confronted with your might
544 Lord, graciously hear us
577 Our Father, we have wandered

591 Return to the Lord
660 You, Israel, return now
673 Ps 50(51) Have mercy on me, God
689 Ps 129(130) Out of the depths
711 Ostende nobis
751 Hear us, almighty Lord
757 In the abundance of your compassion
770 My people, I hear you calling
771 My soul cannot be still
780 O Lord, be not mindful

How God wants us to live

417 But I say unto you
743 Forgive our sins as we forgive
797 The gift of the Holy Spirit
799 The Master came to bring good news

807 We are your people
817 What does the Lord require

Forgiveness

60 Dear Lord and Father
227 O Lord my God
231 O the love of my Lord
260 Praise, my soul, the King of heaven
266 Praise we our God with joy
273 Seasons come, seasons go
340 Walk with me, O my Lord
350 We will walk
477 God forgave my sin
728 Bless the Lord, my soul
750 Who calls my life again
773 Nothing can ever take away
803 To God be the glory
813 We're forgiven

Marriage

 71 Father, within thy house today
139 Into one we all are gathered
165 Lead us, heavenly Father
184 Love divine, all loves excelling
243 O perfect love
280 Sing of the bride
311 The King of love
312 The Lord's my shepherd
320 The Kingdom (The Beatitudes) = AK71
327 This is my will, my one command
358 Where are love and loving-kindness
380 A new commandment
404 As the bridegroom to his chosen
450 Father I place into your hands
699 The Beatitudes
738 Father, we come in prayer = AK78
741 For the beauty
AK78, 83

Psalms

667 Psalm 22(23)
681 Psalm 102(103)

Anniversary

Other suitable hymns may be found under
Thanksgiving.
211 Now thank we all our God
260 Praise, my soul
609 Tell out, my soul
681 Psalm 102(103)
691 Psalm 144(145)
728 Bless the Lord, my soul
741 For the beauty of the earth

Days of Special Prayer

Mass for Justice and Peace

(Celebrated on the 4th Sunday in Ordinary Time)

25 Attend and keep this happy fast	593 Seek first the kingdom
72 Feed us now	608 Tell out, my soul
142 I sing the Lord God's praises	628 This is what Yahweh asks
189 Make me a channel	636 Unite us, Lord, in peace
190 Man of Galilee	644 We gather together
314 The prophet in his hunger	726 As a tree planted
317 There is a world	729 Christ's church shall glory
320 The Kingdom	743 Forgive our sins as we forgive
352 Whatsoever you do	744 Forth in the peace of Christ
376 A certain traveller	749 Great is the Lord
397 Almighty Father, who for us	767 Lead us from death to life
417 But I say unto you	797 The gift of the Holy Spirit
436 Come, Lord Jesus	798 The kingdom of God
462 For the healing of the nations	799 The Master came to bring good news
479 God has gladdened my heart	800 The voice of God
488 Grant us thy peace	817 What does the Lord require?
532 Let all who share one bread	
553 May the peace of the Lord	Responsorial Psalms:
554 Modern man has the city	676 Ps 84(84)
581 Peace is my parting gift	687 Ps 121(122)
591 Return to the Lord	

AK24, 25, 35, 39

Mass for the Unity of Christians

There is no such thing as a definitive list of hymns for this or other ecumenical occasions. The act of worshipping together is a gesture of unity and many other hymns and songs could be chosen which do not have 'unity' as their explicit theme.

Healing divisions

331 Thy hand, O God, has guided
342 We are one in the Spirit
380 A new commandment
443 Divided our pathways
629 Thou whose almighty word
783 O that today
799 The master came
AK77

Christ draws us together (e.g. in Baptism*)

136 In Christ there is no East or West
300 The Church's one foundation
327 This is my will
409 Bind us together
427 Christ is made the sure foundation
472 Glorious things of you are spoken
*621 There is one Lord
622 Thine be the glory
729 Christ's Church shall glory
*826 You have put on Christ
AK81, 83

Eucharist, Sacrament of Unity

249 O thou who at thy Eucharist
399 An upper room
501 I am the bread of life

Unity in Mission

76 Follow Christ
468 Gathered here
605 Sing to the world
612 The Church is wherever
632 To be the body of the Lord
644 We gather together
744 Forth in the peace of Christ
753 How shall they hear
797 The gift of the Holy Spirit
798 The Kingdom of God
807 We are your people
809 We have a Gospel to proclaim

Psalms

667 Psalm 22(23)
680 Psalm 99(100)
687 Ps 121(122)
(see also hymn paraphrases of these Psalms)

AK13, 30, 35

Mass for God's Blessing on Human Work

51	Come, Lord Jesus, come	296	Take my hands
63	Do not worry	411	Blest are you
79	Forth in thy name, O Lord	469	Gifts of bread and wine
135	In bread we bring you	483	God our maker, mighty Father
138	In the earth	547	Lord of creation
181	Lord of all hopefulness	608	Take my life
190	Man of Galilee	637	Upon thy table
211	Now thank we all our God	821	With open hands

Mass in Thanksgiving for the Harvest

4	All creatures of our God and King	402	As long as men on earth
14	All this world belongs to Jesus	410	Blest are you, Lord God
55	Come, ye thankful people	461	For the fruits of his creation
138	In the earth		
211	Now thank we all our God	478	God gives us harvest
218	O Father, take in sign of love	615	The Lord is my shepherd
268	Reap me the earth	821	With open hands
307	The green life rises		Responsorial Psalms:
346	We plough the fields	688	Ps 125(126)

Mass for the Spread of the Gospel (Mission Sunday)

45	Colours of day	661	You must cry out the Word
78/744	Forth in the peace of Christ	703	Go out to the whole world (round)
99	Go tell everyone	724	All the ends of the earth
102	God's Spirit is in my heart	744	see 78
313	The Mass is ended	753	How shall they hear the word
331	Thy hand, O God, has guided	758	In the land there is a hunger
395	Alleluia, give thanks to the risen Lord	788	Praise to you, O Christ
480	God is working his purpose out	797	The gift of the Holy Spirit
500	Our God reigns	809	We have a Gospel
550	Lord, you have come to the lakeside		
574	Oh the word of my Lord		Responsorial Psalms:
619	The Spirit of God rests upon me	685	Psalm 116(117)
629	Thou whose almighty Word		AK29

INDEX OF FIRST LINES